CAROLINE FIELDING

A COURSE OF MATHEMATICS
FOR ENGINEERS AND SCIENTISTS

VOLUME 1

SECOND EDITION

A COURSE OF MATHEMATICS FOR ENGINEERS AND SCIENTISTS

VOLUME 1 — MATHEMATICAL METHODS

BRIAN H. CHIRGWIN

AND

CHARLES PLUMPTON

DEPARTMENT OF MATHEMATICS
QUEEN MARY COLLEGE, MILE END ROAD, LONDON E.1

SECOND EDITION

1966

PERGAMON PRESS

OXFORD · LONDON · EDINBURGH · NEW YORK
TORONTO · SYDNEY · PARIS · BRAUNSCHWEIG

Pergamon Press Ltd., Headington Hill Hall, Oxford
4 & 5 Fitzroy Square, London W.1
Pergamon Press (Scotland) Ltd., 2 & 3 Teviot Place, Edinburgh 1
Pergamon Press Inc., Maxwell House, Fairview Park, Elmsford,
New York 10523
Pergamon of Canada Ltd., 207 Queen's Quay West, Toronto 1
Pergamon Press (Aust.) Pty. Ltd., 19a Boundary Street, Rushcutters Bay,
N.S.W. 2011, Australia
Pergamon Press S.A.R.L., 24 rue des Écoles, Paris 5e
Vieweg & Sohn GmbH, Burgplatz 1, Braunschweig

First edition 1961
Reprinted (with corrections) 1966
Second edition 1970

Library of Congress Catalog Card No. 60-13894

Printed in Hungary
08 006388 8

CONTENTS

PREFACE TO THE SECOND EDITION

THIS book is the first of a series of volumes written to cover the pure and applied mathematics required by students reading for a first degree in engineering or science at British and Commonwealth universities and polytechnics. The series also covers the mathematical methods and mechanics required by students reading honours mathematics.

The first edition of this volume covered the technique and applications of differentiation and integration of one variable, geometry of two dimensions and complex numbers. A number of changes and additions have been made in this edition. Chapter I has been substantially enlarged; material on numerical analysis has been introduced wherever appropriate; a new Chapter VIII, introducing the subject of probability and statistics, and an Appendix on computers have been added. Additional examples and exercises have been included and modifications and extensions have been made to the text wherever required to cover the change in mathematics syllabuses.

In a work of this nature, full rigorous proofs cannot be given, but the assumptions made have been carefully stated and, wherever the existence of a rigorous proof is assumed, some indication of this assumption is given. Many of the worked examples and exercises incorporate proofs of important results or special cases of general theorems. The reader should not ignore these just because they are printed in small type.

We assume only that the reader has a basic knowledge of "pure mathematics" up to G.C.E. O-Level. However, most students of science and technology at British universities and polytechnics have undergone a two-year A-Level course (such as that given in *Sixth Form Pure Mathematics*, Vols. I and II, by C. Plumpton and W. A. Tomkys, Pergamon Press); a knowledge of the more elementary formulae given in such works will be found useful.

The sections, exercises, figures and equations are numbered according to the chapters; e.g. § 6 : 2 is the second section of Chapter VI, Ex. 3 : 8 is the set of exercises at the end of § 3 : 8, eqn. (2.3) is the third (numbered) equation of Chapter II. Only equations to which subsequent reference is made are numbered.

Most of the exercises are taken from examination papers of the University of London. We express our thanks to the Senate of the University of London for permission to use these questions. We also express our thanks to the Northern Universities Joint Matriculation Board for permission to use questions from G.C.E. advanced and scholarship papers.

Our best thanks are also due to Dr. Christine Davies, who has read the proofs, and to all those readers who have made valuable suggestions for improvement on the first edition.

Queen Mary College
London E.1

B. H. CHIRGWIN
C. PLUMPTON

THE GREEK ALPHABET

A	α	alpha	N	ν	nu
B	β	beta	Ξ	ξ	xi
Γ	γ	gamma	O	o	omicron
Δ	δ	delta	Π	π	pi
E	ε	epsilon	P	ϱ	rho
Z	ζ	zeta	Σ	σ	sigma
H	η	eta	T	τ	tau
Θ	θ	theta	Y	υ	upsilon
I	ι	iota	Φ	ϕ	phi
K	$\varkappa$	kappa	X	χ	chi
Λ	λ	lambda	Ψ	ψ	psi
M	μ	mu	Ω	ω	omega

CHAPTER I

INTRODUCTORY CONCEPTS

1:1 Functional notation and fundamental definitions

If a variable number y is determined when a second variable number x is specified, y is said to be a *function* of x. We call x the independent variable and y the dependent variable. The relationship between x and y is expressed symbolically in the form $y = f(x)$ which is to be read as "y is a function of x". If $f(x)$ is a known function, y is said to be an *explicit* function of x. In this case we can illustrate the dependence of y on x by drawing the graph of $y = f(x)$. When we write $|f(x)|$, to be read as "mod $f(x)$", we mean the numerical value of $f(x)$ without regard to sign. For example: $|-7| = 7$; $|x-3| = x-3$ if $x > 3$ and $3-x$ if $x < 3$; if $r > 0$, $|x| \leq r$ means $-r \leq x \leq r$.

We give below four examples of functions defined in specified intervals or ranges of values of x; the graphs of these functions are shown in Fig. 1.1(a)–(d).

(a) $\qquad f(x) = x^2 \quad$ for $\quad -3 \leq x \leq 3$;

(b) $\qquad f(x) = \begin{cases} x & \text{for} \quad 0 \leq x \leq 1, \\ 1 & \text{for} \quad 1 \leq x \leq 2, \\ 3-x & \text{for} \quad 2 \leq x \leq 3; \end{cases}$

(c) $\qquad f(x) = |\sin x| \quad$ for $\quad 0 \leq x \leq 4\pi$;

(d) $\qquad f(x) = \frac{1}{2}\{|\sin x| + \sin x\} \quad$ for $\quad 0 \leq x \leq 4\pi$.

Unless otherwise specified, throughout these volumes we take the angle x in the trigonometric or circular functions $\sin x$, $\tan x$, etc., to be expressed in radians. Example (b) indicates that it may be necessary to specify a functional relationship by several equations each of which defines $f(x)$ in some interval. Examples (c) and (d) give full and half wave rectification of the sine wave.

1

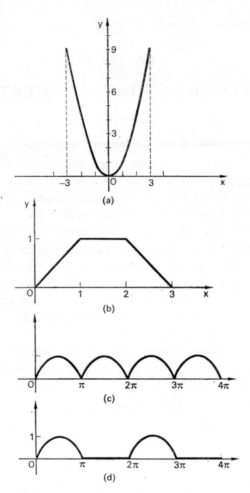

FIG. 1.1. (a) The curve $y = x^2$ for $-3 \leqslant x \leqslant 3$.

$$(b) \text{ The curve } y = \begin{cases} x & \text{for} \quad 0 \leqslant x \leqslant 1, \\ 1 & \text{for} \quad 1 \leqslant x \leqslant 2, \\ 3-x & \text{for} \quad 2 \leqslant x \leqslant 3. \end{cases}$$

(c) The curve $y = |\sin x|$ for $0 \leqslant x \leqslant 4\pi$.

(d) The curve $y = \frac{1}{2}\{|\sin x| + \sin x\}$ for $0 \leqslant x \leqslant 4\pi$.

Different functions may be denoted by different letters, by capitals or by suffixes, e.g. $f(x)$, $g(x)$, $\varphi(x)$, $F(x)$, $f_1(x)$, $f_2(x)$, etc. If the relation between x and y is in the form of an equation, e.g.

$$\sin(xy) - 6x^2 + 1 = 0 \quad \text{or} \quad x^2 + y^2 + 2x - 2y - 7 = 0,$$

we say that y is an *implicit* function of x. This type of relation between x and y is usually expressed symbolically in the form $f(x, y) = 0$ where $f(x, y)$ is a function of the two variables x and y. Solution of the equation $f(x, y) = 0$ for y in terms of x may give one and only one value of y corresponding to each value of x. In this case the function is said to be *single valued*. On the other hand, relations such as $y^2 = |x|$ and $\sin y = x$ define *two-valued* and *many-valued* functions of x respectively.

A polynomial of degree n is a function of the form

$$a_n x^n + a_{n-1} x^{n-1} + \ldots + a_1 x + a_0,$$

in which the a's are constants and n is an integer. The quotient $p(x)/q(x)$ of one polynomial $p(x)$ by another polynomial $q(x)$ is called a *rational* function of x. A rational number is a number which can be expressed in the form r/s where r and s are integers; e.g. $\frac{2}{3}, \frac{4}{7}$ are rational numbers. An irrational number is one which cannot be expressed in this way; $\pi, \sqrt{2}$ are examples of irrational numbers. A function which cannot be obtained from x by a finite number of the elementary operations of addition, subtraction, multiplication and division and taking roots is called a *transcendental* function of x. The exponential, hyperbolic and logarithm functions discussed in Chapter II are transcendental functions and so are the trigonometric functions.

It is convenient at this stage to *define* the circular or trigonometric functions $\sin x$ and $\cos x$ as non-terminating (or infinite) power series by the equations:

$$\sin x = x - \frac{x^3}{3!} + \frac{x^5}{5!} - \ldots = \sum_{r=0}^{\infty} \frac{(-1)^r x^{2r+1}}{(2r+1)!}, \qquad (1.1)$$

$$\cos x = 1 - \frac{x^2}{2!} + \frac{x^4}{4!} - \ldots = \sum_{r=0}^{\infty} \frac{(-1)^r x^{2r}}{(2r)!}. \qquad (1.2)$$

[The symbol ∞ is defined on p. 30.] The remaining trigonometric functions are then defined by the relations

$$\tan x = \frac{\sin x}{\cos x}, \quad \cot x = \frac{1}{\tan x}, \quad \sec x = \frac{1}{\cos x},$$
$$\operatorname{cosec} x = \frac{1}{\sin x}.$$

(1.3)

The graphs of these functions are given in Plumpton and Tomkys, *Sixth Form Pure Mathematics*, Vol. 1, § 4 : 3. The equivalence of these definitions of the trigonometric functions with the more elementary definitions involving projection is given in books on analysis. Alternative but equivalent definitions of sin x and cos x as solutions of differential equations with certain boundary conditions are given in Example 9 on p. 274.

Later we find that many differential equations of applied mathematics cannot be solved in terms of the elementary functions defined in this book. In such cases we *define* new functions which are the solutions of these differential equations and investigate their properties in various ways. [See Example 10 on p. 275, question 18 of Ex. 5 : 5, and also Vol. 4, Chaps. II and III.]

A function $f(x)$ is said to be *periodic* with period l if, for every $x, f(x+l) = f(x)$ for a constant l, i.e., if the function repeats itself at regular intervals. For example cos x is periodic with period 2π, tan x is periodic with period π, sin $(\pi x/a)$ is periodic with period $2a$. These properties together with the usual addition theorems, sum-product transformations (see *P.M.*, Vol. 1, Chap. IV) are established in books on analysis direct from the definitions (1.1)–(1.3) but involve a variety of theorems on multiplication of power series, etc., which we do not consider here.

In some cases functions are defined by definite integrals, see § 3 : 11, where the error function, the gamma function and the beta function are defined.

If $f(x)$ is such that $f(-x) = f(x)$, then $f(x)$ is said to be an *even* function of x; e.g. x^2, cos x and $x \sin x$ are even functions. If, however, $f(-x) = -f(x)$, then $f(x)$ is said to be an *odd* function of x; e.g. x^3, sin x and $x \cos^2 x$ are odd functions. In general an arbitrary function is neither even nor odd. However, the identity

$$f(x) = \tfrac{1}{2}\{f(x)+f(-x)\}+\tfrac{1}{2}\{f(x)-f(-x)\} \qquad (1.4)$$

shows that the arbitrary function $f(x)$ may be expressed as the sum of an even function $\tfrac{1}{2}\{f(x)+f(-x)\}$ and an odd function $\tfrac{1}{2}\{f(x)-f(-x)\}$. If $f(x)$ is even, the graph of $f(x)$ is symmetrical about the y-axis since in this case $f(-x) = f(x)$ implying that the graph of $f(x)$ for $x < 0$ is the optical image in the y-axis of the graph of $f(x)$ for $x > 0$. Similarly, if $f(x)$ is odd, the graph of $f(x)$ for $x < 0$ may be derived by successive reflections, first in the x-axis and then in the y-axis, of the graph of $f(x)$ for $x > 0$. Unless an odd function is discontinuous for $x = 0$, its graph must pass through the origin. [Continuity is defined in § 1 : 4.] Graphs of even and odd functions are shown in Fig. 1.2(a) and 1.2(b) respectively.

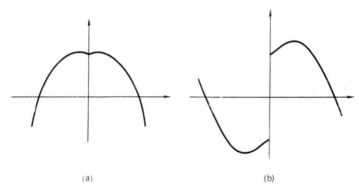

(a)   (b)

FIG. 1.2. (a) Graph of an even function. (b) Graph of an odd function.

Throughout these volumes we make great use of the concept of even and odd functions in integration, power series expansions, Fourier series expansions, etc. [See p. 120; Example 3, p. 131, § 5 : 5; also Vol. 5, Chap. I.]

Frequently, a variable y is determined by more than one independent variable. The functional relation $y = f(x_1, x_2, \ldots, x_n)$ indicates that the dependent variable y is a function of the n independent variables $x_1, x_2, \cdots, x_n$. For example, the volume

V and surface area A of a rectangular parallelepiped or cuboid with edges x_1, x_2, x_3 are given by

$$V = x_1 x_2 x_3, \quad A = 2(x_1 x_2 + x_2 x_3 + x_3 x_1)$$

and are functions of the three independent variables x_1, x_2, x_3.

At this stage we distinguish between equations and identities. Two functions $f(x)$ and $g(x)$ are said to be identically equal to one another over the range $a \leqslant x \leqslant b$, $a < b$, if $f(x) = g(x)$ for *all values of x* in this range and we write the relation between them in the form $f(x) \equiv g(x)$. For example

$$\frac{2x}{x^2 - 1} \equiv \frac{1}{x-1} + \frac{1}{x+1}$$

provided $|x| \neq 1$. On the other hand, equations are usually satisfied for discrete values of x. (See § 1 : 2.)

Suppose, in particular, that $f(x) = \sum_{r=0}^{n} A_r x^r$, $g(x) = \sum_{r=0}^{n} B_r x^r$ and $f(x) \equiv g(x)$ for $a \leqslant x \leqslant b$, $a < b$. Then it can be proved that $A_r = B_r$, (see also § 3 : 6). This is the principle of equating coefficients and, by use of the theory of functions of a complex variable, the principle can be proved to hold in the case when $f(x)$ and $g(x)$ are non-terminating power series.

A further result of importance is that if

$$\sum_{1}^{n} A_r x_r = 0$$

for arbitrary x_r, $r = 1, 2, \ldots, n$, then each of the constants A_r is zero.

Notation. When x is the (independent) variable under consideration, we use the notation (a, b) with round brackets to denote the *open interval* $a < x < b$, whereas $[a, b]$ with square brackets denotes the *closed interval* $a \leqslant x \leqslant b$, i.e. the values (or points) $x = a$, $x = b$ are excluded from the open interval, but are included in the closed interval.

Example 1. By showing that $n!e$ is never an integer (for $n = 1, 2, \ldots$), prove that

$$e = 1 + \frac{1}{1!} + \frac{1}{2!} + \ldots + \frac{1}{r!} + \ldots$$

is irrational.

If a number is rational, it must be capable of being expressed in the form p/q where p and q are integers and so, if e is rational, $n!e$ is an integer for some n. But from the above definition of e,

$$n!e = \text{an integer} + \frac{1}{n+1} + \frac{1}{(n+1)(n+2)} + \ldots$$

However, for n a positive integer,

$$\frac{1}{n+1} + \frac{1}{(n+1)(n+2)} + \ldots < \frac{1}{(n+1)} + \frac{1}{(n+1)^2} + \ldots = \frac{1}{n}.$$

(See § 5 : 1 for the summation of this geometrical series.) It follows that

$$\frac{1}{n+1} + \frac{1}{(n+1)(n+2)} + \ldots < 1 \quad \text{for} \quad n \geqslant 1$$

and so $n!e$ can never be an integer.

Example 2. The function $f(x)$ is real and bounded (see § 1 : 8) for all real values of x and satisfies the functional equation

$$f(x-y) = f(x)f(y) - f(a-x)f(a+y), \tag{1}$$

where a is a positive constant and $f(0) = 1$.

Prove that $f(a) = 0$, and show that $f(x)$ possesses the following properties for all real values of x:

    (i) $f(x) = f(-x)$,   (ii) $f(2a-x) = -f(x)$,

    (iii) $f(x+4a) = f(x)$,   (iv) $\{f(x)\}^2 + \{f(a-x)\}^2 = 1$,

    (v) $-1 \leqslant f(x) \leqslant 1$.

Give an example of a function $f(x)$ possessing all these properties.

Putting $x = a$, $y = 0$ in eqn. (1) we find

$$f(a) = f(a)f(0) - f(0)f(a) = 0 \tag{2}$$

as required. Then putting $x = 0$ in eqn. (1) we obtain

$$f(-y) = f(0)f(y) - f(a)f(a+y)$$

which reduces to

$$f(-y) = f(y) \tag{3}$$

since $f(a) = 0$ and $f(0) = 1$. This is equivalent to the required result (i). [We may write x as the variable instead of y.]

Now we replace x by a and y by $a - x$ in (1) to obtain

$$f(x) = f(a)f(a-x) - f(0)f(2a-x)$$

leading at once to result (ii). Then using the above results

$$f(x+4a) = f\{2a+(2a+x)\} = f\{2a-(-2a-x)\}$$
$$= -f(2a+x) = -f\{2a-(-x)\} = f(-x) = f(x)$$

proving result (iii).

Replacing x in (ii) by $a-t$ we obtain

$$f(a+t) = -f(a-t). \tag{4}$$

Further, writing $y = x$ in (1) we have

$$\{f(x)\}^2 - f(a-x)\,f(a+x) = f(0)$$

and using eqn. (4) and the relation $f(0) = 1$, we arrive at result (iv). This result implies that each of $\{f(x)\}^2$, $\{f(a-x)\}^2$ must not exceed unity. [Each of these quantities is positive being the square of a real number.] It follows that $-1 \leqslant f(x) \leqslant 1$ since $f(x)$ can by definition attain the value 1 when $x = 0$ and from (ii) the value -1 when $x = 2a$.

The function $\cos x$ (with $a = \pi/2$) possesses all the above properties.

Example 3. Sketch the graphs of

$$\text{(a)} \quad y = \frac{x}{x-1}, \qquad \text{(b)} \quad y = \left| \frac{x}{x-1} \right|.$$

Find the range of values of x for which

$$\left| \frac{x}{x-1} \right| < \frac{1}{2}.$$

Detailed information regarding sketching of graphs is contained in § 4:9. Here we presume that the reader is familiar with the elements of curve sketching and the graphs are as shown in Fig. 1.3(a), (b), the asymptotes being dotted. Since

$$\left| \frac{x}{x-1} \right| = \frac{1}{2} \quad \text{when} \quad \frac{x}{x-1} = \pm\frac{1}{2},$$

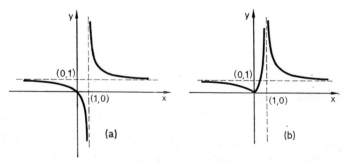

Fig. 1.3. (a) The curve $y = x/(x-1)$. (b) The curve $y = |x/(x-1)|$.

it follows that the graphs of $y = \frac{1}{2}$ and $y = |x/(x-1)|$ intersect when $x = -1$ and when $x = \frac{1}{3}$. Clearly from Fig. 1.3(b) the given inequality holds for $-1 < x < \frac{1}{3}$.

Example 4. Sketch the function

$$y = |2x-1| - |3-x|.$$

Since
$$|2x-1| = \begin{cases} 2x-1 & \text{for} & x \geqslant \frac{1}{2}, \\ 1-2x & \text{for} & x \leqslant \frac{1}{2}, \end{cases}$$

and
$$|3-x| = \begin{cases} x-3 & \text{for} & x \geqslant 3, \\ 3-x & \text{for} & x \leqslant 3, \end{cases}$$

it follows that

$$y = \begin{cases} 2x-1-(x-3) = x+2 & \text{for} & x \geqslant 3, \\ 2x-1-(3-x) = 3x-4 & \text{for} & \frac{1}{2} \leqslant x \leqslant 3, \\ 1-2x-(3-x) = -x-2 & \text{for} & x \leqslant \frac{1}{2}. \end{cases}$$

The graph therefore consists of segments of three straight lines as shown in Fig. 1.4.

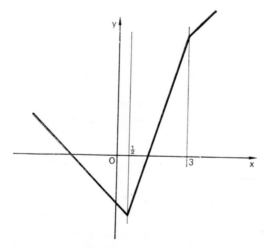

FIG. 1.4. The graph $y = |2x-1| - |3-x|$.

Exercises 1 : 1

1. Sketch the following functions in the given ranges:

(i) $y = |2x| - |1-x|, \quad -3 \leqslant x \leqslant 2.$

(ii) $y = +\sqrt{(1-\cos\theta)}, \quad 0 \leqslant \theta \leqslant 2\pi.$

(iii)
$$y = \begin{cases} x^2, & 0 \leqslant x \leqslant 1, \\ 1, & 1 \leqslant x \leqslant 2, \\ (3-x)^2, & 2 \leqslant x \leqslant 3. \end{cases}$$

(iv)
$$y = \begin{cases} 1+x-x^2, & -1 \leqslant x \leqslant 1, \\ -\tfrac{1}{2}+\tfrac{3}{2}x, & 1 \leqslant x \leqslant 3. \end{cases}$$

(v)
$$y = \begin{cases} \tfrac{1}{4}(x^2+3), & 0 \leqslant x \leqslant 1, \\ \sqrt{x} & 1 \leqslant x \leqslant 2. \end{cases}$$

2. Give specifications of the functions defined in 1 (iii) and 1 (v) for negative values of x, (a) when y is taken to be an odd function and (b) when y is taken to be an even function.

3. Express the functions defined in Qu. 1 (i) and 1 (iv) as the sum of even and odd functions.

4. The following functions are periodic with period a. Sketch the curves for $-a \leqslant x \leqslant 3a$ and give the values of y in each case corresponding to $x = -5a/4$ and $x = 13a/4$:

(i)
$$y = \begin{cases} 0, & 0 < x \leqslant \tfrac{1}{2}a, \quad \text{(square wave)} \\ 1, & \tfrac{1}{2}a < x \leqslant a. \end{cases}$$

(ii)
$$y = x, \quad 0 < x \leqslant a \quad \text{(saw-tooth wave)}.$$

(iii)
$$y = (x-\tfrac{1}{2}a)^2/a, \quad 0 \leqslant x \leqslant a.$$

(iv)
$$y = \cos\left(\frac{\pi x}{a}\right), \quad -\tfrac{1}{2}a \leqslant x \leqslant \tfrac{1}{2}a.$$

(v)
$$y = \begin{cases} -1, & 0 < x \leqslant \tfrac{1}{3}a, \\ 0, & \tfrac{1}{3}a < x \leqslant \tfrac{2}{3}a, \\ 1, & \tfrac{2}{3}a < x \leqslant a. \end{cases}$$

(vi)
$$y = \begin{cases} -(x+\tfrac{1}{4}a), & -\tfrac{1}{2}a \leqslant x \leqslant 0, \\ x-\tfrac{1}{4}a, & 0 \leqslant x \leqslant \tfrac{1}{2}a. \end{cases}$$

5. State which of the functions defined in 4(i)–(vi) are even functions and which are odd.

6. A function $f(x)$ satisfies the relation
$$2f(u) \cos v = f(u+v)+f(u-v)$$

for all real values of u and v.
     Show that for real values of x,

(i) $f(x)+f(-x) = 2a \cos x$,

(ii) $f(\pi-x)+f(-x) = 0$,

(iii) $f(\pi-x)+f(x) = 2b \sin x$,

where a and b are certain constants and hence deduce that, for all real values of x,

(iv) $f(x) = a \cos x + b \sin x.$

1:2 The roots of equations

If $f(a) = 0$, then $x = a$ is said to be a *root* of the equation $f(x) = 0$ or a zero of the function $f(x)$. At present we only consider equations in which the numerical coefficients are real, i.e., the coefficients do not involve $i = \sqrt{(-1)}$ which is a root of the equation $x^2 + 1 = 0$. Consideration of complex roots, i.e., roots involving i, is deferred to Chapter VII. However, it may be stated here that, if $\alpha + i\beta$ is a complex root of an equation with real coefficients, $\alpha - i\beta$ is also a complex root so that complex roots occur in conjugate pairs.

If $f(x)$ is the polynomial $p_n(x)$ where

$$p_n(x) \equiv a_n x^n + a_{n-1} x^{n-1} + \ldots + a_1 x + a_0 \equiv \sum_{r=0}^{n} a_r x^r, \quad (1.5)$$

then it may be shown that the equation $p_n(x) = 0$ has n roots, α_1, α_2, ..., α_n and, by the factor theorem,

$$p_n(x) \equiv a_n(x - \alpha_1)(x - \alpha_2) \ldots (x - \alpha_n) \equiv a_n \prod_{r=1}^{n} (x - \alpha_r). \quad (1.6)$$

Comparison of the coefficients of powers of x in eqns. (1.5) and (1.6) gives

$$\Sigma \alpha_1 = -\frac{a_{n-1}}{a_n}, \quad \Sigma \alpha_1 \alpha_2 = \frac{a_{n-2}}{a_n}, \quad \Sigma \alpha_1 \alpha_2 \alpha_3 = -\frac{a_{n-3}}{a_n},$$

$$\ldots, \alpha_1 \alpha_2 \ldots \alpha_n = (-1)^n \frac{a_0}{a_n}. \quad (1.7)$$

It should be noted that if $\sum_{r=0}^{n} a_r x^r = 0$ for more than n values of x, then $\sum_{r=0}^{n} a_r x^r \equiv 0$ and all the coefficients are zero, i.e. $a_0 = a_1 = a_2 = \ldots = a_n = 0$. Thus an equation of the nth degree in x with more than n roots is satisfied for all values of x.

Example 1. The equation $x^2 - 5x + 4 = 0$ has roots 1, 4. The sum and product of these roots are 5, 4 respectively.

Example 2. The roots α_1, α_2 of $ax^2 + bx + c = 0$ satisfy the equations

$$\alpha_1 + \alpha_2 = -\frac{b}{a}, \quad \alpha_1\alpha_2 = \frac{c}{a}.$$

Example 3. The roots α, β, γ of $x^3 + px^2 + qx + r = 0$ satisfy the equations

$$\alpha + \beta + \gamma = -p, \quad \alpha\beta + \beta\gamma + \gamma\alpha = q, \quad \alpha\beta\gamma = -r.$$

Example 4. The equation

$$ax^4 + bx^3 + cx^2 + dx + e = 0, \tag{1}$$

where a and e are not zero, has roots α, β, γ, δ. Show how it is possible to obtain $s_n = \alpha^n + \beta^n + \gamma^n + \delta^n$ in terms of the coefficients a, b, c, d, e for all values of n, where n is a positive or negative integer.

Obtain the equations whose roots are

(i) α^2, β^2, γ^2, δ^2;

(ii) $\alpha - 3$, $\beta - 3$, $\gamma - 3$, $\delta - 3$.

Since e is not zero, none of α, β, γ, δ vanishes. By eqns. (1.7) above

$$\Sigma\alpha = -b/a, \quad \Sigma\alpha\beta = c/a, \quad \Sigma\alpha\beta\gamma = -d/a, \quad \alpha\beta\gamma\delta = e/a.$$

Hence $\quad s_1 = -b/a, \quad s_2 = (\Sigma\alpha)^2 - 2\Sigma\alpha\beta = (b^2 - 2ac)/a^2$.

Also $\quad s_0 = \Sigma\alpha^0 = 4, \quad s_{-1} = \Sigma\dfrac{1}{\alpha} = \dfrac{\Sigma\alpha\beta\gamma}{\alpha\beta\gamma\delta} = -\dfrac{d}{e}$.

Since $x = \alpha$ satisfies eqn. (1) it also satisfies the equation

$$x^n(ax^4 + bx^3 + cx^2 + dx + e) = 0,$$

i.e. $\quad ax^{n+4} + bx^{n+3} + cx^{n+2} + dx^{n+1} + ex^n = 0, \tag{2}$

for all n. Now writing $x = \alpha$, β, γ, δ in turn in eqn. (2) and adding the four resulting equations gives

$$as_{n+4} + bs_{n+3} + cs_{n+2} + ds_{n+1} + es_n = 0. \tag{3}$$

Putting $n = -1$ in eqn. (3) and using the values of s_2, s_1, s_0, s_{-1} already calculated enables us to calculate s_3. Then s_n for any other value of n can be calculated by successive applications of eqn. (3).

(i) If x satisfies eqn. (1) and

$$y = x^2, \tag{4}$$

then elimination of x between (1) and (4) gives an equation for y whose roots are α^2, etc., thus

$$ay^2 + cy + e + (by + d)\sqrt{y} = 0,$$

i.e. $\quad (ay^2 + cy + e)^2 = (by + d)^2 y,$

which gives the required equation.

(ii) In this case the required equation (in y) is obtained by eliminating x between eqn. (1) and the equation $y = x - 3$.

Example 5. Solve the equations
$$x+y+z = 2, \quad x^2+y^2+z^2 = 14, \quad xyz = -6.$$

These equations are symmetric in x, y, z and we therefore take x, y, z to be the roots of the cubic equation
$$\theta^3 + \lambda\theta^2 + \mu\theta + \nu = 0.$$
Using $\Sigma x = -\lambda$, etc., we find $\lambda = -2$, $\mu = -5$, $\nu = 6$ so that x, y, z are roots of the cubic
$$\theta^3 - 2\theta^2 - 5\theta + 6 = 0.$$

This equation has roots $\theta = -2$, 1, 3 and accordingly the solution of the given equations is that x, y, z can take any of the (six) permutations of the numbers -2, 1, 3.

Example 6. Find the condition that the two equations
$$x^2+2ax+b^2 = 0, \quad x^3+3p^2x+q^3 = 0$$
should have a common root.

If this root is α, then
$$\alpha^2+2a\alpha+b^2 = 0, \quad \alpha^3+3p^2\alpha+q^3 = 0, \qquad (1), (2)$$
and the required relation is obtained by eliminating α from these equations thus:

Equation (2) — α eqn. (1) gives
$$-2a\alpha^2+(3p^2-b^2)\alpha+q^3 = 0. \tag{3}$$
Then $2a$ eqn. (1) + eqn. (3) gives
$$(4a^2+3p^2-b^2)\alpha+(2ab^2+q^3) = 0.$$
Substitution for α in eqn. (1) gives the required result.

If all the α's above are real and different, the equation $p_n(x) = 0$ has n simple roots and $p_n(x)$ is expressible as the product of n linear, i.e., first degree, factors in x. If, however, r of the α's are equal so that $\alpha_1 = \alpha_2 = \ldots = \alpha_r$, then the equation has a multiple (r-fold) root α_1.

Example 1. The equation $x^3-6x^2+11x-6 \equiv (x-1)(x-2)(x-3) = 0$ has three simple roots 1, 2, 3.

Example 2. The equation
$$x^5+3x^4-6x^3-26x^2-27x-9 \equiv (x+1)^3(x-3)(x+3) = 0$$
has the triple root -1 and the simple roots 3, -3. We express this by saying that this equation has roots -1, -1, -1, 3, -3.

Location of roots. Equations arising in practical problems have frequently to be solved by numerical techniques in which the first step is to "locate" the roots by finding their approximate values. Many equations can be expressed in the form $f_1(x) = f_2(x)$ where $f_1(x)$ and $f_2(x)$ are continuous functions [see § 1 : 4] whose graphs are easy to draw. If the curves $y = f_1(x)$ and $y = f_2(x)$, intersect where $x = b$, then $x = b$ is a root of the equation

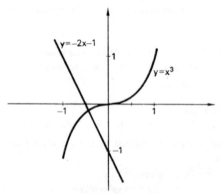

FIG. 1.5. Graphs of $y = x^3$ and $y = -2x - 1$.

$f_1(x) - f_2(x) = 0$. Fig. 1.5 shows the curve $y = x^3$ and the straight line $y = -2x - 1$; we infer from this figure that the equation $x^3 + 2x + 1 = 0$ has a root near $x = -0.45$ and no other real root.

An alternative method for locating the real roots of the polynomial equation $f(x) = 0$ is to consider the alterations of sign of $f(x)$ as x increases from large negative to large positive numbers. If $f(a) < 0, f(b) > 0$ where $a < b$, then $f(x)$ alters its sign at least once as x increases from a to b. This implies that an odd number of real roots of the equation $f(x) = 0$ lie between a and b. The same result holds if $f(a) > 0$ and $f(b) < 0$.

Example. If $f(x) = x^3 + 2x^2 - 3x - 3$, then

$$f(-3) = -3, \quad f(-2) = 3, \quad f(-1) = 1, \quad f(0) = -3, \quad f(1) = -3, \quad f(2) = 7.$$

Therefore the equation $x^3 + 2x^2 - 3x - 3 = 0$ has roots between -3 and -2, between -1 and 0, and between 1 and 2. Since this equation is a cubic in x and therefore has at most 3 real roots, we have located all the roots.

A closer examination shows that $f(1\cdot4) < 0, f(1\cdot5) > 0$; therefore one of the roots lies between $1\cdot4$ and $1\cdot5$. It is left to the reader to locate the other roots more precisely.

It must not be assumed that the equation $f(x) = 0$ has no root in the interval $a \leqslant x \leqslant b$ if $f(a)$ and $f(b)$ have the same sign. The equation may have an even number of real roots in this interval. The location of the roots of an equation is a tentative affair and usually a combination of graphical and "alteration of sign" techniques is advisable. In this connection we may employ *Descartes' rule of signs* which states: *If $f(x)$ is a polynomial, the number of positive roots of the equation $f(x) = 0$ cannot exceed the number of changes of sign of the numerical coefficients of $f(x)$. The number of negative roots cannot exceed the number of changes of sign of the numerical coefficients of $f(-x)$.* Here a "change of sign" occurs when a term with a positive coefficient is followed by one with a negative coefficient or vice versa.

Example 1. The equation $f(x) = x^3 + 4x - 2 = 0$ can have at most one positive root. Since $f(-x) = -x^3 - 4x - 2$, the equation has no negative roots. Further, the equation is a cubic and must have at least one real root (complex roots occur in pairs); therefore the equation has one positive root. Since $f(0) < 0$ and $f(0\cdot5) > 0$ this root lies between 0 and $0\cdot5$.

Example 2. $x^5 + 4x^3 - 18x^2 + 3x + 1 = 0$.

Descartes' rule indicates that this equation has at most two positive roots and one negative root. Further, since $f(-1) < 0$, $f(0) > 0$, $f(1) < 0$, $f(2) < 0$, $f(3) > 0$, the equation has three real roots which lie between -1 and 0, 0 and 1, 2 and 3.

If the equation $f(x) = 0$ involves transcendental functions, it may have an infinite number of real roots. In this case graphical methods usually indicate the approximate values of the roots. Figure 1.6(a), showing the graphs of $y = \tan x$ and $y = x$, indicates that the equation $\tan x = x$ has roots at $x = 0$ and near $\pm(n + \frac{1}{2})\pi$ where n is an integer. Figure 1.6(b), showing the graphs of $y = \sin x$ and $y = 2/x$, gives the location of the roots of the equation $x \sin x = 2$. In this case also alteration of the sign of $f(x)$ between $x = a$ and $x = b$ may imply that an odd number of

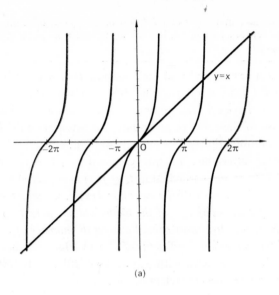

(a)

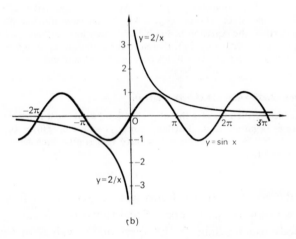

(b)

Fig. 1.6. (a) Graphs of $y = \tan x$ and $y = x$. (b) Graphs of $y = \sin x$ and $y = 2/x$.

roots of the equation $f(x) = 0$ lie between a and b. However, discontinuities in the function $f(x)$ may invalidate this result, cf. § 1 : 4.

Example. *Horner's method.* There is a systematic method, called Horner's method, of obtaining to any desired degree of accuracy the real roots of a polynomial equation. For any particular root this method consists of repeated applications of a cycle of three operations, each cycle providing one integer of the decimal expression of the root. The procedure is as follows:

Suppose the equation $f(x) = 0$, where $f(x)$ is a polynomial, has a root lying between n and $n+1$ where n is an integer. The cycle of operations starts here after n has been found. The substitution $x = n+y_1$ gives an equation for y_1, of the form $f(n+y_1) \equiv g_1(y_1) = 0$, which has a root lying between 0 and 1. The substitution $y_1 = x_1/10$ transforms this equation into $g_1(x_1/10) = 0$, or $f_1(x_1) = 0$, whose roots are ten times those of the equation $g_1(y_1) = 0$. In particular, this equation, $f_1(x_1) = 0$, will have a root lying between 0 and 10, i.e., between n_1 and n_1+1, where n_1 is an integer lying between 0 and 9 inclusive. This completes the first cycle of operations. The substitution $x_1 = n_1+y_2$, followed by $y_2 = x_2/10$ leads to the equation $f_2(x_2) = 0$ which has a root lying between 0 and 10. This lies between n_2 and n_2+1, where n_2 is the figure in the second decimal place of the root. This completes the second cycle of operations. The cycles are repeated until the required degree of accuracy is obtained, the root being $n \cdot n_1 n_2 n_3 \ldots$.

In illustration we find an approximate value of $\sqrt{2}$ by solving the equation $x^2 - 2 = 0$ by Horner's method.

$f(x) = x^2 - 2$, $f(1) = -1$, $f(2) = 2$. Therefore the integral part of the root is $n = 1$.

(i) *First cycle.*

$$g_1(y_1) = (1+y_1)^2 - 2 = y_1^2 + 2y_1 - 1.$$

$$g_1\left(\frac{x_1}{10}\right) = \left(\frac{x_1}{10}\right)^2 + 2\left(\frac{x_1}{10}\right) - 1 = 0.$$

Clearing of fractions leads to $f_1(x_1) = x_1^2 + 20x_1 - 100 = 0$.
Since $f_1(4) = -4$, $f_1(5) = 25$, the first decimal figure is $n_1 = 4$.

(ii) *Second cycle.*

$$g_2(y_2) = (4+y_2)^2 + 20(4+y_2) - 100 = y_2^2 + 28y_2 - 4 = 0.$$

$$f_2(x_2) = x_2^2 + 280x_2 - 400 = 0.$$

Since $f_2(1) = -119$, $f_2(2) = 164$, the second decimal figure is $n_2 = 1$.

(iii) *Third cycle.*

$$g_3(y_3) = (1+y_3)^2 + 280(1+y_3) - 400 = y_3^2 + 282y_3 - 119 = 0.$$

$$f_3(x_3) = x_3^2 + 2820x_3 - 11{,}900 = 0.$$

Since $f_3(4) = -604$, $f_3(5) = 2225$, the third decimal figure is $n_3 = 4$.

The square root of 2 is therefore 1·41 *correct* to two decimal places; the actual value is 1·414 .... It is clear that the coefficients in the later cycles become large, often unmanageably so. This, however, is not always a disadvantage because x_r is always less than 10 so that higher powers may sometimes be neglected and a good approximate value obtained from the last two terms of the equation $f_r(x_r) = 0$. In the third cycle of the above calculation we may take an approximate value

$$x_3 = \frac{11900}{2820} = 4.21\ldots.$$

This indicates that the root of $x^2 - 2 = 0$ is 1·414 *correct* to 3 decimal places.

The derivation of $f_r(x_r)$ from $g_r(y_r)$ is comparatively simple in this example, but, in general, may involve awkward coefficients if decimals occur in the coefficients of $f(x)$. It is therefore essential that the whole process should be set out in tabular form so that checks can easily be carried out. Space does not permit us to give details of such a tabular arrangement here.

Linear equations, i.e. equations of the first order in x, y, z, etc., are considered in detail in Vol. 2, Chap. III.

Exercises 1 : 2

1. Locate the real roots of the following equations to the nearest unit; i.e. find the consecutive integers between which the roots lie:

(i) $x^3 + 2x^2 + 5 = 0,$

(ii) $x^3 - 4x + 2 = 0,$

(iii) $x^3 + 8x^2 - 32x + 14 = 0,$

(iv) $x^4 - 2x - 1 = 0,$

(v) $3x^4 + 4x^3 - 12x^2 + 1 = 0.$

2. Show that the equation $x^{1\cdot5} - 24 \lg x + 4 \sin 2x = 4\cdot12$ has a root lying between $x = 1$ and $x = 2$. [The notation "$\lg x$" stands for $\log_{10} x$.]

3. Show that the equation $x(1 - \ln x) = 0\cdot5$ has a root lying between $x = 0\cdot1$ and $x = 0\cdot2$.

4. Use Horner's method to find the largest real root of each of the eqns. 1(i) − (v) correct to two significant figures.

5. By means of a sketch graph, or otherwise, show that the roots of the equation $x^3 + 3x^2 - 3 = 0$ are all real. Find the positive root correct to three places of decimals.

6. Assuming that the equation

$$4x^3 - 24x^2 + kx - 30 = 0$$

has its roots in arithmetical progression, find the value of k and solve the equation.

7. Find all the real roots of the following equations in x:

(i) $\cos(\pi \sin x) = \frac{1}{2};$

(ii) $\cos 2x + 2 \cos \alpha \cos x - 2 \cos 2\alpha = 1.$

8. Solve the equations

$$x + \frac{1}{yz} = 1, \qquad y + \frac{1}{zx} = 2, \qquad z + \frac{1}{xy} = 4.$$

9. Solve the equations

$$x+y+z = 7,$$
$$x^2+y^2+z^2 = 31,$$
$$x^3+y^3+z^3 = 154.$$

10. Prove that a periodic function cannot be a rational function.

11. Draw on the same graph and with the same scales the graphs of $y = \sin x$ and $4y = 3x - 1$ for values of x between 0 and π. Hence estimate the value of x in this range for which $4 \sin x = 3x - 1$.

1:3 Elementary two-dimensional coordinate geometry

Coordinate systems. In two-dimensional coordinate geometry it is usually convenient to fix the position of a point P by means of its distances x, y from two perpendicular straight lines Oy, Ox respectively [see Fig. 1.7(a)]; i.e. we use *rectangular cartesian axes*

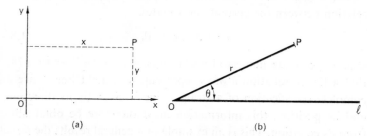

Fig. 1.7. (a) Cartesian coordinates. (b) Polar coordinates.

Ox, Oy with *origin O*. The coordinate x is taken to be positive if P is to the right of Oy and negative if P is to the left; similarly y is positive if P is above Ox and negative if P is below. The coordinate axes divide the plane into four quadrants, the first quadrant being that for which $x > 0$ and $y > 0$, the second that for which $x < 0$, $y > 0$, and so on in the counter-clockwise sense of rotation about O.

Some problems are best handled by using *polar coordinates* (see Fig. 1.7(b)) in which the position of P is determined by its distance r from the origin or *pole O*, and by the angle θ between a line Ol, the *initial line*, and the line OP, θ being measured positively in the counter-clockwise sense .The *radius vector* is the name given to OP and its length r is taken to be positive; the point $(-r, \theta)$ should be interpreted as $(r, \theta+\pi)$. The point $(r, -\theta)$ is the optical image of the point (r, θ) in the initial line. Usually, cartesian and polar coordinates are related by taking the origin at the pole and Ox along the initial line, when $x = r \cos \theta$ and $y = r \sin \theta$.

An equation $y = f(x)$ or $g(x, y) = 0$ represents a curve, the x, y in the equation, which are called *current coordinates*, being the coordinates of an arbitrary unspecified point on the curve. The equation is the condition which these coordinates must satisfy if the point is to lie on the curve. As the coordinates x, y satisfying the equation alter, so the point runs along the curve. Coordinate geometry consists of obtaining geometrical information and properties from the equations of curves.

The straight line. The simplest type of equation is a linear relation between the current coordinates,

$$ax+by+c = 0, \tag{1.8}$$

where a, b, c are numerical coefficients. We prove later (p. 178) that a linear equation always represents a straight line. Since a complete specification of a straight line is given by its direction and its position, this information must therefore be obtainable from its equation. This is an example of a general result: the *form* of the equation (here linear in x, y) gives information about the type of curve (a straight line); the *coefficients* give the details of size, position, etc., of the particular curve or *locus* represented.

The equation of a given curve may be expressed in different forms. Each form displays some specific feature of the curve. In illustration we give now some of the forms which may be assumed by the equation of a straight line.

(i) $$p(x-x_0)+q(y-y_0) = 0. \tag{1.9}$$

This is a straight line through the point (x_0, y_0).

(ii) $$\left(\frac{x}{a}\right) + \left(\frac{y}{b}\right) = 1. \tag{1.10}$$

This is a straight line making (signed) intercepts a, b on the axes

Ox, Oy respectively.

(iii) $\qquad x \cos \alpha + y \sin \alpha = p \quad$ or $\quad lx + my = p \qquad$ (1.11)

where $l^2 + m^2 = 1$. This is the *normal* form of the equation. The term p is the length of the normal (or perpendicular) from the origin to the line, and α is the angle this normal makes with Ox.

(iv) $\qquad\qquad\qquad y = mx + c. \qquad\qquad\qquad$ (1.12)

This is a straight line with gradient m passing through the point $(0, c)$ on Oy. The *gradient* of a line is the tangent of the angle, ψ, (lying in the 1st or 4th quadrants) between the line and Ox.

Example 1. The equation $3x + 4y = 7$ represents a straight line. It may be put in the form

(i) $\qquad\qquad\qquad 3(x-1) + 4(y-1) = 0,$

showing that it passes through $(1, 1)$, or

(ia) $\qquad\qquad\qquad 3(x+1) + 4(y - \tfrac{5}{2}) = 0,$

showing that it passes through $(-1, \tfrac{5}{2})$.

It can be put in the form

(ii) $\qquad\qquad\qquad \dfrac{x}{\tfrac{7}{3}} + \dfrac{y}{\tfrac{7}{4}} = 1,$

showing the intercepts $\tfrac{7}{3}$ and $\tfrac{7}{4}$ on Ox, Oy respectively.

Dividing the equation by $\sqrt{(3^2 + 4^2)} = 5$ gives

(iii) $\qquad \tfrac{3}{5}x + \tfrac{4}{5}y - \tfrac{7}{5} \equiv x \cos \alpha + y \sin \alpha - p = 0.$

This shows that the perpendicular distance from the origin is $\tfrac{7}{5}$ and $\cos \alpha = \tfrac{3}{5}$, $\sin \alpha = \tfrac{4}{5}$.

It can be written

(iv) $\qquad\qquad\qquad y = -\tfrac{3}{4}x + \tfrac{7}{4},$

indicating a gradient $-\tfrac{3}{4}$ and an intercept $\tfrac{7}{4}$ on Oy.

The reader will realise that of these alternative forms the *intercept* form (ii), the *normal* form (iii), and the *gradient-intercept* form (iv), are unique. There are infinitely many possible ways of writing the equation in the form (i).

Example 2. The perpendicular distance of (x_0, y_0) from the line whose equation is given by (1.8).

First we transform this to the normal form

$$x \cos \alpha + y \sin \alpha = p$$

where

$$\cos \alpha = \frac{a}{\sqrt{(a^2 + b^2)}}, \qquad \sin \alpha = \frac{b}{\sqrt{(a^2 + b^2)}}, \qquad p = -\frac{c}{\sqrt{(a^2 + b^2)}}. \qquad (1)$$

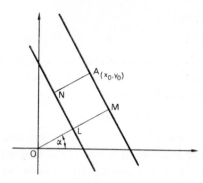

FIG. 1.8.

The line parallel to this through (x_0, y_0) is

$$(x - x_0) \cos \alpha + (y - y_0) \sin \alpha = 0,$$

i.e. $$x \cos \alpha + y \sin \alpha = p_1,$$

where $p_1 = x_0 \cos \alpha + y_0 \sin \alpha$ is the distance of this line from the origin. In Fig. 1.8, $p = OL$, $p_1 = OM$ and the required perpendicular distance is

$$NA = OM - OL = p_1 - p$$
$$= x_0 \cos \alpha + y_0 \sin \alpha - p$$
$$= \frac{ax_0 + by_0 + c}{\sqrt{(a^2 + b^2)}}.$$

In eqn. (1) we may choose either $\pm$ sign for the square root. That sign is chosen so that the value of p is positive. Then the sign of NA is negative if A lies on the side of the given line opposite to the origin.

Example 3. The bisector of the angle between the lines $ax + by + c = 0$, $a'x + b'y + c' = 0$. The bisector is the locus of a point whose perpendicular distances from each of the two lines are numerically equal. If the point is (x_0, y_0), then

$$\frac{ax_0 + by_0 + c}{\sqrt{(a^2 + b^2)}} = \frac{a'x_0 + b'y_0 + c'}{\sqrt{(a'^2 + b'^2)}} \quad \text{or} \quad \frac{ax_0 + by_0 + c}{\sqrt{(a^2 + b^2)}} = -\frac{a'x_0 + b'y_0 + c'}{\sqrt{(a'^2 + b'^2)}}.$$

These are the equations of the two bisectors. [Note that they are both of the form $ax + by + c + \lambda(a'x + b'y + c') = 0$.]

Example 4. If the lines of Example 3 are perpendicular, prove that $aa' + bb' = 0$.

The lines may be written

$$y = -\left(\frac{a}{b}\right)x - \left(\frac{c}{b}\right), \quad y = -\left(\frac{a'}{b'}\right)x - \left(\frac{c'}{b'}\right).$$

Hence their gradients are

$$\tan \psi = -\left(\frac{a}{b}\right), \qquad \tan\left(\psi + \frac{1}{2}\pi\right) = -\left(\frac{a'}{b'}\right).$$

$$\therefore \ -\left(\frac{a}{b}\right) = +\frac{1}{\left(\dfrac{a'}{b'}\right)},$$

i.e.,
$$aa' + bb' = 0.$$

The circle. It is easy to see that the distance r between the points (g, f) and (x, y) is given by

$$r^2 = (x-g)^2 + (y-f)^2.$$

Regarding x, y as variables and keeping r fixed this relation becomes

$$x^2 + y^2 - 2gx - 2fy + g^2 + f^2 - r^2 = 0$$

or
$$x^2 + y^2 - 2gx - 2fy + c = 0, \tag{1.13}$$

where $c = g^2 + f^2 - r^2$, which is the general form of the equation of a circle with centre at (g, f) and radius r. The features which show that an equation represents a circle are the absence of a product term xy and equality of the coefficients of x^2 and y^2. The remaining coefficients determine the size and position of the circle.

For example

$$x^2 + y^2 = a^2, \ a > 0 \tag{1.14}$$

is the equation of a circle with centre at the origin ($f = 0 = g$) and radius a.

Example 1. Find the centres and radii of the circles

    (a) $x^2 + y^2 - 2x - 4y + 1 = 0$,   (b) $3x^2 + 3y^2 - 5x + 4y - 7 = 0$,

    (c) $4x^2 + 4y^2 + 1 = 0$.

Equation (a) may be put in the form

$$(x-1)^2 + (y-2)^2 = -1 + 1 + 4 = 4.$$

Hence the centre is at $(1, 2)$ and the radius is 2.

Equation (b) must first be divided by 3 to give the equation

$$x^2 + y^2 - \tfrac{5}{3}x + \tfrac{4}{3}y - \tfrac{7}{3} = 0.$$

Hence the centre is at $(\tfrac{5}{6}, -\tfrac{2}{3})$ and the radius is $(5\sqrt{5})/6$.

Equation (c). This equation is not satisfied by any real values of x and y, and therefore does not represent any real locus.

Example 2. Obtain equations of the circles whose centres and radii are

$$\text{(a)} \quad (3, 4), 5; \quad \text{(b)} \quad (0, \tfrac{1}{2}), 1.$$

(a) $(x-3)^2+(y-4)^2 = 25$ or $x^2+y^2-6x-8y = 0$.

This circle passes through the origin.

(b) $(x-0)^2+(y-\tfrac{1}{2})^2 = 1$ or $4x^2+4y^2-4y-3 = 0$.

Example 3. Find the condition that the two circles

$$x^2+y^2+2g_rx+2f_ry+c_r = 0, \quad (r = 1, 2),$$

cut at right angles (i.e., cut orthogonally).

If the centres are A_1 and A_2 and B is one of the points of intersection, the triangle A_1BA_2 is right angled at B.

$$\therefore \ A_1A_2^2 = A_1B^2+A_2B^2.$$

Since A_1A_2 is the distance between the centres

$$A_1A_2^2 = (g_2-g_1)^2+(f_2-f_1)^2.$$

The squares of the radii are

$$A_1B^2 = r_1^2 = g_1^2+f_1^2-c_1, \quad A_2B^2 = r_2^2 = g_2^2+f_2^2-c_2.$$
$$\therefore \ (g_2-g_1)^2+(f_2-f_1)^2 = g_1^2+g_2^2+f_1^2+f_2^2-c_1-c_2,$$

i.e. $2g_1g_2+2f_1f_2 = c_1+c_2,$

is the required condition.

Example 4. Find the length of the tangent from a point $A(x_0, y_0)$ to the circle $x^2+y^2+2gx+2fy+c = 0$.

If C is the centre of the circle and T is the point of contact of the tangent, $AT^2 = AC^2-r^2$. Therefore

$$AT^2 = (x_0+g)^2+(y_0+f)^2-(g^2+f^2-c)$$

or

$$AT^2 = x_0^2+y_0^2+2gx_0+2fy_0+c.$$

Note that AT^2 is negative if the point A lies inside the circle. In fact the point A lies outside, on, or inside the circle according as $x_0^2+y_0^2+2gx_0+2fy_0+c$ is positive, zero, or negative respectively.

Example 5. Find the equation of the circle with $A(a, b)$ and $B(c, d)$ as the ends of a diameter.

Let $P(x, y)$ be any point on the circle, then the gradients of AP and BP are $(y-b)/(x-a)$ and $(y-d)/(x-c)$ respectively.

Since AB is a diameter these directions are perpendicular. Therefore

$$\left(\frac{y-b}{x-a}\right) \cdot \left(\frac{y-d}{x-c}\right) = -1.$$

Therefore the required equation is

$$(x-a)(x-c)+(y-b)(y-d) = 0.$$

The equation of the nth degree. Suppose that $f(x, y)$ is a polynomial of the nth degree in x and y together, i.e. if $a_{rs}x^ry^s$ is a typical term of $f(x, y)$, then n is the greatest value of $r+s$. Elimination of y between the equation $f(x, y) = 0$ and the equation $y = mx+c$ of an arbitrary straight line gives $f(x, mx+c) = 0$ which is, in general, an equation of the nth degree in x. The n roots of this equation give the x coordinates (abscissae) of the points in which the line meets the curve. This means that an arbitrary straight line meets a curve whose equation is of the nth degree in n points, some or all of which may be imaginary, i.e. correspond to complex roots of the equation in x.

Example. (i) $x^2+3xy+y^2-1 = 0$ represents a second degree curve or conic.

(ii) $x^3+y^3+3xy = 0$ represents a cubic curve.

(iii) $(x^2+y^2)^2-x^2+y^2 = 0$ represents a quartic curve.

These curves are met by an arbitrary straight line in 2, 3 and 4 points respectively.

The function $f(x, y)$ is said to be *homogeneous* in x and y and of the nth degree if $f(tx, ty) = t^nf(x, y)$ for all t.

Example. (i) $x^6+6x^4y^2+7xy^5$ is homogeneous and of the sixth degree.

(ii) $x \sin (y/x)+(y^2/x) \ln (x^2/y^2)$ is homogeneous and of the first degree.

If $f(x, y)$ is a homogeneous polynomial of the nth degree in x and y, then the equation $f(x, y) = 0$ may be expressed in the form

$$\prod_{r=1}^{n} (y-m_rx) = 0. \qquad (1.15)$$

Corresponding to each of these linear factors is a straight line through the origin and thus the locus represented by eqn. (1.15) consists of n straight lines through the origin.

Example 1. The equation $y^3+3xy^2-x^2y-3x^3 = 0$ is equivalent to $(y-x)(y+x)(y+3x) = 0$ and therefore represents the 3 straight lines $y-x = 0$, $y+x = 0$, $y+3x = 0$.

Example 2. Find the angle, θ, between the two lines represented by $ax^2+2hxy+by^2 = 0$.

The expression has real factors if $ab < h^2$, it is a perfect square if $ab = h^2$, and has no real factors if $ab > h^2$.

(a) $ab < h^2$. Suppose the lines are $y-m_1x = 0$, $y-m_2x = 0$. Then

$$\tan \theta = \frac{(m_1-m_2)}{1+m_1m_2}.$$

The equation $(y-m_1x)(y-m_2x) = 0$ must represent the same locus as $ax^2+2hxy+by^2 = 0$.

$$\therefore ax^2+2hxy+by^2 \equiv b(y-m_1x)(y-m_2x).$$

$$\therefore m_1+m_2 = -\frac{2h}{b}, \quad m_1m_2 = \frac{a}{b},$$

$$(m_1-m_2)^2 = 4\frac{(h^2-ab)}{b^2}.$$

$$\therefore \tan \theta = \pm\frac{2\sqrt{(h^2-ab)}}{(a+b)}.$$

(b) $ab = h^2$. Here $\tan \theta = 0$. This follows from the result (a) or from the fact that, $ax^2+2hxy+by^2$ being a perfect square, the equation represents two coincident straight lines.

(c) $ab > h^2$. There is no angle θ. The only real point on the locus is the origin.

Parametric coordinates. Frequently the equation of a curve is best given by expressing both x and y as functions of an independent variable t in the form

$$x = x(t), \quad y = y(t). \tag{1.16}$$

Here $x = x(t)$ is to be read as "x is a function of t". In this case the cartesian equation of the curve may be obtained by elimination of t between the equations, but in some cases problems are best solved without eliminating the parameter t.

Example 1. $x = g+r \cos t$, $y = f+r \sin t$, $0 \leqslant t \leqslant 2\pi$, are parametric equations of the circle $(x-g)^2+(y-f)^2 = r^2$.

Example 2. If x and y are the linear functions

$$x = \alpha t+\beta, \quad y = \alpha' t+\beta', \tag{1}$$

where α, α', β, β' are constants, the point (x, y) lies on the straight line

$$\frac{x-\beta}{\alpha} = \frac{y-\beta'}{\alpha'} (= t). \tag{2}$$

This straight line passes through the point (β, β') and makes an angle ψ with Ox where $\dfrac{\cos \psi}{\alpha} = \dfrac{\sin \psi}{\alpha'}$.

A fundamental technique of coordinate geometry. Suppose the equations of two plane curves referred to rectangular cartesian axes Oxy are $S_1(x, y) = 0$, $S_2(x, y) = 0$. Then the equation

$$S_1(x, y)+\lambda S_2(x, y) = 0, \tag{1.17}$$

where λ is a constant (parameter), is the equation of a plane curve which is satisfied identically when $S_1 = 0 = S_2$, i.e. eqn. (1.17) represents a plane curve which passes through all the points of intersection of S_1 and S_2. In general the parameter λ can be chosen to satisfy some other geometrical condition. If λ is made to vary, the equation $S_1+\lambda S_2 = 0$ represents different curves passing through these intersections. These curves are a family which is given the collective name of a "pencil".

Example 1. The equation

$$(3x+2y-3)+\lambda(4x-7y+6) = 0$$

represents a straight line l passing through the intersection of the lines l_1, l_2 with equations

$$3x+2y-3 = 0, \quad 4x-7y+6 = 0.$$

Choosing $\lambda (=\frac{1}{2})$ so that l passes through the origin gives the equation of the line through the origin and the intersection of l_1 and l_2.

Example 2. If two circles have equations

$$S_1 = x^2+y^2+2g_1x+2f_1y+c_1 = 0,$$
$$S_2 = x^2+y^2+2g_2x+2f_2y+c_2 = 0,$$

then $S_1+\lambda S_2 = 0$ represents a family of circles, a coaxial system passing through the points of intersection (if any) of S_1 and S_2. In particular the case

$\lambda = -1$ gives a straight line, the radical axis of the system, which passes through these points of intersection. (The system is called coaxial because the circles all have the same radical axis.)

Exercises 1 : 3

1. The following are the equations of four straight lines.

$$l_1 = 3x - 4y + 5 = 0, \quad l_2 = x + 2y - 4 = 0, \quad l_3 = 5x - y + 1 = 0,$$
$$l_4 = 8x + 6y - 3 = 0.$$

(i) Write down the equations of the lines parallel to l_1 passing through (a) the origin $(0, 0)$, (b) the point $(-1, 2)$, (c) the point $(5, 2)$.

(ii) Write down the equations of the lines perpendicular to each of the lines $l_1, \ldots, l_4$ passing through the point $(2, 1)$.

(iii) Find the perpendicular distance of the point $(2, 3)$ from each of the lines $l_1, \ldots, l_4$ and indicate by the sign whether $(2, 3)$ lies on the same, or the opposite, side of the line as the origin.

(iv) Obtain the equations of the bisectors of the angles between l_1 and l_4. Verify that these bisectors are at right angles.

(v) The lines l_1, l_2, l_3 are the sides of a triangle. Find the epuations of the altitudes of this triangle and verify that these altitudes are concurrent.

(vi) Find the equation of the line through the points of intersection of l_1, l_2 and l_3, l_4.

2. One side of an equilateral triangle is the line $x - \sqrt{3}y + 4 = 0$. Find the equations of the other sides if the opposite vertex is $(2, 3)$.

3. Find the condition that the three lines

$$a_r x + b_r y + c_r = 0 \qquad (r = 1, 2, 3)$$

should form a right-angled isosceles triangle with the line given by $r = 3$ as the hypotenuse.

4. Prove that the product of the perpendicular distances from $(ae, 0)$ and $(-ae, 0)$ to the line $(x/a) \cos \theta + (y/b) \sin \theta = 1$ is b^2, where $b^2 = a^2(1 - e^2)$ and θ is an arbitrary angle.

5. The equation of a straight line is given in terms of a parameter r by

$$\frac{x - a}{\cos \alpha} = \frac{y - b}{\sin \alpha} = r.$$

Prove that α is the angle between the direction of the line and Ox and that r is the distance along the line from (a, b) to the point (x, y).

6. Find the equation of the straight lines joining the points:

(i) $(1, 2)$ and $(3, 5)$. (ii) $(am^2, 2am)$ and $(an^2, 2an)$.

(iii) $(a \cos \theta, b \sin \theta)$ and $(a \cos \varphi, b \sin \varphi)$.

7. Find the centres and radii of the following circles:

(i) $$x^2 + y^2 + 6x + 5y = 0.$$

(ii) $$(x - 1)(x - 2) + (y - 3)(y - 4) = 0.$$

(iii) $$x^2 + y^2 - 2x - 4 = 0.$$

(iv) $$8x^2 + 8y^2 + 24x - 8y + 15 = 0.$$

8. Obtain the equations of the circles whose centres and radii are

(i) $(-1, 2)$ 3,   (ii) $(2, 4)$ 1,   (iii) $(3, -2)$ 5,   (iv) $(-\frac{1}{2}, \frac{1}{4})$ 1.

9. Find the equations of the circles whose centres are at $(-3, 2)$ and $(1, 4)$

(i) if the circles pass through the origin,

(ii) if the circles pass through $(1, 3)$.

10. Show that the points $(-1, 2)$, $(3, 1)$, $(-1, 1)$, $(3, 2)$ all lie on the circle

$$x^2 + y^2 - 2x - 3y - 1 = 0.$$

Find the equations of the tangents to the circle at each of these points. (The tangent is perpendicular to the radius at its point of contact.)

1 : 4 Limits and continuity

The two ideas introduced in this section are very important and have to be given precise meanings. Continuity is represented graphically by a curve without gaps; a more formal definition is given below. The idea of a limit is associated with the behaviour of a function $f(x)$ as x approaches a given value from above or below.

If, as x takes values approaching the number a, the function $f(x)$ takes values approaching the number l so that $|f(x) - l|$ may be made less than any assigned positive number ε, however small, provided $|x - a|$ is made sufficiently small, we say that $f(x)$ tends to the *limit l* as x tends to a. We write this symbolically

$$\lim_{x \to a} f(x) = l. \tag{1.18}$$

As an important illustrative example we prove that, if n is a positive integer,

$$\lim_{x \to a} \frac{x^n - a^n}{x - a} = na^{n-1}. \tag{1.19}$$

By long division, we find

$$\frac{x^n - a^n}{x - a} = x^{n-1} + ax^{n-2} + a^2 x^{n-3} + \ldots + a^{n-2}x + a^{n-1}.$$

Letting $x \to a$ the result (1.19) follows. It is proved in books on analysis that this result is valid for all real numbers n and a, rational or irrational, positive or negative except when both $a = 0$ and $n < 0$. Note that $\lim_{x \to a} f(x)$ is not necessarily equal to

$f(a)$. For example, when $x = a$ the function $(x^n - a^n)/(x - a)$ takes the form $0/0$ which is meaningless.

It follows at once from the definition (1.1) of $\sin x$ that

$$\lim_{x \to 0} \frac{\sin x}{x} = 1. \tag{1.20}$$

If $f(x)$ increases indefinitely as x tends to a we say that $f(x)$ tends to infinity and write $f(x) \to \infty$ as $x \to a$. For example, $1/|x| \to \infty$ as $x \to 0$. The function $1/x$ tends to ∞ or $-\infty$ according as $x \to 0$ from positive or negative values of x. We write these results in the form $\lim_{x \to 0+} 1/x = \infty$, $\lim_{x \to 0-} 1/x = -\infty$; here $x \to 0+$ and $x \to 0-$ are to be read as "x tends to zero from above" and "...below" respectively. It must be emphasised that infinity is not a number ∞ in the same sense that two is a number 2. Infinity cannot be used for the arithmetical processes of addition, multiplication, etc., as finite numbers are used.

If $\lim_{x \to a} f(x) = p$ and $\lim_{x \to a} g(x) = q$, where p and q are finite, then it may be shown that

(i)
$$\lim_{x \to a} \{f(x) \pm g(x)\} = p \pm q, \tag{1.21}$$

(ii)
$$\lim_{x \to a} \{f(x) \cdot g(x)\} = pq, \tag{1.22}$$

(iii)
$$\lim_{x \to a} \left\{ \frac{f(x)}{g(x)} \right\} = \frac{p}{q}. \qquad (q \neq 0) \tag{1.23}$$

If $p \neq 0$ and $q = 0$, $\lim_{x \to a} \{f(x)/g(x)\}$ is infinite. If $p = 0 = q$ equation (1.23) is meaningless.

If $\lim_{x \to a+} f(x) = f(a) = \lim_{x \to a-} f(x)$, then $f(x)$ is said to be *continuous* at $x = a$. If $f(x)$ is continuous for all x such that $a \leqslant x \leqslant b$, we say that $f(x)$ is continuous in the interval $a \leqslant x \leqslant b$. Essentially this implies that, if $f(x)$ is a continuous function, the curve C whose equation is $y = f(x)$ has no sudden jumps, i.e. from any point P of the curve C a pencil may be moved along the curve to reach any other point Q of the curve C without being lifted off the paper [see Fig. 1.9(a)].

If $\lim_{x \to a+} f(x) - \lim_{x \to a-} f(x)$ is finite and non zero, $f(x)$ is not

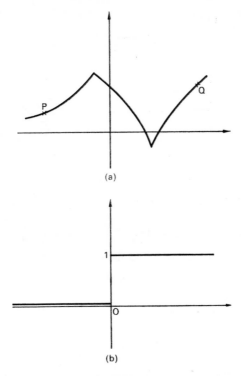

(a)

(b)

FIG. 1.9. (a) Graph of a continuous function. (b) Graph of Heaviside's unit function $H(x)$.

continuous at $x = a$ but it has a finite discontinuity there. For example Heaviside's unit function, $H(x)$, defined by $H(x) = 0$ for $x < 0$, $H(x) = 1$ for $x > 0$, has a finite discontinuity at $x = 0$ [see Fig. 1.9(b)]. The shearing force in a horizontal beam supported on knife edges is discontinuous at a support. If $\lim\limits_{x \to a+} f(x) - \lim\limits_{x \to a-} f(x)$ is infinite, then $f(x)$ has an infinite discontinuity at $x = a$. For example $\tan x$ has infinite discontinuities at the points $x = \pm(n + \frac{1}{2})\pi$ where n is an integer.

Example 1. The graphs of the functions $y = [x]$, $y = x - [x]$, where $[x]$ denotes the greatest integer not exceeding x, are given in Figs. 1.10(a), (b) respectively. Here "integer" includes "negative integer".
　　Note $[7\frac{1}{3}] = 7$, $[-2\frac{1}{2}] = -3$.

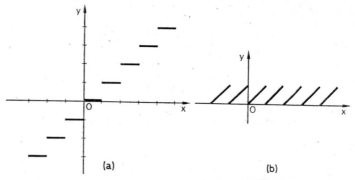

FIG. 1.10. (a) The graph $y = [x]$. (b) The graph $y = x - [x]$.

Example 2. $\lim_{x \to 0} \dfrac{\sin ax}{x} = \lim_{x \to 0} \dfrac{a \sin ax}{ax} = a \lim_{\theta \to 0} \dfrac{\sin \theta}{\theta} = a.$

Here we have written $ax = \theta$ so that we may use eqn. (1.20).

Example 3. $\lim_{\theta \to 0} \dfrac{1 - \cos \theta}{\theta^2} = \lim_{\theta \to 0} \dfrac{1 - \left(1 - \dfrac{\theta^2}{2!} + \dfrac{\theta^4}{4!} - \ldots\right)}{\theta^2}$

$$= \lim_{\theta \to 0} \left(\dfrac{1}{2!} - \dfrac{\theta^2}{4!} + \ldots\right) = \dfrac{1}{2}.$$

Example 4. $\lim_{x \to 0} \dfrac{1 - \sqrt{(1 - x^2)}}{x^2} = \lim_{x \to 0} \dfrac{1 - (1 - x^2)}{x^2\{1 + \sqrt{(1 - x^2)}\}}$

$$= \lim_{x \to 0} \dfrac{x^2}{x^2\{1 + \sqrt{(1 - x^2)}\}}$$

$$= \lim_{x \to 0} \dfrac{1}{1 + \sqrt{(1 - x^2)}} = \dfrac{1}{2}.$$

Example 5. In the equation

$$f(x) = \dfrac{k_1}{x - a_1} + \dfrac{k_2}{x - a_2} + \ldots + \dfrac{k_n}{x - a_n} = 0 \qquad (1)$$

the numbers k_i are positive and the a_i are distinct real numbers. Prove that the roots of the equation are all real.

Without loss of generality we can take $a_1 < a_2 < \ldots < a_{n-1} < a_n$. Then when $x < a_1$ all the quantities on the left hand side of eqn. (1) are negative, i.e. $f(x)$ is negative for $x < a_1$, and the equation has no root less than a_1. But $f(x)$ is continuous for $a_1 < x < a_2$ and $f(x) \to \infty$ as $x \to a_1 + 0$,

$f(x) \to -\infty$ as $x \to a_2 - 0$. Therefore $f(x)$ vanishes (the equation has a root) for some value of x in the interval (a_1, a_2). [Remember (a_1, a_2) represents the open interval $a_1 < x < a_2$.] Similarly, the equation $f(x) = 0$ has roots in each of the open intervals $(a_2, a_3), \ldots, (a_{n-1}, a_n)$ and so has $n-1$ real roots. But multiplication of eqn. (1) by $\prod\limits_{r=1}^{n} (x - a_r)$ shows that it is an equation of the $(n-1)$th degree in x and so has not more than $n-1$ roots and by the above these must be real.

Example 6. The function $\phi(x) = f(x)/|f(x)|$ is a discontinuous function and

$$\phi(x) = 1 \qquad \text{when} \quad f(x) > 0,$$
$$\phi(x) = -1 \qquad \text{when} \quad f(x) < 0.$$

Similarly, if $\psi(x) = \tfrac{1}{2}\{f(x) + |f(x)|\}/|f(x)|$,

$$\psi(x) = 1 \qquad \text{when} \quad f(x) > 0,$$
$$\psi(x) = 0 \qquad \text{when} \quad f(x) < 0.$$

When a function of several variables is considered the definition of continuity is a generalisation of that for a function of one variable. A function of more than one variable, $f(x_1, x_2, \ldots, x_p)$, is continuous "at the point" $x_1 = a_1$, $x_2 = a_2, \ldots, x_p = a_p$, if there is a quantity δ such that

$$|f(x_1, x_2, \ldots, x_p) - f(a_1, a_2, \ldots, a_p)| < \varepsilon \qquad (1.24)$$

for all $x_1, x_2, \ldots, x_p$ satisfying

$$|x_1 - a_1| < \delta, \quad |x_2 - a_2| < \delta, \ldots, |x_p - a_p| < \delta, \quad (1.25)$$

where ε is an arbitrary positive quantity. Expressed less formally this means that we can make the difference $f(x_1, x_2, \ldots, x_p) - f(a_1, a_2, \ldots, a_p)$ numerically as small as we please by choosing $x_1, x_2, \ldots, x_p$ sufficiently close, respectively, to $a_1, a_2, \ldots, a_p$. Another instructive way of expressing this is to say that

$$\lim f(x_1, x_2, \ldots, x_p) = f(a_1, a_2, \ldots, a_p)$$

when $x_1 \to a_1$, $x_2 \to a_2, \ldots, x_p \to a_p$, the variables tending to their respective limits *independently*. This last provision, tending independently to their limits, is important.

Example. Consider the simple function of two variables

$$f(x, y) = (x - y)/(x + y). \qquad (1)$$

When $x = 2, y = 1, f(x, y) = f(2, 1) = 1/3$. If we put $x = 2+\xi, y = 1+\eta$, then

$$f(x, y) = \frac{1+\xi-\eta}{3+\xi+\eta}.$$

Now,

$$\lim_{\xi \to 0} \lim_{\eta \to 0} f(x, y) = \lim_{\xi \to 0} \left(\frac{1+\xi}{3+\xi} \right) = \frac{1}{3},$$

and

$$\lim_{\eta \to 0} \lim_{\xi \to 0} f(x, y) = \lim_{\eta \to 0} \left(\frac{1-\eta}{3+\eta} \right) = \frac{1}{3}.$$

The result we obtain is in each case equal to $f(2, 1)$, however we make x and y tend to their respective limits.

The state of affairs is very different at $x = 0, y = 0$. No meaning attaches to $f(0, 0)$ since it is of the form $0/0$; nor can we give f a special value at this point to make it continuous. By putting $y = kx$, with x and y tending to zero simultaneously

$$\lim_{x, y \to 0} f(x, y) = \lim_{x \to 0} \left\{ \frac{(1-k)x}{(1+k)x} \right\} = \frac{1-k}{1+k}. \tag{2}$$

By a suitable choice of k the last limit can be made to take any value whatever. Hence eqns. (1.24) and (1.25) cannot be satisfied (it is impossible to find δ) and $f(x, y)$ is not continuous at $(0, 0)$.

The result of the above example illustrates an important fact, viz. that the result of two limiting processes may be altered if the order of these limits is interchanged.

Exercises 1 : 4

1. Find the limit of each of the following functions as $x \to 0$:

(i) $\dfrac{\tan ax}{x}$, (ii) $\dfrac{\tan px}{\tan qx}$, (iii) $\dfrac{3x+1}{4x+1}$, (iv) $\cos x$, (v) $\sin\left(\dfrac{1}{x}\right)$.

2. Find the limits of the following functions as $x \to \infty$:

(i) $\sqrt{(1+x+x^2)} - x$, (ii) $\sqrt{(x+1)} - \sqrt{x}$, (iii) $\dfrac{x+2}{x^2+x+1}$,

(iv) $\dfrac{x^2+6x+4}{3x^2+7x+2}$, (v) $\dfrac{7x^2+2x+5}{4x^2+13}$.

3. Find

(i) $\lim\limits_{x \to a} \dfrac{\sqrt{(3x-a)} - \sqrt{(x+a)}}{(x-a)}$, (ii) $\lim\limits_{x \to \frac{1}{2}\pi - 0} (\sec x - \tan x)$.

4. The velocity of a train between two stations is given by

$$v = a(t^3 - 3t^2), \qquad 0 \leqslant t < 2,$$
$$v = b, \qquad 2 \leqslant t < 4,$$
$$v = c(2t^3 - 27t^2 + 120t - 175), \qquad 4 \leqslant t \leqslant 5.$$

Find a and c in terms of b assuming that the velocity is continuous. Draw a rough sketch of the velocity-time curve.

5. Sketch the graphs of the following functions:

(i) $\dfrac{\sin \omega t}{|\sin \omega t|}$,   (ii) $\dfrac{x(x^2-1)}{|x(x^2-1)|}$.

1 : 5 Orders of magnitude

Whenever an approximate relation is used, some knowledge of its accuracy or the error involved is usually required and the term "order of magnitude" is used colloquially in connection with this type of relation. For example, the populations of a small village, of a small town, and of a large city are of the order of 100, 10 000 and 1 000 000 people respectively. The linear dimensions of a room, of a brick, of a dust particle, and of a molecule are of the order of 10^3, 10, 10^{-2}, 10^{-6} cm, respectively. In many contexts the powers of 10, viz. 1, 10, 10^2, 10^3, ..., are used as orders of magnitude. In connection with some specific problem it may be convenient to use the powers of some variable x, viz. x, 1, x^{-1}, x^{-2}, ..., as orders of magnitude.

The use of such a scale of magnitudes normally implies that in matters concerning a given order of magnitude (such as a city, above) variations which are of the next order of magnitude down the scale (i.e. the town) may perhaps be neglected; variations which are two steps down the scale may usually be neglected. In the discussion of any problem involving a sum of terms, where approximations are made, it is most important for the reader to be able to assess the order of magnitude of the terms, to see which term is dominant (i.e., will effectively determine the value of the sum) and to decide whether a term is small enough to be neglected. He should have a scale of "orders of magnitude" by which he decides which terms are important and which terms to retain in order to keep the relation "correct to the first (or second, or higher) order" of magnitude.

We give this concept a precise meaning by using the symbol $O[f(x)]$. A function $g(x)$ is written

$$g(x) = O[f(x)] \quad \text{as} \quad x \to 0$$

(to be read as "$g(x)$ is of the order of $f(x)$") if

$$\left| \frac{g(x)}{f(x)} \right| < M \quad \text{for all } x \text{ such that} \quad |x| < \delta,$$

where M, δ are fixed positive numbers independent of x. The symbol O is also used when x tends to other values such as a, or $\pm \infty$. The definition has then to be modified slightly. It is used when $x \to +\infty$ in the form

$$g(x) = O[f(x)] \quad \text{as} \quad x \to +\infty$$

if $\qquad \left| \dfrac{g(x)}{f(x)} \right| < M \quad \text{for all} \quad x > X,$

where M, X are fixed positive numbers independent of x. (This conception is elaborated and one or two other symbols defined in books on pure mathematics.)

To sum up. The use of the symbol $O[f(x)]$ is a convenient way of exhibiting the behaviour of a function for large or small values of the variable in an easily recognisable form. The reader should become sufficiently familiar with the symbol O to be able to recognise quickly whether it is being used to denote a quantity which is negligible or whether it is the "dominant" term in an expression. We give below, without proof, some illustrative examples.

Example 1. If $g(x) = ax^2 + bx + c$ where $a \neq 0$, $c \neq 0$, then

$$g(x) = O(1) \quad \text{as} \quad x \to 0,$$
$$g(x) = O(x^2) \quad \text{as} \quad x \to \infty.$$

Example 2. $\qquad \sin x = O(x) \quad \text{as} \quad x \to 0,$
$$\sin x = O(1) \quad \text{as} \quad x \to \infty.$$

Example 3. When x is small, $\sqrt{(1+x)} = 1 + \frac{1}{2}x + O(x^2)$, i.e., $1 + \frac{1}{2}x$ is the value of the square root "correct to the first order in x", (c.f. Chapter 5).

Example 4. $\qquad \sin x = x + O(x^3) \quad \text{as} \quad x \to 0,$
$$\cos x = 1 + O(x^2) \quad \text{as} \quad x \to 0.$$

Exercises 1 : 5

Write each of the following functions in the form $O(x^n)$ as (a) $x \to 0$, (b) $x \to \infty$:

(i) $\dfrac{3x+1}{4x+1}$.   (ii) $\dfrac{x^2+3x+2}{x+4}$.   (iii) $\dfrac{x+2}{3x^2+4x+1}$.   (iv) $\dfrac{\sin x}{x^2}$.   (v) $x \cos^2 x$.

1 : 6 Inequalities and quadratic forms

In most branches of mathematics, and particularly in applications to subjects such as stability, problems arise in which the sign of a specified function in a prescribed range needs investigation. Other important problems involve considerations of the ranges of x for which $f(x) > g(x)$ or discussions of the conditions under which a function is always positive. Here we give an introduction to the techniques for investigating elementary inequalities. Later, §§ 5 : 2 and 6 : 8, we apply the techniques of the differential and integral calculus to problems involving inequalities. [See also *P.M.*, Vol. 2, Chap. XIX, for an elementary introduction to this subject.]

Two important features must be stressed when handling inequalities involving real numbers.

First, since the square of any real number is positive or zero,

$$(x-y)^2 \geqslant 0,$$

equality occurring only when $x = y$. This can be written

$$\tfrac{1}{2}(x^2+y^2) \geqslant xy \quad \text{or} \quad \tfrac{1}{2}(p+q) \geqslant \surd(pq), \qquad (1.26)$$

i.e. the arithmetic mean of two positive numbers is always greater than their geometric mean unless the numbers are equal, in which case the two means are equal.

Second, care must be taken when carrying out algebraic operations on inequalities since the operations of multiplication and division can then be carried out with positive factors only. Otherwise the directions of the inequality signs must be reversed.

Example 1. Prove that, if x, y, z are any positive numbers, $(y+z)(z+x)(x+y) \geqslant 8xyz$. Prove also that, if a, b, c are any three positive numbers such that each is less than the sum of the other two,

$$(b+c-a)(c+a-b)(a+b-c) \leqslant abc.$$

Since $y+z \geqslant 2\sqrt{(yz)}$ with two similar eqns., multiplication gives the desired result at once. The second inequality follows on writing

$$y+z = a, \quad z+x = b, \quad x+y = c.$$

Example 2. *The modulus inequality*

$$|a+b| \leqslant |a|+|b|. \tag{1}$$

When a, b are real this result follows immediately from the definition of modulus, equality holding only when a, b both have the same sign. This result can be extended by mathematical induction, see § 1:7, to

$$\left| \sum_{r=1}^{n} a_r \right| \leqslant \sum_{r=1}^{n} |a_r|. \tag{2}$$

Note that by writing $a = x-y$, $b = y-z$, the modulus inequality can be written

$$|x-z| \leqslant |x-y|+|y-z|,$$

and it is in this form that the modulus inequality is frequently employed in analysis.

Example 3. *Cauchy's Inequality.*

Prove that $(a_1^2+a_2^2+ \ldots +a_n^2)(b_1^2+b_2^2+ \ldots +b_n^2) \geqslant (a_1b_1+a_2b_2+ \ldots + +a_nb_n)^2$ and show that equality holds if and only if $\dfrac{a_1}{b_1} = \dfrac{a_2}{b_2} = \ldots = \dfrac{a_n}{b_n}$

Hence, or otherwise, show that

(i)
$$n\left(\sum_{i=1}^{n} a_i^2 \right) \geqslant \left(\sum_{i=1}^{n} a_i \right)^2 ;$$

(ii)
$$\left(\sum_{k=1}^{n} c_k \right) \left(\sum_{k=1}^{n} c_k^{-1} \right) \geqslant n^2 .$$

[All the above numbers are real and positive.]

Cauchy's inequality $\left(\sum_{i=1}^{n} a_i^2 \right) \left(\sum_{j=1}^{n} b_j^2 \right) \geqslant \left(\sum_{i=1}^{n} a_ib_i \right)^2$ is proved as follows:

$$\left(\sum_{i=1}^{n} a_i^2 \right) \left(\sum_{j=1}^{n} b_j^2 \right) = \sum_{i,\,j=1}^{n} a_i^2 b_j^2 , \tag{1}$$

$$\left(\sum_{i=1}^{n} a_ib_i \right)^2 = \sum_{i,\,j=1}^{n} a_ib_ia_jb_j . \tag{2}$$

For a particular pair of values of the suffixes, say $i = p$, $j = q$, in the sum (1) there is a term $a_p^2b_q^2$ and a term $a_q^2b_p^2$. Similarly, in the sum (2) there is a term $a_pb_pa_qb_q$ and a term $a_qb_qa_pb_p$. Hence, when the complete sum in (2) is subtracted from that in (1) we find

$$\left(\sum_{i=1}^{n} a_i^2 \right) \left(\sum_{j=1}^{n} b_j^2 \right) - \left(\sum_{i=1}^{n} a_ib_i \right)^2 \equiv \sum_{p<q} (a_pb_q-a_qb_p)^2 . \tag{3}$$

The terms in $a_p^2 b_p^2$ cancel out. The identity (3) is sometimes called *Lagrange's identity* and, since the right-hand side is a sum of squares, Cauchy's inequality follows. In fact, equality only holds if

$$a_p b_q - a_q b_p = 0, \quad \text{i.e.} \quad \frac{a_p}{a_q} = \frac{b_p}{b_q},$$

for all p, q,

i.e. $$\frac{a_1}{b_1} = \frac{a_2}{b_2} = \ldots = \frac{a_n}{b_n}.$$

The particular cases follow:

(i) by writing $b_1 = b_2 = \ldots = b_n = 1$;

(ii) in this case the right-hand side of Cauchy's inequality is n^2.

Example 4. If the value of the fraction

$$f(x) = \frac{x(2+x)}{2x+1}$$

lies within the range from 0 to 1, find the ranges within one of which x must lie.

We require

(a) $$0 < \frac{x(2+x)}{(2x+1)} \quad \text{and} \quad \text{(b)} \quad \frac{x(2+x)}{(2x+1)} < 1.$$

(a) is true if the numerator and denominator of $f(x)$ have the same sign. Since

$x(2+x) > 0$ if $x > 0$ or < -2 and $(2x+1) > 0$ if $x > -\frac{1}{2}$,

the numerator and denominator are both positive only if $x > 0$. Similarly the numerator and denominator are both negative if $-2 < x < -\frac{1}{2}$.

Therefore (a) is true for $x > 0$ or $-2 < x < -\frac{1}{2}$.

(b) implies that

$$1 - \frac{x(2+x)}{(2x+1)} > 0,$$

i.e. $$\frac{1-x^2}{(2x+1)} = \frac{(1+x)(1-x)}{(2x+1)} > 0.$$

As before this is true if $x < -1$ or $-\frac{1}{2} < x < 1$. Combination of the results for (a) and (b) gives as the required ranges $-2 < x < -1$, $0 < x < 1$.

Note that inequalities (a) and (b) cannot be multiplied by $(2x+1)$ as this leads to wrong conclusions.

Example 5. Find the real values of x for which $|x^2-4| > |x^2+1|$.

This inequality requires

either $\quad\quad\quad x^2 < 4 \quad$ and $\quad 4-x^2 > x^2+1,$ $\quad\quad\quad\quad$ (1)

or $\quad\quad\quad\quad x^2 > 4 \quad$ and $\quad x^2-4 > x^2+1.$ $\quad\quad\quad\quad$ (2)

[Note that $|x^2+1| = x^2+1$ since x^2+1 must be positive.]

There are no real values of x for which inequalities (2) are satisfied and so the only values of x are those for which

$$(x-2)(x+2) < 0 \quad \text{and} \quad [x - \sqrt{(\tfrac{3}{2})}]\,[(x + \sqrt{(\tfrac{3}{2})}] < 0.$$

Clearly the required range is $-\sqrt{3} < \sqrt{2}x < \sqrt{3}$.

The sign of $f(x, y)$ in the x, y plane. We consider the regions of the plane of the coordinate axes Oxy into which it is divided by the curve C with equation $f(x, y) = 0$, where $f(x, y)$ is a continuous function of x and y. All the points in the plane for which $f(x, y) = 0$ lie on C and so $f(x, y)$ cannot vanish at points not on C. Further, $f(x, y)$ cannot change sign from positive at the point P, say, to negative at the point Q, say, or vice versa without passing through zero since it is a continuous function. Hence P, Q must lie on opposite sides of the curve C. In fact $f(x, y)$ must have the same sign at all points of the plane which can be joined by a continuous curve which does not cross C, whereas the signs of $f(x, y)$ can be (and usually are) are opposite in two regions separated by the curve C. To find the sign of $f(x, y)$ in a particular region it is sufficient to consider its sign at some conveniently chosen point as illustrated in the following examples.

Example 1. The circle whose equation is

$$f(x, y) = (x-3)^2 + (y-2)^2 - 16 = 0$$

divides the plane into two regions. Inside the circle $f(x, y) < 0$, [proved by putting $x = 3$, $y = 2$ in $f(x, y)$], outside the circle $f(x, y) > 0$.

This result is confirmed by more elementary considerations for $f(x, y)$ is the square of the length of the tangent from P to the circle, see Fig. 1.11 in which $PT^2 = PC^2 - r^2$.

Example 2. Show in a sketch of the plane of the coordinate axes Oxy the region for which the inequalities

$$x + y - 1 \leqslant 0, \quad x - 2y + 6 \geqslant 0, \quad x + 4y \geqslant 0$$

are satisfied. Hence, find

    (i) the greatest possible value of y,

    (ii) the greatest possible *integral* value of y for which x is also integral.

The straight line $x + y - 1 = 0$ divides the plane into two domains in which the linear function $f(x, y) = x + y - 1$ has constant signs. Since $f(0, 0) = -1$ the function is negative to the left of the line. [The arrows on the lines of Fig.

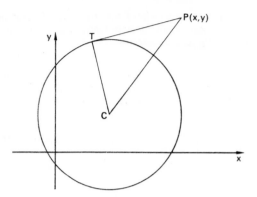

Fig. 1.11.

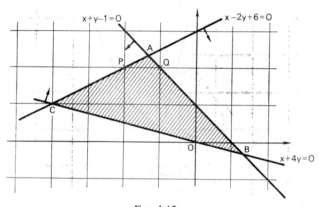

Fig. 1.12.

1.12 point to the correct regions.] Similar considerations for the other two inequalities lead to the conclusion that the three inequalities hold within and on the boundary of the shaded triangle ABC of Fig. 1.12. Clearly the greatest value of y occurs at the point A, $(-\frac{4}{3}, \frac{7}{3})$, and so the greatest value of y is $\frac{7}{3}$.

The greatest possible integral value of y is 2 provided that that part of the line $y = 2$ within or on the triangle contains a point or points with integral x-coordinate. This is in fact the case since the line $y = 2$ cuts AC at $x = -2$ and the line AB at $x = -1$ and so there are two integral solutions of the inequalities, viz. $(-2, 2), (-1, 2)$, corresponding to the points P, Q for which y has its greatest integral value.

Note that a solution of this problem by analytical means would be extremely difficult whereas our graphical approach aided by common sense makes it easy.

This type of problem is associated with the ideas of linear programming in which a large number of simultaneous linear inequalities require solution. Here we consider only simple problems.

Example 3. By considering the signs of $3x-2$ and $x-2y$ in the four regions into which the plane of the coordinate axes is divided by the straight lines $3x-2 = 0$ and $x-2y = 0$, sketch the graph of

$$3y = |3x-2|+|x-2y|.$$

We divide the plane into four domains, labelled A, B, C, D in Fig. 1.13, by the lines $3x-2 = 0$, $x-2y = 0$.

In A, $3y = (2-3x)+(2y-x)$, i.e. $y = 2-4x$.
In B, $3y = (2-3x)+(x-2y)$, i.e. $5y = 2-2x$.
In C, $3y = (3x-2)+(x-2y)$, i.e. $5y = 4x-2$.
In D, $3y = (3x-2)+(2y-x)$, i.e. $y = 2x-2$.

The required graph is shown in heavy type in Fig. 1.13.

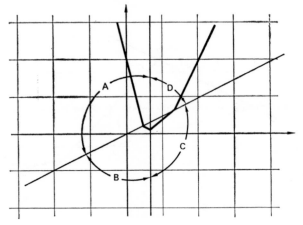

FIG. 1.13. The graph $3y = |3x-2|+|x-2y|$.

Example 4. Sketch the three curves

$$x^2-y^2 = 1,$$
$$x^2+4y^2 = 4,$$
$$3y-x = 0,$$

and shade those regions of the plane whose points satisfy all the inequalities

$$\left.\begin{array}{c} x^2-y^2 \geqslant 1, \\ x^2+4y^2 \leqslant 4, \\ 3y-x \geqslant 0. \end{array}\right\} \tag{1}$$

Find, subject to the conditions (1), the maximum values of x and x^2, and the minimum values of y and y^2.

The curves are shown in Fig. 1.14 and the two shaded areas give the required regions.

Clearly the maximum value of x is $6/\sqrt{13}$ (at P), and of x^2 is 4 (at $x = -2$). The minimum value of y is $-2/\sqrt{13}$ and arises at Q but the minimum value of y^2 is 0 and occurs along the negative x-axis for $-2 \leqslant x \leqslant -1$.

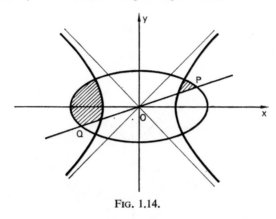

FIG. 1.14.

Example 5. Show in a diagram the positive and negative regions of the function

$$f(x, y) = \cos(x+y)\cos(x-y)$$

within a square whose corners are $(\pm 3\pi/2, 0)$, $(0, \pm 3\pi/2)$.

Sketch the contour $f = \frac{1}{4}$ and find its points of intersection with the coordinate axes. Also find the contours for which $f(x, y) = 1 - \varepsilon$, where ε is small and positive, and consider the case $\varepsilon \to 0$.

The lines upon which $f(x, y)$ vanishes are

$$x \pm y = \pm(2n+1)\pi/2 \quad \text{for} \quad n = 0, \pm 1, \dots.$$

The relevant lines are shown dotted in Fig. 1.15 and the shaded areas are those for which $f(x, y) < 0$.

The contour $f = \frac{1}{4}$ has equation

$$\cos(x+y)\cos(x-y) = \tfrac{1}{2}(\cos 2x + \cos 2y) = \tfrac{1}{4},$$

i.e. $$\cos 2x + \cos 2y = \tfrac{1}{2}.$$

This contour cuts the axis $x = 0$, where $2y = 2n\pi \pm 2\pi/3$ and the axis $y = 0$, where $2x = 2n\pi \pm 2\pi/3$. The relevant points are

on Ox, $(\pm\pi/3, 0)$, $(\pm 2\pi/3, 0)$, $(\pm 4\pi/3, 0)$,

on Oy, $(0, \pm\pi/3)$, $(0, \pm 2\pi/3)$, $(0, \pm 4\pi/3)$.

The contour $f = \frac{1}{4}$ consists of 5 oval curves as shown.

When $f(x, y) = 1 - \varepsilon$, since the cosine factors cannot exceed unity, both $\cos(x+y)$ and $\cos(x-y)$ are nearly equal to 1. Therefore, one such contour must occur near the centre of each positive square of Fig. 1.15. We consider that contour near O, i.e. where x, y are both small. On this contour

$$\cos(x+y)\cos(x-y) = \{1 - \tfrac{1}{2}(x+y)^2 + \ldots\}\{1 - \tfrac{1}{2}(x-y)^2 + \ldots\}$$
$$= 1 - (x^2 + y^2) + O(x^4) = 1 - \varepsilon.$$
$$\therefore \quad x^2 + y^2 = \varepsilon.$$

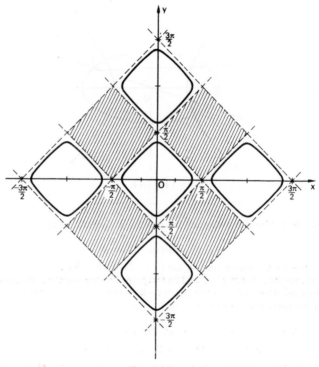

FIG. 1.15.

Hence the contour is a small circle of radius $\varepsilon^{\frac{1}{2}}$. In the limit $\varepsilon \to 0$ this contour reduces to an *isolated point* $(0, 0)$. Similarly, there are other isolated points at the centres of the positive squares for $f = 1$ and at the centres of the negative squares for $f = -1$. These points give the maximum and minimum values of the function $f(x, y)$.

Quadratic forms. Equation (1.6) shows that a polynomial in x with real zeros can be expressed as the product of real linear factors. In particular the quadratic polynomial

$$z \equiv ax^2 + 2hx + b \equiv a(x-\alpha)(x-\beta), \qquad (1.27)$$

where α, β are the roots of the quadratic equation $ax^2 + 2hx + b = 0$. The function z is the most general *quadratic form* in one variable x.

The graph of z is a parabola (see Chapter IV) which is a curve roughly resembling the letter U, whose limbs extend indefinitely. If the coefficient a is positive, the U is upright; if a is negative, the

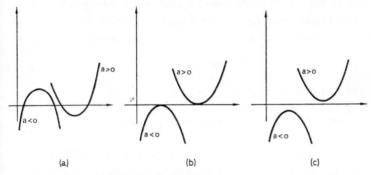

(a)   (b)   (c)

FIG. 1.16. Graphs of the quadratic form $ax^2 + 2hx + b$.

U is inverted. Such a U-shaped graph may either (a) cut the x-axis in two real points (z has real distinct zeros), or (b) it may touch the x-axis (z has two coincident zeros), or (c) it may not cut the x-axis at all (z has complex zeros). Figs. 1.16(a), (b), (c) show that, in case (a) a and z have the same sign for all values of x lying outside the zeros [such values of x give both factors in eqn. (1.27) the same sign]. In case (c), when the zeros are complex, a and z have the same sign for *all* values of x. The case (b) is the limiting case separating these two possibilities.

These results can be proved, without reference to a figure, by "completing the square".

$$z = a\left[x^2 + 2\left(\frac{h}{a}\right)x + \left(\frac{h}{a}\right)^2 + \left(\frac{b}{a}\right) - \left(\frac{h}{a}\right)^2\right]$$

$$= a\left[\left(x + \frac{h}{a}\right)^2 + \frac{ab - h^2}{a^2}\right].$$

(a) If $ab < h^2$, factorising the expression in square brackets by the "difference of two squares" leads to the well-known formula for α, β the roots of a quadratic equation. In this case z has the same sign as a except when $\alpha \leqslant x \leqslant \beta$.

(b) If $ab = h^2$, the expression in square brackets is "a perfect square" and can never be negative although it vanishes for $x = -h/a$.

(c) If $ab > h^2$ the expression in square brackets must be positive for all values of x and z always has the same sign as a.

These same results appear in a slightly different form when z is a *homogeneous quadratic function* of two variables x, y defined by

$$z = ax^2 + 2hxy + by^2.$$

Since this may be written

$$z = y^2 \left[a \left(\frac{x}{y} \right)^2 + 2h \left(\frac{x}{y} \right) + b \right],$$

where (x/y) plays the part of the variable x in eqn. (1.27), we may apply the above results to a homogeneous quadratic form. Such a function (or form) is said to be *definite* if it has the same sign for all possible values of the variables x, y other than $x = 0 = y$. We therefore conclude that:

If $a > 0$ and $ab - h^2 > 0$, then z is a *positive definite* quadratic form.

If $a < 0$ and $ab - h^2 > 0$, then z is a *negative definite* quadratic form.

The above results can be summarised as follows:

Either (1) Necessary and sufficient conditions for $ax^2 + 2hxy + by^2$ to be a positive definite quadratic form are that $a > 0$ and $ab - h^2 > 0$.

Or (2) The quadratic form $ax^2 + 2hxy + by^2$ is positive definite if and only if [sometimes abbreviated to iff] $a > 0$ and $ab - h^2 > 0$.

These statements (1) and (2) are equivalent and they each express a theorem and its converse.

We shall use these results frequently in subsequent work.

Example 1. (i) Show that if p and q are real the expression $(px+q)/(x^2+1)$ can, for real values of x, take only values lying between the limits

$$\tfrac{1}{2}[q - \surd(p^2+q^2)] \leqslant y \leqslant \tfrac{1}{2}[q + \surd(p^2+q^2)].$$

(ii) Show that the expression $(px+q)/(x^2-1)$ can take all real values for real values of x, unless p lies between $-q$ and q.

(i) If $y = (px+q)/(x^2+1)$, then the equation giving the values of x for some specified y is

$$yx^2 - px + y - q = 0.$$

For this quadratic equation in x to have real roots $p^2 \geqslant 4y(y-q)$, i.e.,

$$4y^2 - 4qy - p^2 \leqslant 0.$$

Hence y may not lie outside the roots of the equation $4y^2 - 4qy - p^2 = 0$. This gives the required limits.

(ii) If $y_1 = (px+q)/(x^2-1)$, then for real x we find, as in (i), that y_1 satisfies the condition

$$4y_1^2 + 4qy_1 + p^2 \geqslant 0.$$

If the left-hand side has complex factors or is a perfect square, the condition is satisfied for every value of y_1. If the left-hand side has real factors, then y_1 cannot take all real values but only those lying outside the zeros. The condition for real factors is $q^2 \geqslant p^2$. Therefore y_1 may have any real value unless p lies between $-q$ and q.

Example 2. Prove that the expression

$$10x^2 - 6xy + y^2 - 8x + y + 7$$

is positive for all real values of x and y.

The given expression is

$$(3x - y - 1)^2 + (x - 1)^2 + 6 > 0.$$

Note that we "spot" that this expression is the sum of squares by writing the terms in y^2, xy and y correctly in the first bracket.

Exercises 1 : 6

1. If a, b, c, d are any real numbers, prove that

$$a^4 + b^4 \geqslant 2a^2b^2, \quad a^4 + b^4 + c^4 + d^4 \geqslant 4abcd.$$

Prove also that $(a^2+b^2)^2 + (c^2+d^2)^2 \geqslant 2(ab+cd)^2$.

Show that, if $a^4 + b^4 + c^4 + d^4 \leqslant 1$, then $\dfrac{1}{a^4} + \dfrac{1}{b^4} + \dfrac{1}{c^4} + \dfrac{1}{d^4} \geqslant 16$.

2. Find the range of values of x for which

$$\text{(i)} \quad 1 > \frac{2}{x+2} + \frac{1}{x+1} > 0, \qquad \text{(ii)} \quad \frac{x^2+2x-19}{x-4} > 4.$$

3. (i) Find the real values of λ for which the inequality

$$x^2 + y^2 \geqslant \lambda xy$$

holds for all real values of x and y.

Show that

$$x^2 + y^2 + z^2 \geqslant yz + zx + xy$$

for all real values of x, y and z.

(ii) Find the real values of x for which

$$\frac{1}{x+5} < \frac{2}{5-3x}.$$

4. Find the ranges of values of x for which

(i) $|2x-1| + |4-x| > 4$,

(ii) $\sin kx + \cos 2kx < 1$, where k is constant.

5. Find the real values of x which satisfy each of the following inequalities:

$$\text{(i)} \quad x^4 - 5x^2 + 6 > 0, \qquad \text{(ii)} \quad |3-2x| \leqslant |x+4|.$$

6. (i) Prove that the inequalities

$$3x+2y > 6, \quad x-2y > 2, \quad -2x+y > 2$$

cannot simultaneously be satisfied.

(ii) Find for what values of a the inequalities

$$0 < x+2y < a, \quad xy > 3$$

can be simultaneously satisfied.

7. For the set of contours

$$(x^2-y^2)(x^2+y^2-1) = k$$

in the plane of the coordinate axes Oxy show in a diagram the regions in which k is positive.

8. Sketch in the same diagram the two curves

$$\text{(i)} \quad 4x^2 - 3y^2 = 4, \qquad \text{(ii)} \quad xy = 4.$$

Shade the areas of the plane in which the inequality

$$(4x^2 - 3y^2 - 4)(xy - 4) \geqslant 0 \tag{1}$$

holds. Indicate the points of these areas for which

$$y^2 + 2x = 8. \tag{2}$$

Find the greatest value of x for points satisfying conditions (1) and (2) simultaneously. Show that there is no least value of x for such points.

9. A rectangular hall of length x m, width y m and ceiling height 10 m is to be built with a floor area of at most 400 m². It is to be longer than it is wide and one end wall will have a tapestry 10 m long by 5 m high mounted on it. One side wall is to have a window 5 m high running the whole of its length and the door is to be 8 m high and $2\frac{1}{2}$ m wide. Find the inequalities which x, y must satisfy and, in a sketch, indicate the region of the x, y-plane which satisfies these conditions.

The acoustic specialists recommend that for such a hall at least $625\frac{1}{2}$ m² of acoustic tiling should be used on the walls (excluding door, window and tapestry). Find the limitations imposed on the length of the hall if this minimum area of acoustic tiling is used.

It is finally decided that the greatest possible area of acoustic tiling should be used on the walls; find the dimensions for the hall.

10. Show that the equation

$$\frac{2x^2+4x+3}{x^2-1} - \lambda = 0$$

has real roots in x provided that λ does not lie between -2 and 1. For what values of λ are these roots of opposite sign?

11. Prove that the function $y = \dfrac{x^2+x-2}{x^2-x-2}$ can take all real values, but

that the function $z = \dfrac{x^2+x-2}{x^2-x-2} + \dfrac{x^2-x-2}{x^2+x-2}$ cannot take values between -2 and $+2$.

12. If $E = x^4 - 8x^3 + 23x^2 - 28x + 13$, show, by finding the numerical values of the constants p, q and r, that E can be written in the form

$$E = (x^2+px+q)^2 + (x^2+px+q) + r.$$

Hence, or otherwise, show that E is positive for all real values of x but that $E-1$ can assume both positive and negative values.

13. If $x/(x^2-a)$ takes all real values as x ranges over the real numbers, show that $a > 0$. Sketch the curve $y = x/(x^2-a)$ in each of the cases (i) $a = -1$, (ii) $a = 0$, (iii) $a = 1$.

14. Given that a, h, b are constants and that

$$ax^2+2hxy+by^2 > 0$$

whenever x and y are real and not both zero, prove that a, b, and $ab-h^2$ are all positive.

When a, b, $ab-h^2$ are all positive and

$$A = +\sqrt{\{(a-b)^2+4h^2\}}$$

show that $a+b-A$ is a positive number and prove that, when $x^2+y^2 = r^2$,

$$ax^2+2hxy+by^2 \geqslant \tfrac{1}{2}r^2(a+b-A).$$

1 : 7 Mathematical induction

The process of *mathematical induction* is frequently employed to prove formulae involving an integer n which takes positive integral values. There are two essential parts to any such proof. First, the truth of such a formula for an *arbitrary* value $n = k$

must be proved to imply the truth of this formula for the next value $n = k+1$. Second, an independent proof must be given that the formula is true for the lowest possible value of n. These results then imply the validity of the formula for all positive integers n exceeding this lowest value of n.

It should be pointed out, however, that the process of mathematical induction has one serious drawback. It does not really enable results to be "discovered". Rather it is a method of proving formally results expected to be true. See Example 4 below.

Example 1. Prove by induction that $\sum_1^n \dfrac{1}{r(r+1)} = \dfrac{n}{n+1}$.

If
$$\sum_1^k \frac{1}{r(r+1)} = \frac{k}{k+1},$$
then
$$\sum_1^{k+1} \frac{1}{r(r+1)} = \frac{k}{k+1} + \frac{1}{(k+1)(k+2)}$$
$$= \frac{k(k+2)+1}{(k+1)(k+2)} = \frac{(k+1)^2}{(k+1)(k+2)} = \frac{k+1}{k+2}.$$

Therefore if the statement $\sum_1^n \dfrac{1}{r(r+1)} = \dfrac{n}{n+1}$ is true for any one value of n, it is true for the next value of n. The statement is certainly true for $n = 1$. Therefore it is true for all values of n.

Example 2. If n is a positive integer, prove that $3^{4n+2}+2^{6n+3}$ is divisible by 17.

Let $f(p) = 3^{4p+2}+2^{6p+3}$.

Then $f(p+1) = 3^{4p+6}+2^{6p+9} = 81.3^{4p+2}+64.2^{6p+3}$.

Therefore $f(p+1)-64f(p) = 17.3^{4p+2}$.

Therefore if $f(p)$ is divisible by 17, so is $f(p+1)$.

But
$$f(1) = 3^6+2^9 = 729+512 = 1241 = 17 \times 73.$$

Hence $f(1)$ is divisible by 17. Therefore $f(1+1) = f(2)$ is divisible by 17, and so on. Therefore $f(n)$ is divisible by 17 for all values of n.

Example 3. The *binomial theorem* for a positive integer n can be written
$$(x+a)^n = x^n + {}_nC_1 x^{n-1}a + {}_nC_2 x^{n-2}a^2 + \ldots + {}_nC_r x^{n-r}a^r + \ldots + a^n,$$
where ${}_nC_r = n!/\{(n-r)!\,r!\} = n(n-1)(n-2)\ldots(n-r+1)/(1.2.3\ldots r)$.

We prove the theorem by induction as follows:

If
$$(x+a)^k = x^k + {}_kC_1x^{k-1}a + {}_kC_2x^{k-2}a^2 + \ldots$$
$$+ {}_kC_{r-1}x^{k-r+1}a^{r-1} + {}_kC_rx^{k-r}a^r + \ldots + a^k,$$

then multiplication by $(x+a)$ gives
$$(x+a)^{k+1} = x^{k+1} + ({}_kC_1+1)x^ka + ({}_kC_2+{}_kC_1)x^{k-1}a^2 + \ldots$$
$$+ ({}_kC_{r-1}+{}_kC_r)x^{k-r+1}a^r + \ldots + a^{k+1}.$$

But ${}_kC_1 + 1 = k+1 = {}_{k+1}C_1$ and generally ${}_kC_r + {}_kC_{r-1} = {}_{k+1}C_r$.

The expansion above may therefore be written

$$(x+a)^{k+1} = x^{k+1} + {}_{k+1}C_1x^ka + {}_{k+1}C_2x^{k-1}a^2 + \ldots + {}_{k+1}C_rx^{k-r+1}a^r + \ldots + a^{k+1}.$$

Therefore if the binomial theorem is true for any one value of n, it is true for the next integral value of n.

The theorem is clearly true when $n = 1$.

Hence the theorem is true for $n = 1+1 = 2$ and for $n = 2+1 = 3$ and so on. Therefore the theorem is true for all integral values of n.

Example 4. Find an expression for
$$T_n = (1-\tfrac{1}{4})(1-\tfrac{1}{9})(1-\tfrac{1}{16}) \ldots (1-1/n^2) \qquad (n \geqslant 2)$$
and prove it by mathematical induction.

Since
$$1 - \frac{1}{n^2} = \frac{n^2-1}{n^2} = \frac{(n-1)(n+1)}{n^2},$$

$$T_n = \frac{1\times3}{2^2} \times \frac{2\times4}{3^2} \times \frac{3\times5}{4^2} \ldots \frac{(n-2)n}{(n-1)^2} \frac{(n-1)(n+1)}{n^2},$$

and it appears probable that this product has the value $(n+1)/(2n)$. [This agrees with the results for the cases $n = 1$ and $n = 2$.] Let us then assume that

$$T_n = \frac{n+1}{2n} \quad \text{for} \quad n \geqslant 2. \tag{1}$$

Then
$$T_{n+1} = \frac{n+1}{2n}\left\{1 - \frac{1}{(n+1)^2}\right\} = \frac{(n+1)n(n+2)}{2n(n+1)^2} = \frac{n+2}{2n+2}$$
$$= \frac{(n+1)+1}{2(n+1)}.$$

This is the same formula as (1) but with $n+1$ in place of n. Also $T_2 = \dfrac{3}{4} = \dfrac{2+1}{2(2)}$ and so the formula (1) holds for $n = 2$. Hence it holds for $n = 2+1 = 3$ and so on indefinitely.

Exercises 1 : 7

1. By mathematical induction prove that

$$\sum_{n=1}^{m} nc^{n-1} = \frac{1-(m+1)c^m + mc^{m+1}}{(1-c)^2},$$

where $c \neq 1$. Hence, or otherwise, show that $\sum_{n=1}^{10} n\left(-\frac{1}{2}\right)^{n-1} = \frac{7}{16}$.

2. Establish the generalisation of the modulus inequality, Example 2, eqn. (2), of p. 38, by induction.

3. If $a_1, a_2, \ldots, a_n$ are real numbers each exceeding -1 and all of the same sign, prove that

$$(1+a_1)(1+a_2) \ldots (1+a_n) \geqslant 1 + a_1 + a_2 + \ldots + a_n.$$

(i) Deduce that, if $x > -1$, $(1+x)^n \geqslant 1 + nx$.

(ii) Hence show that, if $|a| < 1$, then $a^n \to 0$ as $n \to \infty$.

(iii) Prove also that, if $k > 0$, then $k^{1/n} \to 1$ as $n \to \infty$.

4. If $x > 0$ and n is a positive integer, prove that

$$(1+x)^n > 1 + nx + nx^2.$$

5. If $3u_{n+1} = 2u_n - 1$ for all positive integral values of n and $u_1 = 1$, prove by induction that

$$u_n = 3(\tfrac{2}{3})^n - 1.$$

6. Prove by induction that

$$1 + \frac{1}{\sqrt{2}} + \frac{1}{\sqrt{3}} + \ldots + \frac{1}{\sqrt{n}} < 2\sqrt{n}.$$

7. Prove by induction that $3^{2n+1} + 2^{n+2}$ is divisible by 7 for any positive integer n.

8. Use induction to prove that, for every positive integer n,

$$1^3 + 2^3 + 3^3 + \ldots + n^3 = \tfrac{1}{4} n^2(n+1)^2.$$

1 : 8 The concept of convergence

We consider a set of quantities $u_1, u_2, u_3, \ldots, u_n, \ldots$ defined for every positive integer n so that $u_n = f(n)$. Such a set is called a sequence. Examples of sequences are the set of positive integers

$$1, 2, 3, \ldots, n, \ldots,$$

and the terms of a geometrical progression

$$a, ar, ar^2, \ldots, ar^{n-1}, \ldots.$$

Here we concern ourselves with the meaning of the term limit applied to a sequence u_n as $n \to \infty$. Later, § 5 : 1, we consider the convergence of series.

Following § 1 : 4 we say that the sequence u_n converges to the finite limit l if

$$|u_n - l| < \varepsilon, \tag{1.28}$$

however small the assigned positive number ε may be, for all n exceeding some number $n_0(\varepsilon)$, that is a number n_0 which depends on ε. We express this in the form

$$\lim_{n \to \infty} u_n = l. \tag{1.28a}$$

If a sequence does not converge, then it may:

(i) tend to ∞, i.e. exceed any assigned positive number N for all n sufficiently large [by "for all n sufficiently large" we mean for all n exceeding some number n_1 which depends on N]; or

(ii) tend to $-\infty$, i.e. be less than any assigned negative number $-N$, $(N > 0)$, for all n sufficiently large; or

(iii) oscillate, that is, does not tend to a limit or to $+\infty$ or to $-\infty$. A sequence oscillates boundedly if there exists ($\exists$) a positive number M such that $|u_n| < M$ for all n. Otherwise the sequence oscillates unboundedly.

Example 1. The sequence $(n+1)/n$ coverges to the limit 1.

Example 2. The sequence n^2 diverges to ∞.

Example 3. The sequence $-n^4$ diverges to $-\infty$.

Example 4. The sequence $\cos n\pi$ oscillates boundedly (between the values -1 and 1).

Example 5. The sequence $\{1 + 2(-1)^n\} n$ oscillates unboundedly.

A sequence u_n is said to be *monotonic increasing* when $u_{n+1} \geqslant u_n$ for $n = 1, 2, \ldots$ and to be *strictly monotonic increasing* if $u_{n+1} > u_n$. Similarly, monotonic decreasing and strictly mono-

.c decreasing sequences are those for which $u_{n+1} \leqslant u_n$, $u_{n+1} < u_n$ respectively.

It is proved in books on analysis that if a sequence is monotonic increasing, then it either tends to a finite limit or diverges to ∞. In particular, if this sequence is bounded above, i.e. $\exists$ a number K such that $u_n \leqslant K$ for all n, then the sequence tends to a finite limit which cannot exceed K. Similarly a monotonic decreasing sequence tends to a finite limit or diverges to $-\infty$, and must tend to a finite limit if it is bounded below.

Example 1. The sequence $1-(1/n)$ is strictly monotonic increasing, bounded above (every term is less than 1), and tends to the limit 1.

Example 2. The sequence $-n$ is strictly monotonic decreasing and diverges to $-\infty$.

Example 3. *The limit of $u_n = x^n$ for real x.*

Here we illustrate the importance in analysis of considering all the cases which arise.

The results for the cases $x = 0$, ± 1 are obvious (trivial) thus:

(i) When $x = 0$, $x^n = 0$ for all n and u_n converges to zero.

(ii) When $x = 1$, $x^n = 1$ for all n and u_n converges to 1.

(iii) When $x = -1$, $x^n = (-1)^n$ and u_n oscillates boundedly between -1 and 1.

Now we consider the general cases when $x > 0$.

(iv) If $x > 1$, then $u_{n+1} = xu_n > u_n$ and so u_n increases monotonically. Hence $u_n \to \infty$ or to a finite limit $l > 1$. Suppose that this latter result holds so that $\lim_{n \to \infty} x^n = l$. Then clearly

$$xl = x \lim_{n \to \infty} x^n = \lim_{n \to \infty} x^{n+1} = l$$

by definition. Therefore $xl = l$. But $l > 1$ and so $x = 1$ contrary to the fact that $x > 1$. Hence our assumption that the sequence converges gives rise to a contradiction and so must be false. Therefore $\lim_{n \to \infty} x_n^n \to \infty$ for $x > 1$.

Note: The above illustrates a standard technique of proof in mathematics. Thus: *If two and only two mutually exclusive conclusions A, B are possible and the assumption that A is true leads to a contradiction then B must be true.*

(v) If $0 < x < 1$, then $x = 1/y$, where $y > 1$. Then by (iv) above $y^n \to \infty$ as $n \to \infty$ and so x^n converges to 0.

(vi) If $-1 < x < 0$, then $x^n = (-1)^n |x|^n$ and, by (v), $|x|^n \to 0$ and so $x^n \to 0$.

(vii) If $x < -1$, then $x^n = (-1)^n |x|^n$ and, by (iv), $|x|^n \to \infty$. Hence, in this case x^n oscillates unboundedly.

[We use the results of this example in § 5 : 1.]

Example 4. *The general principle of convergence.*

A necessary and sufficient condition that the sequence u_n converges is that, given $\varepsilon > 0$, ∃ an integer $N(\varepsilon)$ such that

$$\left| u_{n_1} - u_{n_2} \right| < \varepsilon \tag{1}$$

for all integers n_1, n_2 exceeding N.

If the series converges to l, then, by the definition of convergence, given $\varepsilon' > 0$, Ǝ $N(\varepsilon')$ such that

$$\left| u_n - l \right| < \varepsilon'$$

for $n > N(\varepsilon')$. Hence, if n_1, n_2 both exceed N,

$$\left| u_{n_1} - l \right| < \varepsilon', \quad \left| u_{n_2} - l \right| < \varepsilon',$$

and so

$$\left| u_{n_1} - u_{n_2} \right| \leqslant \left| u_{n_1} - l \right| + \left| u_{n_2} - l \right| < 2\varepsilon'$$

which, on writing $\varepsilon' = \tfrac{1}{2}\varepsilon$ implies that condition (1) is necessary.

It is proved in books on analysis that condition (1) is also sufficient for convergence of the sequence.

Example 5. A positive quantity a_n satisfies the relationship

$$a_n = \frac{1}{2}\left(a_{n-1} + \frac{a^2}{a_{n-1}} \right), \tag{1}$$

where n is a positive integer greater than unity and a is positive. Prove that, provided $a_1 > 0$,

> (i) $a_n \geqslant a$ for $n \geqslant 2$.
>
> (ii) $a_{n-1} \geqslant a_n$ for $n \geqslant 3$.
>
> (iii) $a_n - a \leqslant \tfrac{1}{2}(a_{n-1} - a)$ for $n \geqslant 3$.

Hence show that a_n tends to the limit a as n tends to infinity.

Since $a_1 > 0$, it follows from eqn. (1) that $a_2 > 0$. Clearly by mathematical induction $a_n > 0$ for $n \geqslant 1$.

(i) From eqn. (1),

$$a_n - a = \frac{(a - a_{n-1})^2}{2a_{n-1}} \geqslant 0 \quad \text{for} \quad n \geqslant 2. \tag{2}$$

Hence $a_n \geqslant a$ for $n \geqslant 2$.

(ii) From eqn. (1),

$$a_n - a_{n-1} = \frac{a^2 - a_{n-1}^2}{2a_{n-1}} \leqslant 0 \quad \text{for} \quad n \geqslant 3$$

from result (i).

(iii) Also eqn. (2) can be written

$$a_n - a = \frac{1}{2}(a_{n-1} - a)\left(1 - \frac{a}{a_{n-1}}\right)$$

and since $a/a_{n-1} \geqslant 0$ this implies that $a_n - a \leqslant \frac{1}{2}(a_{n-1} - a)$ for $n \geqslant 3$. It follows that

$$(a_n - a) \leqslant (\tfrac{1}{2})^{n-2}(a_2 - a_1)$$

and by the results of Example 3 above $|a_n - a| < \varepsilon$ for n sufficiently large. Therefore $a_n \to a$ as $n \to \infty$.

Note: We could derive this result from (i), (ii) by noting that a_n is a decreasing sequence of positive terms bounded below and we derive the limit l by writing $a_{n-1} = a_n = l$ in (1) and solving the resulting quadratic equation, taking the positive root.

Exercises 1 : 8

1. Consider the behaviour as $n \to \infty$ of the sequences whose nth terms are the following:

(i) $\dfrac{n}{n^2+1}$; (ii) $\dfrac{n^2+1}{2n}$; (iii) $\cos(n\pi/3)$; (iv) $n\cos(n\pi/3)$;

(v) $n^r x^n$ where r is a positive integer.

2. (i) Give an example of a sequence $s_1, s_2, s_3, \ldots, s_n, \ldots$ of real number which does not have a limit, and justify your answer.

(ii) Sketch roughly the graphs of $\sin^3 x$ and $\sin(x^3)$. Show that if $P_1, P_2, \ldots, P_n, \ldots$ are the successive positive zeros of $\sin(x^3)$, then

$$P_n - P_{n-1} \to 0 \quad \text{as} \quad n \to \infty.$$

3. If n is any positive integer and

$$x_n = \frac{1}{n} + \frac{1}{n+1} + \ldots + \frac{1}{2n}.$$

show that

$$x_{n+1} < x_n \quad \text{and} \quad \tfrac{1}{2} < x_n \leqslant \tfrac{3}{2}.$$

Deduce that x_n tends to a limit as n tends to infinity.

4. If a is positive, discuss the limits of

$$\frac{a^n - 1}{a^n + 1}$$

as the positive integer n tends to infinity.

5. The numbers x_n ($n = 1, 2, \ldots$) satisfy the recurrence relation

$$x_{n+1} = \frac{x_n^2 + x_n + 1}{x_n + 2}.$$

If $x_1 > -2$, show that $(x_n - x_{n+1})$, $(x_n - 1)$, $(x_{n+1} - 1)$ all have the same sign when $n > 1$.

If $x_1 > -2$, show that $x_n \to 1$ as $n \to \infty$.

1 : 9 Tabulated functions—difference tables

1. Introduction. When a body falls freely under gravity from rest the "solution of the problem" is given by $s = \frac{1}{2}gt^2$; the "solution of the problem of the simple pendulum" is given, for small amplitudes, by $x = a \cos(\omega t + \alpha)$. Because we are familiar with the functions involved, these formulae give us an idea of what is happening. However, in a practical problem it may be necessary to know (exactly) the position of the particle or the pendulum at a given instant or even at a number of instants. The formula $s = \frac{1}{2}gt^2$ enables us to calculate s for any value of t; the formula $x = a \cos(\omega t + \alpha)$ enables the value of x to be calculated *provided we have trigonometric tables available.* In other cases the solution of a problem may involve a function such as the *error function* erf x (see § 3 : 11) which cannot be written in familiar terms, or the analytic solution (formula) may not be known. In these cases either we must find methods of calculating the new function or the information is given by means of a table of figures. In fact, even the calculation of s from $\frac{1}{2}gt^2$ relies ultimately on certain tables of figures (multiplication tables) which we carry in our heads. Most people are familiar with tables of trigonometric functions, sine, cosine and tangent, and with common logarithms (to the base 10). In addition many of the less familiar functions such as exponential functions, Bessel functions, error functions, natural logarithms, etc., have been tabulated.

In this section we introduce tabulated functions and some numerical methods associated with them. Practical numerical analysis may involve calculations by hand, with the aid of slide rules, logarithm tables or desk calculators, or possibly the preparation of the problem for computer solution according to the scale of the problem on hand. Here we do not attempt to give *practical* advice concerning layout, methods of checking and other matters concerning the use of these tools, or detail for programming of digital computers. Later we consider numerical methods for the approximate solution of equations, interpolation, differentiation and integration.

2. Tabulated functions. In order to develop a systematic method for handling numerical data and tabulated functions we use a more or less standard notation. When a function $y = f(x)$ is tabulated the values of x chosen are equally spaced and are denoted by

$$x_r = x_0 + rh \qquad (r = \ldots, -2, -1, 0, 1, 2, \ldots.) \qquad (1.29)$$

The table may start with $r = 0$, but this is not necessarily the case. The corresponding values of y are denoted by

$$y_r = f(x_r).$$

(Frequently the symbol f_r is used instead of y_r.)

The table then is:

TABLE 1

x	x_{-2}	x_{-1}	x_0	x_1	x_2	x_3	$\ldots$
$y = f(x)$	y_{-2}	y_{-1}	y_0	y_1	y_2	y_3	$\ldots$

All tabulated functions are effectively two rows or columns of figures, though in practice they may be printed as rectangular blocks, cf. tables of common logarithms.

The accuracy to which the figures of y_r are given is specified by the number of figures after the decimal place, zeros being used, if necessary, to complete the required number of significant figures. For example, Tables 8 and 9 (printed at the end of this book) give y_r (and the difference columns) correct to 4 and 6 places respectively. The range and spacing of the independent variable is denoted by the initial and final values of x with the spacing in brackets between. Thus Table 1 is given (apart from the dots) for the range $x_{-2}\,(h)\,x_3$; the Tables 8 and 9 are both given for the range $-1\cdot0\,(0\cdot2)\,2\cdot0$.

3. Differences. Tables 8 and 9 give not only the functions y_r but also the differences. These differences are constructed according to the scheme shown in Table 2 opposite.

We could construct one further entry in Table 2, a 4th difference, viz.

$$(y_4 - 3y_3 + 3y_2 - y_1) - (y_3 - 3y_2 + 3y_1 - y_0)$$
$$= y_4 - 4y_3 + 6y_2 - 4y_1 + y_0. \qquad (1.30)$$

TABLE 2

x	$y = f(x)$	1st difference	2nd difference	3rd difference
x_0	y_0			
		$y_1 - y_0$		
x_1	y_1		$(y_2 - y_1) - (y_1 - y_0)$	
		$y_2 - y_1$		$(y_3 - 2y_2 + y_1) - (y_2 - 2y_1 + y_0)$
x_2	y_2		$(y_3 - y_2) - (y_2 - y_1)$	
		$y_3 - y_2$		$(y_4 - 2y_3 + y_2) - (y_3 - 2y_2 + y_1)$
x_3	y_3		$(y_4 - y_3) - (y_3 - y_2)$	
		$y_4 - y_3$		
x_4	y_4			

The reader should notice that from a table with n entries, columns of differences up to the $(n-1)$th can be obtained; further, the coefficients in the expressions for the various, mth, orders of difference are the binomial coefficients, $_mC_r$, $r = 0, 1, \ldots, m$. In a table with n ($> m$) entries the coefficient of y_r in the mth difference column is $(-1)^r {}_mC_r$, i.e. the mth difference is

$$\sum_{r=0}^{m} (-1)^r {}_mC_r y_r. \qquad (1.31)$$

In Tables 8 and 9 there are no decimal points in the difference columns. The convention is that the last digit of a difference entry corresponds to the last significant figure of the y_r entries. Thus the first difference in Table 8 stands for $-2\cdot0460$; the fourth difference in Table 9 opposite $x = -0\cdot6$ stands for $0\cdot002935$. The alignment of the difference entries should also be noted: all differences are entered on a level halfway between the values from which they come. Consequently, odd-order differences occur between the y_r entries and even-order differences occur on the levels of the y_r entries.

A glance at Tables 8 and 9 shows that the column of 5th (and higher) differences is zero for Table 8 but that the 6th and 7th differences in Table 9 are small compared with y but vary more or less at random. This is an important feature. Table 8 lists the

values of
$$y = x^4 - 2 \cdot 6x^3 + 1 \cdot 01x^2 + 0 \cdot 884x - 0 \cdot 198$$

for the range $-1 \cdot 0 \ (0 \cdot 2) \ 2 \cdot 0$, i.e. a polynomial of degree 4. Table 9 lists the values of $y = e^{-x}$, which is a transcendental function, (see § 2 : 4). The kth differences of a table of values of a polynomial of degree k are equal (see Table 8) and therefore the $(k+1)$th differences are zero. This follows because the difference between two polynomials with the same leading term (the term of highest degree) is a polynomial of degree one less than the degree of the original polynomials. Hence the first differences of a polynomial of degree k are polynomials of degree $k-1$; the second differences are therefore of degree $k-2$; and so on. This should be compared with the case of differentiation; for a polynomial of degree k, $d^k y/dx^k = $ constant, $d^{k+1} y/dx^{k+1} = 0$. (See Chapter II.) For other functions this is not true. This property enables us to extend a table of values of a polynomial of degree k when $k+1$ equally spaced values are given, as illustrated in the following example.

Example. The table below gives above the dotted line the values of $y = x^4$ for five values. Extend the table to $x = 2, 3$.

x	$y = x^4$	Δf	$\Delta^2 f$	$\Delta^3 f$	$\Delta^4 f$
-3	81				
		-65			
-2	16		50		
		-15		-36	
-1	1		14		24
		-1		-12	
0	0		2		24
		$+1$		$+12$	
1	1		14		24
		15		36	
2	16		50		
		65			
3	81				

Since we are given that the function is a polynomial of degree 4 we can enter 24 in the 4th difference column opposite zero. We now construct the entry

+12 in the 3rd difference column from $12 = -12 + 24$, the next entry below the dotted line is $14 = 2 + 12$, the next $15 = 1 + 14$, and $16 = 1 + 15$. We construct the next line from this and so on, as far as is required.

Note that in the above table we have used the symbols Δf, $\Delta^2 f$, $\Delta^3 f$, $\Delta^4 f$ to denote the 1st, 2nd, 3rd, and 4th differences respectively.

Difference entries can also indicate the occurrence of a mistake in a table of values, for such a mistake gives increasing oscillations in the higher difference columns, as illustrated in Table 3.

TABLE 3

x	y	Δ	Δ^2	Δ^3	Δ^4	Δ^5	Δ^6
0	0						
		0					
1	0		0				
		0		e			
2	0		e		$-4e$		
		e		$-3e$		$10e$	
3	e		$-2e$		$6e$		$20e$
		$-e$		$3e$		$-10e$	
4	0		e		$-4e$		
		0		$-e$			
5	0		0				
		0					
6	0						

Note that the coefficients of e in the rth difference column are the same as in the binomial expansion of $(1-x)^r$.

Example. The first two columns of the table on page 62 give x, y for a low degree polynomial but contain an error. Locate the error and correct it.

When the differences are evaluated the top four entries in the 3rd difference column appear wrong particularly as subsequent differences oscillate considerably. It also appears from the last two entries that each entry in this column should be 6. The error pattern is now immediately apparent. In fact $e = 9$ and the error pattern is e, $-4e$, $+6e$, $-4e$, e giving 9, -36, $+54$, -36, etc., as shown. The corrected entries for the 2nd differences are constructed in the small section from the new column and lead to the correct figure 44 in the small section; these corrected entries are now used to correct the 1st differences, and are checked by the appearance of the correct entry

x	y	Δ	Δ^2	Δ^3	Δ^4	Δ^5
2	15					
		25				
3	40		20			
		45		15		
4	85		35		−36	
		80		−21		90
5	165		14		54	
		94		33		−90
6	259		47		−36	
		141		−3		45
7	400		44		9	
		185		6		−9
8	585		50		0	
		235		6		
9	820		56			
		291				
10	1111					

y	Δ	Δ^2
	45	20
85		↓ ↘6
	71	26
156		↓ ↘6
	103	32
259		↓ ↘6
	141	38
		↓ ↘6
		44

141. The corrected entry 156 in the y-column then completes the corrections. The transposition of two digits in this manner is a mistake which can easily occur in copying.

If there are two errors whose "fans" overlap the location of mistakes may be difficult; or if there are only a few entries in the table there is insufficient space for the errors to show themselves clearly. If the table does not represent a polynomial, then the correction of an error is uncertain, for there is no constant value for any one column. The occurrence of an error is then indicated by widely oscillating values and an "improved" value may be deduced for the mistaken entry. Another reason for differences which do not ultimately vanish is the necessity of "rounding-off" entries when entries are given correct to a fixed number of decimal places. When rounding has occurred the entries in the mth difference column lie in the range $\pm 2^{m-1}$ multiplied by (the last decimal place given) when they should be zero.

Another feature of difference tables is shown by the (approximate) tabulation of the function $y = 1/x^2$ (Table 4).

TABLE 4

x	y	Δ	Δ^2	Δ^3	Δ^4
$-1 \cdot 0$	1				
		1			
$-0 \cdot 7$	2		3		
		4		87	
$-0 \cdot 4$	6		90		-346
		94		-259	
$-0 \cdot 1$	100		-169		482
		-75		223	
$0 \cdot 2$	25		54		-258
		-21		-35	
$0 \cdot 5$	4		19		
		-2			
$0 \cdot 8$	2				

In Table 4 the difference terms increase in value, especially within the dotted lines, and to an even greater extent within the inner pair. This happens because the function $1/x^2$ has a singularity at $x = 0$, a value which is straddled by the values of x being used. In general, the higher differences only diminish in value where the function is "well-behaved". Since a polynomial is "well-behaved" for all finite values of x, the occurrence of small values for the higher differences means that a function resembles a polynomial fairly closely. We shall see later that small values for the higher differences are necessary for a good approximation to a function by a polynomial to be possible.

Exercises 1 : 9

1. By taking alternate entries from the table of the example on p. 62 construct a table of differences and show that fifth differences are zero.

2. From a table giving squares of numbers correct to 4 significant figures construct a table with 11 entries for the range 1·0(0·1)2·0 and test whether 3rd differences are zero.

3. From a table giving square roots of numbers correct to 4 significant figures construct a similar table.

4. The following values refer to a polynomial; find any error in the entries and determine the degree of the polynomial.

x	−0·2	0·0	0·2	0·4	0·6	0·8	1·0
y	0·379	0·710	1·175	1·811	2·666	3·810	5·292

x	1·2	1·4	1·6	1·8
y	7·232	9·633	12·728	16·673

5. Find and correct, by the use of a difference table, the error in the following table:

x	$f(x)$	x	$f(x)$
1	0·00000	6	0·20411
2	0·03612	7	0·25178
3	0·07464	8	0·30163
4	0·11550	9	0·35362
5	0·15897		

Draw up the correct difference table.

6. The following table contains one incorrect entry for $f(x)$. Locate the error; suggest a possible cause and a suitable correction.

x	0·1	0·2	0·3	0·4	0·5	0·6	0·7
$f(x)$	35·743	33·959	32·511	31·486	30·969	31·046	31·800

x	0·8	0·9	1·0	1·1
$f(x)$	33·341	35·673	38·965	43·274

Miscellaneous Exercises I

1. The periodic function $f(x)$ is defined by

$$f(x) = \begin{cases} \dfrac{A(x-3nl)}{l}, & 3nl \leqslant x \leqslant (3n+1)l, \\[2mm] A, & (3n+1)l \leqslant x \leqslant (3n+2)l, \\[2mm] \dfrac{A[(3n+3)l-x]}{l}, & (3n+2)l \leqslant x \leqslant (3n+3)l. \end{cases}$$

Sketch the graph of $f(x)$ in the range $-6l \leqslant x \leqslant 9l$.

2. What can we say about (i) $f(x)g(x)$, (ii) $f(x)/g(x)$ in the following cases: (a) $f(x)$ and $g(x)$ both even functions, (b) both odd functions, (c) one even and one odd?

3. If the function $f(x)$ satisfies the relation $f(x).f(y) = f(x+y)$ for all x, y and $f(0) = 1$ prove that $f(nx) = [f(x)]^n$ for positive and negative values of n either integral or fractional.

4. A function which is finite and continuous for all x is defined by

$$f(x) = \begin{cases} \left(\dfrac{A}{x^2}\right) + x + B, & 0 \leqslant x \leqslant a, \\[3mm] \left(\dfrac{C}{x^2}\right) + Dx, & a \leqslant x \leqslant \infty, \end{cases}$$

where A, B, C, D are numerical coefficients. If $f(0) = 1$ and $\lim\limits_{x \to \infty} f(x)$ is zero, find these coefficients.

5. By considering separately the signs of $x-1$ and $x-y$ in the four regions into which the plane is divided by the straight lines $x-1 = 0$ and $x-y = 0$, sketch the graph of

$$2y = |x-1| + |x-y|.$$

6. Find the number of real roots of the equation

$$x^3 + 8x^2 - 32x + 14 = 0$$

and determine their signs.

Evaluate the smallest positive root *correct* to 3 decimal places.

7. Show that when λ is large and positive the equation $x^3 - \lambda x + 1 = 0$ has a small positive root given by $1/\lambda$ to a first approximation, and that a better approximation to this root is $1/\lambda + 1/\lambda^4$.

Find the smaller positive root of $x^3 - 5x + 1 = 0$ correct to four decimal places.

8. By the substitution $y = x + 1/x$, solve the *reciprocal* equation

$$6x^4 - 25x^3 + 37x^2 - 25x + 6 = 0.$$

9. Sketch the curves

$$y = x^3 - 3x^2 + 4 \quad \text{and} \quad y = x^2 + 4,$$

and determine into how many regions they together divide the plane.

(*Continued overleaf*)

Find the greatest possible number of regions into which the plane can be divided by

(i) the graphs of a cubic and of a quadratic polynomial,

(ii) the graphs of two cubic polynomials.

10. By means of a sketch-graph, or otherwise, show that the equation $2x^3 - 4x^2 + 1 = 0$ has two positive roots and one negative root. Calculate the negative root and the larger positive root correct to three significant figures.

11. By the substitution $y = 1/x$ find the equation in y whose roots are the reciprocals of the roots α, β, γ of the equation

$$x^3 + px^2 + qx + r = 0.$$

What are the roots of the equations in y obtained by elimination of x between the above equation and (i) $y^2 = x$, (ii) $y = x^2$, (iii) $y = x+c$, (iv) $y = ax+b$?

12. Find the equation whose roots are the roots of the following quartic equation, each augmented by 2:

$$x^4 + 8x^3 + 12x^2 - 16x - 28 = 0.$$

Hence, or otherwise, solve the given equation.

13. Show that the expression

$$\frac{x^2 - 3ax + 2a^2}{x^2 - 3x + 2} \qquad (a \neq 1)$$

can assume any real value for real values of x only if $\frac{1}{2} \leqslant a \leqslant 2$.

Show that, if $a = 0$, there will be two extreme values between which the expression cannot lie, and determine these values.

14. Prove that the expression

$$x^2 - 4xy + 5y^2 + 2x - 8y + 6$$

is positive for all real values of x and y, but that the expression

$$x^2 - 4xy + 3y^2 + 2x - 8y + 6$$

can take all real values for real values of x and y.

15. Show on the plane of the cartesian axes Oxy the area within which the following inequalities are satisfied: $x - y \geqslant -1$, $2x + y \leqslant 7$, $2y - x \geqslant 3$. Hence find the greatest possible value of (i) x, (ii) y.

16. Sketch the graph of

$$y = \frac{2x-1}{3x+2}.$$

Find the values of x for which

$$\frac{2x-1}{3x+2} < \frac{1}{x},$$

and verify that they form two intervals the sum of whose lengths is $\frac{8}{3}$.

17. Show that the equation
$$ax^2 + 2\lambda xy - ay^2 = 0$$
represents two perpendicular straight lines.

Show that the pair of straight lines joining the origin O to the intersections A and B of the line $lx + my = 1$ with the conic $ax^2 + by^2 = 1$ has the equation
$$(a - l^2)x^2 - 2lmxy + (b - m^2)y^2 = 0.$$

Deduce that if AOB is a right angle, then the line AB touches the circle
$$(a + b)(x^2 + y^2) = 1.$$

[If $f(x, y) = 0$ and $g(x, y) = 0$ are the equations of two curves C_1, C_2, then the equation of the straight lines joining the origin to the points of intersection of C_1 and C_2 may be obtained by making the equations of C_1 and C_2 homogeneous in x, y and z by the introduction of a variable z and eliminatng z from the equations so obtained.]

18. A sequence is defined by $x_1 = 3$, $x_{n+1} = 2 + 4/x_n \,(n \geqslant 1)$; it tends to a limit l. By evaluating the terms of the sequence find l, to three significant figures, and confirm the result by obtaining and solving an equation for l.

19. (i) Prove that the parabola $y^2 - 4x = 0$ divides the plane of the coordinate axes Oxy into two regions in which the function $f(x, y) = y^2 - 4x$ has opposite signs. By drawing suitable curves show on the plane Oxy the area within which both the following inequalities are satisfied:
$$y^2 - 4x \leqslant 0, \qquad y - x + 3 \geqslant 0.$$

Hence find the greatest possible value of x and the least possible value of y.

(ii) Find the ranges of values of x for which
$$x - \frac{6}{x} < 1.$$

20. If $f(x, y) = (x + 3)(x^2 + y^2 - 9)$, sketch the curve $f = 0$ and indicate on the graph the positive and negative regions of the function $f(x, y)$. Sketch *roughly* contours $f = C$ in each region. Show that there is just one isolated point.

21. The function $f(x)$ is defined and takes real finite values for all real finite x, is not identically zero and satisfies the functional equation $f(x + y) = f(x)f(y)$. Show that $f(x)$ is positive for every x and that $f(0) = 1$.

If there exists a fixed positive constant K such that $f(x) < K$ for all x, show that $f(x) \leqslant 1$ for all x and hence prove that $f(x) = 1$ for every x.

22. (i) Prove that
$$2x^2 - 6xy + 5y^2 + 2x - 8y + 14 > 0$$
for all real x, y.

(ii) Find all the ranges of values of x for which
$$x^3 - 4x^2 - x + 4 > 0.$$

Shade in a diagram of the (x, y) plane the regions for which
$$x^3 - 4x^2y - xy^2 + 4y^3 > 0.$$

23. The circles C_1 and C_2 have radii r_1 and r_2, and their centres are at the points (α_1, β_1) and (α_2, β_2) respectively. Sketch the relative positions of the circles if

$$(\alpha_1 - \alpha_2)^2 + (\beta_1 - \beta_2)^2 = (r_1 \pm r_2)^2,$$

distinguishing carefully between the two cases.

Hence, or otherwise, show that the two circles $x^2 + y^2 = 1$ and $x^2 - 2x + y^2 = 3$ touch one another.

Obtain the equation of a circle which touches these circles and the x-axis.

24. Show, by means of a suitable counter example, that the following proposition is false: If $f(x)$ is a real function of a real variable x defined on $a \leqslant x \leqslant b$, and if $f(a)$ and $f(b)$ are of opposite sign, then $f(\zeta) = 0$ for some $\zeta, a < \zeta < b$. State a further condition on the function which will turn the proposition into a correct theorem, the theorem of Bolzano. Illustrate by sketching the graphs of

$$\text{(i)} \quad y = \frac{1}{3 - 2x}; \qquad \text{(ii)} \quad y = \ln\left[\tfrac{1}{2}(5 - 2x)\right]$$

taking, in each case, $a = 0$ and $b = 2$.

25. The domain R is the semicircular region of the plane defined by $x^2 + y^2 \leqslant 1$, $x \geqslant 0$. Find the largest and smallest values attained in R by each of the following functions: (i) $x + y$; (ii) $(x + y)^2$; (iii) $x(x^2 + y^2 - 1)$; (iv) $x^2 + 2y^2 + 6y$.

26. The values of $f(x)$, a low degree polynomial, are given by the table

x	2	3	4	5	6	7	8	9	10
$f(x)$	15	40	85	165	259	400	585	820	1111

It is suspected that there is a transposition error in one of the values of x).

(By differencing locate and correct this error.

27. Prove that the sum of the numbers in any column of a difference table is equal to the difference between the first and last numbers in the preceding column.

Set out a table showing the first and second differences for the following entries. Use the above result to check the arithmetical work.

$$0 \cdot 0000 \quad -0 \cdot 0104 \quad -0 \cdot 0206 \quad -0 \cdot 0307 \quad -0 \cdot 0404 \quad -0 \cdot 0496$$

CHAPTER II

THE TECHNIQUE OF DIFFERENTIATION

2 : 1 Differentiation from first principles

If $y = f(x)$, we define the rate of increase or rate of change of y with respect to x as $\lim_{h \to 0} \dfrac{f(x+h)-f(x)}{h}$ provided this limit exists. This rate of change is variously denoted by $f'(x)$, Dy or $\dfrac{dy}{dx}$, (dy/dx), and is called the differential coefficient or derivative of y with respect to (w.r. to) x. The process of finding the derivative is called differentiation.

We now find the derivatives of (i) x^n, (ii) $\sin x$.

(i) $f(x) = x^n$;

$$f'(x) = \lim_{h \to 0} \frac{(x+h)^n - x^n}{h} = \lim_{h \to 0} \frac{(x+h)^n - x^n}{(x+h)-x} = nx^{n-1} \quad (2.1)$$

on using eqn. (1.19) with $x+h$ and x written in place of x and a respectively.

(ii) Assuming that term by term differentiation of an infinite power series is legitimate (see § 5 : 1), it follows at once from definitions (1.1) and (1.2) for $\sin x$, $\cos x$ that

$$\frac{d(\sin x)}{dx} = \cos x, \quad (2.2)$$

similarly,

$$\frac{d(\cos x)}{dx} = -\sin x. \quad (2.3)$$

69

We now use a slightly different approach. Suppose $y = f(x)$ and x increases to $x + \delta x$. Here δx stands for "a small increment in x" and is *not* δ multiplied by x. Then y increases to $y + \delta y$, where δy is the increment in y corresponding to the increment δx in x, i.e. $y + \delta y = f(x + \delta x)$. The definition of differentiation then implies that

$$\frac{dy}{dx} = \lim_{\delta x \to 0} \frac{\delta y}{\delta x}. \tag{2.4}$$

At this stage we regard $d\{f(x)\}/dx$ as the result of the operation of a differentiation carried out on $f(x)$; in fact d/dx is an operator not a number.

It follows from the definitions of continuity and differentiation that, if $f'(x)$ exists in the range $a \leqslant x \leqslant b$, then $f(x)$ is continuous in this range. However, continuity of $f(x)$ does not imply differentiability, e.g. if $f(x) = x$ for $0 \leqslant x \leqslant a$, $f(x) = 2a - x$ for $a \leqslant x \leqslant 2a$, then $f(x)$ is continuous for $0 \leqslant x \leqslant 2a$ but $f'(x)$ is undefined at $x = a$.

Exercises 2 : 1

Differentiate from first principles

(i) $\tan x$,   (ii) $(ax+b)^3$,   (iii) $\sin (x^2)$,   (iv) $\sqrt{x}$,   (v) $\sec 2x$.

2 : 2 The rules of differentiation

1. The sum and difference rules. If $u_1, u_2, \ldots, u_n$ are all functions of x and n is finite, then it follows from the definition of differentiation and eqn. (1.21) that

$$\frac{d}{dx}(u_1 + u_2 + \ldots + u_n) = \frac{du_1}{dx} + \frac{du_2}{dx} + \ldots + \frac{du_n}{dx}. \tag{2.5}$$

This result has been anticipated in deriving eqns. (2.2) and (2.3). It does not follow from this that an infinite series (i.e. a series which does not terminate) may necessarily be differentiated term by term.

Example. $\dfrac{d}{dx}\left(\sum_{r=1}^{n} x^r\right) = \sum_{r=1}^{n} r x^{r-1}.$

2. The product rule. If u and v are functions of x and $y = uv$, then

$$y + \delta y = (u + \delta u)(v + \delta v).$$

$$\therefore \quad \delta y = (u + \delta u)(v + \delta v) - uv = v\,\delta u + u\,\delta v + \delta u \cdot \delta v.$$

$$\therefore \quad \frac{dy}{dx} = \lim_{\delta x \to 0} \frac{\delta y}{\delta x} = \lim_{\delta x \to 0} \left(v\,\frac{\delta u}{\delta x} + u\,\frac{\delta v}{\delta x} + \delta u\,\frac{\delta v}{\delta x} \right).$$

Since we assume that du/dx exists, u must be continuous and $\delta u \to 0$ as $\delta x \to 0$. We obtain therefore the product rule

$$\frac{dy}{dx} = \frac{d(uv)}{dx} = v\,\frac{du}{dx} + u\,\frac{dv}{dx}. \tag{2.6}$$

The product rule may be generalised to

$$\frac{d}{dx}(u_1 u_2 \ldots u_n)$$

$$= (u_1 u_2 \ldots u_n)\left(\frac{1}{u_1}\,\frac{du_1}{dx} + \frac{1}{u_2}\,\frac{du_2}{dx} + \ldots + \frac{1}{u_n}\,\frac{du_n}{dx} \right). \tag{2.7}$$

This will be proved in § 2 : 4.

Example. (i) $\dfrac{d}{dx}(x^3 \sin x) = 3x^2 \sin x + x^3 \cos x.$

(ii) If c is a constant, so that $\dfrac{dc}{dx} = 0$, then $\dfrac{d(cu)}{dx} = c\,\dfrac{du}{dx}.$

(iii) $\dfrac{d}{dx}(x \sin x \cos x) = \sin x \cos x + x \cos^2 x - x \sin^2 x.$

---

3. The quotient rule. If

$$y = \frac{u}{v},$$

then

$$y + \delta y = \frac{(u + \delta u)}{(v + \delta v)}$$

and

$$\delta y = \frac{(v\,\delta u - u\,\delta v)}{v(v + \delta v)}.$$

$$\therefore \quad \frac{dy}{dx} = \lim_{\delta x \to 0} \frac{\delta y}{\delta x} = \lim_{\delta x \to 0} \frac{v(\delta u/\delta x) - u(\delta v/\delta x)}{v(v + \delta v)}.$$

Since in general $\delta v \to 0$ as $\delta x \to 0$ we obtain the quotient rule

$$\frac{\mathrm{d}}{\mathrm{d}x}\left(\frac{u}{v}\right) = \frac{v(\mathrm{d}u/\mathrm{d}x) - u(\mathrm{d}v/\mathrm{d}x)}{v^2}.\qquad(2.8)$$

Example.

$f(x)$	$f'(x)$
$\dfrac{1}{v}$	$-\dfrac{1}{v^2}\dfrac{\mathrm{d}v}{\mathrm{d}x}$
$\tan x$	$\sec^2 x$
$\cot x$	$-\operatorname{cosec}^2 x$
$\sec x$	$\sec x \tan x$
$\operatorname{cosec} x$	$-\operatorname{cosec} x \cot x.$

4. Differentiation of a function of a function. If $y = F(u)$ where $u = f(x)$, clearly y is a function of x. We say that y is a function of a function, i.e., the function F of the function f.

Example. (i) $(x^4 + a^4)^6$ is the function u^6 of the function $u = x^4 + a^4$.

(ii) $\cos(x^3)$ is the function $\cos u$ of the function $u = x^3$.

(iii) $(\cos x)^3$ or $\cos^3 x$ is the function u^3 of the function $u = \cos x$.

Suppose that, corresponding to an increment δx in x, the increments in u and y are δu and δy respectively. Then, assuming that $\delta u \to 0$ when $\delta x \to 0$, the identity

$$\frac{\delta y}{\delta x} = \frac{\delta y}{\delta u} \cdot \frac{\delta u}{\delta x}$$

gives

$$\frac{\mathrm{d}y}{\mathrm{d}x} = \lim_{\delta x \to 0} \frac{\delta y}{\delta x} = \lim_{\delta x \to 0}\left(\frac{\delta y}{\delta u} \cdot \frac{\delta u}{\delta x}\right) = \lim_{\delta u \to 0} \frac{\delta y}{\delta u} \cdot \lim_{\delta x \to 0} \frac{\delta u}{\delta x}.$$

$$\therefore \quad \frac{\mathrm{d}y}{\mathrm{d}x} = \frac{\mathrm{d}y}{\mathrm{d}u} \cdot \frac{\mathrm{d}u}{\mathrm{d}x} = F'(u) \cdot f'(x),\qquad(2.9)$$

where $F'(u) = \mathrm{d}\{F(u)\}/\mathrm{d}u$ and $f'(x) = \mathrm{d}\{f(x)\}/\mathrm{d}x$. This is the chain rule for the differentiation of a function of a function.

Example. (i) $y = F(ax+b)$ where a and b are constants. Then $y = F(u)$, where $u = ax+b$.

$$\therefore \quad \frac{\mathrm{d}y}{\mathrm{d}x} = F'(u) \cdot \frac{\mathrm{d}u}{\mathrm{d}x} = aF'(ax+b).$$

Here $F'(ax+b)$ means $F'(u)$ with u put equal to $ax+b$ after differentiation, i.e. the derivative of $F(ax+b)$ w.r. to $ax+b$.

For example, $\mathrm{d}\{\cos(ax+b)\}/\mathrm{d}x = -a\sin(ax+b)$.

(ii) $\dfrac{\mathrm{d}}{\mathrm{d}x}(x^4+a^4)^6 = \dfrac{\mathrm{d}(u^6)}{\mathrm{d}u}\cdot\dfrac{\mathrm{d}}{\mathrm{d}x}(x^4+a^4) = 6u^5\cdot4x^3 = 24x^3(x^4+a^4)^5.$

(iii) $\dfrac{\mathrm{d}}{\mathrm{d}x}[\cos(x^3)] = \dfrac{\mathrm{d}}{\mathrm{d}u}(\cos u)\cdot\dfrac{\mathrm{d}(x^3)}{\mathrm{d}x} = -\sin u\cdot3x^2 = -3x^2\sin(x^3).$

(iv) $\dfrac{\mathrm{d}}{\mathrm{d}x}[\cos^3 x] = \dfrac{\mathrm{d}(u^3)}{\mathrm{d}u}\cdot\dfrac{\mathrm{d}}{\mathrm{d}x}(\cos x) = 3u^2\cdot(-1)\sin x$

$\qquad\qquad = -3\sin x\cos^2 x.$

The chain rule may be generalised. For, if y is a function of u and u is a function of v which is a function of x, then

$$\frac{\mathrm{d}y}{\mathrm{d}x} = \frac{\mathrm{d}y}{\mathrm{d}u}\cdot\frac{\mathrm{d}u}{\mathrm{d}v}\cdot\frac{\mathrm{d}v}{\mathrm{d}x}. \tag{2.10}$$

This result may be extended to any number of functions.

Example. $\dfrac{\mathrm{d}}{\mathrm{d}x}(1+5\sin^3 2x)^4 = 4(1+5\sin^3 2x)^3\dfrac{\mathrm{d}}{\mathrm{d}x}(5\sin^3 2x)$

$\qquad\qquad = 20(1+5\sin^3 2x)^3\cdot3\sin^2 2x\dfrac{\mathrm{d}}{\mathrm{d}x}(\sin 2x)$

$\qquad\qquad = 120\sin^2 2x\cos 2x(1+5\sin^3 2x)^3.$

---

5. Differentiation of parametric equations. Suppose that x and y are expressed as functions of t so that $x = x(t)$, $y = y(t)$. Then, if $\delta x \to 0$ as $\delta t \to 0$, the identity

$$\frac{\delta y}{\delta x} = \frac{\delta y/\delta t}{\delta x/\delta t}$$

gives

$$\frac{\mathrm{d}y}{\mathrm{d}x} = \lim_{\delta x \to 0}\frac{\delta y}{\delta x} = \lim_{\delta t \to 0}\frac{\delta y/\delta t}{\delta x/\delta t} = \frac{\lim_{\delta t \to 0}\delta y/\delta t}{\lim_{\delta t \to 0}\delta x/\delta t}.$$

$$\therefore\ \frac{\mathrm{d}y}{\mathrm{d}x} = \frac{\mathrm{d}y/\mathrm{d}t}{\mathrm{d}x/\mathrm{d}t}. \tag{2.11}$$

It is standard practice to put a dot over a variable to denote differentiation w.r. to t, e.g. $\mathrm{d}x/\mathrm{d}t = \dot{x}$. Then eqn. (2.11) may be written $\mathrm{d}y/\mathrm{d}x = \dot{y}/\dot{x}$.

Example. (i) If $x = at^2$, $y = 2at$, then $\dfrac{dy}{dx} = \dfrac{1}{t}$.

(ii) If $x = a \cos t$, $y = b \sin t$, then $\dfrac{dy}{dx} = \dfrac{(-b \cot t)}{a}$.

(iii) If $x = a(\theta - \sin \theta)$, $y = a(1 - \cos \theta)$, then $\dfrac{dy}{dx} = \cot \left(\tfrac{1}{2}\theta\right)$.

Exercises 2 : 2

Differentiate the following functions w.r. to x:

1. $x(1-x^2)$ **2.** $x(1-x)$ **3.** $x(1-x)^2$ **4.** $x(1-x^2)^2$

5. $x^2(1-x^2)$ **6.** $x^4(1-x)$ **7.** $x^4(1-x)^2$ **8.** $x^m(1-x^n)$

9. $x^m(1-x^2)^n$ **10.** $x + \dfrac{1}{x}$ **11.** $\left(x - \dfrac{1}{x}\right)^2$ **12.** $x^2\left(x - \dfrac{1}{x}\right)^2$

13. $\left(x + \dfrac{1}{2x}\right)^3$ **14.** $\left(5x - \dfrac{1}{3x}\right)^2$ **15.** $x^6\left(2x - \dfrac{1}{3x}\right)^3$ **16.** $\dfrac{x}{1-x}$

17. $\dfrac{x}{1-x^2}$ **18.** $\dfrac{x^2}{1-x}$ **19.** $\dfrac{x^2}{1-x^2}$ **20.** $(x^m + x^{-m})^n$

21. $\dfrac{1+x}{1-x}$ **22.** $\dfrac{1+x}{(1-x)^2}$ **23.** $\dfrac{x}{1-2x}$ **24.** $\dfrac{x}{1-3x^2}$

25. $\dfrac{1+x^2}{1-x^2}$ **26.** $\dfrac{1-x^2}{1+x^3}$ **27.** $\dfrac{1+x^m}{1-x^m}$ **28.** $\dfrac{2+3x^2}{1-4x^2}$

29. $\dfrac{a+bx^n}{c-dx^m}$ **30.** $\dfrac{1+x+x^2}{1-x+x^2}$ **31.** $\sin^2 x$ **32.** $\sin x \cos x$

33. $\sin^n x \cos^n x$ **34.** $\tan(x^2)$ **35.** $\sec 3x$ **36.** $\cot(1+3x^3)$

37. $\sec^2 4x$ **38.** $\cos^2 \tfrac{1}{2} x$ **39.** $\tan^2(ax+b)$

40. $\tan x + \tfrac{1}{3}\tan^3 x$ **41.** $\dfrac{\sin x}{1+\sin x}$ **42.** $\dfrac{\sin x}{1-\sin x}$

43. $\dfrac{1-\cos x}{1+\cos x}$ **44.** $\sec x + \tan x$ **45.** $\dfrac{1-\sin 2x}{1+\sin 2x}$ **46.** $\cos 3x \cos x$

47. $\cos(x^3) \cos x$ **48.** $\dfrac{\cos x + \sin x}{\cos x - \sin x}$ **49.** $x \sin x$ **50.** $x^2 \sec x$

51. $\dfrac{\sin x}{x}$ **52.** $x \tan x$ **53.** $\sin \dfrac{1}{x}$ **54.** $\cot^2\left(\dfrac{1}{x}\right)$

55. $x \tan\left(\dfrac{1}{3x}\right)$ **56.** $x^2 \cos\left(\dfrac{4}{x}\right)$ **57.** $\sqrt{(1+x)}$

58. $\sqrt{(a-x)} \cdot \sqrt{(b+x)}$ **59.** $x\sqrt{(a^2-x^2)}$

60. $(1+x)\sqrt{(1+x^2)}$ **61.** $\dfrac{\sqrt{(1-x^2)}}{1+x^2}$ **62.** $\dfrac{1-x}{\sqrt{(1+x^2)}}$

63. $\sqrt{\left(\dfrac{1-x}{1+x}\right)}$ **64.** $\dfrac{1}{\sqrt{(1-x^2)}}$ **65.** $\dfrac{\sqrt{(a^2+x^2)}}{x}$ **66.** $\dfrac{1}{x+\sqrt{(1+x^2)}}$

67. $\dfrac{1}{x-\sqrt{(x^2-1)}}$ **68.** $\dfrac{x}{x+\sqrt{(1+x^2)}}$ **69.** $\sqrt{\left(\dfrac{1+x+x^2}{1-x+x^2}\right)}$

70. $\sqrt{(a\sin^2 x+b\cos^2 x)}$ **71.** $\sqrt{(x^2+3x+4)}$.

Find dy/dx in terms of t in the following cases:

72. $x=ct,\quad y=\dfrac{c}{t}$ **73.** $x=a\cos^n t,\quad y=b\sin^n t,\quad n\neq 0$

74. $x=a\left(\dfrac{t^2+1}{t}\right),\quad y=b\left(\dfrac{t^2-1}{t}\right)$.

2 : 3 Repeated differentiation

If $y=f(x)$, then dy/dx is also a function of x and we can by differentiation find the value of $\dfrac{d}{dx}\left(\dfrac{dy}{dx}\right)$. This we call the second derivative of y w.r. to x and denote it by $\dfrac{d^2y}{dx^2}$, (d^2y/dx^2), $f''(x)$ or D^2y. Most functions of physical interest can be differentiated a number of times and we denote the result of differentiating $f(x)$ n times, i.e. the nth derivative of $f(x)$, by $\dfrac{d^ny}{dx^n}$, (d^ny/dx^n), $f^{(n)}(x)$ or D^ny.

Example.   (i) $\dfrac{d^2(x^n)}{dx^2}=n(n-1)x^{n-2}$.   (ii) $\dfrac{d^3(\sin x)}{dx^3}=-\cos x$.

When $x=x(t)$, $y=y(t)$, eqn. (2.11) implies that $d/dx\equiv(1/\dot{x})(d/dt)$, i.e. the operation of differentiation w.r. to x is equivalent to differentiation w.r. to t followed by division by $\dot{x}$. Then

$$\frac{d^2y}{dx^2}=\frac{1}{\dot{x}}\frac{d}{dt}\left(\frac{\dot{y}}{\dot{x}}\right)=\frac{\dot{x}\ddot{y}-\ddot{x}\dot{y}}{\dot{x}^3}, \tag{2.12}$$

where $\ddot{x}$ denotes d^2x/dt^2, etc.

The convention for the representation of a sequence of operations is to write the operators in the opposite order to that in which the operations are carried out so that the last symbol represents the first operation to be carried out and so on.

Example. $x^4 \, \mathrm{D} \, [x^2 \, \mathrm{D} \, \{(\sin x)/x\}]$ is obtained by the following sequence:

   (i) division of $\sin x$ by x,

   (ii) differentiation w.r. to x,

   (iii) multiplication by x^2,

   (iv) differentiation w.r. to x,

   (v) multiplication by x^4.

The final result is $-x^5 \sin x$.

Exercises 2 : 3

1. Find $\mathrm{D}^n(x^m)$ considering separately the three cases (a) $n < m$, (b) $n = m$, (c) $n > m$.

2. Show that $\mathrm{D}[\sin(ax+b)] = a \sin\left(ax+b+\tfrac{1}{2}\pi\right)$.

Deduce by mathematical induction that

$$\mathrm{D}^n[\sin(ax+b)] = a^n \sin\left(ax+b+\tfrac{1}{2}n\pi\right).$$

Express $\mathrm{D}^n[\cos(ax+b)]$ in this form.

3. Show by mathematical induction that

$$\mathrm{D}^n\left\{\frac{1}{(ax+b)^r}\right\} = \frac{(-1)^n a^n (n+r-1)!}{(r-1)! \, (ax+b)^{n+r}} \,.$$

2 : 4 Exponentials, logarithms and hyperbolic functions

The exponential function. We define the exponential function $y = \exp(x)$ as that solution of the (differential) equation $\mathrm{d}y/\mathrm{d}x = y$ for which $y = 1$ when $x = 0$, i.e. we define $\exp(x)$ as the function which is equal to its own derivative and takes the value unity when $x = 0$.

The unique function which satisfies the above conditions may be shown (see § 5 : 5) to be expressible as an infinite series in the form

$$\exp(x) = 1 + \frac{x}{1!} + \frac{x^2}{2!} + \frac{x^3}{3!} + \ldots + \frac{x^n}{n!} + \ldots. \qquad (2.13)$$

It is proved in books on analysis that

$$\exp(x)\cdot\exp(y) = \exp(x+y), \quad [\exp(x)]^n = \exp(nx),$$
$$\exp(x)\cdot\exp(-x) = 1;$$

in fact it is shown that we may write $\exp(x) = \mathrm{e}^x$, where e is the irrational number defined by

$$\mathrm{e} = 1 + \frac{1}{1!} + \frac{1}{2!} + \frac{1}{3!} + \ldots + \frac{1}{n!} + \ldots; \qquad (2.14)$$

e = 2·71828 approximately. The function e^x is clearly positive for $x \geqslant 0$. Since $e^{-x} = 1/e^x$, it must be positive for $x < 0$ also. Further, $e^0 = 1$ and $\lim_{x \to \infty} e^{-x} = \lim_{x \to \infty} 1/e^x = 0$. The graph of e^x is shown in Fig. 2.1.

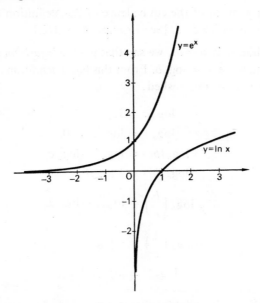

FIG. 2.1. The graph of e^x and $\ln x$.

Example 1. $D[e^{f(x)}] = f'(x)e^{f(x)}$.

Example 2. If p is an integer,

$$\lim_{x \to \infty} x^p e^{-x} = \lim_{x \to \infty} \left[\frac{x^p}{\left\{ 1 + x + \dfrac{x^2}{2!} + \ldots + \dfrac{x^{p+1}}{(p+1)!} + \ldots \right\}} \right]$$

$$= \lim_{x \to \infty} \left[\frac{1}{\left\{ x^{-p} + x^{-p+1} + \dfrac{x^{-p+2}}{2!} + \ldots + \dfrac{x}{(p+1)!} + \ldots \right\}} \right] = 0$$

whatever the value of p. A similar result holds if p is not an integer; the proof requires only slight modification. This limit indicates that, for large values of x, e^x is of a higher order of magnitude than any power of x.

An alternative definition of the exponential function is

$$e^x = \lim_{n \to \infty} \left(1 + \frac{x}{n}\right)^n = \lim_{n \to \infty} \left(1 + \frac{1}{n}\right)^{nx}. \qquad (2.15)$$

We defer a proof of the equivalence of this definition to the one given above until § 5 : 5. [See Example 4, p. 272.]

Logarithms. If $b = a^y$, we say that y is the *logarithm* of b to the base a and write $y = \log_a b$. From this basic definition the following rules may be established:

(i) $$\log_a a = 1,$$

(ii) $$\log_a 1 = \log_a a^0 = 0,$$

(iii) $$\log_a (bc) = \log_a b + \log_a c,$$

(iv) $$\log_a (b^k) = k \log_a b,$$

(v) $$\log_a \left(\frac{b}{c}\right) = \log_a b - \log_a c,$$

(vi) $$\log_a \left(\frac{1}{c}\right) = -\log_a c,$$

(vii) $$\log_b N = \log_a N \cdot \log_b a.$$

Writing $N = b$ in (vii) gives $\log_a b \cdot \log_b a = 1$. Another particular case of (vii) is $\log_{10} [f(x)] = \log_e [f(x)] \cdot \log_{10} e$. Logarithms to the base e are called natural logarithms; the notation "ln" for "$\log_e$" has now been adopted as the standard British convention and will be used in the second and later editions of these volumes. If "log" to any other base is required, that base will be indicated. An important identity, used in the solution of linear differential equations (cf. Vol. 2., Chap. I, § 1 : 4) is $e^{\log_e f(x)} = f(x)$.

Before finding the derivative of ln x we establish an important preliminary theorem or lemma. The relation $y = f(x)$ implies that x is some function of y, $g(y)$ say; treating y as the independent variable we may find dx/dy. Then, assuming that $\delta y \to 0$ as $\delta x \to 0$,

$$\frac{dy}{dx} = \lim_{\delta x \to 0} \frac{\delta y}{\delta x} = \lim_{\delta y \to 0} \left[\frac{1}{(\delta x / \delta y)}\right] = \frac{1}{dx/dy}, \qquad (2.16)$$

i.e.

$$\frac{dy}{dx} \cdot \frac{dx}{dy} = 1. \qquad (2.17)$$

If $y = \ln x$, by definition $x = e^y$ and hence $dx/dy = e^y = x$. Therefore eqn. (2.17) gives

$$\frac{d}{dx}(\ln x) = \frac{1}{x}. \qquad (2.18)$$

The chain rule gives at once

$$\frac{d}{dx}[\ln f(x)] = \frac{f'(x)}{f(x)}. \qquad (2.19)$$

Example 1. $D[\ln (x^p + a^p)] = \dfrac{px^{p-1}}{(x^p + a^p)}.$

Example 2. $D[\ln (x^2 + a^2)^n] = D[n \ln (x^2 + a^2)] = \dfrac{2nx}{(x^2 + a^2)}.$

Example 3. $D\left[\ln\left(\dfrac{x+a}{x-a}\right)\right] = D[\ln (x+a) - \ln (x-a)]$

$$= \frac{1}{x+a} - \frac{1}{x-a} = \frac{-2a}{x^2 - a^2}.$$

Example 4. Express d^2x/dy^2 in terms of dy/dx, d^2y/dx^2.

Since

$$\frac{dx}{dy} = \frac{1}{dy/dx},$$

then

$$\frac{d^2x}{dy^2} = \frac{d}{dy}\left(\frac{1}{dy/dx}\right) = \frac{d}{dx}\left(\frac{1}{dy/dx}\right) \cdot \frac{dx}{dy}$$

by the chain rule.

$$\therefore \frac{d^2x}{dy^2} = -\frac{d^2y/dx^2}{(dy/dx)^3}.$$

We now find $\lim\limits_{x \to 0+} \ln x$. Writing $x = 1/N$ where $N \to \infty$, $\ln x = \ln (1/N) = -\ln N$. Therefore $\ln x \to -\infty$ as $x \to 0+$.

Logarithms of negative numbers are complex and will be considered in Chapter VII. The graph of $\ln x$ is shown in Fig. 2.1 and is the reflection in the line $y = x$ of the graph of e^x.

By writing $x = e^t$ and using example 2 of page 77, it is easy to show that

$$
\text{(i)} \qquad \lim_{x \to \infty} \frac{(\ln x)}{x^\alpha} = 0 \quad \text{if} \quad \alpha > 0,
$$

$$
\text{(ii)} \qquad \lim_{x \to 0+} x^\beta \ln x = 0 \quad \text{if} \quad \beta > 0.
$$

$$(2.20)$$

These limits indicate that, for large values of x, any positive power of x is of a higher order of magnitude than $\ln x$. Also, for small positive values of x, $-\ln x$ is of a lower order of magnitude than any negative power of x.

We now prove the generalisation (2.7) of the product rule for differentiation. If $y = u_1 u_2 \ldots u_n$, then

$$
\ln y = \ln u_1 + \ln u_2 + \ldots + \ln u_n.
$$

Differentiation w.r. to x gives

$$
\frac{1}{y} \frac{dy}{dx} = \frac{1}{u_1} \frac{du_1}{dx} + \frac{1}{u_2} \frac{du_2}{dx} + \ldots + \frac{1}{u_n} \frac{du_n}{dx}.
$$

Multiplication by y leads to eqn. (2.7). This method of *logarithmic differentiation* may be used directly for the differentiation of products, complicated surds, etc.

Example 1. $\qquad y = \dfrac{x^3(x+1)}{(3x-2)^4}.$

$$
\ln y = 3 \ln x + \ln (x+1) - 4 \ln (3x-2).
$$

$$
\therefore \quad \frac{1}{y} \frac{dy}{dx} = \frac{3}{x} + \frac{1}{x+1} - \frac{12}{(3x-2)} = -\frac{(11x+6)}{x(x+1)(3x-2)}.
$$

$$
\therefore \quad \frac{dy}{dx} = -\frac{(11x+6)x^2}{(3x-2)^5}.
$$

Example 2. $\quad y = \sqrt{\left(\dfrac{p+x}{p-x}\right)} \cdot \sqrt{\left(\dfrac{q+x}{q-x}\right)},$

$$
\ln y = \tfrac{1}{2} [\ln (p+x) + \ln (q+x) - \ln (p-x) - \ln (q-x)].
$$

$$
\therefore \quad \frac{1}{y} \frac{dy}{dx} = \frac{1}{2} \left[\frac{1}{p+x} + \frac{1}{q+x} + \frac{1}{p-x} + \frac{1}{q-x} \right] = \frac{(p+q)(pq-x^2)}{(p^2-x^2)(q^2-x^2)},
$$

whence we derive at once the value of dy/dx.

If $y = [f(x)]^{g(x)}$, we can only find dy/dx by logarithmic differentiation. Taking logarithms gives

$$\ln y = g(x) \ln f(x).$$

$$\therefore \frac{1}{y} \frac{dy}{dx} = g'(x) \ln f(x) + \frac{g(x) \cdot f'(x)}{f(x)}.$$

$$\therefore \frac{dy}{dx} = [f(x)]^{g(x)} \left\{ g'(x) \ln f(x) + \frac{g(x) f'(x)}{f(x)} \right\}.$$

Example 1.   If $y = a^x$,   then $\ln y = x \ln a$.

$$\frac{1}{y} \frac{dy}{dx} = \ln a \text{ and therefore } \frac{d(a^x)}{dx} = a^x \ln a.$$

Example 2.   If $y = x^x$,   then $\ln y = x \ln x$;

$$\frac{1}{y} \frac{dy}{dx} = 1 + \ln x, \quad \therefore \frac{d(x^x)}{dx} = x^x (1 + \ln x).$$

Hyperbolic functions. There exist certain combinations of the exponential functions e^x and e^{-x} with properties which bear a close formal analogy with those of the trigonometric functions. We define these *hyperbolic* functions as follows:

$$\sinh x = \frac{1}{2} (e^x - e^{-x}) = x + \frac{x^3}{3!} + \frac{x^5}{5!} + \cdots + \frac{x^{2n+1}}{(2n+1)!} + \cdots,$$

$$\cosh x = \frac{1}{2} (e^x + e^{-x}) = 1 + \frac{x^2}{2!} + \frac{x^4}{4!} + \cdots + \frac{x^{2n}}{2n!} + \cdots,$$

$$\tanh x = \frac{\sinh x}{\cosh x} = \frac{e^x - e^{-x}}{e^x + e^{-x}},$$

$$\coth x = \frac{1}{\tanh x}, \quad \text{sech } x = \frac{1}{\cosh x}, \quad \text{cosech } x = \frac{1}{\sinh x}.$$

Clearly $\cosh x$ is an even function and $\cosh x \geqslant 1$ whereas $\sinh x$ and $\tanh x$ are odd functions with $|\tanh x| < 1$. The graphs of $\sinh x$, $\cosh x$ and $\tanh x$ are shown in Fig. 2.2.

From the formal definitions given above we derive at once the identities

(i) $\cosh x \pm \sinh x = e^{\pm x}$,   (2.21)

(ii) $\cosh^2 x - \sinh^2 x = (\cosh x - \sinh x)(\cosh x + \sinh x) = 1.$

$$\therefore \cosh^2 x = 1 + \sinh^2 x. \tag{2.22}$$

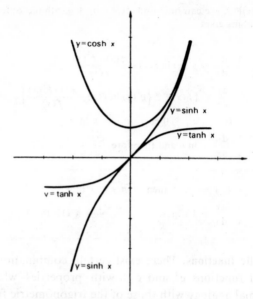

FIG. 2.2. The graphs of sinh x, cosh x, and tanh x.

Division by $\cosh^2 x$ gives

(iii) $$\operatorname{sech}^2 x = 1 - \tanh^2 x. \qquad (2.23)$$

Identities involving hyperbolic functions resemble closely corresponding identities for trigonometric functions. For example,

$$\cosh(x+y) = \tfrac{1}{2}(e^{x+y} + e^{-x-y}) \equiv \tfrac{1}{2}(e^x + e^{-x}) \cdot \tfrac{1}{2}(e^y + e^{-y})$$
$$+ \tfrac{1}{2}(e^x - e^{-x}) \cdot \tfrac{1}{2}(e^y - e^{-y}).$$

$$\therefore \quad \cosh(x+y) = \cosh x \cosh y + \sinh x \sinh y.$$

Similarly

$$\sinh(x+y) = \sinh x \cosh y + \cosh x \sinh y.$$

A hyperbolic identity may be formally obtained from a trigonometric identity simply by changing "sin" into "sinh" and "cos" into "cosh" except that wherever the product of two sines occurs in the trigonometric identity a negative sign must be introduced in the hyperbolic identity. This result follows directly from eqns. (7.9).

Example.

(i) $\cos 5x = \cos^5 x - 10 \cos^3 x \sin^2 x + 5 \cos x \sin^4 x.$

∴ $\cosh 5x = \cosh^5 x - 10 \cosh^3 x(-1)\sinh^2 x + 5 \cosh x(-1)^2 \sinh^4 x.$

∴ $\cosh 5x = \cosh^5 x + 10 \cosh^3 x \sinh^2 x + 5 \cosh x \sinh^4 x.$

(ii) $\sin 5x = 5 \sin x - 20 \sin^3 x + 16 \sin^5 x.$

∴ $\sinh 5x = 5 \sinh x - 20(-1)\sinh^3 x + 16(-1)^2 \sinh^5 x.$

∴ $\sinh 5x = 5 \sinh x + 20 \sinh^3 x + 16 \sinh^5 x.$

The derivatives of the hyperbolic functions follow at once from the definitions, viz.

$f(x)$	$f'(x)$
$\sinh x$	$\cosh x$
$\cosh x$	$\sinh x$
$\tanh x$	$\operatorname{sech}^2 x$
$\coth x$	$-\operatorname{cosech}^2 x$
$\operatorname{sech} x$	$-\operatorname{sech} x \tanh x$
$\operatorname{cosech} x$	$-\operatorname{cosech} x \coth x$

Exercises 2 : 4

Differentiate the following functions w.r. to x:

1. e^{x^2}.   **2.** $\dfrac{e^{ax^2}}{x}$.   **3.** $e^{\sin x}$.   **4.** $e^{ax} \sin bx$.   **5.** $\sinh^n x \cosh^m x$.

6. $\dfrac{(e^x - 1)}{(e^x + 1)}$.   **7.** $\tanh x - \dfrac{1}{3}\tanh^2 x$.   **8.** $\ln \sin x$.   **9.** $\ln \cos x$.

10. $\ln\left(\dfrac{1+x}{1-x}\right)$.   **11.** $\ln\left(\dfrac{1+\sqrt{x}}{1-\sqrt{x}}\right)$.   **12.** $\ln[x + \sqrt{(x^2 - 1)}]$.

13. $\sqrt{x} + \ln(1 - \sqrt{x})$.   **14.** $\dfrac{\cosh x + \sinh x}{\cosh x - \sinh x}$.   **15.** $\dfrac{\cosh x + \cos x}{\sinh x + \sin x}$.

16. $\ln\left[\dfrac{x}{\sqrt{(x^2+1)} - x}\right]$.   **17.** $\tan(a + b^x)$.   **18.** $x^{x \ln x}$.

19. $\ln\left[\dfrac{(x-4)}{\sqrt{(2x-3)}}\right]$.   **20.** $\dfrac{(x^3+1)^{\frac{3}{4}}}{(x^4-1)^{\frac{1}{2}}}$.

21. Solve the equation $\sinh x = e^{-x} + 1$.

22. Express $\tanh x$ in terms of e^{2x} and show directly from the definitions of the hyperbolic functions that

$$\tanh(x+y) = \frac{\tanh x + \tanh y}{1 + \tanh x \tanh y}.$$

23. Prove the formula $\sinh \frac{1}{2}u = \sqrt{\{\frac{1}{2}(\cosh u - 1)\}}$ where $u > 0$.

24. If two variables u and θ are connected by the relation $\sinh u = \tan \theta$, where θ is in the first quadrant, prove that $u = \ln \tan (\frac{1}{2}\theta + \frac{1}{4}\pi)$.

2 : 5 Inverse functions

If $\sin y = x$, then y is a function of x. We express y explicitly in terms of x in the form $y = \sin^{-1} x$ to be read as "sine to the minus one x" or the "inverse sine of x;" this means the angle whose sine is x. The notation arc $\sin x$ is used by some writers. We define $\cos^{-1} x, \tan^{-1} x, \cot^{-1} x, \sec^{-1} x$ and $\mathrm{cosec}^{-1} x$ similarly. The graphs of $\sin^{-1} x$, $\cos^{-1} x$ and $\tan^{-1} x$ are shown in Figs. 2.3(a), (b), (c). Clearly $y = \sin^{-1} x$ is a many-valued function, since, corresponding to any value of x in the range $|x| \leqslant 1$, there exists an infinite number of values of y, e.g. $\sin^{-1}(\frac{1}{2}) = \pm n\pi + (-1)^n \pi/6$ where n is 0 or an integer. We define the principal value of $y = \sin^{-1} x$ as that value which lies in the range $-\frac{1}{2}\pi \leqslant y \leqslant \frac{1}{2}\pi$. Similarly, the other inverse trigonometric functions are many-valued. We choose the principal values of $u = \cos^{-1} x$ and $v = \tan^{-1} x$ to lie in the ranges $0 \leqslant u \leqslant \pi$ and $-\frac{1}{2}\pi \leqslant v \leqslant \frac{1}{2}\pi$ respectively.

If $y = \sin^{-1}(x/a)$, where $a > 0$, then $x = a \sin y$.

$$\therefore \quad \frac{\mathrm{d}x}{\mathrm{d}y} = a \cos y = \pm a \sqrt{(1 - \sin^2 y)} = \pm \sqrt{(a^2 - x^2)}.$$

$$\therefore \quad \frac{\mathrm{d}y}{\mathrm{d}x} = \frac{\pm 1}{\sqrt{(a^2 - x^2)}}.$$

If we consider the principal value of $\sin^{-1}(x/a)$ only, so that, as x increases from $-a$ to a, $\sin^{-1}(x/a)$ increases from $-\frac{1}{2}\pi$ to $\frac{1}{2}\pi$ then $\mathrm{d}y/\mathrm{d}x$ is positive, and the positive sign must be taken.

[Alternatively we see that the gradient of the curve $y = \sin^{-1}(x/a)$ is positive (cf. § 4 : 2) and hence $\mathrm{d}y/\mathrm{d}x > 0$.]

$$\therefore \quad \frac{\mathrm{d}}{\mathrm{d}x}\left[\sin^{-1}\left(\frac{x}{a}\right)\right] = \frac{1}{\sqrt{(a^2 - x^2)}}. \tag{2.24}$$

Similarly, taking the principal value of $\cos^{-1}(x/a)$ we find

$$\frac{\mathrm{d}}{\mathrm{d}x}\left[\cos^{-1}\left(\frac{x}{a}\right)\right] = \frac{-1}{\sqrt{(a^2 - x^2)}}. \tag{2.25}$$

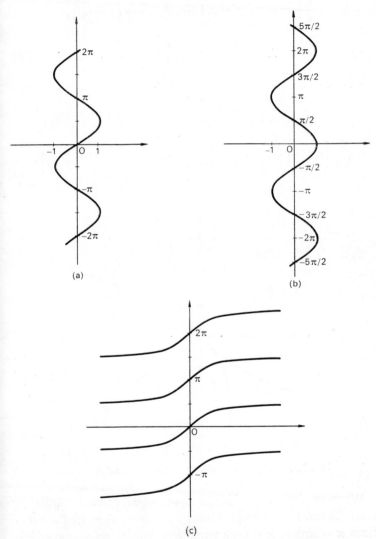

FIG. 2.3. (a) The graph of $\sin^{-1} x$. (b) The graph of $\cos^{-1} x$. (c) The graph of $\tan^{-1} x$.

If $y = \tan^{-1}(x/a)$ so that $x = a \tan y$, then

$$\frac{\mathrm{d}x}{\mathrm{d}y} = a \sec^2 y = a(1 + \tan^2 y) = a\left(1 + \frac{x^2}{a^2}\right).$$

$$\therefore \quad \frac{\mathrm{d}}{\mathrm{d}x}\left[\tan^{-1}\left(\frac{x}{a}\right)\right] = \frac{a}{a^2 + x^2}. \qquad (2.26)$$

Similarly,

$$\frac{\mathrm{d}}{\mathrm{d}x}\left[\cot^{-1}\left(\frac{x}{a}\right)\right] = -\frac{a}{a^2 + x^2},$$

$$\frac{\mathrm{d}}{\mathrm{d}x}\left[\sec^{-1}\left(\frac{x}{a}\right)\right] = \frac{a}{x\sqrt{(x^2 - a^2)}} = -\frac{\mathrm{d}}{\mathrm{d}x}\left[\operatorname{cosec}^{-1}\left(\frac{x}{a}\right)\right].$$

$$(2.27)$$

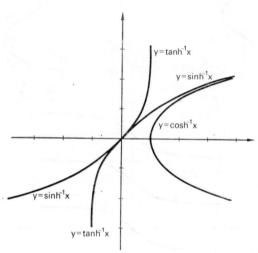

FIG. 2.4. The graphs of $\sinh^{-1}x$, $\cosh^{-1}x$ and $\tanh^{-1}x$.

We now define the inverse hyperbolic functions $\sinh^{-1}x$, $\cosh^{-1}x$ and $\tanh^{-1}x$ as the functions y determined by the equations $x = \sinh y$, $x = \cosh y$ and $x = \tanh y$ respectively. The graphs of these three functions are given in Fig. 2.4 and are the reflections in the line $y = x$ of the corresponding graphs of Fig. 2.2.

If $y = \sinh^{-1}(x/a)$ where $a > 0$, then

$$x = a \sinh y. \qquad (2.28)$$

$$\therefore \; x^2 + a^2 = a^2 \sinh^2 y + a^2 = a^2 \cosh^2 y.$$

$$\therefore \; \sqrt{(x^2 + a^2)} = a \cosh y. \qquad (2.29)$$

Here we retain the positive square root only since $a \cosh y > 0$. Addition of eqns. (2.28) and (2.29) gives

$$x + \sqrt{(x^2 + a^2)} = a(\cosh y + \sinh y) = a\,e^y.$$

$$\therefore \; y = \sinh^{-1}\left(\frac{x}{a}\right) = \ln\left\{\frac{x + \sqrt{(x^2 + a^2)}}{a}\right\} \qquad (2.30)$$

and is a single-valued odd function of x as shown by its graph.

If

$$y = \cosh^{-1}\left(\frac{x}{a}\right), \quad \text{where} \quad a > 0,$$

then

$$x = a \cosh y. \qquad (2.31)$$

$$\therefore \; x^2 - a^2 = a^2 (\cosh^2 y - 1) = a^2 \sinh^2 y.$$

$$\therefore \; \pm\sqrt{(x^2 - a^2)} = a \sinh y. \qquad (2.32)$$

Addition of eqns. (2.31) and (2.32) gives

$$x \pm \sqrt{(x^2 - a^2)} = a\,e^y.$$

$$\therefore \; y = \cosh^{-1}\left(\frac{x}{a}\right) = \ln\left[\frac{x \pm \sqrt{(x^2 - a^2)}}{a}\right]. \qquad (2.33)$$

Since

$$\frac{x - \sqrt{(x^2 - a^2)}}{a} = \frac{x^2 - (x^2 - a^2)}{a[x + \sqrt{(x^2 - a^2)}]} = \frac{a}{x + \sqrt{(x^2 - a^2)}},$$

we may rewrite eqn. (2.33) in the form

$$y = \cosh^{-1}\left(\frac{x}{a}\right) = \pm\ln\left[\frac{x + \sqrt{(x^2 - a^2)}}{a}\right] \qquad (2.34)$$

and thus $\cosh^{-1}(x/a)$ is a two-valued even function of x as shown by its graph. We take the positive sign in eqn. (2.34) to define the principal value of $\cosh^{-1}(x/a)$.

If

$$y = \tanh^{-1}\left(\frac{x}{a}\right), \quad \text{where} \quad a > 0, \text{ then } x = a \tanh y$$

so that

$$\frac{x}{a} = \frac{e^y - e^{-y}}{e^y + e^{-y}}.$$

$$\therefore \ e^{2y} = \frac{a+x}{a-x}.$$

$$\therefore \ y = \tanh^{-1}\left(\frac{x}{a}\right) = \frac{1}{2}\ln\left(\frac{a+x}{a-x}\right). \tag{2.35}$$

Differentiation of the inverse hyperbolic functions may be carried out by use of the chain rule and eqns. (2.30), (2.34) and (2.35). Alternatively we may proceed directly as for the trigonometric functions. For example, if $y = \sinh^{-1}(x/a)$ where $a > 0$, so that $x = a \sinh y$, then

$$\frac{dx}{dy} = a \cosh y = \pm a\sqrt{(\sinh^2 y + 1)} = \pm\sqrt{(x^2 + a^2)}.$$

Figure 2.4 shows that $\sinh^{-1}(x/a)$ is an increasing function of x and so we take the positive sign and find

$$\frac{d}{dx}\left[\sinh^{-1}\left(\frac{x}{a}\right)\right] = \frac{1}{\sqrt{(x^2 + a^2)}}. \tag{2.36}$$

Similarly,

$$\frac{d}{dx}\left[\cosh^{-1}\left(\frac{x}{a}\right)\right] = \frac{1}{\sqrt{(x^2 - a^2)}}, \tag{2.37}$$

where we have taken the positive (principal) value of $\cosh^{-1}(x/a)$, and

$$\frac{d}{dx}\left[\tanh^{-1}\left(\frac{x}{a}\right)\right] = \frac{a}{a^2 - x^2}. \tag{2.38}$$

Although we have considered only the logarithm, inverse trigonometric and inverse hyperbolic functions as examples of inverse functions, nevertheless we can apply the techniques employed above to other (similar) cases. Thus, if there is a functional relation denoted by $y = f(x)$, then the relation $x = f(y)$ defines the inverse function $y = f^{-1}(x)$.

Further, the graph of the inverse function $y = f^{-1}(x)$ can be obtained from that of $y = f(x)$ by interchanging the labelling of the coordinate axes Oxy and, in fact, the curve $y = f^{-1}(x)$ is the optical image (or reflection) of the curve $y = f(x)$ in the line $y = x$.

Exercises 2 : 5

1. Verify the identities:

(i)　　$\sin^{-1} x \pm \sin^{-1} y = \sin^{-1} \{x \sqrt{(1-y^2)} \pm y \sqrt{(1-x^2)}\}$.

(ii)　　$\cos^{-1} x \pm \cos^{-1} y = \cos^{-1} \{xy \mp \sqrt{(1-x^2)} \cdot \sqrt{(1-y^2)}\}$.

(iii)　　$\tan^{-1} x \pm \tan^{-1} y = \tan^{-1} \left(\dfrac{x \pm y}{1 \mp xy} \right)$.

2. Find the functions F inverse to the following functions $f(x)$, i.e. if $y = f(x)$ then $x = F(y)$:

(i) $f(x) = x^2$.　　(ii) $f(x) = \dfrac{1-x}{1+x}$,　　$(x \neq -1)$.

(iii) $f(x) = \sqrt{\left(\dfrac{1+x}{x} \right)}$　$(x \neq 0)$.　　(iv) $f(x) = \tan^{-1} (\cot x)$.

(v) $f(x) = \tan^{-1} \left(\dfrac{1}{x} \right)$.　　(vi) $y = 10^x$.

(vii) $f(x) = \cos^{-1} [\sqrt{(1-x^2)}]$,　$(-1 \leqslant x \leqslant 1)$.

3. Solve the equation $\tan^{-1}(x) + 2 \cot^{-1}(x) = \frac{2}{3}\pi$ where the principal values of the inverse functions are taken.

4. If $x > 0$, show that

$$\tan^{-1}(2x+1) - \tan^{-1}(2x-1) = \tan^{-1} \left(\frac{1}{2x^2} \right).$$

Hence show that $\displaystyle\sum_{r=1}^{\infty} \tan^{-1} \left(\frac{1}{2r^2} \right) = \frac{\pi}{4}$ where the principal values of the inverse tangent are taken.

5. Solve the simultaneous equations:

$$\cosh x + \cosh y = 4,$$
$$\sinh x - \sinh y = 2.$$

6. (i) Express $\operatorname{cosech}^{-1} x$ in the form $\ln [f(x)]$ distinguishing between the two cases, x positive and x negative.

(ii) Show that

$$\operatorname{sech}^{-1} x = \ln \left[\frac{1 \pm \sqrt{(1-x^2)}}{x} \right], \quad \text{if} \quad 0 \leqslant x \leqslant 1.$$

7. Prove that

$$\tanh^{-1} \left(\frac{x^2 - a^2}{x^2 + a^2} \right) = \ln \left(\frac{x}{a} \right).$$

8. If $y = \ln \tan x$, prove the following:

(i) $\sinh ny = \tfrac{1}{2}(\tan^n x - \cot^n x)$,

(ii) $2 \cosh ny \operatorname{cosec} 2x = \cosh (n+1)y + \cosh (n-1)y$.

Differentiate the following functions w.r. to x:

9. $\sin (n \sin^{-1} x)$.   **10.** $\ln (\tan^{-1} x)$.   **11.** $\tan^{-1}\left(\dfrac{a}{x} \tan \dfrac{x}{a}\right)$.

12. $\tan^{-1} \dfrac{2x}{1-x^2}$.   **13.** $\tan^{-1} [\sqrt{(x^2+1)} - x]$. **14.** $\tan^{-1} (e^x \cos x)$.

15. $x e^x \sin^2 x \tan^{-1} x$. **16.** $\tan^{-1}\left(\dfrac{ax-b}{bx+a}\right)$.   **17.** $\sinh^{-1} (\cos x)$.

18. $\sinh^{-1}\left[\tan\left(\dfrac{1+x}{1-x}\right)\right]$. **19.** $\coth^{-1}\left(\dfrac{x}{a}\right)$.   **20.** $\operatorname{sech}^{-1}\left(\dfrac{x}{a}\right)$.

21. $\operatorname{cosech}^{-1}\left(\dfrac{x}{a}\right)$.

22. Find the values when $x = 1$ of the differential coefficients with respect to x of the following functions:

(i) $(x-2)^3 (6-2x)^4$;   (ii) x^{2x};   (iii) $\sinh^{-1} [\sqrt{(1+x^2)}]$;

(iv) $x^3 e^{-x} \sin \pi x$;   (v) $\ln\left(\dfrac{2x^2-1}{2x^2+1}\right)$.

23. A and B are positive constants. Show that when $|B^2 - A^2| < 1$ the equations

$$A \sinh u + B \cosh u = 1 \quad \text{and} \quad B \sinh v + A \cosh v = 1$$

each have at least one real solution. Show also that whatever the values of A and B they cannot both have two real solutions.
    Solve the equation

$$6 \sinh x + 9 \cosh x = 23.$$

24. Solve for x and y the simultaneous equations

(i) $\cosh x = 3 \sinh y$, $2 \sinh x + 6 \cosh y = 5$,

(ii) $\cosh x \cosh y = 2$, $\sinh x \sinh y = 1$,

where x and y are real, expressing your answers as logarithms.

25. If

$$2 \sinh x + 3 \cosh x = 3 + k,$$

where k is small, prove that $x = \tfrac{1}{3}k$ and

$$x = \frac{k}{2} - \frac{3k^2}{16}$$

are successive approximations to a real root of this equation.

2 : 6 Differentiation of equations

If $f(x, y) = 0$, where x and y are the independent and dependent variables respectively, so that y is an implicit function of x, the differential coefficient dy/dx is defined as before to be $\lim_{\delta x \to 0} \delta y/\delta x$. However, expression of y as an explicit function of x may be difficult or even impossible. Accordingly we usually obtain dy/dx in terms of x and y by differentiating the equation $f(x, y) = 0$ as it stands w.r. to x using the chain rule where necessary for differentiating terms involving y. This process may be repeated to obtain second and higher derivatives.

Example 1. If $\ln (x^2+y^2) = 2 \tan^{-1} (y/x)$, find dy/dx and d^2y/dx^2 in terms of x and y.

Differentiation gives

$$\frac{2x+2y\dfrac{dy}{dx}}{x^2+y^2} = \frac{2\left(x\dfrac{dy}{dx}-y\right)}{x^2+y^2}.$$

$$\therefore \quad \frac{dy}{dx} = \frac{x+y}{x-y}.$$

$$\therefore \quad \frac{d^2y}{dx^2} = \frac{(x-y)\left(1+\dfrac{dy}{dx}\right)-(x+y)\left(1-\dfrac{dy}{dx}\right)}{(x-y)^2} = -\frac{2y}{(x-y)^2}+\frac{2x\dfrac{dy}{dx}}{(x-y)^2}$$

$$= -\frac{2y}{(x-y)^2}+\frac{2x(x+y)}{(x-y)^3} = \frac{2(x^2+y^2)}{(x-y)^3}.$$

Example 2. If $x e^y = \cos y$, find dy/dx and d^2y/dx^2 when $x = 1$, $y = 0$.

$$e^y+xe^y \frac{dy}{dx} = -\sin y \frac{dy}{dx}. \tag{1}$$

Putting $x = 1$, $y = 0$ we find $\left(\dfrac{dy}{dx}\right)_{1,0} = -1$. The notation $\left(\dfrac{dy}{dx}\right)_{1,0}$ means the numerical value of $\dfrac{dy}{dx}$ obtained on putting $x = 1$, $y = 0$ after differentiation.

To find $\left(\dfrac{d^2y}{dx^2}\right)_{1,0}$, rather than solve eqn. (1) for $\dfrac{dy}{dx}$, etc., it is more convenient to differentiate eqn. (1) as it stands w.r. to x. This gives

$$2e^y \frac{dy}{dx}+xe^y \left(\frac{dy}{dx}\right)^2+xe^y \frac{d^2y}{dx^2} = -\cos y \left(\frac{dy}{dx}\right)^2-\sin y \frac{d^2y}{dx^2}.$$

Putting $x = 1$, $y = 0$ gives

$$2\left(\frac{dy}{dx}\right)_{1,0}+\left(\frac{dy}{dx}\right)^2_{1,0}+\left(\frac{d^2y}{dx^2}\right)_{1,0} = -\left(\frac{dy}{dx}\right)^2_{1,0},$$

whence
$$\left(\frac{\mathrm{d}^2 y}{\mathrm{d}x^2}\right)_{1,0} = 0.$$

Example 3. If $y = [\sin^{-1}(x/a)]^2$, show that $(a^2 - x^2)\dfrac{\mathrm{d}^2 y}{\mathrm{d}x^2} - x\dfrac{\mathrm{d}y}{\mathrm{d}x} - 2 = 0$.

We may verify this result directly but it is quicker to proceed as follows:
$$\frac{\mathrm{d}y}{\mathrm{d}x} = \frac{2\sin^{-1}(x/a)}{\sqrt{(a^2 - x^2)}}.$$
$$\therefore \ (a^2 - x^2)\left(\frac{\mathrm{d}y}{\mathrm{d}x}\right)^2 = 4\left[\sin^{-1}\left(\frac{x}{a}\right)\right]^2 = 4y.$$

Differentiation w.r. to x and cancellation of $\mathrm{d}y/\mathrm{d}x$ gives the required equation. Note that in this way we *derive* rather than *verify* the stated result.

Example 4. If $x = \cos t$, $y = \cos 2pt$, show that
$$(1 - x^2)\frac{\mathrm{d}^2 y}{\mathrm{d}x^2} - x\frac{\mathrm{d}y}{\mathrm{d}x} + 4p^2 y = 0.$$
$$\frac{\mathrm{d}y}{\mathrm{d}x} = \frac{\dfrac{\mathrm{d}y}{\mathrm{d}t}}{\dfrac{\mathrm{d}x}{\mathrm{d}t}} = \frac{2p\sin 2pt}{\sin t} = \pm\frac{2p\sqrt{(1 - y^2)}}{\sqrt{(1 - x^2)}}.$$
$$\therefore \ (1 - x^2)\left(\frac{\mathrm{d}y}{\mathrm{d}x}\right)^2 = 4p^2(1 - y^2).$$

Differentiation w.r. to x and cancellation of $\mathrm{d}y/\mathrm{d}x$ gives the required equation.

Exercises 2 : 6

1. If $y = \mathrm{e}^{-kx}(a\cos nx + b\sin nx)$, and a, b, n, k are constants, show that
$$\frac{\mathrm{d}^2 y}{\mathrm{d}x^2} + 2k\frac{\mathrm{d}y}{\mathrm{d}x} + (n^2 + k^2)y = 0.$$

2. If $y^n = x + \sqrt{(1 + x^2)}$, prove that $n\sqrt{(1 + x^2)}\dfrac{\mathrm{d}y}{\mathrm{d}x} = y$.

3. If $y = \sin(a\sin^{-1} x)$, prove that
$$(1 - x^2)\frac{\mathrm{d}^2 y}{\mathrm{d}x^2} - x\frac{\mathrm{d}y}{\mathrm{d}x} + a^2 y = 0.$$

4. If $y = \left[x + (1 + x^2)^{\frac{1}{2}}\right]^p$, show that
$$(1 + x^2)\frac{\mathrm{d}^2 y}{\mathrm{d}x^2} + x\frac{\mathrm{d}y}{\mathrm{d}x} - p^2 y = 0.$$

5. If $xy^2 - \ln y = x + \sin x$, find the values of y, dy/dx and d^2y/d^2x when $x = 0$.

6. If y is a function of x and $x = e^t/(e^t + 1)$, prove that

$$x(1-x)\frac{dy}{dx} = \frac{dy}{dt}.$$

7. If $y = t^m + t^{-m}$ and $x = t + t^{-1}$, prove that

(i) $$(x^2 - 4)\left(\frac{dy}{dx}\right)^2 = m^2(y^2 - 4).$$

(ii) $$(x^2 - 4)\frac{d^2y}{dx^2} + x\frac{dy}{dx} - m^2y = 0.$$

8. If $u = \sin^p \theta - \csc^p \theta$ and $v = \sin \theta - \csc \theta$, prove that

(i) $$(v^2 + 4)\left(\frac{du}{dv}\right)^2 = p^2(u^2 + 4),$$

(ii) $$(v^2 + 4)\frac{d^2u}{dv^2} + v\frac{du}{dv} - p^2u = 0.$$

9. (i) If

$$x = a\left(t + \frac{1}{t}\right) \quad \text{and} \quad y = a\left(t - \frac{1}{t}\right),$$

prove that

$$y^3 \frac{d^2y}{dx^2} + 4a^2 = 0.$$

(ii) When

$$y = \frac{x}{x + \sqrt{(1 + x^2)}}$$

show that

$$\sqrt{(1 + x^2)}\frac{dy}{dx} = \frac{y^2}{x^2}.$$

(iii) If

$$\ln(x^2 + y^2) = 2 \tan^{-1}\left(\frac{y}{x}\right),$$

prove that dy/dx and d^2y/dx^2 are positive when $x > y > 0$.

10. Given that $u = J_0(\alpha x)$ and $v = J_0(\beta x)$ satisfy the equations

$$\frac{d}{dx}\left(x\frac{du}{dx}\right) + \alpha^2 xu = 0, \qquad \frac{d}{dx}\left(x\frac{dv}{dx}\right) + \beta^2 xv = 0,$$

verify the following results by carrying out the differentiations:

(i) $$\frac{d}{dx}\left\{x\left(u\frac{dv}{dx} - v\frac{du}{dx}\right)\right\} = (\alpha^2 - \beta^2)\,xuv,$$

(ii) $$\frac{d}{dx}\left[x^2\left\{\alpha^2 u^2 + \left(\frac{du}{dx}\right)^2\right\}\right] = 2\alpha^2 xu^2.$$

[The functions $J_0(\alpha x)$, $J_0(\beta x)$ are *Bessel functions*. See Vol. 4, § 3 : 1.]

11. If $x = r \cos \theta$, $y = r \sin \theta$ where r, θ are functions of t, prove that

$$\frac{d^2 x}{dt^2} \cos \theta + \frac{d^2 y}{dt^2} \sin \theta = \frac{d^2 r}{dt^2} - r \left(\frac{d\theta}{dt} \right)^2 .$$

[See also eqn. (7.13), p. 421.]

12. Variables x, y are given in terms of new variables t, u by the equations $x = e^t$, $y = ue^{-t}$. If $y = f(x)$ prove that

(a) $$x^2 \frac{dy}{dx} = \frac{du}{dt} - u,$$

(b) $$x^3 \frac{d^2 y}{dx^2} = \frac{d^2 u}{dt^2} - 3 \frac{du}{dt} + 2u.$$

2 : 7 Leibniz's theorem on repeated differentiation

In many problems it is necessary to find the second or higher derivative of a product of two functions. Repeated use of the product rule (2.6) can be tedious and conducive to error. A useful result is **Leibniz's theorem** which states that if u and v are functions of x, then

$$D^n(uv) = u_0 v_n + \binom{n}{1} u_1 v_{n-1} + \binom{n}{2} u_2 v_{n-2} + \dots$$

$$+ \binom{n}{r} u_r v_{n-r} + \dots + \binom{n}{n-1} u_{n-1} v_1 + u_n v_0. \quad (2.39)$$

Here $\binom{n}{r}$ denotes the binomial coefficient $_nC_r = {}^nC_r = \dfrac{n!}{r!\,(n-r)!}$ and suffixes denote differentiation w.r. to x, e.g. $u_0 = u$, $u_r v_{n-r} = D^r u \, D^{n-r} v$.

We prove this theorem by mathematical induction as follows:

Assuming the truth of the theorem for an integer $n = k$ and differentiating w.r. to x, we obtain

$$D^{k+1}(uv) = (u_0 v_{k+1} + u_1 v_k) + \binom{k}{1} (u_1 v_k + u_2 v_{k-1})$$

$$+ \binom{k}{2} (u_2 v_{k-1} + u_3 v_{k-2}) + \dots$$

$$+ \binom{k}{r} (u_r v_{k+1-r} + u_{r+1} v_{k-r}) + \dots$$

$$+ (u_k v_1 + u_{k+1} v_0).$$

The coefficient of the term involving $u_r v_{k+1-r}$ is

$$\binom{k}{r-1} + \binom{k}{r} = \frac{k!}{(r-1)!\,(k+1-r)!} + \frac{k!}{r!\,(k-r)!}$$

$$= \frac{(k+1)!}{r!\,(k+1-r)!} = \binom{k+1}{r}.$$

$$\therefore \; D^{k+1}(uv) = u_0 v_{k+1} + \binom{k+1}{1} u_1 v_k$$

$$+ \binom{k+1}{2} u_2 v_{k-1} + \cdots$$

$$+ \binom{k+1}{r} u_r v_{k+1-r} + \cdots$$

$$+ \binom{k+1}{k} u_k v_1 + u_{k+1} v_0. \qquad (2.40)$$

But eqn. (2.40) is merely the statement of the theorem with $k+1$ in place of k, and the theorem is true when $k = 1$ by virtue of the product rule (2.6). Hence it is true for $k = 1+1 = 2$ and therefore for $k = 2+1 = 3$ and so on for all integral k.

Example 1. Writing $u = x^2$, $v = e^{ax}$ gives, if $n \geqslant 2$,

$$D^n(x^2 e^{ax}) = x^2 \cdot D^n(e^{ax}) + n\,D(x^2) \cdot D^{n-1}(e^{ax}) + \tfrac{1}{2} n(n-1)\,D^2(x^2) \cdot D^{n-2}(e^{ax}).$$

The remaining terms vanish since $D^r(x^2) = 0$ for $r > 2$.

$$\therefore \; D^n(x^2 e^{ax}) = [a^2 x^2 + 2nax + n(n-1)]\,a^{n-2} e^{ax}.$$

Example 2. If $y = (x^2-1)^n$, where n is a positive integer, prove that

$$(1-x^2)\frac{dy}{dx} + 2nxy = 0.$$

By differentiating this equation $(n+1)$ times and using Leibniz's theorem, or otherwise, show that the function $p_n(x)$, defined by

$$p_n(x) = \frac{d^n}{dx^n}\{(x^2-1)^n\},$$

satisfies the equation

$$. \;(1-x^2)\frac{d^2 p_n}{dx^2} - 2x\frac{dp_n}{dx} + n(n+1)p_n = 0.$$

Show also that $p_n(1) = (-1)^n\,p_n(-1) = 2^n n!$

If $y = (x^2 - 1)^n$, then

$$\ln y = n \ln (x^2 - 1), \quad \frac{1}{y} \frac{dy}{dx} = \frac{2nx}{x^2 - 1},$$

i.e.
$$(1 - x^2) \frac{dy}{dx} + 2nxy = 0. \tag{1}$$

Differentiating $(n+1)$ times by using Leibniz's theorem we have

$$(1 - x^2) \frac{d^{n+2}y}{dx^{n+2}} - 2(n+1)x \frac{d^{n+1}y}{dx^{n+1}} - (n+1)n \frac{d^n y}{dx^n}$$
$$+ 2n \left\{ x \frac{d^{n+1}y}{dx^{n+1}} + (n+1) \frac{d^n y}{dx^n} \right\} = 0.$$

This reduces to the given equation on writing $p_n(x) = d^n/dx^n\{(x^2 - 1)^n\}$. To find $p_n(1)$ we need $D^n[(x+1)^n (x-1)^n]$ when $x = 1$. Writing $u = (x+1)^n$, $v = (x-1)^n$ and noting that $D^r[(x-1)^n] = n!(x-1)^{n-r}/(n-r)!$ vanishes when $x = 1$ except in the case $r = n$, we obtain the required value as

$$[(x+1)^n D^n \{(x-1)^n\}]_{x=1} = 2^n \cdot n!. \tag{2}$$

Similarly, to find $p_n(-1)$ we need $D^n\{(x+1)^n (x-1)^n\}$ when $x = -1$ and this time the required value is

$$[(x-1)^n D^n \{(x+1)^n\}]_{x=-1} = (-2)^n n!. \tag{3}$$

Equations (2) and (3) are equivalent to the required results. The functions $P_n(x) = \{2^n(n!)\}^{-1} p_n(x)$ are called *Legendre polynomials*. [See Vol. 4, § 3 : 2.]

Example 3. If $y = f(x) = [x + \sqrt{(1 + x^2)}]^m$, find $f^{(2p)}(0)$ and $f^{(2p+1)}(0)$, i.e., find the values of the $2p^{th}$ and $(2p+1)^{th}$ derivatives of y w.r. to x when x is put equal to zero after differentiation.

$$\frac{dy}{dx} = m[x + \sqrt{(1+x^2)}]^{m-1} \left[1 + \frac{x}{\sqrt{(1+x^2)}} \right] = \frac{m[x + \sqrt{(1+x^2)}]^m}{\sqrt{(1+x^2)}}$$
$$= \frac{my}{\sqrt{(1+x^2)}}.$$
$$\therefore \quad (1+x^2) \left(\frac{dy}{dx} \right)^2 = m^2 y^2.$$

Differentiation w.r. to x and cancellation of dy/dx gives

$$(1+x^2) f''(x) + x f'(x) - m^2 f(x) = 0.$$

Differentiation n times by Leibniz's theorem gives

$$(1+x^2) f^{(n+2)}(x) + 2nx f^{(n+1)}(x) + n(n-1) f^{(n)}(x) + x f^{(n+1)}(x)$$
$$+ n f^{(n)}(x) - m^2 f^{(n)}(x) = 0,$$

i.e. $(1+x^2) f^{(n+2)}(x) + (2n+1)x f^{(n+1)}(x) + (n^2 - m^2) f^{(n)}(x) = 0$. Putting $x = 0$ gives $f^{(n+2)}(0) = (m^2 - n^2) f^{(n)}(0)$.

But $f(0) = 1, f'(0) = m$ (from the expression for dy/dx above).

$$\therefore \quad f^{(2p)}(0) = 1 \cdot m^2(m^2 - 2^2)(m^2 - 4^2) \ldots [m^2 - (2p-2)^2],$$
$$f^{(2p+1)}(0) = m(m^2 - 1^2)(m^2 - 3^2) \ldots [m^2 - (2p-1)^2].$$

Example 4. Show that

$$(-1)^n e^{x^2} \frac{d^n e^{-x^2}}{dx^n}$$

is a polynomial of degree n in x. Call this polynomial $H_n(x)$, and show that

(i) $\dfrac{d}{dx} H_n(x) = 2nH_{n-1}(x)$;

(ii) $H_{n+1}(x) - 2xH_n(x) + 2nH_{n-1}(x) = 0$;

(iii) $\dfrac{d^2 H_n(x)}{dx^2} - 2x \dfrac{dH_n(x)}{dx} + 2nH_n(x) = 0$.

We prove that $H_n(x)$ is a polynomial in x of degree n by mathematical induction. Clearly $H_1(x) = 2x$, $H_2(x) = 4x^2 - 2$, and so are polynomials in x of the stated degrees. Assuming the result to be proved for $n = k$ and $n = k-1$, we have

$$H_{k+1}(x) = (-1)^{k+1} e^{x^2} \frac{d^{k+1}}{dx^{k+1}} (e^{-x^2})$$

$$= (-1)^{k+1} e^{x^2} \frac{d^k}{dx^k} (-2xe^{-x^2})$$

$$= (-1)^{k+1} e^{x^2} \left\{ -2x \frac{d^k}{dx^k} (e^{-x^2}) - 2k \frac{d^{k-1}(e^{-x^2})}{dx^{k-1}} \right\}$$

$$= 2xH_k(x) - 2kH_{k-1}(x).$$

This shows that $H_{k+1}(x)$ is the sum of two terms each of which is a polynomial, the degree of the highest term [from $2xH_k(x)$] being $k+1$. Therefore $H_{k+1}(x)$ is a polynomial of degree $k+1$ and the required result follows by induction. Note that, replacing k by n, we have established the result (ii).

To derive (i) we consider

$$\frac{dH_n(x)}{dx} = \frac{d}{dx} \left\{ (-1)^n e^{x^2} \frac{d^n}{dx^n} e^{-x^2} \right\}$$

$$= (-1)^n 2xe^{x^2} \frac{d^n}{dx^n} (e^{-x^2}) + (-1)^n e^{x^2} \frac{d^{n+1}(e^{-x^2})}{dx^{n+1}}$$

$$= (-1)^n 2xe^{x^2} \frac{d^n}{dx^n} (e^{-x^2}) + (-1)^n e^{x^2} \frac{d^n (-2xe^{-x^2})}{dx^n}$$

$$= (-1)^n 2xe^{x^2} \frac{d^n}{dx^n} (e^{-x^2})$$

$$+ (-1)^n e^{x^2} \left\{ -2x \frac{d^n}{dx^n} (e^{-x^2}) - 2n \frac{d^{n-1}(e^{-x^2})}{dx^{n-1}} \right\},$$

from Leibniz's theorem,

$$= 2n(-1)^{n-1} e^{x^2} \frac{d^{n-1}}{dx^{n-1}} (e^{-x^2}) = 2n H_{n-1}(x).$$

To derive (iii) we first replace $H_{n-1}(x)$ in (ii) by its value as given by (i) thus:

$$H_{n+1}(x) - 2xH_n(x) + \frac{d}{dx} H_n(x) = 0.$$

Differentiating w.r. to x and using (i) again in the form

$$\frac{d}{dx} H_{n+1}(x) = 2(n+1)H_n(x)$$

to eliminate $H_{n+1}(x)$, we obtain the required eqn. (iii) satisfied by $H_n(x)$. The functions $H_n(x)$ are called *Hermite polynomials*. [See Vol. 4, § 3 : 3.]

Exercises 2 : 7

1. If $y = e^{-x} \cos x$, prove that $d^4y/dx^4 + 4y = 0$.

2. If $y = (x^3 - 3x^2) e^{2x}$, find d^6y/dx^6.

3. If $x(1-x) D^2y + 2y = 0$, prove that

$$x(1-x) D^{n+2}y + n(1-2x) D^{n+1}y = (n+1)(n-2) D^ny.$$

4. If $y = \sinh (m \sinh^{-1} x)$, and $y_n = d^ny/dx^n$, prove that

$$(1+x^2) y_{n+2} + (2n+1) xy_{n+1} + (n^2 - m^2) y_n = 0.$$

5. Prove that $D^{n+1}(x y) = (n+1) D^ny + x D^{n+1}y$.
By taking $y = x^{n-1} e^{1/x}$ prove, by induction, that

$$D^n(x^{n-1} e^{1/x}) = (-1)^n \frac{e^{1/x}}{x^{n+1}}.$$

6. If $y = \dfrac{\sin x}{1-x^2}$, show that

(i) $$\qquad (1-x^2) \frac{d^2y}{dx^2} - 4x \frac{dy}{dx} - (1+x^2) y = 0,$$

(ii) $$\qquad y_{n+2} - (n^2 + 3n + 1) y_n - n(n-1) y_{n-2} = 0,$$

where y_n is the value of d^ny/dx^n when $x = 0$.

7. Find d^6y/dx^6 for each of the following:

(i) $y = x^5 \ln x$, (ii) $y = e^{2x} \sin 2x$.

8. If $y = (\sin^{-1} x)^2$, prove that

$$(1-x^2) \frac{d^2y}{dx^2} - x \frac{dy}{dx}$$

is independent of x and deduce that

$$(1-x^2) \frac{d^{n+2}y}{dx^{n+2}} - x(2n+1) \frac{d^{n+1}y}{dx^{n+1}} - n^2 \frac{d^ny}{dx^n} = 0$$

for $n \geqslant 1$. Show that $d^{2n-1}y/dx^{2n-1}$ is zero at $x = 0$ and find the value of $d^{2n}y/dx^{2n}$ at $x = 0$.

9. The polynomials $f_n(x)$ are defined by the formula

$$f_n(x) = e^{-x}\frac{d^n}{dx^n}(e^x x^n).$$

(i) Prove that   (a) $f_{n+1}(x) = xf_n'(x)+(x+n+1)f_n(x)$,

               (b) $f_{n+1}(x)-(2n+1+x)f_n(x)+n^2f_{n-1}(x) = 0$.

(ii) Verify that $y = e^x x^n$ is a solution of the differential equation

$$x\frac{d^2y}{dx^2}-(x+n-1)\frac{dy}{dx}-y = 0,$$

and deduce that $xf_n''(x)+(x+1)f_n'(x)-nf_n(x) = 0$.

2 : 8 Elementary partial differentiation

If $f(x, y)$ is a function of the two independent variables x and y, we define the partial derivatives of $f(x, y)$ w.r. to x and y as

$$\lim_{h \to 0}\frac{f(x+h, y)-f(x, y)}{h} \quad \text{and} \quad \lim_{k \to 0}\frac{f(x, y+k)-f(x, y)}{k}$$

respectively when these limits exist. The partial derivative of f w.r. to x is effectively the derivative of f w.r. to x when y is treated as a constant. This partial derivative we denote by $\partial f/\partial x$ or f_x. Similarly the partial derivative of f w.r. to y is the derivative of f w.r. to y when x is treated as a constant. We denote this partial derivative by $\partial f/\partial y$ or f_y.

Example 1. If $f = x\,e^y \ln(2x+3y)+\sin(x^2y)$, then

$$\frac{\partial f}{\partial x} = e^y \ln(2x+3y)+\frac{2xe^y}{2x+3y}+2xy \cos(x^2y),$$

$$\frac{\partial f}{\partial y} = x\,e^y \ln(2x+3y)+\frac{3x\,e^y}{2x+3y}+x^2 \cos(x^2y).$$

Example 2. If $z = F(ax+by)+G(x^m y^p)$, where a, b, m, p are constants, find $\partial z/\partial x$, $\partial z/\partial y$.

Here $F(ax+b)$ is the function $F(u)$ of the function $u = ax+by$, $G(x^m y^p)$ is the function $G(v)$ of the function $v = x^m y^p$.

Then $\partial z/\partial x = F'(ax+by)(\partial(ax+by)/\partial x)+G'(x^m y^p)(\partial(x^m y^p)/\partial x)$ where $F'(ax+by)$ denotes the function $F'(u)$ of the function $u = ax+by$. In fact we may consider $F'(ax+by)$ as the derivative of $F(ax+by)$, where $ax+by$ is regarded as a single variable.

$$\therefore \frac{\partial z}{\partial x} = aF'(ax+by)+mx^{m-1}y^p G'(x^m y^p).$$

Similarly

$$\frac{\partial z}{\partial y} = bF'(ax+by)+px^m y^{p-1}G'(x^m y^p).$$

Example 3. If $u = \sin^{-1}(y/2x)$, find $\partial u/\partial x$ and $\partial u/\partial y$ and *verify* that

$$x\frac{\partial u}{\partial x}+y\frac{\partial u}{\partial y} = 0.$$

By the chain rule

$$\frac{\partial u}{\partial x} = \frac{1}{\sqrt{\{1-(y/2x)^2\}}}\ \frac{\partial}{\partial x}\left(\frac{y}{2x}\right)$$

$$= \frac{-y}{2x^2\sqrt{\{1-(y/2x)^2\}}} = \frac{-y}{x\sqrt{(4x^2-y^2)}}.$$

Similarly

$$\frac{\partial u}{\partial y} = \frac{1}{\sqrt{\{1-(y/2x)^2\}}}\ \frac{\partial}{\partial y}\left(\frac{y}{2x}\right)$$

$$= \frac{1}{2x\sqrt{\{1-(y/2x)^2\}}} = \frac{1}{\sqrt{(4x^2-y^2)}}.$$

It follows at once by substitution that

$$x\frac{\partial u}{\partial x}+y\frac{\partial u}{\partial y} = \frac{-y}{\sqrt{(4x^2-y^2)}}+\frac{y}{\sqrt{(4x^2-y^2)}} = 0.$$

Since $\partial f/\partial x$ is a function of x and y, we may differentiate it w.r. to x giving $\dfrac{\partial}{\partial x}\left(\dfrac{\partial f}{\partial x}\right)$, the result being denoted by $\partial^2 f/\partial x^2$ or f_{xx}. Similarly, $\dfrac{\partial}{\partial y}\left(\dfrac{\partial f}{\partial y}\right)$ is denoted by $\partial^2 f/\partial y^2$ or f_{yy}. In addition we have the "mixed" derivatives $\dfrac{\partial}{\partial y}\left(\dfrac{\partial f}{\partial x}\right)$ and $\dfrac{\partial}{\partial x}\left(\dfrac{\partial f}{\partial y}\right)$.

Except in special circumstances, rarely if ever encountered in physical problems, the order of differentiation is immaterial and we denote either of these derivatives by $\partial^2 f/\partial x\partial y$ or f_{xy}. Similarly by $\partial^n f/(\partial x^p\partial y^q)$, where $p+q = n$, we denote the result of q successive differentiations of f w.r. to y followed by p successive derivatives w.r. to x.

Example 1. Show that $\Phi = e^{-x^2/y}$ satisfies the equation

$$\frac{\partial^2\Phi}{\partial x^2} = 4\,\frac{\partial\Phi}{\partial y} - \frac{2\Phi}{y}\,.$$

$$\frac{\partial\Phi}{\partial x} = -\frac{2x\,e^{-x^2/y}}{y} = -\frac{2x\Phi}{y}\,.$$

$$\therefore\quad \frac{\partial^2\Phi}{\partial x^2} = -\frac{2\Phi}{y} - \frac{2x}{y}\,\frac{\partial\Phi}{\partial x} = -\frac{2\Phi}{y} + \frac{4x^2\Phi}{y^2}\,.$$

$$\frac{\partial\Phi}{\partial y} = \frac{x^2\,e^{-x^2/y}}{y^2} = \frac{x^2\Phi}{y^2}\,.$$

$$\therefore\quad \frac{\partial^2\Phi}{\partial x^2} - 4\,\frac{\partial\Phi}{\partial y} + \frac{2\Phi}{y} = -\frac{2\Phi}{y} + \frac{4x^2\Phi}{y^2} - \frac{4x^2\Phi}{y^2} + \frac{2\Phi}{y} = 0.$$

$$\therefore\quad \frac{\partial^2\Phi}{\partial x^2} = 4\,\frac{\partial\Phi}{\partial y} - \frac{2\Phi}{y}\,.$$

Example 2. *Verify* that
$$V = f(x+ct) + g(x-ct),$$

where f and g are arbitrary differentiable functions and c is constant, satisfies the partial differential equation (the one-dimensional wave equation)

$$\frac{\partial^2 V}{\partial t^2} = c^2\,\frac{\partial^2 V}{\partial x^2}\,.$$

If $V = 0$ at $x = 0$ for all t, show that $g(u) = -f(-u)$. If also $V = 0$ at $x = l$ for all t show that $f(u+l) = f(u-l)$. Deduce that $f(u)$ is periodic with period $2l$.

$$\frac{\partial V}{\partial t} = f'(x+ct)\,\frac{\partial(x+ct)}{\partial t} + g'(x-ct)\,\frac{\partial(x-ct)}{\partial t}$$
$$= cf'(x+ct) - cg'(x-ct).$$

$$\frac{\partial^2 V}{\partial t^2} = cf''(x+ct)\,\frac{\partial(x+ct)}{\partial t} - cg''(x-ct)\,\frac{\partial(x-ct)}{\partial t}$$
$$= c^2[f''(x+ct) + g''(x-ct)].$$

Similarly $\partial^2 V/\partial x^2 = f''(x+ct) + g''(x-ct)$ and the required result follows.
If $V = 0$, at $x = 0$ for all t, then
$$f(ct) + g(-ct) = 0 \qquad \text{for all } t,$$

i.e.
$$g(u) = -f(-u) \tag{1}$$

on writing $ct = -u$.

If $V = 0$ at $x = l$ for all t, then
$$f(l+ct) + g(l-ct) = 0 \quad \text{for all } t,$$

i.e.
$$f(l+u) + g(l-u) = 0 \quad \text{for all } u.$$

But, from (1), $g(l-u) = -f(u-l)$, and so
$$f(u+l) = f(u-l) \tag{2}$$

as required. Finally, writing $u = v+l$, we have

$$f(v+2l) = f(v)$$

indicating that $f(v)$ is periodic with period $2l$.

Example 3. If $\psi = F(y+x)+G(y+2x)$, where F and G are arbitrary functions, satisfies the equation

$$a\frac{\partial^2\psi}{\partial x^2} - 3\frac{\partial^2\psi}{\partial x\,\partial y} + b\frac{\partial^2\psi}{\partial y^2} = 0,$$

find the values of the constants a and b.

Substitution gives

$$(a-3+b)\,F''(y+x)+(4a-6+b)\,G''(y+2x) = 0. \tag{1}$$

Therefore since F and G are arbitrary functions the coefficients of F'' and G'' in equation (1) must vanish identically.

$$\therefore \quad a-3+b = 0, \quad 4a-6+b = 0,$$

whence $a = 1$, $b = 2$.

Example 4. If the arbitrary function $z = g(x+my)$, where m is a numerical constant, satisfies the partial differential equation

$$6\frac{\partial^2 z}{\partial x^2} + \frac{\partial^2 z}{\partial x\,\partial y} - \frac{\partial^2 z}{\partial y^2} = 0,$$

find the two possible values of m.

Making the given substitution we find

$$(6+m-m^2)\,g''(x+my) = 0.$$

Since g is arbitrary, we must have

$$6+m-m^2 = 0.$$

This quadratic equation has roots $m = -2, 3$ and these are the possible values of m.

This example illustrates a technique for solving certain linear partial differential equations with constant coefficients. In fact the general solution of the given equation is

$$z = g_1(x-2y)+g_2(x+3y),$$

where g_1 and g_2 are arbitrary functions.

Example 5. If z is defined implicitly in terms of the independent variables x and y by the relation

$$xy = f(x+z), \tag{1}$$

prove that

$$x \frac{\partial z}{\partial x} - y \frac{\partial z}{\partial y} + x = 0, \tag{2}$$

$$x^2 \frac{\partial^2 z}{\partial x^2} = y^2 \frac{\partial^2 z}{\partial y^2}. \tag{3}$$

Differentiating the given relation (1) partially w.r. to x we find, using the chain rule, that

$$y = f'(x+z) \frac{\partial}{\partial x} (x+z) = \left(1 + \frac{\partial z}{\partial x}\right) f'(x+z).$$

$$\therefore \quad \frac{\partial z}{\partial x} = \frac{y - f'(x+z)}{f'(x+z)}. \tag{4}$$

Similarly,

$$x = f'(x+z) \frac{\partial z}{\partial y}$$

so that

$$\frac{\partial z}{\partial y} = \frac{x}{f'(x+z)}. \tag{5}$$

Elimination of $f'(x+z)$ from eqns. (4) and (5) leads at once to eqn. (2).

To derive eqn. (3) we differentiate eqn. (2) first partially w.r. to x and second partially w.r. to y obtaining respectively

$$x \frac{\partial^2 z}{\partial x^2} + \frac{\partial z}{\partial x} - y \frac{\partial^2 z}{\partial x \, \partial y} + 1 = 0, \tag{6}$$

$$x \frac{\partial^2 z}{\partial x \, \partial y} - y \frac{\partial^2 z}{\partial y^2} - \frac{\partial z}{\partial y} = 0. \tag{7}$$

Then x eqn. (6) $- y$ eqn. (7) and use of eqn. (2) leads to the required result. [Note that in this case we do not have to find $\partial^2 z/\partial x^2$, $\partial^2 z/\partial y^2$ explicitly in terms of the derivatives of f.]

If $f(x_1, x_2, \ldots, x_n)$ is a function of the n independent variables $x_1, x_2, \ldots, x_n$, we define the partial derivative of f w.r. to x_r, $\partial f/\partial x_r$, $(r = 1, 2, \ldots, n)$ as the derivative of f w.r. to x_r when the remaining $n-1$ variables are treated as constants. Similarly, we define partial derivatives of higher orders.

Example 1. Find the relation between the constants a_1, a_2, a_3, p, c, if the (three-dimensional) wave equation

$$\frac{\partial^2 \Phi}{\partial x_1^2} + \frac{\partial^2 \Phi}{\partial x_2^2} + \frac{\partial^2 \Phi}{\partial x_3^2} = \frac{1}{c^2} \frac{\partial^2 \Phi}{\partial t^2}$$

is satisfied by $\Phi = \sin(x_1/a_1) \sin(x_2/a_2) \sin(x_3/a_3) \cos pt$.

$$\frac{\partial^2 \Phi}{\partial x_1^2} = -\frac{1}{a_1^2} \sin\left(\frac{x_1}{a_1}\right) \sin\left(\frac{x_2}{a_2}\right) \sin\left(\frac{x_3}{a_3}\right) \cos pt = \frac{-\Phi}{a_1^2}.$$

Similarly for

$$\frac{\partial^2 \Phi}{\partial x_2^2}, \quad \frac{\partial^2 \Phi}{\partial x_3^2}.$$

Also

$$\frac{1}{c^2}\frac{\partial^2 \Phi}{\partial t^2} = -\frac{p^2}{c^2}\sin\left(\frac{x_1}{a_1}\right)\sin\left(\frac{x_2}{a_2}\right)\sin\left(\frac{x_3}{a_3}\right)\cos pt = -\frac{p^2 \Phi}{c^2}.$$

Therefore the required condition is

$$\left(\frac{p^2}{c^2} - \frac{1}{a_1^2} - \frac{1}{a_2^2} - \frac{1}{a_3^2}\right)\Phi = 0,$$

i.e.

$$\frac{1}{a_1^2} + \frac{1}{a_2^2} + \frac{1}{a_3^2} = \frac{p^2}{c^2}.$$

Example 2. Show that $V = 1/r$, where $r^2 = (x-a)^2 + (y-b)^2 + (z-c)^2$ and a, b, c are constants, satisfies Laplace's equation

$$\frac{\partial^2 V}{\partial x^2} + \frac{\partial^2 V}{\partial y^2} + \frac{\partial^2 V}{\partial z^2} = 0.$$

$$\frac{\partial V}{\partial x} = -\frac{1}{r^2}\frac{\partial r}{\partial x}, \quad \frac{\partial^2 V}{\partial x^2} = \frac{2}{r^3}\left(\frac{\partial r}{\partial x}\right)^2 - \frac{1}{r^2}\frac{\partial^2 r}{\partial x^2}.$$

But

$$2r\frac{\partial r}{\partial x} = 2(x-a) \quad \text{and} \quad r\frac{\partial^2 r}{\partial x^2} + \left(\frac{\partial r}{\partial x}\right)^2 = 1.$$

$$\therefore \quad \frac{\partial r}{\partial x} = \frac{x-a}{r}, \quad \frac{\partial^2 r}{\partial x^2} = \frac{1}{r} - \frac{(x-a)^2}{r^3}.$$

$$\therefore \quad \frac{\partial^2 V}{\partial x^2} = \frac{2(x-a)^2}{r^5} - \frac{1}{r^3} + \frac{(x-a)^2}{r^5} = \frac{3(x-a)^2}{r^5} - \frac{1}{r^3}.$$

Therefore by symmetry

$$\frac{\partial^2 V}{\partial x^2} + \frac{\partial^2 V}{\partial y^2} + \frac{\partial^2 V}{\partial z^2} = \frac{3[(x-a)^2 + (y-b)^2 + (z-c)^2]}{r^5} - \frac{3}{r^3} = 0,$$

since $(x-a)^2 + (y-b)^2 + (z-c)^2 = r^2$.

The definition of the partial derivative $\partial f/\partial x$ requires that the other independent variable y (or all the others if there are more than two) is kept constant. On considering $f(x, y)$ it is clear that x and y are the independent variables and therefore in finding the derivative $\partial f/\partial y$ it is the independent variable x which is kept constant; there is no need to denote this in any special way. However, in some applications of partial differentiation, notably in thermodynamics, it is not always clear which variables of a group, such as p, v, T, φ, u, are the independent and which the dependent variables. When the context does not make this clear a suffix is put after the brackets enclosing a derivative to indicate the other independent variable. For example, the symbol $(\partial p/\partial v)_T$ denotes the derivative of p w.r. to v when v is one of the independent variables, the other being T which is being kept constant. Or again, $(\partial v/\partial T)_p$ denotes the rate of increase of volume, v, with temperature, T, while the pressure, p, is constant, p and T being the independent variables. In this type of application to thermodynamics there are usually only two independent variables.

Example 1. The thermodynamical quantities are related by the equations

$$T = \left(\frac{\partial u}{\partial \varphi}\right)_v, \quad p = -\left(\frac{\partial u}{\partial v}\right)_\varphi .$$

In these relations u is the dependent variable, v, φ being the independent variables. Taking the two forms of the mixed derivative of u gives the relation

$$\left(\frac{\partial T}{\partial v}\right)_\varphi = -\left(\frac{\partial p}{\partial \varphi}\right)_v .$$

Example 2. If $x^a y^b = z^c$ where x, y, z are variables and a, b, c are non-zero constants, prove that

(i) $bx\dfrac{\partial z}{\partial x} = ay\dfrac{\partial z}{\partial y}$,   (ii) $\left(\dfrac{\partial y}{\partial x}\right)\left(\dfrac{\partial x}{\partial z}\right)\left(\dfrac{\partial z}{\partial y}\right) = -1$.

Here, since there are three variables only, writing down a symbol such as $\partial z/\partial x$ without a suffix is quite unambiguous since, in this case, z must be a function of x and y and $\partial z/\partial x$ means differentiation of z w.r. to x keeping y constant.

Partial differentiation of the given relation first with respect to x and then with respect to y gives

$$ax^{a-1}y^b = cz^{c-1}\frac{\partial z}{\partial x}, \quad bx^a y^{b-1} = cz^{c-1}\frac{\partial z}{\partial y} .$$

Cross-multiplication of these equations leads to result (i). Also

$$\frac{\partial z}{\partial y} = \frac{bx^a y^{b-1}}{cz^{c-1}} . \tag{1}$$

Now consider the given relation as defining x in terms of z and y. Then differentiating partially w.r. to z we have

$$ax^{a-1}y^b \frac{\partial x}{\partial z} = cz^{c-1} ,$$

i.e. $$\frac{\partial x}{\partial z} = \frac{cz^{c-1}}{ax^{a-1}y^b} . \tag{2}$$

Similarly, regarding y as function of x and z and differentiating partially w.r. to x we find

$$ax^{a-1}y^b + x^a by^{b-1} \frac{\partial y}{\partial x} = 0,$$

or

$$\frac{\partial y}{\partial x} = -\frac{ay}{bx}. \tag{3}$$

Multiplication of eqns. (1), (2) and (3) gives

$$\left(\frac{\partial y}{\partial x} \right) \left(\frac{\partial x}{\partial z} \right) \left(\frac{\partial z}{\partial y} \right) = -1.$$

Exercises 2 : 8

1. Show that $u = x^2 \sin (\ln y)$ satisfies

$$2y^2 \frac{\partial^2 u}{\partial y^2} + 2y \frac{\partial u}{\partial y} + x \frac{\partial u}{\partial x} = 0.$$

2. If $V = (Ar^n + Br^{-n}) \sin n\theta$, where A, B, n are constants, prove that

$$r \frac{\partial}{\partial r} \left(r \frac{\partial V}{\partial r} \right) + \frac{\partial^2 V}{\partial \theta^2} = 0.$$

3. (i) If $r\Phi = \sin pr \cos cpt$, where p and c are constants, show that

$$\frac{\partial^2 \Phi}{\partial r^2} + \frac{2}{r} \frac{\partial \Phi}{\partial r} = \frac{1}{c^2} \frac{\partial^2 \Phi}{\partial t^2}.$$

(ii) If $z = f(x-2y) + g(3x+y)$, where f and g are arbitrary functions and if

$$\frac{\partial^2 z}{\partial x^2} + a \frac{\partial^2 z}{\partial x \, \partial y} + b \frac{\partial^2 z}{\partial y^2} = 0,$$

find a, b.

4. (i) Show that $\Phi = e^{-2x} \sin x \sin t$ satisfies the equation

$$\frac{\partial^2 \Phi}{\partial x^2} + 4 \frac{\partial \Phi}{\partial x} = 5 \frac{\partial^2 \Phi}{\partial t^2}.$$

(ii) If $u = \ln (1 + xy^2)$, show that

$$2x \frac{\partial u}{\partial x} = y \frac{\partial u}{\partial y} \quad \text{and} \quad 2 \frac{\partial^2 u}{\partial x^2} + y^3 \frac{\partial^2 u}{\partial x \, \partial y} = 0.$$

5. (i) If $z = \ln r$, where $r^2 = x^2 + y^2$, prove that

$$\frac{\partial^2 z}{\partial x^2} + \frac{\partial^2 z}{\partial y^2} = 0.$$

(ii) If $z = f(x+ay) + \Phi(x-ay) - \dfrac{x}{2a^2} \cos (x+ay)$, where f and Φ are arbitrary functions, prove that

$$a^2 \frac{\partial^2 z}{\partial x^2} - \frac{\partial^2 z}{\partial y^2} = \sin(x + ay).$$

6. If $r^2 = x^2 + y^2$, prove that

$$\frac{\partial r}{\partial x} = \frac{x}{r} \quad \text{and} \quad \frac{\partial^2 r}{\partial x^2} = \frac{y^2}{r^3}.$$

If $V = e^{k(r-x)}$, where k is constant, prove that

(i) $$\left(\frac{\partial V}{\partial x}\right)^2 + \left(\frac{\partial V}{\partial y}\right)^2 + 2Vk \frac{\partial V}{\partial x} = 0,$$

(ii) $$\frac{\partial^2 V}{\partial x^2} + \frac{\partial^2 V}{\partial y^2} + 2k \frac{\partial V}{\partial x} = \frac{Vk}{r}.$$

7. If $r^2 = x^2 + y^2$ and $u = \cos kr$, where k is constant, prove that

(i) $$\frac{\partial r}{\partial x} = \frac{x}{r},$$ (ii) $$y \frac{\partial u}{\partial x} = x \frac{\partial u}{\partial y},$$

(iii) $$\frac{\partial^2 u}{\partial x^2} + \frac{\partial^2 u}{\partial y^2} + k^2 u = -\frac{k}{r} \sin kr.$$

8. (i) Find for what values of n the function $v = r^n(3\cos^2\theta - 1)$ satisfies the equation

$$\frac{\partial}{\partial r}\left(r^2 \frac{\partial v}{\partial r}\right) + \frac{1}{\sin\theta} \frac{\partial}{\partial\theta}\left(\sin\theta \frac{\partial v}{\partial\theta}\right) = 0.$$

(ii) Find k so that $U = t^k \exp(-r^2/4t)$ satisfies the equation

$$\frac{1}{r^2} \frac{\partial}{\partial r}\left(r^2 \frac{\partial U}{\partial r}\right) = \frac{\partial U}{\partial t}.$$

9. Show that $u = e^{-3y} \cos 4y \cos 5x$ satisfies the equation

$$\frac{\partial^2 u}{\partial x^2} = \frac{\partial^2 u}{\partial y^2} + 6 \frac{\partial u}{\partial y}.$$

10. If $z = y^2 f\left(\frac{x}{y}\right)$, prove that

$$x^2 \frac{\partial^2 z}{\partial x^2} + 2xy \frac{\partial^2 z}{\partial x \partial y} + y^2 \frac{\partial^2 z}{\partial y^2} = 2z.$$

11. Show that the numerical values of a and b (other than zero) can be found so that $u = \exp(-ax + bt^2)$ satisfies the equation

$$\frac{\partial^2 u}{\partial t^2} - 4t \frac{\partial u}{\partial t} = 100 \frac{\partial^2 u}{\partial x^2}$$

for all values of x and t, and find a and b.

12. If $f(x, y) = (x^4 + y^4)^{\frac{1}{2}}$, evaluate the partial derivatives $f_x, f_y, f_{xx}, f_{xy}, f_{yy}$ and hence show that

(i) $x f_x + y f_y = 2f(x, y),$ and   (ii) $x^2 f_{xx} + 2xy f_{xy} + y^2 f_{yy} = 2f(x, y).$

13. (i) If

$$f(x, y) = \frac{1}{y} \exp \left\{ \frac{-(x-1)^2}{y^2} \right\},$$

prove that

$$y \frac{\partial^2 f}{\partial x^2} = 2 \frac{\partial f}{\partial y}.$$

(ii) If $z = x^2 F(u)$, where $u = xy$, prove that

(a) $$x \frac{\partial z}{\partial x} - y \frac{\partial z}{\partial y} = 2z,$$

(b) $$x \frac{\partial^2 z}{\partial x \, \partial y} - y \frac{\partial^2 z}{\partial y^2} = 3 \frac{\partial z}{\partial y}.$$

14. If $f(z)$ is an arbitrary function of z, where $z = xy$, and if $V = (x^2 - y^2) f(z)$, show that

$$\frac{\partial^2 V}{\partial x^2} + \frac{\partial^2 V}{\partial y^2} = (x^4 - y^4) f''(z).$$

15. If $u = x f(z)$, where $z = y/x$, prove that

$$\frac{\partial^2 u}{\partial x^2} + \frac{\partial^2 u}{\partial y^2} = \frac{x^2 + y^2}{x^3} f''(z).$$

2 : 9 Differentials

If $y = f(x)$ and $f(x)$ is differentiable, i.e. $f'(x)$ exists, then corresponding to a small increment δx in x, the definition of $f'(x)$ implies that the increment δy in y is given by

$$\delta y = [f'(x) + \eta] \, \delta x, \tag{2.41}$$

where $\eta \to 0$ as $\delta x \to 0$.

$$\therefore \quad \delta y \approx f'(x) \, \delta x, \tag{2.42}$$

a result of importance in the discussion of small errors and small increments (see § 5 : 7). We now define the *differential* of y, written dy, by the equation

$$dy = f'(x) \, \delta x, \tag{2.43}$$

i.e. dy is the principal or dominant part of δy. In particular, putting $y = x$ in eqn. (2.43) gives $dx = \delta x$ so that

$$dy = f'(x) \, dx. \tag{2.44}$$

A geometrical interpretation of differentials is given in § 5 : 3.

Example. (i) $d(\cos ax) = -a \sin ax \, dx.$

(ii) $$x e^{x^2} \, dx = d(\tfrac{1}{2} e^{x^2}).$$

(iii) $$\frac{dx}{a^2 + x^2} = \frac{1}{a} d \left[\tan^{-1} \left(\frac{x}{a} \right) \right].$$

(iv) $$\frac{dx}{x} = d(\ln x).$$

(v) $$d(uv) = u\,dv + v\,du.$$

(vi) $$d\left(\frac{u}{v}\right) = \frac{v\,du - u\,dv}{v^2}.$$

(vii) $$\frac{dv}{v^2} = -d\left(\frac{1}{v}\right).$$

Miscellaneous Exercises II

Differentiate w.r. to x the following functions:

1. $e^{cx} \sin^m rx.$

2. $\ln\left[x + (x^2 + a^2)^{\frac{1}{2}}\right] + \sec^{-1}\left(\frac{x}{a}\right).$

3. $\tan^{-1}\left[\dfrac{x}{x^2 + 1}\right].$

4. $\cos^{-1}\left[\dfrac{1 + 2\cos x}{2 + \cos x}\right].$

5. $\ln\left[\dfrac{\cos x - \sin x}{\cos x + \sin x}\right].$

6. $\exp(e^x).$

7. $x \ln\left[(x^2 + a^2)^{\frac{1}{2}}\right] - x + a \tan^{-1}\left(\dfrac{x}{a}\right).$

8. $x \sqrt{(a^2 - x^2)} + a^2 \sin^{-1}\left(\dfrac{x}{a}\right).$

9. $\sqrt{\left(\dfrac{a^2 + ax + x^2}{a^2 - ax + x^2}\right)}.$

10. $\dfrac{(x^2 - 1)^{\frac{3}{2}}}{(x^4 + 1)^{\frac{1}{3}}}.$

11. $\cosh^{-1} \sqrt{(1 + x)}.$

12. $\lg\left(\dfrac{x^2 - x + 1}{x^2 + x - 1}\right).$

13. $\tan^{-1}\left(\dfrac{\cos x - \sin x}{\cos x + \sin x}\right).$

14. $\left(\dfrac{x}{1 + x^2}\right)^{\frac{x}{1 - x^2}}.$

15. $\sin(x^{\cos x}).$

16. $x^{\frac{a}{x}}.$

17. $\tan^{-1}\left(\dfrac{1 - \sqrt{x}}{1 + \sqrt{x}}\right).$

18. $(\cosh x)^x.$

19. $\ln\left[\sqrt{(x^2 + 1)} + \sqrt{(x^2 - 1)}\right].$

20. $(2 - x)\sqrt{\left(\dfrac{3 - x}{1 + x}\right)}.$

21. $\sec^{-1}\left[\dfrac{1 + x}{1 - x}\right].$

22. $\ln[\ln(\ln x)].$

23. (i) If $\sinh x = \cot\theta$, $(0 < \theta < \frac{1}{2}\pi)$, prove that $x = \ln\cot(\frac{1}{2}\theta)$.

(ii) Express y in terms of x if $\tanh^{-1}(\sqrt{x}) = \cosh^{-1} y$.

24. Find a pair of real values (x, y) satisfying
$$12(\cosh x - \cosh y) = 5,$$
$$12(\sinh x - \sinh y) = 7.$$

25. Verify equation (2,30) by expressing the equation $y = \sinh^{-1}(x/a)$ as a quadratic equation in e^y and solving this equation. Verify equation (2.33) similarly.

26. If $y = x - \tan^{-1} x$, prove that $\dfrac{d^2x}{dy^2} = -2x^{-5}(1+x^2)$.

27. If $y = \sin(\ln x)$, evaluate $x^2 \dfrac{d^2y}{dx^2} + x\dfrac{dy}{dx} + y$.

28. If $y = \sec x$, prove that $y\dfrac{d^2y}{dx^2} = \left(\dfrac{dy}{dx}\right)^2 + y^4$.

29. If $\ln y = 2ax - x^2$, where a is a constant, prove that

$$y\frac{d^2y}{dx^2} - \left(\frac{dy}{dx}\right)^2 + 2y^2 = 0.$$

30. (i) If $y(a^2+x^2)^{\frac{1}{2}} = x$, find the value of

$$(a^2+x^2)^2\frac{d^2y}{dx^2} + 2x(a^2+x^2)\frac{dy}{dx} + a^2y.$$

(ii) Find all values of x that make $\dfrac{d^2y}{dx^2} = 0$ when $y = \ln\tan\left(2x+\dfrac{\pi}{4}\right)$.

31. If $y = \tan^{-1}(\sinh x)$ prove that

$$\frac{d^2y}{dx^2} + (\tan y)\left(\frac{dy}{dx}\right)^2 = 0.$$

32. Find (i) $\dfrac{dy}{dx}$ if $y = \sin(x+y)^2$,

(ii) $\dfrac{d^2y}{dx^2}$ if $x = 3\cos\theta - \cos 3\theta$, $y = 3\sin\theta - \sin 3\theta$.

33. If $y = \cosh n\theta$ and $x = \cosh\theta$ show that

$$(x^2-1)\frac{d^2y}{dx^2} + x\frac{dy}{dx} - n^2y = 0.$$

34. If $y = \sinh^{-1} x$ prove (i), $(x^2+1)\dfrac{d^2y}{dx^2} + x\dfrac{dy}{dx} = 0$, and

(ii) $(x^2+1)\dfrac{d^{n+2}y}{dx^{n+2}} + x(2n+1)\dfrac{d^{n+1}y}{dx^{n+1}} + n^2\dfrac{d^ny}{dx^n} = 0$

where n is a positive integer.

35. Find the nth differential coefficients of the following functions:

(i) $x^3 \ln x$, $n > 3$, (ii) $\cos^3 2x$, (iii) $\ln\left[\dfrac{1-x}{1+x}\right]$, (iv) $x^2\cos 2x$.

36. If $y = e^{ax}\cos bx$, show that $\dfrac{d^ny}{dx^n} = r^n e^{ax}\cos(bx+n\theta)$ where $r^2 = a^2 + b^2$ and $\tan\theta = b/a$.

37. If $x = \cos t$, $y = \cos 2pt$, show that, if $y_r = d^r y / dx^r$,

(i) $\qquad (1-x^2)y_2 - xy_1 + 4p^2 y = 0,$

(ii) $\qquad (1-x^2)y_{n+2} - (2n+1)xy_{n+1} + (4p^2 - n^2)y_n = 0.$

38. If $x+y+z = f(x-z)$, prove that

$$\frac{\partial z}{\partial x} - 2\frac{\partial z}{\partial y} = 1.$$

39. If $z = x^n f(y/x)$ prove that

$$x\frac{\partial z}{\partial x} + y\frac{\partial z}{\partial y} = nz.$$

If $V = z \ln r$, where $r^2 = x^2 + y^2$, prove that

$$x\frac{\partial V}{\partial x} + y\frac{\partial V}{\partial y} = nV + z.$$

40. Find the possible values of n if the function $U = xr^n$ satisfies the equation

$$\frac{\partial^2 U}{\partial x^2} + \frac{\partial^2 U}{\partial y^2} = 0,$$

where $r^2 = x^2 + y^2$.

For each value of n obtain the function V which is such that $\dfrac{\partial V}{\partial y} = \dfrac{\partial U}{\partial x}$ and $\dfrac{\partial V}{\partial x} = -\dfrac{\partial U}{\partial y}$, and V is zero on the x-axis.

41. If (x, y) are the cartesian coordinates of a point and (r, θ) are its polar coordinates, find $\partial x/\partial r$ and $\partial r/\partial x$ and show their meaning on a diagram. Prove also that

(i) $\qquad \dfrac{\partial^2 r}{\partial x^2} \cdot \dfrac{\partial^2 r}{\partial y^2} = \left(\dfrac{\partial^2 r}{\partial x\,\partial y}\right)^2,$

(ii) $\qquad \dfrac{\partial^2 \theta}{\partial x^2} + \dfrac{\partial^2 \theta}{\partial y^2} = 0.$

42. Show that $u = Ae^{mx}\cos(\omega t + mx) + Be^{-mx}\cos(\omega t - mx)$ is a solution of $\dfrac{\partial^2 u}{\partial x^2} = 2\dfrac{\partial u}{\partial t}$, where A, B, m and ω are constants provided that $m^2 = \omega$.

Find the values of the constants, given the conditions (i) $m > 0$, (ii) u remains finite as $x \to \infty$, (iii) $u = \cos t$ when $x = 0$.

43. The function $f(x)$ satisfies the equation $f(x+y) = f(x) + f(y) - 2$ for all values of x and y. Find the value of $f(0)$.

Given that $f(x)$ is differentiable for all values of x and that $f'(0) = 3$, prove that $f'(x) = 3$ for all values of x, and find the function $f(x)$.

44. Given the following thermodynamical relations

$$T = \left(\frac{\partial H}{\partial \varphi}\right)_p, \qquad v = \left(\frac{\partial H}{\partial p}\right)_\varphi; \qquad \varphi = -\left(\frac{\partial F}{\partial T}\right)_v, \qquad p = -\left(\frac{\partial F}{\partial v}\right)_T;$$

$$\varphi = -\left(\frac{\partial G}{\partial T}\right)_p, \qquad v = \left(\frac{\partial G}{\partial p}\right)_T;$$

state the independent variables for each of the functions H, F, G.

Obtain the Maxwell relations,

$$\left(\frac{\partial T}{\partial p}\right)_{\varphi} = \left(\frac{\partial v}{\partial \varphi}\right)_{p}, \quad \left(\frac{\partial \varphi}{\partial v}\right)_{T} = \left(\frac{\partial p}{\partial T}\right)_{v}, \quad \left(\frac{\partial \varphi}{\partial p}\right)_{T} = -\left(\frac{\partial v}{\partial T}\right)_{p}.$$

45. (i) Find dy/dx if (a) $y = \sqrt{\{(x+1)/(x-1)\}}$,

(b) $y = x^y$.

(ii) If $y = x^n \ln x$, prove that

$$x \frac{dy}{dx} = x^n + ny.$$

Hence prove that, if n is a positive integer

$$\frac{d^{n+1}y}{dx^{n+1}} = \frac{n!}{x}.$$

46. Sketch the functions

$$\frac{e^{1/x} - e^{-1/x}}{e^{1/x} + e^{-1/x}}, \quad x \frac{e^{1/x} - e^{-1/x}}{e^{1/x} + e^{-1/x}}$$

over the whole range of values of x, paying particular attention to their behaviour as x passes through the value 0 and as $x \to \pm \infty$.

47. If $y = \exp(\tan^{-1} x)$, show that

(i) $(1+x^2) \, Dy = y$;

(ii) $(1+x^2) \, D^{n+1}y + (2nx-1) \, D^n y + n(n-1) \, D^{n-1}y = 0$ $(n \geqslant 1)$;

(iii) if $D^n y = y \, \Phi_n(x)/(1+x^2)^n$, then $\Phi_n(x)$ is a polynomial in x of degree $\leqslant n-1$ such that

$$\Phi_{n+1}(x) + (2nx-1) \, \Phi_n(x) + n(n-1)(1+x^2) \, \Phi_{n-1}(x) = 0 \quad (n \geqslant 1),$$
$$\Phi_n'(x) = -n(n-1) \, \Phi_{n-1}(x) \quad (n \geqslant 1).$$

48. (i) If $r = (x^2+y^2+z^2)^{\frac{1}{2}}$ and $u = (r+z)^{\frac{1}{2}}$, prove that

$$\left(\frac{\partial u}{\partial x}\right)^2 + \left(\frac{\partial u}{\partial y}\right)^2 + \left(\frac{\partial u}{\partial z}\right)^2 = \frac{1}{2r}.$$

(ii) The variables p, v, t are connected by the relation

$$pv = Rt \quad (R = \text{constant}).$$

If w is a differentiable function of p and v, prove that

$$\left(\frac{\partial w}{\partial p}\right)_t = \left(\frac{\partial w}{\partial p}\right)_v - \left(\frac{\partial w}{\partial v}\right)_p \frac{v}{p}.$$

49. (i) If $z = y^2 f(xy)$, prove that

(a) $$x \frac{\partial z}{\partial x} - y \frac{\partial z}{\partial y} + 2z = 0,$$

(b) $$x \frac{\partial^2 z}{\partial x^2} - y \frac{\partial^2 z}{\partial x \, \partial y} + 3 \frac{\partial z}{\partial x} = 0.$$

(ii) Find the two values of m for which $u = F(x+my)$, where F is an arbitrary function, satisfies the partial differential equation

$$8\frac{\partial^2 u}{\partial x^2} - 2\frac{\partial^2 u}{\partial x\,\partial y} - 3\frac{\partial^2 u}{\partial y^2} = 0.$$

50. If $\omega(r)$ is a function of r, where $r^2 = x^2 + y^2 + z^2$, prove that

$$x\frac{\partial^2 \omega}{\partial y\,\partial z} = y\frac{\partial^2 \omega}{\partial z\,\partial x} = z\frac{\partial^2 \omega}{\partial x\,\partial y}.$$

51. The series of polynomials $\phi_n(x)$ for $n = 0, 1, 2, \ldots$ are defined by

$$\phi_n(x) = x^{2n+2}e^{1/x}(\mathrm{d}/\mathrm{d}x)^{n+1}\,e^{-1/x}.$$

Prove that for $n \geqslant 1$

$$\phi_n(x) = -(2nx-1)\,\phi_{n-1}(x) + x^2\,\phi'_{n-1}(x).$$

Hence show by induction that $\phi_n(x)$ is a polynomial in x of degree n.

CHAPTER III

THE TECHNIQUE OF INTEGRATION

3:1 Definitions and standard forms

Given a function $f(x)$ of the independent variable x, we define the *indefinite integral* of $f(x)$ w.r. to x as the function $F(x)$ which satisfies the equation

$$\frac{\mathrm{d}}{\mathrm{d}x}\{F(x)\} = f(x). \tag{3.1}$$

We denote the integral of $f(x)$ by $\int f(x)\,\mathrm{d}x$ where the symbols $\int \ldots \mathrm{d}x$ denote the operation of *integration* which is effectively the reverse of differentiation. Finding the integral of $f(x)$ is the process of finding the function $F(x)$ whose derivative is $f(x)$. The function $f(x)$ is called the integrand. The indefinite integral of a specified function is indeterminate to the extent of an arbitrary constant C since, if $\mathrm{D}\,F(x) = f(x)$, then $\mathrm{D}[F(x)+C] = f(x)$. The Table of Standard Integrals given on page 115 is obtained from the standard derivatives of Chapter II. For brevity we have omitted the constant of the integration in the table. However, in applications to differential equations and physical problems an arbitrary constant must be added at each integration. In the table we have, without loss of generality, taken $a > 0$ and the values of $\sin^{-1}(x/a)$, $\tan^{-1}(x/a)$, $\sec^{-1}(x/a)$, $\cosh^{-1}(x/a)$ to be principal values, i.e.

$$-\tfrac{1}{2}\pi \leqslant \sin^{-1}(x/a) \leqslant \tfrac{1}{2}\pi, \quad -\tfrac{1}{2}\pi \leqslant \tan^{-1}(x/a) \leqslant \tfrac{1}{2}\pi,$$
$$0 \leqslant \sec^{-1}(x/a) \leqslant \pi, \quad \cosh^{-1}(x/a) \geqslant 0.$$

Since the logarithm of a negative number is complex (see Chapter VII) the argument of ln in an entry in the Table of Standard Integrals must be positive; hence the use of the modulus

TABLE OF STANDARD INTEGRALS

$f(x)$	$\int f(x)\,\mathrm{d}x$
$x^n, n \neq -1$	$\dfrac{x^{n+1}}{n+1}$
$\dfrac{1}{x},\ x > 0$	$\ln|x|$
e^{ax}	$\dfrac{1}{a}\mathrm{e}^{ax}$
$\sin x$	$-\cos x$
$\cos x$	$\sin x$.
$\tan x$	$-\ln|\cos x| = \ln|\sec x|$
$\cot x$	$\ln|\sin x|$
$\sec x$	$\ln|\sec x+\tan x| = \ln\tan|(\tfrac{1}{4}\pi+\tfrac{1}{2}x)|$
$\operatorname{cosec} x$	$-\ln|\operatorname{cosec} x+\cot x| = \ln|\tan(\tfrac{1}{2}x)|$
$\sec^2 x$	$\tan x$
$\operatorname{cosec}^2 x$	$-\cot x$
$\sec x \tan x$	$\sec x$
$\operatorname{cosec} x \cot x$	$-\operatorname{cosec} x$
$\sinh x$	$\cosh x$
$\cosh x$	$\sinh x$
$\operatorname{sech}^2 x$	$\tanh x$
$\operatorname{cosech}^2 x$	$-\coth x$
$\tanh x$	$\ln\cosh x$
$\coth x$	$\ln|\sinh x|$
$\operatorname{sech} x \tanh x$	$-\operatorname{sech} x$
$\operatorname{cosech} x \coth x$	$-\operatorname{cosech} x$
$\dfrac{1}{a^2+x^2}$	$\dfrac{1}{a}\tan^{-1}\left(\dfrac{x}{a}\right)$
$\dfrac{1}{a^2-x^2}$	$\dfrac{1}{2a}\ln\dfrac{a+x}{a-x}\ (x<a)$
$\dfrac{1}{\sqrt{(a^2-x^2)}}$	$\sin^{-1}\left(\dfrac{x}{a}\right)$
$\dfrac{1}{\sqrt{(a^2+x^2)}}$	$\sinh^{-1}\left(\dfrac{x}{a}\right) = \ln\left[\dfrac{x+\sqrt{(x^2+a^2)}}{a}\right]$
$\dfrac{1}{\sqrt{(x^2-a^2)}}$	$\cosh^{-1}\left(\dfrac{x}{a}\right) = \ln\left[\dfrac{x+\sqrt{(x^2-a^2)}}{a}\right]$
$\dfrac{1}{x\sqrt{(x^2-a^2)}}$	$\dfrac{1}{a}\sec^{-1}\left(\dfrac{x}{a}\right)$.

sign in the table. Particularly in the case of indefinite integrals, but sometimes with definite integrals, it is not always clear whether the integrand is positive or negative. In these volumes it is to be understood that the range of variables in an indefinite integral, or the range of integration of a definite integral, is such that the integrand is positive in an integral leading to a ln expression. With this proviso, in general, modulus signs will not be used (cf. the corresponding convention for expressions under a square root sign). If the denominator of the integrand in a definite integral becomes zero somewhere in the range of integration, then problems of convergence arise.

If $\int f(x)\,dx = F(x)$, we define the *definite integral* of $f(x)$ w.r. to x between the limits $x = a$ and $x = b$, written $\int_a^b f(x)\,dx$, by

$$\int_a^b f(x)\,dx = \left[F(x)\right]_a^b = F(b) - F(a). \tag{3.2}$$

Example 1.
$$\int_0^1 x^2\,dx = \left[\tfrac{1}{3}x^3\right]_0^1 = \tfrac{1}{3} - 0 = \tfrac{1}{3}.$$

Example 2.
$$\int_0^{2\pi/\omega} \sin(\omega t + \varepsilon)\,dt = \left[-\frac{1}{\omega}\cos(\omega t + \varepsilon)\right]_0^{2\pi/\omega}$$
$$= -\frac{1}{\omega}\left[\cos(2\pi + \varepsilon) - \cos\varepsilon\right] = 0.$$

Example 3.
$$\int_0^2 \frac{dx}{4 + x^2} = \left[\frac{1}{2}\tan^{-1}\left(\frac{x}{2}\right)\right]_0^2 = \frac{1}{2}\left[\tan^{-1} 1 - \tan^{-1} 0\right]$$
$$= \frac{1}{2}\left[\frac{\pi}{4} - 0\right] = \frac{\pi}{8}.$$

Two simple rules which follow at once from the definition of the definite integral are

(i)
$$\int_a^b f(x)\,dx = -\int_b^a f(x)\,dx, \tag{3.3}$$

i.e. reversal of the limits changes the sign of the integral, and

(ii) $$\int_a^b f(x)\,dx = \int_a^c f(x)\,dx + \int_c^b f(x)\,dx, \qquad (3.4)$$

when c lies between a and b, i.e. we may express one definite integral as the sum of two others. The generalisation of eqn. (3.4) is

$$\int_{a_0}^{a_n} f(x)\,dx = \sum_{r=0}^{n-1} \int_{a_r}^{a_{r+1}} f(x)\,dx \qquad (3.5)$$

which follows from the identity

$$F(a_n) - F(a_0) \equiv \sum_{r=0}^{n-1} [F(a_{r+1}) - F(a_r)].$$

Example. If

$$f(x) = \begin{cases} x^2, & 0 \leqslant x \leqslant 3a, \\ 9a^2, & 3a \leqslant x \leqslant 4a, \\ 25a^2 - x^2, & 4a \leqslant x \leqslant 5a, \end{cases}$$

then
$$\int_0^{5a} f(x)\,dx = \int_0^{3a} x^2\,dx + \int_{3a}^{4a} 9a^2\,dx + \int_{4a}^{5a} (25a^2 - x^2)\,dx$$

$$= \left[\tfrac{1}{3}x^3\right]_0^{3a} + \left[9a^2 x\right]_{3a}^{4a} + \left[25a^2 x - \tfrac{1}{3}x^3\right]_{4a}^{5a}$$

$$= 9a^3 + 9a^2(4a - 3a) + 25a^2(5a - 4a) - \tfrac{1}{3}a^3(125 - 64)$$

$$= 68a^3/3.$$

3:2 The definite integral as the limit of a sum

An important feature of the definite integral is that it may be regarded as the limit of a sum. Complete and rigorous discussions of the theories of definite integration are to be found in books on analysis. These theories take as starting point the concept of a definite integral as the limit of a sum. Here, covering most practical problems, we give an intuitive account of the case in which the integrand $f(x)$ is continuous. If $f(x)$ is not continuous over the range of integration but has a finite number of finite discontinuities, i.e. $f(x)$ is *piecewise* continuous, then we use eqn. (3.5) after dividing the range of integration into a finite number of ranges in each of which $f(x)$ is continuous.

Suppose we divide the range of integration $[a, b]$, i.e. $a \leqslant x \leqslant b$, into a large number, n, of intervals each of length $h = (b-a)/n$. Then eqn. (3.5) gives

$$\int_a^b f(x) \, dx = \sum_{r=0}^{n-1} \int_{x_r}^{x_{r+1}} f(x) \, dx = \sum_{r=0}^{n-1} [F(x_{r+1}) - F(x_r)],$$

where $x_r = a + r(b-a)/n = a + rh$. But since $D F(x) = f(x)$, the definition of differentiation gives $F(x_{r+1}) - F(x_r) = (x_{r+1} - x_r)f(x_r)$ + infinitesimals (small quantities) of higher order than $x_{r+1} - x_r = h$. Therefore

$$\int_a^b f(x) \, dx = \sum_{r=0}^{n-1} h f(x_r) + \text{terms of higher order in } h.$$

Letting $n \to \infty$ so that $h \to 0$ we obtain $\int_a^b f(x) \, dx$ as the limit of a sum.

To fix our ideas we obtain the expression for the area ABB_1A_1 bounded by the curve $y = f(x)$, Ox and the ordinates $x = a$, $x = b$, see Fig. 3.1. In the first instance we consider only the case

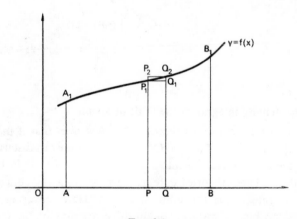

FIG. 3.1.

in which $f(x) > 0$ for $a \leqslant x \leqslant b$ so that the arc A_1B_1 lies wholly above Ox. Suppose that the area APP_1A_1 is $S(x)$ where $OP = x$. If $PQ = \delta x$, the area of the narrow strip PQQ_2P_1 lies between the areas of the rectangles PQQ_1P_1 and PQQ_2P_2, i.e. between

$f(x)\,\delta x$ and $f(x+\delta x)\,\delta x$.

$$\therefore \quad \delta S(x) = S(x+\delta x) - S(x) \approx f(x)\,\delta x.$$

The error in this approximation clearly has the same order of magnitude as $(\delta x)^2$.

$$\therefore \quad S(x+\delta x) - S(x) = f(x)\,\delta x + O\{(\delta x)^2\}. \tag{3.6}$$

If the whole area ABB_1A_1 is divided into strips of width δx there is an equation corresponding to (3.6) for each strip. Addition of all these equations leads to

$$S(b) - S(a) = \Sigma f(x)\,\delta x + \frac{b-a}{\delta x}\,O\{(\delta x)^2\} = \Sigma f(x)\,\delta x + O(\delta x)$$

since

$$\frac{O\{(\delta x)^2\}}{\delta x} = O(\delta x).$$

Hence, letting $\delta x \to 0$,

$$S(b) - S(a) = \int_a^b f(x)\,\mathrm{d}x$$

because the limiting value of the sum $\Sigma f(x)\,\delta x$ is the integral $\int_a^b f(x)\,\mathrm{d}x$ and the limiting value of $O(\delta x)$ is zero. From the definition of $S(x)$ it is clear that $S(a) = 0$ and that $S(b) =$ area $ABB_1A_1 = \int_a^b f(x)\,\mathrm{d}x$.

If $f(x)$ is negative over part of the range of integration, say for $a_1 \leqslant x \leqslant b_1$, then the magnitude of the corresponding area between the curve $y = f(x)$ and Ox is $\int_{a_1}^{b_1} \{-f(x)\}\,\mathrm{d}x$. This result is of great value in the evaluation of certain definite integrals since any definite integral $\int_a^b f(x)\,\mathrm{d}x$ may be considered as the area between the curve $y = f(x)$, Ox and the ordinates $x = a$ and $x = b$; areas above Ox count as numerically positive whereas areas below Ox count as numerically negative. Hence, if $f(x)$ is even, cf. Fig. 1.2(a), $\int_{-a}^{a} f(x)\,\mathrm{d}x = 2\int_0^a f(x)\,\mathrm{d}x$, whereas if $f(x)$ is odd, cf. Fig. 1.2(b), $\int\limits_{-a}^{a} f(x)\, dx = 0$. An analytical proof of these results is given in Example 3 on page 131. Similarly, if $f(x)$ is periodic with period l, and n is an integer

$$\int\limits_{0}^{nl} f(x)\, dx = n \int\limits_{0}^{l} f(x)\, dx.$$

Example 1. The area between the curve $y = \sin x$ and Ox for $0 \leqslant x \leqslant \pi$ is $\int\limits_{0}^{\pi} \sin x\, dx = 2$.

Example 2. If p is an integer, $\int\limits_{0}^{2\pi} \sin^{2p} x\, dx = 4 \int\limits_{0}^{\pi/2} \sin^{2p} x\, dx$ and $\int\limits_{0}^{2\pi} \sin^{2p+1} x\, dx = 0$.

Example 3. $$\int\limits_{-a}^{a} \frac{x^5\, dx}{(x^4 + b^4)^2} = 0.$$

Example 4. Evaluate $\int\limits_{0}^{2} |x(x-1)(x-2)|\, dx$.

The graphs of $y = x(x-1)(x-2)$, $y = |x(x-1)(x-2)|$ are sketched in Figs. 3.2(a), (b), respectively. From the definition of modulus (or using the *idea* of a definite integral as the area under a curve) it follows that

$$\int\limits_{0}^{2} |x(x-1)(x-2)|\, dx = \int\limits_{0}^{1} x(1-x)(2-x)\, dx + \int\limits_{1}^{2} x(x-1)(2-x)\, dx = \tfrac{1}{2}$$

after term by term integration and some reduction.

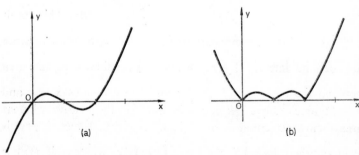

Fig. 3.2.(a) The graph $y = x(x-1)(x-2)$. (b) The graph $y = |x(x-1)(x-2)|$.

Note that, if $f(x)$ is a function with simple zeros at

$\alpha_1, \alpha_2, \ldots, \alpha_n$ and $a < \alpha_1 < \alpha_2 < \ldots < \alpha_n < b$, $f(a) < 0$,   then

$$\int_a^b |f(x)|\ dx = \int_a^{\alpha_1} (-f)\ dx + \int_{\alpha_1}^{\alpha_2} f\ dx + \int_{\alpha_2}^{\alpha_3} (-f)\ dx + \ldots + \int_{\alpha_n}^b (-1)^{n+1} f\ dx.$$

Example 5. Prove that, for $x > 0$,

$$\int_0^x [t]\ dt = (x - \tfrac{1}{2})\ [x] - \tfrac{1}{2}\ [x]^2,$$

where $[t]$ is the greatest integer $\leqslant t$.

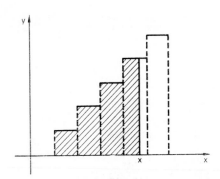

Fig. 3.3.

The graph of $y = [x]$ is sketched in Fig. 3.3 (see p. 31 for the definition of $[x]$). Clearly $\int_0^x [t]\ dt$ is the sum of the areas of $[x]$ rectangles shown shaded in that figure. The first $[x-1]$ of these rectangles are of areas 1, 2, ..., $[x-1]$ units^2 and the last rectangle is of area $(x - [x])\ [x]$ units^2. Hence

$$\int_0^x [t]\ dt = (1 + 2 + \ldots + [x-1]) + (x - [x])\ [x]$$

$$= \tfrac{1}{2}\ [x-1]\ [x] + (x - [x])\ [x]$$

and, using the relation $[x-1] = [x] - 1$, we have the required result.

A definite integral with infinity as one of its limits is to be interpreted by the relation

$$\int_a^\infty f(x)\ dx = \lim_{X \to \infty} \left\{ \int_a^X f(x)\ dx \right\}$$

provided this limit exists in which case the integral is said to converge to this limit [see § 3 : 10]. If $f(x) > 0$ for $x > a$, the existence of this limiting value of the integral implies that the area between Ox, the line $x = a$ and the curve $y = f(x)$ is finite.

Example 1. If $a > 0$,

$$\int_0^\infty e^{-ax}\,dx = \lim_{X \to \infty}\left[-\frac{e^{-ax}}{a}\right]_0^X = \lim_{X \to \infty}\frac{[1-e^{-aX}]}{a} = \frac{1}{a}.$$

Example 2.

$$\int_0^\infty \frac{dx}{a^2+x^2} = \lim_{X \to \infty}\left[\frac{1}{a}\tan^{-1}\left(\frac{x}{a}\right)\right]_0^X = \lim_{X \to \infty}\left[\frac{1}{a}\tan^{-1}\left(\frac{X}{a}\right)\right] = \frac{\pi}{2a}.$$

Exercises 3 : 2

Evaluate the following integrals:

1. $\displaystyle\int_0^\infty \frac{dx}{e^{4x-3}}.$ **2.** $\displaystyle\int_0^2 \frac{dx}{(4x+3)^2}.$ **3.** $\displaystyle\int_1^3 \frac{(y-1)^4\,dy}{y^2}.$

4. $\displaystyle\int_0^{\pi/4} (\sec\theta+1)^2\,d\theta.$ **5.** $\displaystyle\int_0^5 \frac{3\,dx}{(6x+5)}.$

6. Show without integration that $\displaystyle\int_{-1}^1 \left(\frac{e^x-1}{e^x+1}\right)dx = 0.$

7. Find the area between the parabola $y = x^2$ and the line $y = 4x-3$.

8. Evaluate the integrals

     (i) $\displaystyle\int_0^{2\pi/\omega} |\sin\omega t|\,dt,$ (ii) $\displaystyle\int_0^2 |x(1-x)|\,dx.$

3 : 3 Elementary rules and examples

We now list a number of simple rules and techniques which follow directly from the definition of integration. To save space, wherever indefinite integrals occur we have omitted the constant of the integration. The result of any integration may usually be rapidly checked by differentiation.

(i) If k is constant, $\int k f(x) \, dx = k \int f(x) \, dx.$

(ii) If n is finite

$$\int (f_1 + f_2 + \ldots + f_n) \, dx = \int f_1 \, dx + \int f_2 \, dx + \ldots + \int f_n \, dx.$$

(3.7)

It does not follow from this result that an infinite series may be integrated term by term. We consider this point later (§ 5 : 1).

(iii) If $\displaystyle\int f(u) \, du = F(u),$ then $\displaystyle\int f(ax+b) \, dx = \frac{1}{a} F(ax+b).$

This result may be verified by differentiation or as on page 127, Example 1.

Example. $\displaystyle\int (ax+b)^n \, dx = \frac{(ax+b)^{n+1}}{(n+1)a}$ if $n \neq -1, = \dfrac{1}{a} \ln (ax+b)$ if $n = -1.$

(iv) Simple expressions involving trigonometric or hyperbolic functions may be evaluated by the use of the techniques illustrated in the following examples:

$$\int \sin^2 x \, dx = \int \tfrac{1}{2}(1-\cos 2x) \, dx = \tfrac{1}{2}\left(x - \tfrac{1}{2} \sin 2x\right)$$
$$= \tfrac{1}{2}(x - \sin x \cos x).$$
$$\int \cos^3 x \, dx = \int \tfrac{1}{4}(3 \cos x + \cos 3x) \, dx = \tfrac{1}{4}\left(3 \sin x + \tfrac{1}{3} \sin 3x\right).$$
$$\int \tan^2 x \, dx = \int (\sec^2 x - 1) \, dx = \tan x - x.$$
$$\int \cosh^2 x \, dx = \int \tfrac{1}{2}(1 + \cosh 2x) \, dx = \tfrac{1}{2}\left(x + \tfrac{1}{2} \sinh 2x\right)$$
$$= \tfrac{1}{2}(x + \sinh x \cosh x).$$

Note that $\displaystyle\int_0^{\pi/2} \sin^2 x \, dx = \tfrac{1}{4}\pi = \int_0^{\pi/2} \cos^2 x \, dx,$ a result frequently required.

(v) If m and n are positive integers and $I = \displaystyle\int_\alpha^{2\pi+\alpha} \cos mx \cos nx \, dx,$ then $I = 0$ if $m \neq n, I = \pi$ if $m = n.$

For, if $m \neq n$,

$$I = \frac{1}{2} \int\limits_{\alpha}^{2\pi+\alpha} \{\cos(m-n)x + \cos(m+n)x\} \, dx$$

$$= \frac{1}{2} \left[\frac{\sin\{(m-n)x\}}{m-n} + \frac{\sin\{(m+n)x\}}{m+n} \right]_{\alpha}^{2\pi+\alpha}$$

$$= \frac{1}{2} \left\{ \frac{\sin\{(m-n)(2\pi+\alpha)\} - \sin\{(m-n)\alpha\}}{m-n} \right.$$

$$\left. + \frac{\sin\{(m+n)(2\pi+\alpha)\} - \sin\{(m+n)\}\alpha}{m+n} \right\} = 0.$$

If $m = n > 0$,

$$I = \int\limits_{\alpha}^{2\pi+\alpha} \cos^2 mx \, dx = \frac{1}{2} \int\limits_{\alpha}^{2\pi+\alpha} (1 + \cos 2mx) \, dx$$

$$= \frac{1}{2} \left[x + \frac{1}{2m} \sin 2mx \right]_{\alpha}^{2\pi+\alpha}$$

$$= \frac{1}{2} \left[2\pi + \alpha - \alpha + \frac{1}{2m} (\sin\{2m(2\pi+\alpha)\} - \sin 2m\alpha) \right] = \pi.$$

Note that if $m = n = 0$, $I = \int\limits_{\alpha}^{2\pi+\alpha} 1 \, dx = 2\pi$.

We leave as an exercise for the reader to prove in a similar manner that, for positive integers m and n,

$$\int\limits_{\alpha}^{2\pi+\alpha} \sin mx \sin nx \, dx = 0 \quad \text{if} \quad m \neq n,$$

$$= \pi \quad \text{if} \quad m = n,$$

$$\int\limits_{\alpha}^{2\pi+\alpha} \sin mx \cos nx \, dx = 0 \quad \text{for all integers } m \text{ and } n.$$

These results are of importance in connection with Fourier series. [See Vol. V, Chap. I.]

(vi) If $a > 0$, $b > 0$, extensions of the results given in the table of standard forms are

$$\int \frac{dx}{\sqrt{(b^2 - a^2 x^2)}} = \frac{1}{a} \int \frac{dx}{\sqrt{[(b^2/a^2) - x^2]}} = \frac{1}{a} \sin^{-1} \left[\frac{x}{b/a} \right]$$

$$= \frac{1}{a} \sin^{-1} \left(\frac{ax}{b} \right).$$

$$\int \frac{dx}{b^2 + a^2 x^2} = \frac{1}{a^2} \int \frac{dx}{(b^2/a^2) + x^2} = \frac{1}{a^2(b/a)} \tan^{-1} \left(\frac{x}{b/a} \right)$$

$$= \frac{1}{ab} \tan^{-1} \left(\frac{ax}{b} \right).$$

Similarly

$$\int \frac{dx}{\sqrt{(b^2 + a^2 x^2)}} = \frac{1}{a} \sinh^{-1} \left(\frac{ax}{b} \right),$$

$$\int \frac{dx}{\sqrt{(a^2 x^2 - b^2)}} = \frac{1}{a} \cosh^{-1} \left(\frac{ax}{b} \right).$$

These results may be further extended to the following:

$$\int \frac{dx}{\sqrt{[b^2 - (ax + c)^2]}} = \frac{1}{a} \sin^{-1} \left(\frac{ax + c}{b} \right), \qquad (3.8)$$

$$\int \frac{dx}{b^2 + (ax + c)^2} = \frac{1}{ab} \tan^{-1} \left(\frac{ax + c}{b} \right), \qquad (3.9)$$

$$\int \frac{dx}{\sqrt{[(ax + c)^2 + b^2]}} = \frac{1}{a} \sinh^{-1} \left(\frac{ax + c}{b} \right), \qquad (3.10)$$

$$\int \frac{dx}{\sqrt{[(ax + c)^2 - b^2]}} = \frac{1}{a} \cosh^{-1} \left(\frac{ax + c}{b} \right). \qquad (3.11)$$

The evaluation of $\int \dfrac{dx}{\sqrt{(Ax^2 + 2Hx + C)}}$, where A, H, C are constants is effected by "completing the square" and using (3.8), (3.10) or (3.11). Similarly $\int \dfrac{dx}{Ax^2 + 2Hx + C}$, where $H^2 < AC$ reduces to the type (3.9).

Example 1. $\int \dfrac{dx}{\sqrt{(1 - 2x - 4x^2)}} = \int \dfrac{dx}{\sqrt{[\frac{5}{4} - (\frac{1}{2} + 2x)^2]}} = \dfrac{1}{2} \sin^{-1} \left(\dfrac{4x + 1}{\sqrt{5}} \right).$

Example 2.

$$\int \frac{dx}{\sqrt{(3x^2+2x)}} = \int \frac{dx}{\sqrt{\left[\left(\sqrt{3}x+\frac{1}{\sqrt{3}}\right)^2 - \frac{1}{3}\right]}} = \frac{1}{\sqrt{3}} \cosh^{-1}(3x+1).$$

Example 3. $\int \dfrac{dx}{25+16x+4x^2} = \int \dfrac{dx}{9+(2x+4)^2} = \dfrac{1}{6} \tan^{-1}\left(\dfrac{2x+4}{3}\right).$

(vii) If $F(x) = \int\limits_a^x f(t)\,dt$, where $f(t)$ is continuous, then $F'(x) = f(x)$.

For

$$F(x+\delta x)-F(x) = \int\limits_a^{x+\delta x} f(t)\,dt - \int\limits_a^x f(t)\,dt$$

$$= \int\limits_x^{x+\delta x} f(t)\,dt = f(x)\,\delta x + O\{(\delta x)^2\}.$$

Dividing by δx and letting $\delta x \to 0$ gives the stated result.

Exercises 3:3

Integrate w.r. to x the following expressions:

1. $(6x+5)^7$.　　　　2. $2\sin^2 x - 3\cos^2 x$.　　　3. $\sin(x/a)$.

4. $5\tan(3x+4)$.　　　5. $\sin^4 x$.　　　6. $\cosh^3 x$.

7. $(2x^2+1)^{-\frac{1}{2}}$.　　8. $(1+4x-x^2)^{-\frac{1}{2}}$.　　9. $(1+x+x^2)^{-\frac{1}{2}}$.

10. $(9+8x+2x^2)^{-\frac{1}{2}}$.　　11. $(25-6x-x^2)^{-\frac{1}{2}}$.　　12. $(25-6x+x^2)^{-\frac{1}{2}}$.

13. $(13+12x+9x^2)^{-1}$.

Evaluate the following definite integrals:

14. $\int\limits_0^\infty \dfrac{dx}{9+16x^2}$.　　15. $\int\limits_0^\pi \cos x \cos 2x \cos 3x \, dx$.

16. $\int\limits_0^{\pi/4} \sin^3 \theta \, d\theta$.　　17. $\int\limits_0^1 \dfrac{dx}{\sqrt{(x^2+4x+8)}}$.　　18. $\int\limits_0^1 \dfrac{dx}{\sqrt{(x^2-4x+8)}}$.

19. $\displaystyle\int_0^1 \frac{dx}{\sqrt{(8-4x-x^2)}}$.   **20.** $\displaystyle\int_{-2}^0 \frac{dx}{x^2+4x+8}$.

21. Evaluate

$$F(x) = \int_{\pi/4}^x \sin^2 t \cos^2 t \, dt \text{ and verify that } F'(x) = \sin^2 x \cos^2 x.$$

3 : 4 Integration by substitution

If we change the independent variable to t by the substitution $x = \varphi(t)$ in the indefinite integral $I = \int f(x) \, dx$, so that by definition $dI/dx = f(x)$, then

$$\frac{dI}{dt} = \frac{dI}{dx} \frac{dx}{dt} = f(x) \frac{dx}{dt} = f\{\varphi(t)\} \varphi'(t).$$

Hence, integrating w.r. to t,

$$I = \int f(x) \frac{dx}{dt} \, dt = \int f\{\varphi(t)\} \varphi'(t) \, dt.$$

Conversely, when the integral to be evaluated is of the form $J = \displaystyle\int h(u) \frac{du}{dx} \, dx$ then, since $du = \dfrac{du}{dx} \, dx$, the integral may be replaced by $J = \int h(u) \, du$ which may be recognisable as a standard form or one of the simple types considered earlier. This method of integration is known as *integration by substitution*. Skill in integration is largely derived from experience. The reader should study the illustrative examples carefully and try as many exercises as possible.

Example 1. $\int f(ax+b) \, dx.$ Put $ax+b = u.$
Then

$$a \, dx = du \quad \text{and} \quad I = \frac{1}{a} \int f(u) \, du.$$

For example,

$$\int \cos^2 (ax+b) \, dx = \frac{1}{a} \int \cos^2 u \, du = \frac{1}{2a} \int (1+\cos 2u) \, du$$

$$= \frac{1}{2a} \left\{ u + \frac{1}{2} \sin 2u \right\} = \frac{1}{2a} \left\{ ax+b+\frac{1}{2} \sin 2(ax+b) \right\}.$$

Example 2. $\int x f(x^2)\, dx$. Put $x^2 = u$.

Then

$$2x\, dx = du \quad \text{and} \quad I = \tfrac{1}{2} \int f(u)\, du.$$

For example,

$$\int x(a+bx^2)^5\, dx = \frac{1}{2} \int (a+bu)^5\, du = \frac{(a+bu)^6}{12b} = \frac{(a+bx^2)^6}{12b}.$$

Example 3. $\int f'(x)\, \psi\{f(x)\}\, dx$. Put $f(x) = u$.

Then

$$f'(x)\, dx = du \quad \text{and} \quad I = \int \psi(u)\, du.$$

In illustration we consider $\int \sin^n x \cos x\, dx$. Put $\sin x = u$ and then $I = \int u^n\, du = \dfrac{u^{n+1}}{n+1}$, if $n \neq -1$, and therefore $I = \dfrac{\sin^{n+1} x}{n+1}$.

A special case of the above result is

$$\int \frac{f'(x)\, dx}{f(x)} = \ln f(x).$$

For example,

$$\int \frac{(3x+2)\, dx}{3x^2+4x+7} = \frac{1}{2} \int \frac{(6x+4)\, dx}{3x^2+4x+7} = \frac{1}{2} \ln |3x^2+4x+7|.$$

Example 4. The examples considered in 1, 2, 3 above may also be solved by the use of differentials. For example

$$\int x f(x^2)\, dx = \tfrac{1}{2} \int f(x^2)\, d(x^2),$$
$$\int f'(x)\, \psi\{f(x)\}\, dx = \int \psi\{f(x)\}\, d\{f(x)\},$$
$$\int \sin^n x \cos x\, dx = \int \sin^n x\, d(\sin x),$$
$$\int \sin^6 x \cos^3 x\, dx = \int \sin^6 x\, (1-\sin^2 x)\, d(\sin x) = \frac{\sin^7 x}{7} - \frac{\sin^9 x}{9}.$$

Example 5. $\int \sqrt{(a^2 - x^2)}\, dx$. Here the surd may be removed by the substitution $x = a \sin \theta$ (thereby making $a^2 - x^2$ a perfect square). Then $dx = a \cos \theta\, d\theta$ and

$$I = \int a^2 \cos^2 \theta\, d\theta = \frac{1}{2} a^2(\theta + \sin \theta \cos \theta) = \frac{1}{2} \left\{ a^2 \sin^{-1}\left(\frac{x}{a}\right) + x \sqrt{(a^2 - x^2)} \right\}.$$

Similarly the substitution $x = a \sinh u$ may be used to show that

$$K = \int \sqrt{(x^2 + a^2)}\, dx = \frac{1}{2} \left\{ a^2 \sinh^{-1}\left(\frac{x}{a}\right) + x \sqrt{(x^2 + a^2)} \right\}$$

and the substitution $x = a \cosh t$ to show that

$$L = \int \sqrt{(x^2 - a^2)}\, dx = \frac{1}{2}\left\{ x \sqrt{(x^2 - a^2)} - a^2 \cosh^{-1}\left(\frac{x}{a}\right)\right\}.$$

Alternatively the substitutions $x = a \tan u$, $x = \sec t$ may be used to evaluate K, L respectively (but integration by parts must then be employed).

Example 6. $\displaystyle\int \frac{(px + q)\, dx}{\sqrt{(ax^2 + 2hx + b)}}$ where a, h, b, p, q are constants.

Since $$px + q \equiv \frac{p}{2a}(2ax + 2h) + q - \frac{ph}{a},$$

$$\int \frac{(px + q)\, dx}{\sqrt{(ax^2 + 2hx + b)}} = \frac{p}{2a} \int \frac{(2ax + 2h)\, dx}{\sqrt{(ax^2 + 2hx + b)}}$$
$$+ \frac{aq - ph}{a} \int \frac{dx}{\sqrt{(ax^2 + 2hx + b)}}. \qquad (3.12)$$

Here we have expressed the numerator in the integral as (a multiple of the derivative of the quadratic form inside the square root in the denominator) + a constant. Each of the integrals on the right hand side of eqn. (3.12) is of known type. By Example 3 above the first of these integrals is $(p/a) \sqrt{(ax^2 + 2hx + b)}$ and the second is one of the types considered in § 3 : 3 (vi).

For example,

$$\int \frac{(4x + 7)\, dx}{\sqrt{(3x^2 + 7x + 2)}} = \frac{2}{3} \int \frac{(6x + 7)\, dx}{\sqrt{(3x^2 + 7x + 2)}}$$
$$+ \frac{7}{3} \int \frac{dx}{\sqrt{[\{\sqrt{3}x + 7/(2\sqrt{3})\}^2 - \frac{25}{12}]}}$$
$$= \frac{4}{3} \sqrt{(3x^2 + 7x + 2)} + \frac{7}{3\sqrt{3}} \cosh^{-1}\left(\frac{6x + 7}{5}\right).$$

In the evaluation of a definite integral by a substitution, the working is usually simplified by changing the limits of integration in accordance with the following rule (proved in books on analysis). "If we make the substitution $x = \psi(u)$ in the definite integral $I = \int_{x_1}^{x_2} f(x)\, dx$ and u_1, u_2 are defined by the equations $x_1 = \psi(u_1)$, $x_2 = \psi(u_2)$, where $\psi'(u)$ does not change sign for any value of u lying between u_1 and u_2, then $I = \int_{u_1}^{u_2} f\{\psi(u)\}\, \psi'(u)\, du$." Briefly, we alter the limits to the corresponding values of the new variable of integration, but it is important that $\psi'(u)$ should not change sign in the range of integration.

Example 1. If $I = \int_0^a \sqrt{(a^2 - x^2)}\,dx$, putting $x = a \sin\theta$ gives $dx = a\cos\theta\,d\theta$. Also $x = 0,\,a$, correspond to $\theta = 0,\,\pi/2$ respectively and $dx/d\theta$ does not change sign for $0 < \theta < \pi/2$. Therefore $I = a^2 \int_0^{\pi/2} \cos^2\theta\,d\theta = \pi a^2/4$.

Example 2. $\int_0^1 \sqrt{\left(\dfrac{x}{1-x}\right)}\,dx$. Putting $x = \sin^2\theta$ leads to $2\int_0^{\pi/2} \sin^2\theta\,d\theta = \pi/2$.

Example 3. $J = \int_a^b \dfrac{dx}{\sqrt{(x-a)}\,\sqrt{(b-x)}}$ where $0 < a < b$. This may be evaluated by completion of the square. A better method is to use the substitution $x = a\cos^2\theta + b\sin^2\theta$ leading to $dx = 2(b-a)\sin\theta\cos\theta\,d\theta$; the limits change to $0,\,\pi/2$.

Then
$$J = 2\int_0^{\pi/2} d\theta = \pi.$$

Example 4. $K = \int_0^a \dfrac{dx}{(a^2 + x^2)^2}$, $a > 0$. Putting $x = a\tan\theta$ gives $dx = a\sec^2\theta\,d\theta$. Moreover $x = 0$ corresponds to $\theta = 0$, $x = a$ corresponds to $\theta = \tfrac{1}{4}\pi$.

$$\therefore K = \frac{1}{a^3}\int_0^{\pi/4}\cos^2\theta\,d\theta = \frac{(\pi+2)}{8a^3}.$$

We now prove an important theorem concerning definite integrals

$$\int_0^a f(x)\,dx = \int_0^a f(a-x)\,dx. \tag{3.13}$$

Let $I = \int_0^a f(x)\,dx$. Making the substitution $x = a - u$, so that $dx = -du$ and $x = 0,\,a$, correspond to $u = a,\,0$ respectively, $I = -\int_a^0 f(a-u)\,du = \int_0^a f(a-u)\,du$ by eqn. (3.3). This establishes the result since the integral $\int\limits_0^a f(a-u)\,\mathrm{d}u$ depends on a but not upon u. In fact any definite integral is independent of the variable of integration. For example, $\int\limits_b^c \varphi(x)\,\mathrm{d}x = \int\limits_b^c \varphi(t)\,\mathrm{d}t$, and for this reason the variable of integration is called a *dummy* variable.

Example 1. $\int\limits_0^{\pi/2} \sin^m x \cos^n x \,\mathrm{d}x = \int\limits_0^{\pi/2} \sin^m (\tfrac{1}{2}\pi - x) \cos^n (\tfrac{1}{2}\pi - x) \,\mathrm{d}x$

$$= \int\limits_0^{\pi/2} \cos^m x \sin^n x \,\mathrm{d}x.$$

Example 2. $\int\limits_0^{\pi/2} \dfrac{\sin\theta \,\mathrm{d}\theta}{\sin\theta + \cos\theta} = \int\limits_0^{\pi/2} \dfrac{\sin(\tfrac{1}{2}\pi - \theta) \,\mathrm{d}\theta}{\sin(\tfrac{1}{2}\pi - \theta) + \cos(\tfrac{1}{2}\pi - \theta)}$

$$= \int\limits_0^{\pi/2} \dfrac{\cos\theta \,\mathrm{d}\theta}{\cos\theta + \sin\theta} \,.$$

Therefore, by addition each integral has the value $\tfrac{1}{2} \int\limits_0^{\pi/2} 1 \,\mathrm{d}\theta = \pi/2$.

Example 3. $\int\limits_{-a}^{a} f(x)\,\mathrm{d}x = \int\limits_{-a}^{0} f(x)\,\mathrm{d}x + \int\limits_{0}^{a} f(x)\,\mathrm{d}x.$

The substitution $x = -u$ gives

$$\int\limits_{-a}^{0} f(x)\,\mathrm{d}x = -\int\limits_{a}^{0} f(-u)\,\mathrm{d}u = \int\limits_{0}^{a} f(-u)\,\mathrm{d}u = \int\limits_{0}^{a} f(-x)\,\mathrm{d}x$$

and hence

$$\int\limits_{-a}^{a} f(x)\,\mathrm{d}x = \int\limits_{0}^{a} [f(-x) + f(x)]\,\mathrm{d}x.$$

Therefore if $f(x)$ is an even function, $\int\limits_{-a}^{a} f(x)\,\mathrm{d}x = 2 \int\limits_{0}^{x} f(x)\,\mathrm{d}x$, whereas if $f(x)$ is an odd function $\int\limits_{-a}^{a} f(x)\,\mathrm{d}x = 0$, confirming the results of § 3 : 2.

Example 4. In books on analysis the logarithmic function is defined by

$$\ln x = \int_1^x \frac{dt}{t}, \qquad x > 0.$$

From this definition we can prove the rules given on page 78. For example,

$$\ln (xy) = \int_1^{xy} \frac{dt}{t} = \int_1^x \frac{dt}{t} + \int_x^{xy} \frac{dt}{t}.$$

Writing $t = xu$ transforms the integral $\int_x^{xy} \dfrac{dt}{t}$ into $\int_1^y \dfrac{du}{u}$. Therefore

$$\ln (xy) = \int_1^x \frac{dt}{t} + \int_1^y \frac{du}{u} = \ln x + \ln y.$$

As an exercise the reader should prove from this definition the other properties of the logarithm function.

Exercises 3 : 4

Integrate w.r. to x the following expressions:

1. $x\,e^{-x^2}$.

2. $\sec^2 x \tan x$.

3. $\sec^4 x$.

4. $x^{-1} \ln x$.

5. $\cos^3 x \sin^4 x$.

6. $\dfrac{x^3}{1-x^4}$.

7. $\dfrac{x}{9+x^4}$.

8. $x \sqrt{(a^2+x^2)}$.

9. $\dfrac{e^x}{5+3e^x}$.

10. $x^3 \sqrt{(a^2-x^2)}$.

11. $\dfrac{\sin x}{16+9 \cos^2 x}$.

12. $\dfrac{e^{ax}}{\sqrt{(b^2+e^{2ax})}}$.

13. $\sqrt{\left[\dfrac{x}{c-x}\right]}$.

14. $\dfrac{e^{3x}}{1+e^{6x}}$.

15. $\sinh^n x \cosh^3 x$.

16. $\dfrac{\sin x}{a+b \cos x}$.

17. $\dfrac{1}{2+\cos^2 x}$.

18. $\dfrac{1}{5 \cosh x + 4 \sinh x}$.

19. $\sec^{\frac{3}{2}} x \tan^3 x$.

20. $x \sqrt{\left[\dfrac{a+x}{a-x}\right]}$.

Evaluate the following definite integrals:

21. $\displaystyle\int_1^2 \frac{dx}{e^x-1}$.

22. $\displaystyle\int_0^{\pi/2} \frac{\sin x \cos x \, dx}{a \cos^2 x + b \sin^2 x}$.

23. $\displaystyle\int_0^1 2^{3x}\, dx$.

24. $\displaystyle\int_0^{\pi/4} \frac{\sin^6 \theta}{\cos^{10} \theta}\, d\theta.$ **25.** $\displaystyle\int_0^\infty \frac{dx}{x^2+1+x\,\sqrt{(x^2+1)}}\cdot$ **26.** $\displaystyle\int_{a/2}^a \frac{dx}{x^2\sqrt{(a^2-x^2)}}\cdot$

27. $\displaystyle\int_0^1 \frac{x\,dx}{(x^2+1)^{\frac{3}{2}}}\cdot$ **28.** $\displaystyle\int_2^\infty \frac{dx}{x\,\sqrt{(x^2+4)}}\cdot$ **29.** $\displaystyle\int_a^\infty \frac{dx}{x^2(a^2+x^2)^{\frac{1}{2}}}\cdot$

30. $\displaystyle\int_0^1 \frac{dx}{\sqrt{(x-x^2)}}\cdot$ **31.** $\displaystyle\int_1^{\sqrt 2} x(3x^2-2)^{\frac{3}{2}}\, dx.$ **32.** $\displaystyle\int_0^\pi \frac{\cos x\, dx}{4-\cos^2 x}\cdot$

33. $\displaystyle\int_1^{10} \frac{(10-x)^{\frac{1}{2}}}{(x-1)^{\frac{1}{2}}}\, dx.$

Prove the results:

34. $\displaystyle\int_0^1 x^2\,\sqrt{(1-x^2)}\, dx = \frac{\pi}{16}\cdot$ **35.** $\displaystyle\int_0^{\pi/2} \frac{1-\cos x}{1+\cos x}\, dx = 2 - \frac{1}{2}\,\pi.$

36. $\displaystyle\int_{-\infty}^\infty \frac{dx}{\cosh x + \cos \alpha} = \frac{2\alpha}{\sin \alpha} \qquad (0 < \alpha < \pi).$

37. $\displaystyle\int_1^{\sqrt 3} \frac{dx}{(1+x^2)\tan^{-1} x} = \ln\left(\frac{4}{3}\right).$

38. $\displaystyle\int_0^{\ln 2} \frac{dx}{\sinh x + 5\cosh x} = \frac{1}{\sqrt 6}\left[\tan^{-1}(\sqrt 6) - \tan^{-1}\left(\frac{1}{2}\,\sqrt 6\right)\right].$

39. Use the substitution $x = \tan \theta$ to evaluate $\displaystyle\int \frac{x^2(x+1)}{(x^2+1)^3}\, dx.$

40. Put $x = \sinh \theta$ and hence evaluate $\displaystyle\int_0^\infty \frac{1}{[x+\sqrt{(1+x^2)}]^2}\, dx.$

41. Evaluate $\displaystyle\int \frac{dx}{x(x-1)^{\frac{3}{2}}}$ by writing $x-1 = t^2$, or otherwise.

42. Prove that $\displaystyle\int_a^b f(x)\, dx = \int_a^b f(a+b-x)\, dx.$

Evaluate $\displaystyle\int_0^\pi x \sin^3 x\, dx.$

43. Prove that $\displaystyle\int_0^a \frac{x^2\,\mathrm{d}x}{x^2+(x-a)^2} = \int_0^a \frac{(x-a)^2\,\mathrm{d}x}{x^2+(x-a)^2} = \frac{1}{2}\,a.$

44. Show that, if $f(x) \equiv f(a-x)$,

$$\int_0^a xf(x)\,\mathrm{d}x = \tfrac{1}{2}a\int_0^a f(x)\,\mathrm{d}x.$$

Evaluate　　$\displaystyle\int_0^\pi \frac{x\,\mathrm{d}x}{1+\cos\alpha\sin x}$　　$(0 < \alpha < \pi).$

45. Evaluate the integral

$$\int_0^a \frac{x\sin x}{1+\cos^2 x}\,\mathrm{d}x$$

in the cases (i) $a = \pi$, (ii) $a = 2\pi$.
(*Hint.* Use the theorem of Q. 44.)

3 : 5 Integration by parts

The rule (2.6) for the differentiation of the product uv of two functions of x is

$$\frac{\mathrm{d}(uv)}{\mathrm{d}x} = u\frac{\mathrm{d}v}{\mathrm{d}x} + v\frac{\mathrm{d}u}{\mathrm{d}x}.$$

Integrating this relation w.r. to x gives

$$uv = \int u\frac{\mathrm{d}v}{\mathrm{d}x}\,\mathrm{d}x + \int v\frac{\mathrm{d}u}{\mathrm{d}x}\,\mathrm{d}x,$$

the constant of integration being absorbed into the integrals. This equation can be rewritten

$$\int u\frac{\mathrm{d}v}{\mathrm{d}x}\,\mathrm{d}x = uv - \int v\frac{\mathrm{d}u}{\mathrm{d}x}\,\mathrm{d}x \tag{3.14}$$

which is the formula for *integration by parts*. Using differentials, equation (3.14) can be expressed in the form

$$\int u\,\mathrm{d}v = uv - \int v\,\mathrm{d}u. \tag{3.15}$$

Example 1. $\displaystyle\int x\,\mathrm{e}^{az}\,\mathrm{d}x = \int x\,\mathrm{d}\left(\frac{\mathrm{e}^{az}}{a}\right) = \frac{x\,\mathrm{e}^{az}}{a} - \int\left(\frac{\mathrm{e}^{az}}{a}\right)\mathrm{d}x = (ax-1)\frac{\mathrm{e}^{az}}{a^2}.$

Example 2. $\int \sin^{-1} x \, dx = (\sin^{-1} x) \, x - \int x \, d(\sin^{-1} x)$

$$= x \sin^{-1} x - \int \frac{x \, dx}{\sqrt{(1-x^2)}} = x \sin^{-1} x + \sqrt{(1-x^2)}.$$

Example 3. $\int x^n \ln x \, dx = \int \ln x \, d\left(\frac{x^{n+1}}{n+1}\right) = \frac{(\ln x) \, x^{n+1}}{n+1} - \frac{1}{n+1} \int x^{n+1} \, d(\ln x)$

$$= \frac{x^{n+1} \ln x}{n+1} - \frac{1}{n+1} \int x^{n+1} \cdot \frac{1}{x} \, dx$$

$$= \frac{x^{n+1} \ln x}{n+1} - \frac{x^{n+1}}{(n+1)^2} \qquad (n \neq -1).$$

Example 4. $\int x^2 \cos ax \, dx = \int x^2 \, d\left(\frac{1}{a} \sin ax\right) = \frac{x^2 \sin ax}{a} - \int \frac{\sin ax \, d(x^2)}{a}$

$$= \frac{x^2 \sin ax}{a} - \frac{2}{a} \int x \sin ax \, dx.$$

Here the original integral cannot be evaluated in one operation of integration by parts; a second integration is necessary, i.e.

$$\int x \sin ax \, dx = \int x \, d\left(-\frac{1}{a} \cos ax\right) = \frac{-x \cos ax}{a} + \frac{1}{a} \int \cos ax \, dx$$

$$= -\frac{x \cos ax}{a} + \frac{\sin ax}{a^2} .$$

Finally, we have $\int x^2 \cos ax \, dx = (a^2 x^2 \sin ax + 2ax \cos ax - 2 \sin ax)/a^3$.

Example 5. In some cases the original integral reappears after one or more integrations by parts. For example,

$$\int \sec^3 x \, dx = \int \sec x \, d(\tan x) = \sec x \tan x - \int \tan x \, d(\sec x)$$
$$= \sec x \tan x - \int \tan^2 x \sec x \, dx$$
$$= \sec x \tan x - \int (\sec^2 x - 1) \sec x \, dx$$
$$= \sec x \tan x - \int \sec^3 x \, dx + \int \sec x \, dx.$$

$\therefore \ 2 \int \sec^3 x \, dx = \sec x \tan x + \int \sec x \, dx.$

$\therefore \ \int \sec^3 x \, dx = \frac{1}{2} \sec x \tan x + \frac{1}{2} \ln (\sec x + \tan x).$

Example 6. If $I = \int e^{az} \cos bx \, dx$, $J = \int e^{az} \sin bx \, dx$, integration by parts gives

$$I = \int \cos bx \, d\left(\frac{e^{az}}{a}\right) = \frac{e^{az} \cos bx}{a} - \int \frac{e^{az}}{a} \, d(\cos bx),$$

i.e.

$$I = \frac{e^{az} \cos bx}{a} + \frac{bJ}{a}. \tag{1}$$

Similarly,

$$J = \frac{e^{az} \sin bx}{a} - \frac{bI}{a}. \tag{2}$$

Solution of eqns. (1) and (2) gives

$$I = e^{az} \frac{(a \cos bx + b \sin bx)}{(a^2 + b^2)},$$

$$J = e^{az} \frac{(a \sin bx - b \cos bx)}{(a^2 + b^2)}.$$

Example 7. In some cases the methods of integration by parts and by substitution must be combined. For example, the substitution $kx^2 = u$ transforms

$$\int x^3 e^{-kx^2} \, dx \quad \text{into} \quad \frac{1}{2k^2} \int u e^{-u} \, du = \frac{1}{2k^2} (-ue^{-u} - e^{-u})$$

on integration by parts.

$$\therefore \int x^3 e^{-kx^2} \, dx = -\frac{(kx^2 + 1)e^{-kx^2}}{2k^2}.$$

Exercises 3 : 5

Integrate w.r. to x the following expressions:

1. $x \sec^2 x.$ **2.** $\sec x \tan^2 x.$ **3.** $\ln x.$

4. $x \ln x.$ **5.** $\tanh^{-1} x.$ **6.** $\sinh^{-1} (x/a).$

7. $\sinh^{-1} (a/x).$ **8.** $(x-1)^2 \ln x.$ **9.** $(1+x^2) \tan^{-1} x.$

10. $\dfrac{x \sin^{-1} x}{\sqrt{(1-x^2)}}.$ **11.** $x(\ln x)^2.$ **12.** $x \sin^2 x \cos x.$

13. $\sec^{-1}\left(\dfrac{x}{a}\right).$ **14.** $\dfrac{x^2}{\sqrt{(a^2-x^2)}}.$ **15.** $\sin x \ln (1-a \cos x).$

16. $x \sin^{-1} x.$

Evaluate the following definite integrals:

17. $\displaystyle\int_0^{\pi/4} \sin x \ln (\cos x) \, dx.$ **18.** $\displaystyle\int_0^{\pi/4} \theta \sec^2 \theta \, d\theta.$ **19.** $\displaystyle\int_0^{\pi/4} x \tan^2 x \, dx.$

20. $\displaystyle\int_0^{\pi/2} \sin \theta \ln (1+\sin \theta) \, d\theta.$ **21.** $\displaystyle\int_{\frac{1}{2}}^1 \sin^{-1} (\sqrt{x}) \, dx.$ **22.** $\displaystyle\int_0^{\pi/2} x \sin^2 x \, dx.$

23. $\displaystyle\int_0^1 x^2 \sin^{-1} x \; \mathrm{d}x.$　　　　**24.** $\displaystyle\int_0^{\pi/4} \frac{x \; \mathrm{d}x}{1 + \cos 2x}.$

25. If $f(x) = \varphi(x) + \varphi'(x),$　show that　$\displaystyle\int \mathrm{e}^x f(x) \; \mathrm{d}x = \mathrm{e}^x \varphi(x).$

26. Prove the results stated on pages 128–9, that

(i)　　$\displaystyle\int \sqrt{(x^2 + a^2)} \; \mathrm{d}x = \frac{1}{2} \left\{ a^2 \sinh^{-1}\left(\frac{x}{a}\right) + x \sqrt{(x^2 + a^2)} \right\},$

(ii)　　$\displaystyle\int \sqrt{(x^2 - a^2)} \; \mathrm{d}x = \frac{1}{2} \left\{ x \sqrt{(x^2 - a^2)} - a^2 \cosh^{-1}\left(\frac{x}{a}\right) \right\}.$

27. Evaluate

(i)　$\displaystyle\int_0^{2n\pi/\omega} \mathrm{e}^{-pt} \cos \omega t \; \mathrm{d}t,$　where n is a positive integer,

(ii)　$\displaystyle\int_0^{\infty} \mathrm{e}^{-\alpha x} \cos \beta x \cos \gamma x \; \mathrm{d}x,$　where $\alpha > 0.$

3 : 6 Partial fractions

Before considering integrals of the form $\displaystyle\int \frac{f(x) \; \mathrm{d}x}{g(x)}$ where $f(x)$ and $g(x)$ are polynomials, we give a brief account of the resolution of a rational function of x into partial fractions. We assume that the reader has some knowledge of this process and therefore enumerate without proof the various cases which arise.

Without loss of generality we consider only cases in which $f(x)$ is of lower degree than $g(x)$ which is taken to be of degree n with the coefficient of x^n unity. It is shown in § 7 : 4, that, if the coefficients of $g(x)$ are all real, then $g(x)$ may be expressed as the product of linear and quadratic factors with real coefficients. Resolution of $f(x)/g(x)$ into partial fractions consists of expressing $f(x)/g(x)$ as the sum of a number of fractions, each partial fraction corresponding to a real factor of $g(x)$. The various cases are tabulated below.

Factor of $g(x)$	*Corresponding partial fractions*
1. Unrepeated linear factor $(x - \alpha)$:	$\dfrac{A}{x - \alpha}$
2. Repeated linear factor $(x - \alpha)^r$:	$\dfrac{A_1}{x - \alpha} + \dfrac{A_2}{(x - \alpha)^2} + \cdots + \dfrac{A_r}{(x - \alpha)^r}$

3. Unrepeated quadratic factor (x^2+ax+b): $\dfrac{Bx+C}{(x^2+ax+b)}$

4. Repeated quadratic factor $(x^2+ax+b)^s$: $\dfrac{B_1x+C_1}{x^2+ax+b}+\dfrac{B_2x+C_2}{(x^2+ax+b)^2}$

$$+ \cdots +\dfrac{B_sx+C_s}{(x^2+ax+b)^s}.$$

To determine the coefficients A, B, etc., in the partial fractions we use the fact that $f(x)/g(x)$ is identically equal to the sum of its partial fractions. Multiplication by $g(x)$ gives an identity between two polynomials, each of degree $n-1$ at most. Two polynomials in x, each of degree m, are *identically* equal if there are more than m values of x for which they are equal. In two identical polynomials the coefficients of any given power of x are the same, i.e. if $\sum\limits_{r=1}^{m} a_rx^r \equiv \sum\limits_{r=1}^{m} b_rx^r$, then $a_r = b_r$. (See p. 6.) The expansion of $f(x)/g(x)$ as a sum of partial fractions must be true for *all* the values of x in a given range, i.e. for more than n values of x. The coefficients A, B, etc., may therefore be determined either by substituting special values of x or by equating coefficients or by a combination of both these processes.

Example 1. $\dfrac{1}{x(x-1)(x-2)(x-3)} = \dfrac{A}{x}+\dfrac{B}{x-1}+\dfrac{C}{x-2}+\dfrac{D}{x-3}.$

Multiply through by the denominator $g(x)$. Then

$$1 \equiv A(x-1)(x-2)(x-3)+Bx(x-2)(x-3)+Cx(x-1)(x-3)$$
$$+Dx(x-1)(x-2).$$

In this identity put, in succession, x equal to 0, 1, 2, 3, and obtain

$$1 = A(-1)(-2)(-3), \quad 1 = B\times1\times(-1)(-2), \quad 1 = C\times2\times1(-1),$$
$$1 = D\times3\times2\times1, \quad \text{or} \quad A = -\tfrac{1}{6}, \quad B = \tfrac{1}{2}, \quad C = -\tfrac{1}{2}, \quad D = \tfrac{1}{6}.$$

$$\therefore \quad \dfrac{1}{x(x-1)(x-2)(x-3)} \equiv -\dfrac{1}{6x}+\dfrac{1}{2(x-1)}-\dfrac{1}{2(x-2)}+\dfrac{1}{6(x-3)}.$$

Example 2. $\dfrac{x^2+x+1}{(x^2-1)(x^2-4)} = \dfrac{A}{x+1}+\dfrac{B}{x-1}+\dfrac{C}{x+2}+\dfrac{D}{x-2}.$

Multiplying by the denominator clears the fractions and gives the identity

$$x^2+x+1 \equiv A(x-1)(x^2-4)+B(x+1)(x^2-4)$$
$$+C(x^2-1)(x-2)+D(x^2-1)(x+2).$$

At this point we could use the method of Example 1 by putting $x = 1$, -1, 2, -2. However, we shall evaluate A, B, C, D by equating coefficients. The reader should verify the results by the method of Example 1.

Coefficient of x^3; $\quad 0 = A + B + C + D.$

$\qquad\qquad\qquad x^2; \quad 1 = -A + B - 2C + 2D.$

$\qquad\qquad\qquad x; \quad 1 = -4A - 4B - C - D.$

Independent term (i.e., x^0); $1 = 4A - 4B + 2C - 2D$.

The solution of these equations is $A = \frac{1}{6}$, $B = -\frac{1}{2}$, $C = -\frac{1}{4}$, $D = \frac{7}{12}$, so that

$$\frac{x^2 + x + 1}{(x^2 - 1)(x^2 - 4)} \equiv \frac{1}{6(x+1)} - \frac{1}{2(x-1)} - \frac{1}{4(x+2)} + \frac{7}{12(x-2)}.$$

Example 3. $\quad \dfrac{x^3}{(x-1)^4(x-2)} = \dfrac{A}{x-2} + \dfrac{B_1}{x-1} + \dfrac{B_2}{(x-1)^2} + \dfrac{B_3}{(x-1)^3} + \dfrac{B_4}{(x-1)^4}.$

This is most conveniently handled by putting $z = x - 1$. Then

$$\frac{x^3}{(x-1)^4(x-2)} = \frac{(z+1)^3}{z^4(z-1)} = \frac{A}{z-1} + \frac{B_1}{z} + \frac{B_2}{z^2} + \frac{B_3}{z^3} + \frac{B_4}{z^4}.$$

$\therefore \quad (z+1)^3 \equiv z^3 + 3z^2 + 3z + 1 \equiv Az^4 + (B_1z^3 + B_2z^2 + B_3z + B_4)(z-1).$

Put $\qquad\qquad z = 1; \qquad 2^3 = A, \qquad\quad \therefore \ A = 8,$

$\qquad\qquad\qquad z = 0; \qquad 1 = B_4(-1), \quad \therefore \ B_4 = -1.$

Equate coefficients of $\quad z^3; \qquad 1 = -B_1 + B_2,$

$\qquad\qquad\qquad\qquad\quad z^2; \qquad 3 = -B_2 + B_3,$

$\qquad\qquad\qquad\qquad\quad z; \qquad 3 = -B_3 + B_4.$

$\therefore \ B_3 = -4, \quad B_2 = -7, \quad B_1 = -8.$

$$\therefore \quad \frac{x^3}{(x-1)^4(x-2)} \equiv \frac{8}{x-2} - \frac{8}{x-1} - \frac{7}{(x-1)^2} - \frac{4}{(x-1)^3} - \frac{1}{(x-1)^4}.$$

Example 4. $\quad \dfrac{x}{x^3 + x^2 + x + 1} \equiv \dfrac{x}{(x^2+1)(x+1)} = \dfrac{A}{x+1} + \dfrac{Bx + C}{x^2 + 1}.$

Remove the fractions to obtain

$$x \equiv A(x^2 + 1) + (Bx + C)(x + 1).$$

Put

$$x = -1; \qquad -1 = 2A. \quad \therefore \ A = -\tfrac{1}{2}.$$

Evaluate coefficients of

$\qquad\qquad\qquad x^2; \qquad 0 = A + B, \quad \therefore \ B = \tfrac{1}{2},$

$\qquad\qquad\qquad x; \qquad 1 = B + C, \quad \therefore \ C = \tfrac{1}{2}.$

$$\therefore \quad \frac{x}{(x^2+1)(x+1)} \equiv -\frac{1}{2(x+1)} + \frac{x+1}{2(x^2+1)}.$$

Example 5. $\dfrac{x}{(x-1)(x^2+2x+3)^2} = \dfrac{A}{x-1} + \dfrac{B_1x+C_1}{x^2+2x+3} + \dfrac{B_2x+C_2}{(x^2+2x+3)^2}$.

$\therefore \quad x \equiv A(x^2+2x+3)^2 + (B_1x+C_1)(x-1)(x^2+2x+3) + (B_2x+C_2)(x-1)$.

Put

$$x = 1; \qquad 1 = A(6)^2. \quad \therefore \ A = \tfrac{1}{36}.$$

Equate coefficients of

$$
\begin{aligned}
x^4; & \quad 0 = A+B_1, \quad \therefore \ B_1 = -\tfrac{1}{36}, \\
x^3; & \quad 0 = 4A - B_1 + C_1 + 2B_1, \quad \therefore \ C_1 = -\tfrac{A}{12}, \\
x; & \quad 1 = 12A - 2C_1 + 3C_1 - 3B_1 + C_2 - B_2, \\
x^0; & \quad 0 = 9A - 3C_1 - C_2, \\
& \therefore \ C_2 = \tfrac{1}{2}, \quad B_2 = -\tfrac{1}{6}.
\end{aligned}
$$

$$\therefore \quad \frac{x}{(x-1)(x^2+2x+3)^2} \equiv \frac{1}{36(x-1)} - \frac{x+3}{36(x^2+2x+3)} - \frac{x-3}{6(x^2+2x+3)^2} .$$

The above examples suggest that the coefficient of the partial fraction corresponding to an unrepeated linear factor can always be obtained by the substitution of a special value of x. If $(x-\alpha)$ is an unrepeated factor of $g(x)$ the corresponding partial fraction is $A/(x-\alpha)$.

$$\therefore \quad \frac{f(x)}{g(x)} = \frac{A}{x-\alpha} + \varphi(x),$$

where $\varphi(x)$ is a rational function whose denominator does not contain the factor $(x-\alpha)$.

$$\therefore \quad f(x) = \frac{Ag(x)}{(x-\alpha)} + g(x)\,\varphi(x). \tag{3.16}$$

But $g(\alpha) = 0$.

$$\therefore \quad g'(\alpha) = \lim_{x \to \alpha} \frac{g(x)-g(\alpha)}{x-\alpha} = \lim_{x \to \alpha} \frac{g(x)}{x-\alpha}. \tag{3.17}$$

In eqn. (3.16) we let $x \to \alpha$ and obtain $f(\alpha) = Ag'(\alpha)$ or

$$A = \frac{f(\alpha)}{g'(\alpha)} = \lim_{x \to \alpha} \frac{(x-\alpha)f(x)}{g(x)}. \tag{3.18}$$

Hence the procedure to obtain A is as follows. Remove the factor $x-\alpha$ from the denominator and put $x = \alpha$ in what remains. This is *Heaviside's rule*. A study of the above examples will show that this always gives the coefficients corresponding to unrepeated linear factors. In fact the coefficient of $1/(ax+b)$ in the partial fraction corresponding to the *linear* factor $(ax+b)$ in the denominator of a rational function can be obtained by "covering-up" the factor $(ax+b)$ in the original expression and putting $x = -b/a$ in the expression which remains. For this reason, Heaviside's rule is sometimes called the *cover-up* rule.

Example. Express $\dfrac{x-1}{(2x+1)(3x+1)}$ in partial fractions.

The coefficient of $\dfrac{1}{3x+1}$ is $\dfrac{-\frac{1}{3}-1}{-\frac{2}{3}+1} = -4$.

The coefficient of $\dfrac{1}{2x+1}$ is $\dfrac{-\frac{1}{2}-1}{-\frac{3}{2}+1} = +3$.

$$\therefore \quad \frac{x-1}{(2x+1)(3x+1)} \equiv \frac{3}{2x+1} - \frac{4}{3x+1}.$$

Exercises 3 : 6

Resolve the following expressions into partial fractions:

1. $\dfrac{1}{(x+3)(x^2+x+1)}$.

2. $\dfrac{x^2-2x}{(2x+1)(x^2+1)}$.

3. $\dfrac{x^3+x+1}{x^4+x^2}$.

4. $\dfrac{4+2x}{1-x^3}$.

5. $\dfrac{6x+1}{x(2x+1)^2}$.

6. $\dfrac{1}{6-x-4x^2-x^3}$.

7. $\dfrac{3x-4}{(x+1)^2(x^2-x+1)}$.

8. $\dfrac{1}{x^2(x^2+1)}$.

9. $\dfrac{x^2}{x^4+1}$ [use $x^4+1 = (x^2-\sqrt{2}x+1)(x^2+\sqrt{2}x+1)$].

10. Find the nth differential coefficient of $\dfrac{1}{(x+1)^2(x+2)}$.

3 : 7 Integration of rational functions

With the help of partial fractions the evaluation of $\displaystyle\int \frac{f(x)\,dx}{g(x)}$, where $f(x)$ and $g(x)$ are polynomials can be reduced to the evaluation of integrals of the following types:

(i) $\displaystyle\int \frac{dx}{(mx+l)^r}$,   (ii) $\displaystyle\int \frac{(px+q)\,dx}{(ax^2+2hx+b)^r}$,   where $h^2 < ab$.

If $f(x)$ is of higher degree than $g(x)$, then $f(x)/g(x)$ must be reduced to a suitable form by long division. Type (i) above has been considered earlier and takes the value

$$\frac{1}{m}\ln(mx+l) \quad \text{when} \quad r = 1, \quad \text{and} \quad -\frac{1}{m(r-1)(mx+l)^{r-1}}$$

otherwise. Type (ii) may be evaluated as follows [cf. Example 6, p. 129]:

$$\int \frac{(px+q)\,dx}{(ax^2+2hx+b)^r} = \frac{p}{2a}\int \frac{(2ax+2h)\,dx}{(ax^2+2hx+b)^r}$$
$$+ \frac{(qa-ph)}{a}\int \frac{dx}{(ax^2+2hx+b)^r}. \quad (3.19)$$

But $\displaystyle\int \frac{(2ax+2h)\,dx}{(ax^2+2hx+b)^r} = \ln(ax^2+2hx+b)$ if $r = 1$ and

$$= \frac{-1}{(r-1)(ax^2+2hx+b)^{r-1}} \quad \text{otherwise.}$$

Since $h^2 < ab$ the remaining integral $\displaystyle\int \frac{dx}{(ax^2+2hx+b)^r}$ may be reduced to an integral of the form $\displaystyle\int \frac{dx}{[(x-\alpha)^2+\beta^2]^r}$, where α and β are real. When $r = 1$ this integral takes the value $\frac{1}{\beta}\tan^{-1}\left(\frac{x-\alpha}{\beta}\right)$; when $r > 1$ the substitution $x - \alpha = \beta\tan\theta$ transforms the integral to a multiple of $\int \cos^{2r-2}\theta\,d\theta$. For moderate values of r this integral may be evaluated by the methods of § 3 : 3 (iv); otherwise the reduction formulae of § 3 : 9 may be used for definite integrals. Formulae which can be used in indefinite integrals of this type are developed in Chapter VII.

Examples. We integrate the expressions resolved into partial fractions in § 3 : 6.

1. $\displaystyle\int \frac{dx}{x(x-1)(x-2)(x-3)}$

$$= \int \left\{ -\frac{1}{6x} + \frac{1}{2(x-1)} - \frac{1}{2(x-2)} + \frac{1}{6(x-3)} \right\}dx$$

$$= -\frac{1}{6}\ln x + \frac{1}{2}\ln(x-1) - \frac{1}{2}\ln(x-2) + \frac{1}{6}\ln(x-3).$$

2. $\displaystyle\int \frac{(x^2+x+1)\ \mathrm{d}x}{(x^2-1)\,(x^2-4)}$

$\displaystyle = \int \left\{ \frac{1}{6(x+1)} - \frac{1}{2(x-1)} - \frac{1}{4(x+2)} + \frac{7}{12(x-2)} \right\}\ \mathrm{d}x$

$\displaystyle = \frac{1}{6}\ \ln\ (x+1) - \frac{1}{2}\ \ln\ (x-1) - \frac{1}{4}\ \ln\ (x+2) + \frac{7}{12}\ \ln\ (x-2).$

---

3. $\displaystyle\int \frac{x^3\ \mathrm{d}x}{(x-1)^4\,(x-2)}$

$\displaystyle = \int \left\{ \frac{8}{x-2} - \frac{8}{x-1} - \frac{7}{(x-1)^2} - \frac{4}{(x-1)^3} - \frac{1}{(x-1)^4} \right\}\ \mathrm{d}x$

$\displaystyle = 8\ \ln\ \left(\frac{x-2}{x-1}\right) + \frac{7}{x-1} + \frac{2}{(x-1)^2} + \frac{1}{3(x-1)^3}\,.$

---

4. $\displaystyle\int \frac{x\ \mathrm{d}x}{x^3+x^2+x+1} = \int \left\{ \frac{-1}{2(x+1)} + \frac{x+1}{2(x^2+1)} \right\}\ \mathrm{d}x$

$\displaystyle \qquad\qquad\qquad = -\frac{1}{2}\ \ln\ (x+1) + \frac{1}{4}\ \ln\ (x^2+1) + \frac{1}{2}\ \tan^{-1}\ x.$

---

5. $\displaystyle\int \frac{x\ \mathrm{d}x}{(x-1)\,(x^2+2x+3)^2}$

$\displaystyle = \int \left\{ \frac{1}{36(x-1)} - \frac{(x+3)}{36(x^2+2x+3)} - \frac{(x-3)}{6(x^2+2x+3)^2} \right\}\ \mathrm{d}x$

$\displaystyle = \frac{1}{36}\ \ln\ (x-1) - \frac{1}{72} \int \frac{(2x+2)\ \mathrm{d}x}{(x^2+2x+3)}$

$\displaystyle \quad - \frac{1}{36} \int \frac{2\ \mathrm{d}x}{(x+1)^2+2} - \frac{1}{12} \int \frac{(2x+2)\ \mathrm{d}x}{(x^2+2x+3)^2} + \frac{4}{6} \int \frac{\mathrm{d}x}{[(x+1)^2+2]^2}$

$\displaystyle = \frac{1}{36}\ \ln\ (x-1) - \frac{1}{72}\ \ln\ (x^2+2x+3)$

$\displaystyle \quad - \frac{1}{18\ \sqrt{2}}\ \tan^{-1}\left(\frac{x+1}{\sqrt{2}}\right) + \frac{1}{12(x^2+2x+3)}$

$\displaystyle \quad + \frac{1}{3\ \sqrt{2}} \int \cos^2\ \theta\ \mathrm{d}\theta, \quad \text{where} \quad x+1 = \sqrt{2}\ \tan\ \theta.$

It is easy to show that

$\displaystyle \int \cos^2\ \theta\ \mathrm{d}\theta = \frac{1}{2}\ (\theta + \sin\ \theta\ \cos\ \theta) = \frac{1}{2}\ \left\{ \tan^{-1}\left(\frac{x+1}{\sqrt{2}}\right) + \frac{(x+1)\ \sqrt{2}}{(x^2+2x+3)} \right\},$

and the required integral follows at once.

Exercises 3 : 7

Integrate w.r. to x the expressions 1–9 of Exercises 3 : 6.

Evaluate the following integrals:

10. $\displaystyle\int_0^\infty \frac{dx}{(x+1)(x^2+1)}$.   **11.** $\displaystyle\int_0^\infty \frac{e^{-x}\,dx}{\cosh x}$.   **12.** $\displaystyle\int_{\pi/4}^{\pi/3} \frac{dx}{\sin x \cos^2 x}$.

13. $\displaystyle\int_{\frac{1}{2}}^1 \frac{dx}{1+x^3}$.   **14.** $\displaystyle\int_0^{\frac{1}{2}} \left(\frac{x^2+x+1}{x^2-x+1}\right) dx$.   **15.** $\displaystyle\int_0^{\frac{1}{2}} x \ln(1-x^2)\,dx$.

16. $\displaystyle\int_0^1 x^2 \tan^{-1} x\,dx$.

17. Show that
$$\frac{x^5}{(x+1)(x-2)} = x^3+x^2+3x+5+\frac{1}{3(x+1)}+\frac{32}{3(x-2)}.$$
Hence integrate this function.

18. (i) Using the identity $x^4+x^2+1 \equiv (x^2+1)^2-x^2$, show that
$$\int_0^1 \frac{x^2\,dx}{x^4+x^2+1} = \frac{\pi}{4\sqrt{3}} - \frac{1}{4}\ln 3.$$

19. (i) Find the indefinite integrals
$$(i) \quad \int \frac{(1+x^3)\,dx}{x^2(1-x)}, \quad\quad (ii) \quad \int \frac{dx}{x(1+x^5)}$$

3 : 8 Miscellaneous methods

(i) *Rational functions of* sin x *and cos* x. In general, integrals of the type $\displaystyle\int \frac{f(\sin x, \cos x)}{g(\sin x, \cos x)}\,dx$, where f and g are polynomials in $\sin x$ and $\cos x$, can be evaluated by the substitution $\tan\left(\frac{1}{2}x\right) = t$. In this case $\frac{1}{2}\sec^2\left(\frac{1}{2}x\right)dx = dt$, or $dx = 2\,dt/(1+t^2)$. Together with the trigonometric identities $\sin x = 2t/(1+t^2)$, $\cos x = (1-t^2)/(1+t^2)$, this substitution reduces an integral of the above type to an integral of a rational function of t.

Example 1. $\displaystyle\int \frac{dx}{4+5\sin x} = \int \frac{dt}{(2t^2+5t+2)} = \int \left\{\frac{2}{3(2t+1)} - \frac{1}{3(t+2)}\right\} dt$
$$= \frac{1}{3}\ln\left[\frac{1+2t}{2+t}\right] = \frac{1}{3}\ln\left[\frac{1+2\tan\left(\frac{1}{2}x\right)}{2+\tan\left(\frac{1}{2}x\right)}\right].$$

Example 2.
$$\int_0^{\pi/2} \frac{dx}{(2+\cos x)} = 2 \int_0^1 \frac{dt}{(t^2+3)} = \left[\frac{2}{\sqrt{3}} \tan^{-1}\left(\frac{t}{\sqrt{3}}\right)\right]_0^1 = \frac{\pi}{3\sqrt{3}}.$$

The above technique may be employed in the evaluation of integrals of the form $\int \dfrac{dx}{a \cos x + b \sin x}$, but, since

$a \cos x + b \sin x = r \cos(x-\alpha)$ where $a = r \cos \alpha$, $b = r \sin \alpha$, this integral can be expressed as

$$\frac{1}{r} \int \sec(x-\alpha)\,dx = \frac{1}{r} \ln[\sec(x-\alpha)+\tan(x-\alpha)].$$

The integrals of some rational functions of $\sin x$ and $\cos x$ are more easily obtained by other substitutions.

Example 1.
$$\int \frac{\cos x\,dx}{3+4 \sin x} = \int \frac{d(\sin x)}{3+4 \sin x} = \frac{1}{4} \ln(3+4 \sin x).$$

Example 2.
$$\int \frac{\sin x\,dx}{9+16 \cos^2 x} = -\int \frac{d(\cos x)}{9+16 \cos^2 x} = -\frac{1}{12} \tan^{-1}\left(\frac{4 \cos x}{3}\right).$$

It is important that any integral of this type should be carefully examined for a simple substitution before application of the $\tan\left(\frac{1}{2}x\right) = t$ substitution. For example a rational function of $\sin^2 x$, $\sin x \cos x$, $\cos^2 x$, which is itself a rational function of $\sin 2x$ and $\cos 2x$ by virtue of the identities $\sin^2 x = \frac{1}{2}(1-\cos 2x)$, $\sin x \cos x = \frac{1}{2} \sin 2x$, $\cos^2 x = \frac{1}{2}(1+\cos 2x)$, can be evaluated by changing the variable of integration to $\tan x$.

Example.
$$\int \frac{dx}{a^2 \cos^2 x + b^2 \sin^2 x} = \int \frac{\sec^2 x\,dx}{a^2+b^2 \tan^2 x} = \int \frac{d(\tan x)}{a^2+b^2 \tan^2 x}$$
$$= \frac{1}{ab} \tan^{-1}\left(\frac{b \tan x}{a}\right).$$

(ii) *Surds.* No general rules can be laid down when the integrand involves surds. However, we give below some examples which are intended to serve as a guide.

Example 1. If the integrand involves $\sqrt{(ax+b)}$, then the substitution $ax+b = u^2$ may reduce the integral to one of the types considered earlier, e.g.

$$\int \left\{ \frac{1+\sqrt{(ax+b)}}{1-\sqrt{(ax+b)}} \right\} dx = \frac{2}{a} \int \frac{u(1+u)\, du}{(1-u)} = \frac{2}{a} \int \left(-u-2+\frac{2}{1-u} \right) du$$

$$= \frac{-u^2-4u-4 \ln (1-u)}{a}$$

$$= \frac{-ax-b-4\sqrt{(ax+b)}-4 \ln \{1-\sqrt{(ax+b)}\}}{a}.$$

Example 2. If the integrand involves $\sqrt{(ax^2+2hx+b)}$, then the techniques of the type given on page 129 may be appropriate, e.g.

$$\int (5x+4) \sqrt{(x^2+2x+5)}\, dx = \tfrac{5}{2} \int (2x+2) \sqrt{(x^2+2x+5)}\, dx$$

$$- \int \sqrt{(x^2+2x+5)}\, dx$$

$$= \tfrac{5}{3} (x^2+2x+5)^{\frac{3}{2}} - \int \sqrt{[(x+1)^2+4]}\, dx.$$

This last integral can be evaluated by using the substitution $x+1 = 2 \sinh \theta$.

Example 3. $$\int_{\frac{1}{2}}^{1} \frac{dx}{x \sqrt{(5x^2-4x+1)}}.$$

Putting $x = 1/u$ transforms this integral into

$$\int_{1}^{2} \frac{du}{\sqrt{(5-4u+u^2)}} = \int_{1}^{2} \frac{du}{\sqrt{[1+(u-2)^2]}} = [\sinh^{-1}(u-2)]_1^2 = -\sinh^{-1}(-1)$$

$$= \sinh^{-1} 1 = \ln (1+\sqrt{2}).$$

(iii) *Hyperbolic functions.* Integration of a polynomial in $\sinh x$, $\cosh x$ or $\tanh x$ can usually be evaluated by methods akin to those used for similar trigonometric functions [cf. type (iv), p. 123]. In other cases, however, this method may not be suitable and the substitution $e^x = u$ is appropriate. It is particularly advisable that results should be checked by differentiation.

Example 1. $\int \sinh^4 x\, dx = \tfrac{1}{8} \int (\cosh 4x - 4 \cosh 2x + 3)\, dx$
$$= \tfrac{1}{32} (\sinh 4x - 8 \sinh 2x + 12x).$$

Example 2. $\int \cosh^5 x \, dx = \int (1+\sinh^2 x)^2 \, d \, (\sinh x)$
$$= \sinh x + \tfrac{2}{3} \sinh^3 x + \tfrac{1}{5} \sinh^5 x.$$

Example 3. $\int \operatorname{cosech} x \, dx = \int \dfrac{2 \, dx}{e^x - e^{-x}} = 2 \int \dfrac{d \, (e^x)}{e^{2x} - 1} = \ln \left(\dfrac{e^x - 1}{e^x + 1} \right)$
$$= \ln \tanh \frac{x}{2}.$$

Example 4. $\int \operatorname{sech} x \, dx = \int \dfrac{2 \, dx}{e^x + e^{-x}} = 2 \int \dfrac{d \, (e^x)}{e^{2x} + 1} = 2 \tan^{-1} (e^x).$

Exercises 3 : 8

Integrate w.r. to x the following expressions:

1. $\dfrac{1}{1+\sin x}.$

2. $\dfrac{\cos x}{3+\cos x}.$

3. $\dfrac{1}{1+8 \sin^2 x}.$

4. $\dfrac{\sqrt{(x-1)}}{x}.$

5. $\dfrac{1}{(1-\sqrt{x}) \sqrt{x}}.$

6. $\dfrac{5 \cos x}{2 \cos x + \sin x + 2}.$

7. $\dfrac{1}{8 - x^{\frac{3}{2}}}.$

8. $\dfrac{x+1}{x \sqrt{(x-1)}}.$

9. $\dfrac{4x+5}{\sqrt{(2x^2 + 7x + 3)}}.$

10. $\dfrac{\sin x}{5 - 3 \sin^2 x}.$

11. $\dfrac{3 + \sin x}{1 + \cos x}.$

12. $\dfrac{1}{(1-x) \sqrt{(x+1)}}.$

13. $\dfrac{1}{1 + \sin x + \cos x}.$

14. $\dfrac{\cos x - \sin x}{\cos x + \sin x}.$

15. $(x+1) \sqrt{(x^2 + x + 1)}.$

16. $\operatorname{sech}^4 x.$

17. $\dfrac{1}{5 + 3 \cosh x}.$

Evaluate the following integrals:

18. $\displaystyle\int_0^{\pi/2} \dfrac{dx}{3 \sin x + 2}.$

19. $\displaystyle\int_0^{\pi/2} \dfrac{d\theta}{4 - \cos^2 \theta}.$

20. $\displaystyle\int_1^2 \dfrac{(x-1) \, dx}{\sqrt{(8 + 2x - x^2)}}.$

21. $\displaystyle\int_1^{\infty} \dfrac{dx}{x \sqrt{(25x^2 - 1)}}.$

22. $\displaystyle\int_0^{\pi/2} \dfrac{d\theta}{3 \sin \theta + \cos \theta + 1}.$

23. $\displaystyle\int_0^{\pi/6} \dfrac{d\theta}{\cos \theta + \cos^3 \theta}.$

24. $\displaystyle\int_0^1 \dfrac{dx}{(1+x) \sqrt{(1-x^2)}}.$

25. $\displaystyle\int_0^{\pi} \dfrac{\sin 2x \, dx}{2 - \cos x}.$

26. $\displaystyle\int_0^{\pi/4} \frac{2\,dx}{3\sin 2x + 4\cos 2x}$.
  27. $\displaystyle\int_0^{\pi/2} \frac{\sin 2x\,dx}{1+\cos^2 x}$.

28. $\displaystyle\int_0^{\pi/2} \frac{d\theta}{1-2a\cos\theta + a^2}$, $|a| \neq 1$.

29. $\displaystyle\int_0^{\infty} \frac{dx}{1-2x\cos\alpha + x^2}$,   when $0 < \alpha \leq \tfrac{1}{2}\pi$.

30. $\displaystyle\int_0^{\pi/2} \frac{\sin 3x}{1+\cos^2 x}\,dx$.
  31. $\displaystyle\int_{\frac{1}{8}}^{\frac{1}{3}} \frac{dx}{\sqrt{x}\sqrt{(1+x)}}$.
  32. $\displaystyle\int_0^{\pi/2} \frac{\cos x\,dx}{7+\cos 2x}$.

33. $\displaystyle\int_0^{\pi} \frac{dx}{2+\cos x}$.
  34. $\displaystyle\int_1^2 \left(\frac{x-1}{2-x}\right)^{\frac{1}{2}} dx$.

35. Show that $\displaystyle\int_0^{\pi} \frac{d\theta}{5+3\cos\theta} = \frac{\pi}{4}$. Hence, or otherwise, evaluate

$$\int_0^{\pi} \frac{(\cos\theta + 2\sin\theta)\,d\theta}{5+3\cos\theta}.$$

36. Find the indefinite integrals

(i) $\displaystyle\int \cosh^4 x\,dx$;
  (ii) $\displaystyle\int (1+x)^{-2}\sin^{-1} x\,dx$;
  (iii) $\displaystyle\int \frac{2\cos x\,dx}{\sin x - 3\cos x}$,

(iv) $\displaystyle\int \frac{(2+x)\,dx}{x\sqrt{(4-x)}}$;
  (v) $\displaystyle\int \frac{dx}{(x^2-1)\sqrt{(x^2+1)}}$;
  (vi) $\displaystyle\int \frac{dx}{(1-x)(1+x)^{\frac{1}{2}}}$;

(vii) $\displaystyle\int \frac{(x+1)\,dx}{x\sqrt{(x^2-4)}}$.

37. Evaluate the integrals

(i) $\displaystyle\int_0^a \frac{\sqrt{(ax)}}{x+a}\,dx$,
  (ii) $\displaystyle\int_0^1 \frac{e^x-1}{e^x+1}\,dx$,
  (iii) $\displaystyle\int_0^1 \frac{x\,dx}{1+\sqrt{x}}$,

(iv) $\displaystyle\int_0^{\frac{1}{2}\pi} \frac{\cos^2\theta\,d\theta}{a^2\cos^2\theta + b^2\sin^2\theta}$,
  (v) $\displaystyle\int_{\frac{1}{2}}^1 \frac{\sqrt{(1-x^2)}}{x}\,dx$,

(vi) $\displaystyle\int_1^2 \frac{\sqrt{(x^2-1)}}{x}\,dx$.

38. Show that

(i) $\displaystyle\int_{1}^{2\sqrt{2}-1} \frac{x+2}{\sqrt{(x^2+2x-3)}}\ \mathrm{d}x = 2 + \ln{(1+\sqrt{2})}.$

(ii) $\displaystyle\int_{0}^{\pi/2} \frac{\mathrm{d}x}{3\sin x + 2} = \frac{1}{\sqrt{5}}\ln\left(\frac{\sqrt{5}+1}{\sqrt{5}-1}\right).$

3 : 9 Reduction formulae

It may happen that we are unable to complete the evaluation of an integral in one operation. However, we may be able, by some means or other, to reduce the integral to a similar kind but of lower order in a parameter occurring in the integrand. This process usually but not always involves integration by parts. For example,

$$\int x^n \mathrm{e}^{ax}\ \mathrm{d}x = \int x^n\ \mathrm{d}\left(\frac{\mathrm{e}^{ax}}{a}\right) = \frac{x^n \mathrm{e}^{ax}}{a} - \left(\frac{n}{a}\right)\int x^{n-1}\mathrm{e}^{ax}\ \mathrm{d}x.$$

Denoting $\int x^n \mathrm{e}^{ax}\ \mathrm{d}x$ by I_n, this equation can be written

$$aI_n = x^n \mathrm{e}^{ax} - nI_{n-1}. \tag{3.20}$$

A relation such as (3.20) is called a *reduction formula*. If n is an integer, repeated application of eqn. (3.20) reduces I_n to the evaluation of $I_0 = \int \mathrm{e}^{ax}\ \mathrm{d}x = \mathrm{e}^{ax}/a$. In fact

$$I_n = \left\{\frac{x^n}{a} - \frac{nx^{n-1}}{a^2} + \frac{n(n-1)x^{n-2}}{a^3} - \ \cdots\ + \frac{(-1)^n n!}{a^{n+1}}\right\}\mathrm{e}^{ax}.$$

Denoting $\int_{0}^{\infty} x^n \mathrm{e}^{-x}\ \mathrm{d}x$ by J_n, eqn. (3.20) implies that, if $n \geqslant 1$,

$$J_n = nJ_{n-1} \tag{3.21}$$

since $\lim\limits_{x\to\infty} (x^n \mathrm{e}^{-x}) = 0$ and $x^n \mathrm{e}^{-x}$ vanishes when $x = 0$, provided $n > 0$. If n is an integer, successive applications of eqn. (3.21) give

$$\int_{0}^{\infty} x^n \mathrm{e}^{-x}\ \mathrm{d}x = n!. \tag{3.22}$$

We now derive the important reduction formulae for $\int \sin^n x\ \mathrm{d}x$.

Writing s for $\sin x$ and c for $\cos x$ and integrating by parts

$$\int \sin^n x \, dx = \int s^n \, dx = -\int s^{n-1} \, dc = -s^{n-1}c + \int c \, d(s^{n-1})$$
$$= -s^{n-1}c + (n-1) \int s^{n-2}c^2 \, dx$$
$$= -s^{n-1}c + (n-1) \int s^{n-2}(1-s^2) \, dx,$$

on using the relation $c^2 = 1 - s^2$. (The use of such identities is usually the key to the solution of this type of problem.) Transposing $(n-1) \int s^n \, dx$ gives finally

$$n \int \sin^n x \, dx = -\sin^{n-1} x \cos x + (n-1) \int \sin^{n-2} x \, dx. \quad (3.23)$$

Thus in one operation we have reduced the parameter n by 2. If $I_n = \int\limits_0^{\pi/2} \sin^n x \, dx$ and $n > 1$, eqn. (3.23) implies

$$I_n = \frac{n-1}{n} I_{n-2}. \quad (3.24)$$

The condition $n > 1$ is necessary since otherwise I_{n-2} becomes infinite, i.e. the integral I_{n-2} does not converge [see § 3 : 10].

Similarly $I_{n-2} = \dfrac{n-3}{n-2} I_{n-4}$ if $n > 3$, etc. In fact, if m is an integer, successive applications of eqn. (3.24) give

$$I_{2m} = \frac{(2m-1)(2m-3) \ldots 3 \times 1}{2m(2m-2) \ldots 4 \times 2} I_0$$

$$= \frac{(2m-1)(2m-3) \ldots 3 \times 1}{2m(2m-2) \ldots 4 \times 2} \frac{\pi}{2},$$

$$I_{2m+1} = \frac{2m(2m-2) \ldots 4 \times 2}{(2m+1)(2m-1) \ldots 5 \times 3} I_1$$

$$= \frac{2m(2m-2) \ldots 4 \times 2}{(2m+1)(2m-1) \ldots 5 \times 3}, \quad (3.25)$$

since $I_0 = \int\limits_0^{\pi/2} 1 \, dx = \tfrac{1}{2}\pi$ and $I_1 = \int\limits_0^{\pi/2} \sin x \, dx = 1$. The formulae (3.25) are known as *Wallis's formulae* and can be written

$$I_{2m} = \frac{(2m)! \, \pi}{2^{2m+1}(m!)^2}, \qquad I_{2m+1} = \frac{2^{2m}(m!)^2}{(2m+1)!}. \quad (3.25a)$$

Writing $a = \frac{1}{2}\pi$, $f(x) = \sin^n x$ in eqn. (3.13) gives

$$\int_0^{\pi/2} \sin^n x \, dx = \int_0^{\pi/2} \sin^n \left(\tfrac{1}{2}\pi - x\right) dx = \int_0^{\pi/2} \cos^n x \, dx. \qquad (3.26)$$

Hence, if n is an integer, $\int_0^{\pi/2} \cos^n x \, dx$ may be written down by Wallis's formulae.

Example 1. $\displaystyle\int_0^{\pi/2} \sin^2 x \, dx = \frac{1}{2} \cdot \frac{\pi}{2} = \frac{\pi}{4}$.

Example 2. $\displaystyle\int_0^{\pi/2} \cos^5 x \, dx = \frac{4 \times 2}{5 \times 3} = \frac{8}{15}$.

Example 3. $\displaystyle\int_0^{\pi/2} \cos^8 x \, dx = \frac{7 \times 5 \times 3 \times 1}{8 \times 6 \times 4 \times 2} \cdot \frac{\pi}{2} = \frac{35\pi}{256}$.

Example 4. $\displaystyle\int_0^{\infty} \frac{dx}{(a^2 + x^2)^4}$. Putting $x = a \tan \theta$ gives

$$\frac{1}{a^7} \int_0^{\pi/2} \cos^6 \theta \, d\theta = \frac{1}{a^7} \frac{5 \times 3 \times 1}{6 \times 4 \times 2} \frac{\pi}{2} = \frac{5\pi}{32a^7} .$$

Example 5. $\displaystyle\int_{\alpha}^{\infty} \frac{dx}{[(x-\alpha)^2 + \beta^2]^2}$. Putting $x - \alpha = \beta \tan \theta$ gives

$$\frac{1}{\beta^3} \int_0^{\pi/2} \cos^2 \theta \, d\theta = \frac{\pi}{4\beta^3} .$$

We now evaluate

$$I_{m,n} = \int_0^{\pi/2} \sin^m x \cos^n x \, dx.$$

$$\int \sin^m x \cos^n x \, dx = \int s^m c^n \, dx = \int s^m c^{n-1} \, ds$$
$$= s^{m+1} c^{n-1} - \int s \, d(s^m c^{n-1})$$
$$= s^{m+1} c^{n-1} - \int [m s^m c^n - (n-1) s^{m+2} c^{n-2}] \, dx$$
$$= s^{m+1} c^{n-1}$$
$$\quad - \int [m s^m c^n - (n-1) s^m (1 - c^2) c^{n-2}] \, dx$$
$$= s^{m+1} c^{n-1}$$
$$\quad - \int [(m+n-1) s^m c^n - (n-1) s^m c^{n-2}] \, dx.$$

Hence, transposing the first term inside this last integral,

$$(m+n) \int \sin^m x \cos^n x \, dx$$
$$= \sin^{m+1} x \cos^{n-1} x + (n-1) \int \sin^m x \cos^{n-2} x \, dx. \quad (3.27)$$
$$\therefore \quad (m+n) I_{m, n} = (n-1) I_{m, n-2} \quad (3.28)$$

provided $n > 1$. (This last condition ensures that $\sin^{m+1} x \cos^{n-1} x$ vanishes at $x = \pi/2$ and that $I_{m, n-2}$ converges.) When m and n are integers, eqn. (3.28) enables us to reduce the evaluation of $I_{m, n}$ to writing down $I_{m, 1}$ or $I_{m, 0}$ according as n is odd or even. But

$$I_{m, 1} = \int_0^{\pi/2} \sin^m x \cos x \, dx = \left[\frac{\sin^{m+1} x}{m+1} \right]_0^{\pi/2} = \frac{1}{m+1}, \quad (3.29)$$

and $I_{m, 0} = \int_0^{\pi/2} \sin^m x \, dx$ which may be written down by Wallis's formulae.

Example 1 (p. 131) shows that $I_{m, n} = I_{n, m}$ and hence from eqn. (3.28)

$$(m+n) I_{m, n} = (m-1) I_{m-2, n}. \quad (3.30)$$

In practice we employ the formula which reduces the lower of the two integers m and n.

Example. (i) $\displaystyle\int_0^{\pi/2} \sin^6 x \cos^4 x \, dx = \frac{3 \times 1}{10 \times 8} \int_0^{\pi/2} \sin^6 x \, dx$

$$= \frac{3 \times 1 \times 5 \times 3 \times 1}{10 \times 8 \times 6 \times 4 \times 2} \frac{\pi}{2} = \frac{3\pi}{512}.$$

(ii) $\displaystyle\int_0^{\pi/2} \sin^3 x \cos^7 x\, dx = \frac{2}{10}\int_0^{\pi/2} \sin x \cos^7 x\, dx = \frac{2}{10}\left[\frac{-\cos^8 x}{8}\right]_0^{\pi/2}$

$$= \frac{2\times 1}{10\times 8} = \frac{1}{40}.$$

(iii) $\displaystyle\int_0^a x^m(a^2-x^2)^{n/2}\, dx$.   Writing $x = a\sin\theta$ gives

$a^{m+n+1}\displaystyle\int_0^{\pi/2} \sin^m\theta\cos^{n+1}\theta\, d\theta$ which is of the above type.

(iv)   Similarly the substitution $x = a\sin^2\theta$ transforms

$\displaystyle\int_0^a x^m(a-x)^n\, dx$ into $2a^{m+n+1}\displaystyle\int_0^{\pi/2} \sin^{2m+1}\theta\cos^{2n+1}\theta\, d\theta.$

We now give illustrative examples of other types of reduction formulae.

Example 1. If $I_n = \displaystyle\int \frac{dx}{(x^3+a^3)^n}$, show that

$$3(n-1)a^3 I_n = \frac{x}{(x^3+a^3)^{n-1}} + (3n-4)I_{n-1}. \tag{1}$$

Show that $\displaystyle\int_0^\infty \frac{dx}{x^3+1} = \frac{2\pi}{3\sqrt{3}}$ and hence deduce the value of $\displaystyle\int_0^\infty \frac{dx}{(x^3+1)^n}$

for positive integer values of n.

Integrating by parts using $(x^3+a^3)^{-n}$ and x as the u and v of eqn. (3.15) gives

$$I_n = \frac{x}{(x^3+a^3)^n} - \int x\, d\left\{\frac{1}{(x^3+a^3)^n}\right\} = \frac{x}{(x^3+a^3)^n} + \int \frac{3nx^3\, dx}{(x^3+a^3)^{n+1}}.$$

Writing the numerator of this final integrand as $3n[(x^3+a^3)-a^3]$ we find

$$I_n = \frac{x}{(x^3+a^3)^n} + 3n\int \frac{dx}{(x^3+a^3)^n} - 3na^3\int \frac{dx}{(x^3+a^3)^{n+1}},$$

i.e. $\displaystyle I_n = \frac{x}{(x^3+a^3)^n} + 3nI_n - 3na^3 I_{n+1},$

or $\displaystyle 3na^3 I_{n+1} = \frac{x}{(x^3+a^3)^n} + (3n-1)I_n.$

Writing $n-1$ for n gives the required formula.

This example illustrates two features of common occurrence in the derivation of reduction formulae. Firstly, rewriting the term x^3 in the numerator of the integrand after integration by parts in the form $(x^3+a^3-a^3)$ enables us to recover the form of the original integral. Secondly, we derive a relation between I_n and I_{n+1} which is equivalent to the required result.

A simple but artificial method of deriving reduction formulae involving *indefinite* integrals lies in differentiation of the term not included within integral signs followed by rearrangement and integration. For the example given above,

$$\frac{d}{dx}\left\{\frac{x}{(x^3+a^3)^{n-1}}\right\} = \frac{1}{(x^3+a^3)^{n-1}} - \frac{3(n-1)x^3}{(x^3+a^3)^n}$$

$$= \frac{1}{(x^3+a^3)^{n-1}} - \frac{3(n-1)\left[(x^3+a^3)-a^3\right]}{(x^3+a^3)^n}.$$

$$\therefore \frac{d}{dx}\left\{\frac{x}{(x^3+a^3)^{n-1}}\right\} = \frac{3(n-1)a^3}{(x^3+a^3)^n} - \frac{(3n-4)}{(x^3+a^3)^{n-1}}.$$

Integrating this equation w.r. to x gives

$$\frac{x}{(x^3+a^3)^{n-1}} = 3(n-1)a^3 \int \frac{dx}{(x^3+a^3)^n} - (3n-4) \int \frac{dx}{(x^3+a^3)^{n-1}}$$

which gives the required relation.

Using the identity $(x^3+1) \equiv (x+1)(x^2-x+1)$ to express $(x^3+1)^{-1}$ in partial fractions we have

$$\int_0^\infty \frac{dx}{x^3+1} = \frac{1}{3}\int_0^\infty \left\{\frac{1}{x+1} - \frac{(x-2)}{x^2-x+1}\right\} dx$$

$$= \lim_{X \to \infty} \frac{1}{3}\left[\ln(x+1) - \frac{1}{2}\ln(x^2-x+1) + \sqrt{3}\tan^{-1}\left(\frac{2x-1}{\sqrt{3}}\right)\right]_0^X$$

$$= \lim_{X \to \infty}\left[\frac{1}{6}\ln\left\{\frac{(X+1)^2}{X^2-X+1}\right\} + \frac{1}{\sqrt{3}}\tan^{-1}\left(\frac{2X-1}{\sqrt{3}}\right) - \frac{1}{\sqrt{3}}\tan^{-1}\left(-\frac{1}{\sqrt{3}}\right)\right]$$

$$= 0 + \frac{1}{\sqrt{3}}\frac{\pi}{2} - \frac{1}{\sqrt{3}}\left(-\frac{\pi}{6}\right) = \frac{2\pi}{3\sqrt{3}}.$$

Writing $J_n = \int_0^\infty \frac{dx}{(x^3+1)^n}$ and using eqn. (1) with $a=1$ and n an integer we find

$$J_n = \frac{(3n-4)}{3(n-1)} J_{n-1} \quad \text{for} \quad n > 1. \tag{2}$$

[The condition $n > 1$ is required in order that the integral J_{n-1} should converge at the upper limit. See § 3 : 10.] Successive applications of formula (2) give

$$J_n = \frac{(3n-4)(3n-7)\dots 5.2}{3^{n-1}(n-1)!} J_1.$$

But $J_1 = 2\pi/(3\sqrt{3})$, proved above, and hence

$$\int_0^\infty \frac{dx}{(x^3+1)^n} = \frac{2(3n-4)(3n-7)\dots 5.2.\pi}{3^n(n-1)!\sqrt{3}}.$$

Example 2. Prove that $\dfrac{d^2}{dx^2} \sin^n x + n^2 \sin^n x = n(n-1) \sin^{n-2} x$, where n is

any constant. If $I_n = \displaystyle\int_0^{\pi} e^{-x} \sin^n x \, dx$, show that $I_n = \dfrac{n(n-1)}{n^2+1} I_{n-2}$ where n

is an integer $\geqslant 2$. Show that $I_6 = \dfrac{144}{629} (1-e^{-\pi})$.

$$\frac{d^2}{dx^2} \sin^n x = \frac{d}{dx} (n \sin^{n-1} x \cos x)$$

$$= n(n-1) \sin^{n-2} x \cos^2 x - n \sin^n x$$

$$= n(n-1) \sin^{n-2} x (1 - \sin^2 x) - n \sin^n x.$$

$$\therefore \quad \frac{d^2}{dx^2} \sin^n x + n^2 \sin^n x = n(n-1) \sin^{n-2} x. \tag{1}$$

$$\int e^{-x} \sin^n x \, dx = - \int \sin^n x \, d(e^{-x})$$

$$= -e^{-x} \sin^n x + \int e^{-x} \frac{d}{dx} (\sin^n x) \, dx$$

$$= -e^{-x} \sin^n x - \int \frac{d}{dx} (\sin^n x) \, d(e^{-x})$$

$$= -e^{-x} \sin^n x - e^{-x} \frac{d}{dx} (\sin^n x) + \int e^{-x} \frac{d^2}{dx^2} (\sin^n x) \, dx.$$

Therefore, using eqn. (1)

$$\int e^{-x} \sin^n x \, dx = -e^{-x}(\sin^n x + n \sin^{n-1} x \cos x)$$
$$+ \int e^{-x}[n(n-1) \sin^{n-2} x - n^2 \sin^n x] \, dx.$$

$$\therefore \quad (n^2+1) \int e^{-x} \sin^n x \, dx = -e^{-x}(\sin^n x + n \sin^{n-1} x \cos x)$$
$$+ n(n-1) \int e^{-x} \sin^{n-2} x \, dx.$$

$$\therefore \quad (n^2+1) I_n = n(n-1) I_{n-2}, \quad \text{if} \quad n \geqslant 2.$$

$$I_6 = \frac{6 \times 5}{(6^2+1)} I_4, \quad I_4 = \frac{4 \times 3}{(4^2+1)} I_2,$$

$$I_2 = \frac{2 \times 1}{(2^2+1)} I_0,$$

$$I_0 = \int_0^{\pi} e^{-x} \, dx = \left[-e^{-x} \right]_0^{\pi} = 1 - e^{-\pi}.$$

$$\therefore \quad I_6 = \frac{6!(1-e^{-\pi})}{(6^2+1)(4^2+1)(2^2+1)} = \frac{144}{629} (1-e^{-\pi}).$$

Exercises 3 : 9

1. Evaluate the following integrals:

(i) $\int_0^{\pi/2} \sin^{10} x \, dx$,   (ii) $\int_0^{\pi/2} \cos^{11} x \, dx$,   (iii) $\int_0^{\pi/2} \sin^8 x \cos^5 x \, dx$

(iv) $\int_0^{\pi/2} \sin^5 x \cos^5 x \, dx$,   (v) $\int_0^{\pi/2} \sin^4 x \cos^{11} x \, dx$,   (vi) $\int_0^1 x^2(1-x)^{\frac{3}{2}} \, dx$,

(vii) $\int_0^1 x^2(1-x^2)^{\frac{3}{2}} \, dx$,   (viii) $\int_{-1}^1 (1+x)^6 (1-x)^2 \, dx$ (put $1+x = 2\cos^2 \theta$),

(ix) $\int_a^b x^2 \sqrt{\{(x-a)(b-x)\}} \, dx$,   where $0 < a < b$.

2. If $I_n = \int \tan^n \theta \, d\theta$ show that $(n-1)[I_n + I_{n-2}] = \tan^{n-1}\theta$, and evaluate $\int_0^{\pi/4} (\tan^5 \theta - \tan^6 \theta) \, d\theta$.

3. If $I_n = \int \sec^n \theta \, d\theta$, show that, when $n \geqslant 1$,
$$(n-1)I_n = \sec^{n-2}\theta \tan \theta + (n-2)I_{n-2}.$$

Show that $8\int_0^{\pi/4} \sec^5 \theta \, d\theta = 7\sqrt{2} + 3\ln(1+\sqrt{2})$ and evaluate $\int_0^a \dfrac{dx}{(2a^2-x^2)^3}$.

4. If $u_n = \int x^n \cos x \, dx$ and $v_n = \int x^n \sin x \, dx$ prove $u_n = x^n \sin x - nv_{n-1}$ and $v_n = -x^n \cos x + nu_{n-1}$. Hence find u_3 and v_5.

5. By differentiating $\dfrac{\sin \theta \cos \theta}{(1+\sin^2 \theta)^n}$ with respect to θ, and expressing the result in powers of y where $y = 1 + \sin^2 \theta$, or otherwise, show that if
$$I_n = \int_0^{\pi/2} \frac{d\theta}{(1+\sin^2 \theta)^n},$$

then
$$4nI_{n+1} = (6n-3)I_n - 2(n-1)I_{n-1}.$$

Show that $I_1 = \dfrac{\pi}{2\sqrt{2}}$, and hence that $I_2 = \dfrac{3\pi}{8\sqrt{2}}$.

6. If $I_n = \int x^{a-1}(\ln x)^n \, dx$, where $a \neq 0$, find a reduction formula giving I_n in terms of I_{n-1}. Hence show that
$$\int_1^e x^{a-1}(\ln x)^n \, dx = \frac{(-1)^n e^a n!}{a^{n+1}} \left\{ 1 - \frac{a}{1!} + \frac{a^2}{2!} - \frac{a^3}{3!} + \right.$$
$$\left. \cdots + \frac{(-1)^n a^n}{n!} \right\} - \frac{(-1)^n n!}{a^{n+1}}.$$

7. If $V_n = \int\limits_0^x \dfrac{\mathrm{d}t}{(t^2+a^2)^n}$ and $W_{m,n} = \int\limits_0^x \dfrac{t^m\,\mathrm{d}t}{(t^2+a^2)^n}$,

where m, n are positive integers, obtain the reduction formulae

$$V_{n+1} = \frac{1}{2na^2}\,\frac{x}{(x^2+a^2)^n} + \frac{2n-1}{2na^2}\,V_n,$$

$$W_{m,n} = -\frac{1}{2(n-1)}\,\frac{x^{m-1}}{(x^2+a^2)^{n-1}} + \frac{m-1}{2(n-1)}\,W_{m-2,\,n-1}.$$

Evaluate $W_{4,\,4}$.

8. If $I_n = \int\limits_0^x \dfrac{t^n}{\sqrt{(1+t+t^2)}}\,\mathrm{d}t$, prove that

$$(n+1)I_{n+1}+(n+\tfrac{1}{2})I_n+nI_{n-1} = x^n\sqrt{(1+x+x^2)}.$$

Hence, or otherwise, prove that

$$\int\limits_0^1 \frac{x^3}{\sqrt{(1+x+x^2)}}\,\mathrm{d}x = \frac{\left\{21\ln\left(1+\dfrac{2\sqrt{3}}{3}\right)-2(3\sqrt{3}-1)\right\}}{48}.$$

9. If $I_{m,n} = \int \cos^m x \sin nx\,\mathrm{d}x$, prove that

$$(m+n)\,I_{m,n} = -\cos^m x \cos nx + mI_{m-1,\,n-1}.$$

Hence, or otherwise, prove that

$$\int\limits_0^{\pi/4} \cos^2 x \sin 4x\,\mathrm{d}x = \frac{5}{12}.$$

10. Obtain the reduction formula for

(a) $I_n = \int (\ln x)^n\,\mathrm{d}x$ and   (b) $J_n = \int \sec^n x\,\mathrm{d}x$.

Find I_3 and J_5.

11. If $I_n = \int x^n(x^2+c^2)^{-1/2}\,\mathrm{d}x$, where $n > 1$, prove the relation

$$nI_n+(n-1)\,c^2I_{n-2} = x^{n-1}(x^2+c^2)^{\frac{1}{2}}.$$

Hence, or otherwise, evaluate

$$\int\limits_0^c \frac{x^4\,\mathrm{d}x}{\sqrt{(x^2+c^2)}}.$$

12. If $I_n = \int\limits_0^2 (2-x)^n \sin x\,\mathrm{d}x$, show that for $n \geqslant 2$,

$$I_n+n(n-1)I_{n-2}-2^n = 0.$$

Evaluate I_4.

13. Find a reduction formula for

$$I_n = \int \frac{dx}{(5+4\cos x)^n}$$

in terms of I_{n-1} and I_{n-2} ($n \geqslant 2$), and use it to show that

$$\int\limits_0^{2\pi/3} \frac{dx}{(5+4\cos x)^2} = \frac{1}{81}(5\pi - 6\sqrt{3}).$$

14. If

$$J_n = \int\limits_a^b \frac{x^n \, dx}{\sqrt{\{(b-x)(x-a)\}}},$$

where $b > a$, $n \geqslant 0$, show that

$$2J_1 = (a+b)J_0,$$
$$2nJ_n = (2n-1)(a+b)J_{n-1} - 2(n-1)abJ_{n-2}, \qquad (n \geqslant 2).$$

Evaluate

$$\int\limits_{-1}^2 \frac{x^3 \, dx}{\sqrt{\{2+x-x^2\}}}.$$

3:10 The convergence of integrals

Thus far, in order to obtain $\int\limits_a^b f(x)\, dx$ we have assumed that the function $f(x)$ is finite for all values of x in the range $a \leqslant x \leqslant b$.

We defined $\int\limits_a^\infty f(x)\, dx$ as $\lim\limits_{t\to\infty} \int\limits_a^t f(x)\, dx$. The existence of the infinite integral thus defined is dependent upon the existence of the limit. If this limit exists, the integral is said to *converge*.

Thus $\int\limits_0^\infty \frac{dx}{1+x}$ does not exist because $\lim\limits_{t\to\infty} \ln(1+t)$ is not finite.

But

$$\int\limits_0^\infty \frac{dx}{(1+x)^{\frac{3}{2}}} = \lim\limits_{t\to\infty} \int\limits_0^t \frac{dx}{(1+x)^{\frac{3}{2}}} = \lim\limits_{t\to\infty} \int\limits_1^{t+1} \frac{dy}{y^{\frac{3}{2}}}$$

$$= \lim\limits_{t\to\infty} \left[-2y^{-\frac{1}{2}} \right]_1^{t+1} = \lim\limits_{t\to\infty} \left[-2(t+1)^{-\frac{1}{2}} + 2 \right] = 2$$

and hence

$$\int_0^\infty \frac{dx}{(1+x)^{\frac{3}{2}}}$$ converges to the value 2.

The graph of $f(x) = (1+x)^{-\frac{3}{2}}$ is shown in Fig. 3.4 (a) and the graph of $f(x) = (1+x)^{-1}$ is shown in Fig. 3.4 (b). In each case the shaded area is equal to $\int_0^t f(x)\,dx$ for the function concerned. In

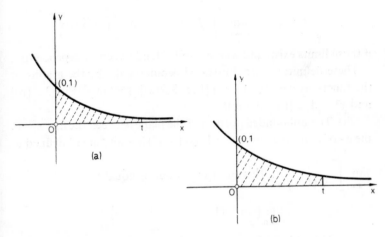

Fig. 3.4. (a) The graph of $y = (1+x)^{-\frac{3}{2}}$. (b) The graph of $y = (1+x)^{-1}$.

the first case there is a limiting value to this area as $t \to \infty$ and $\int_0^\infty f(x)\,dx$ is *defined* as the area of the unbounded portion of the plane between the curve, the x-axis and the line $x = 0$.

In the second case $\int_0^t f(x)\,dx$ has no finite limit and the unbounded portion of the plane between the curve, the x-axis and the line $x = 0$ has no finite "area" as defined above.

Now consider $\int_a^b f(x)\,dx$, where $f(x) \to \infty$ as $x \to b$. If $\varepsilon > 0$ and

$\lim\limits_{\varepsilon \to 0} \int\limits_{a}^{b-\varepsilon} f(x) \, dx$ is finite and equal to L (say), then we *define* L as

the value of $\int\limits_{a}^{b} f(x) \, dx$. Similarly, if $\varphi(x) \to \infty$ as $x \to a$ and

$\lim\limits_{\varepsilon \to 0} \int\limits_{a+\varepsilon}^{b} \varphi(x) \, dx = L'$, then L' is defined as the value of

$\int\limits_{a}^{b} \varphi(x) \, dx$. If $f(x) \to \infty$ as $x \to c$, where $a < c < b$ and $f(x)$ is

finite and continuous for all other values of x in the given range,
then by definition

$$\int\limits_{a}^{b} f(x) \, dx = \lim_{\varepsilon \to 0} \int\limits_{a}^{c-\varepsilon} f(x) \, dx + \lim_{\varepsilon' \to 0} \int\limits_{c+\varepsilon'}^{b} f(x) \, dx$$

if those limits exist, and where ε and ε' tend to zero independently.

These definitions are illustrated geometrically by the graphs of
the functions $y = 1/\sqrt{(1-x^2)}$ [Fig. 3.5 (a)], $y = \tan x$ [Fig. 3.5 (b)]
and $y^3 = 1/x$ [Fig. 3.5 (c)].

(a) The unbounded portion of the plane between the line $x = 0$,
the x-axis and the curve $y = 1/\sqrt{(1-x^2)}$ has an "area" defined as

$$\lim_{\varepsilon \to 0} \int\limits_{0}^{1-\varepsilon} \frac{dx}{\sqrt{(1-x^2)}} \, .$$ This limit exists and is equal to

$$\lim_{\varepsilon \to 0} [\sin^{-1}(1-\varepsilon) - \sin^{-1} 0] = \tfrac{1}{2}\pi.$$

(b) The unbounded portion of the plane between the curve
$y = \tan x$, the x-axis and the line $x = \tfrac{1}{2}\pi$ has no finite "area" as
thus defined because $\int \tan x \, dx = \ln \sec x$ and $\lim\limits_{\varepsilon \to 0} \ln \sec \left(\tfrac{1}{2}\pi - \varepsilon\right)$
is not finite.

(c) The unbounded portion of the plane between the curve
$y^3 = 1/x$, the x-axis and the lines $x = -1$ and $x = +1$ has an
"area" defined as

$$\lim_{\varepsilon \to 0} \int\limits_{-1}^{0-\varepsilon} x^{-\frac{1}{3}} \, dx + \lim_{\varepsilon' \to 0} \int\limits_{0+\varepsilon'}^{1} x^{-\frac{1}{3}} \, dx$$

$$= \lim_{\varepsilon \to 0} \left[\frac{3}{2} x^{\frac{2}{3}} \right]_{-1}^{0-\varepsilon} + \lim_{\varepsilon' \to 0} \left[\frac{3}{2} x^{\frac{2}{3}} \right]_{0+\varepsilon'}^{1} = -\frac{3}{2} + \frac{3}{2} = 0.$$

The area in the positive quadrant is $\frac{3}{2}$ sq. units.

If $I = \int\limits_a^\infty f(x)\,\mathrm{d}x$ and if the integral $\int\limits_a^\infty |f(x)|\,\mathrm{d}x$ is convergent,

then I is said to be *absolutely convergent*. It can be proved that an absolutely convergent integral is convergent. If I is convergent but not absolutely convergent it is said to be *conditionally convergent*.

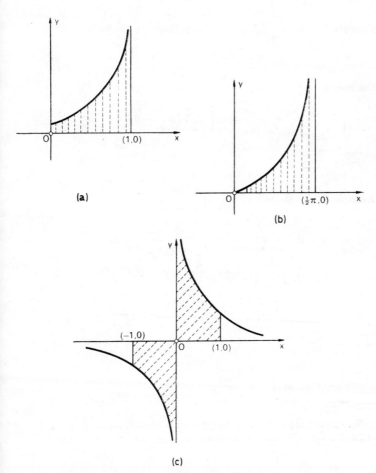

FIG. 3.5. (a) The graph of $y = 1/\sqrt{(1-x^2)}$. (b) The graph of $y = \tan x$. (c) The graph of $y^3 = 1/x$.

Example 1. $\int_0^\infty \cosh x \, dx$ does not exist because $\lim\limits_{t \to \infty} [\sinh t]$ is not finite.

Example 2. $\quad \int_0^\infty \dfrac{dx}{1+x^2} = \lim\limits_{t \to \infty} \left[\tan^{-1} t - \tan^{-1} 0\right] = \dfrac{1}{2} \pi.$

Example 3. $\quad \int_0^a \dfrac{dx}{(x-a)^2}$ does not exist because $\lim\limits_{\varepsilon \to 0} \dfrac{1}{\varepsilon}$ is not finite.

Example 4.

$$\int_0^2 \frac{dx}{(4x-x^2)^{\frac{1}{2}}} = \lim_{\varepsilon \to 0} \left[\sin^{-1}\left(\frac{x-2}{2}\right)\right]_{0+\varepsilon}^2 = 0 - \left(-\frac{1}{2}\pi\right) = \frac{1}{2}\pi.$$

Example 5. Evaluate $I = \int_0^1 \sqrt{\left(\dfrac{1+x}{1-x}\right)} \, dx.$

$$\int \sqrt{\left(\frac{1+x}{1-x}\right)} \, dx = \int \frac{1+x}{\sqrt{(1-x^2)}} \, dx$$

$$= -\frac{1}{2} \int \frac{-2x \, dx}{\sqrt{(1-x^2)}} + \int \frac{dx}{\sqrt{(1-x^2)}} = -\sqrt{(1-x^2)} + \sin^{-1} x.$$

$$\therefore \ I = \lim_{\varepsilon \to 0} \left[\sin^{-1} x - \sqrt{(1-x^2)}\right]_0^{1-\varepsilon}$$

$$= \tfrac{1}{2}\pi - (-1) = \tfrac{1}{2}\pi + 1.$$

Example 6. Evaluate $I = \int_0^\infty \dfrac{dx}{(1+x^2)^2}.$

We can use the method of substitution with such a definite integral provided that the substitution is a valid one.

Let $\qquad\qquad\qquad I_1 = \int_0^t \dfrac{dx}{(1+x^2)^2}.$

Put $x = \tan\theta$. Then $dx/d\theta = \sec^2\theta$ and θ increases continuously from 0 to $\tan^{-1} t$ as x increases from 0 to t.

Then
$$I_1 = \int_0^{\tan^{-1} t} \cos^2\theta \; d\theta = \left[\frac{1}{2}\theta + \frac{1}{4}\sin 2\theta\right]_0^{\tan^{-1} t}$$

$$\therefore \; I = \lim_{\theta \to \pi/2}\left[\frac{1}{2}\theta + \frac{1}{4}\sin 2\theta\right] = \frac{\pi}{4}.$$

Example 7. Consider $J = \int_a^\infty x^{-k} f(x)\,dx$ where $f(x)$ is finite for all x. The condition on $f(x)$ implies that $|f(x)| < M$ where M is a constant, so that, for $a > 0$,

$$\int_a^\infty \left|\frac{f(x)}{x^k}\right|\,dx < \int_a^\infty \frac{M\,dx}{x^k}.$$

If $k > 1$, $I = \int_a^\infty \frac{dx}{x^k} = \frac{1}{(k-1)a^{k-1}}$, but I diverges for other values of k. Hence J is absolutely convergent if $k > 1$. For example, $\int_\pi^\infty \frac{\sin x}{x^2}\,dx$ is absolutely convergent and therefore convergent; but it can be shown that $\int_\pi^\infty \frac{\sin x\,dx}{x}$ is conditionally convergent only.

Example 8. Show that $\int_a^\infty x^k e^{-x}\,dx$, where $a > 0$, converges for all k.

Since $\lim_{x \to \infty} x^n e^{-x} = 0$ (§ 2 : 4), for sufficiently large values of x, $x^{k+2}e^{-x} < 1$ (choosing $n = k+2$).

$$\therefore \; x^k e^{-x} < x^{-2}$$

for sufficiently large values of x, and, by Example 7 above, the required result follows.

Example 9. If $f(x) = O(1)$ for $a \leqslant x \leqslant b$, then $\int_a^b \frac{f(x)\,dx}{(|x-c|)^\alpha}$ is convergent if $\alpha < 1$. It may happen that

$$I(\varepsilon, \varepsilon') = \left(\int_a^{c-\varepsilon} + \int_{c+\varepsilon'}^b\right)\frac{f(x)\,dx}{(|x-c|)^\alpha}$$

tends to a unique limit only if $\varepsilon' = \varepsilon$; this limit is called the *principal value* of the integral. In illustration we consider the integral $\displaystyle\int_{-1}^{2} \frac{dx}{x^3}$.

The integrand tends to infinity at the point $x = 0$ in the range of integration. In this case

$$I(\varepsilon, \varepsilon') = \int_{-1}^{-\varepsilon} \frac{dx}{x^3} + \int_{\varepsilon'}^{2} \frac{dx}{x^3} = -\frac{1}{2\varepsilon^2} + \frac{1}{2} - \frac{1}{8} + \frac{1}{2\varepsilon'^2} = \frac{3}{8} - \frac{1}{2\varepsilon^2} + \frac{1}{2\varepsilon'^2}.$$

f ε, ε' tend to zero independently, $I(\varepsilon, \varepsilon')$ does not tend to a limit. But, if $\varepsilon = \varepsilon'$, $I(\varepsilon, \varepsilon) = 3/8$. Therefore the principal value of $\displaystyle\int_{-1}^{2} \frac{dx}{x^3}$ is 3/8.

Exercises 3 : 10

1. Verify the results stated for the convergence of the following integrals:

(i) $\displaystyle\int_{0}^{1} \frac{dx}{x^n}$　　(converges if $n < 1$, diverges if $n \geqslant 1$),

(ii) $\displaystyle\int_{1}^{\infty} \frac{dx}{x^n}$　　(converges if $n > 1$, diverges if $n \leqslant 1$),

(iii) $\displaystyle\int_{0}^{\infty} \frac{dx}{x^n}$ (diverges for all n),　(vii) $\displaystyle\int_{0}^{\infty} \frac{x \ln x \, dx}{(1+x^3)}$　　(convergent),

(iv) $\displaystyle\int_{0}^{\infty} \frac{dx}{(1+x^2)^2}$ (convergent),　(viii) $\displaystyle\int_{0}^{1} \frac{dx}{e^x - 1}$　　(divergent),

(v) $\displaystyle\int_{1}^{\infty} \frac{dx}{x(1+x)}$ (convergent),　　(ix) $\displaystyle\int_{1}^{3} \frac{dx}{x(2-x)^{\frac{1}{3}}}$　　(convergent),

(vi) $\displaystyle\int_{0}^{1} \frac{dx}{x(1+x)}$　　(divergent),　　(x) $\displaystyle\int_{a}^{b} \frac{dx}{\{(x-a)(b-x)^2\}^{\frac{1}{3}}}$ (convergent),

(xi) $\displaystyle\int_{0}^{1} x^m(1-x)^n \, dx$　　(convergent if $m > -1$ and $n > -1$).

2. Show that

$$\int_0^\infty \frac{x \, dx}{(1+x^2)(4+x^2)} = \frac{1}{3} \ln 2.$$

3. Prove that $\int_1^\infty \frac{(x^2+2) \, dx}{x^2(x^2+1)} = 2 - \frac{1}{4}\pi.$

4. Show that $\int_0^1 \frac{dx}{(1+x)\sqrt{(1-x^2)}} = 1.$

Discuss the existence of each of the integrals in nos. 5–10 and, where possible, evaluate the integral.

5. $\int_0^\infty \frac{dx}{4+9x^2}$ **6.** $\int_0^4 \sqrt{\left(\frac{x}{4-x}\right)} \, dx$ **7.** $\int_1^4 \frac{dx}{\sqrt{\{(x-1)(4-x)\}}}.$

8. $\int_0^1 x^2 \ln x \, dx.$ (Prove and use the result $\lim_{x \to 0+} x^n \ln x = 0$ if $n > 0$.)

9. $\int_0^\infty x e^{-x} \, dx.$ **10.** $\int_0^\infty \frac{dx}{1+2\cosh x}.$

11. Evaluate

(i) $\int_0^\infty \frac{x \tan^{-1} x}{(1+x^2)^2} \, dx,$ (ii) $\int_1^\infty \frac{dx}{x^2(a^2+x^2)^{\frac{1}{2}}},$ (iii) $\int_0^\infty \frac{dx}{\cosh^3 x},$

(iv) $\int_0^\infty \frac{dx}{1+e^{2x}},$ (v) $\int_0^\infty e^{-ax} \sin x \, dx$ $(a > 0).$

12. Evaluate $\int \frac{dx}{\sinh x}.$

Find $\lim_{k \to \infty} k e^k \int_1^\infty \frac{dx}{\sinh (kx)}.$

$\left[\text{Hint: See p. 269, for the expansion of } \ln \left(\frac{1-x}{1+x}\right).\right]$

13. If $F(m, n) = \int_1^\infty (x-1)^m x^{-n} \, dx,$ where m and n are positive integers satisfying $n > m+2$, find relations between $F(m, n-1)$ and $F(m, n)$, and between $F(m-1, n)$ and $F(m, n)$.

Hence find the value of $F(m, n).$

14. Prove

$$\int\limits_1^\infty \frac{\ln x}{x^m}\,\mathrm{d}x = \frac{1}{(m-1)^2}\,,$$

when m is an integer $\geqslant 2$.

Evaluate

$$I_{n,\,m} = \int\limits_1^\infty \frac{(\ln x)^n}{x^m}\,\mathrm{d}x$$

when m and n are integers, $m > 1$, $n > 0$. Discuss the case $m = 1$.

3 : 11 Functions defined by integrals

We now amplify the concept that functions may be defined by means of definite integrals. In general, two distinct types of definition of a function arise according as the argument of the function occurs in the limits of integration or as part of the integrand.

1. The *error function*, erf x, is defined by

$$\operatorname{erf} x = \frac{2}{\sqrt\pi} \int\limits_0^x \mathrm{e}^{-t^2}\,\mathrm{d}t. \tag{3.31}$$

[See also Vol. 2, § 6 : 6.] The indefinite integral $\int \mathrm{e}^{-t^2}\,\mathrm{d}t$ cannot be evaluated in closed form, i.e. in terms of a finite number of the elementary functions introduced in Chapter II. However, various methods of numerical integration, see § 6 : 9, have been used to tabulate erf x. This function is of importance in statistics, see § 8 : 5, and diffusion problems.

2. The *gamma function* $\Gamma(x)$ is defined by

$$\Gamma(x) = \int\limits_0^\infty t^{x-1}\mathrm{e}^{-t}\,\mathrm{d}t \quad \text{for} \quad x > 0. \tag{3.32}$$

The condition $x > 0$ is required for the integral to converge at the lower limit. [Near $x = 0$, the integral for $\Gamma(x)$ behaves like

$\int_0^a t^{x-1} \, dt$ where $a > 0$. But

$$\int_0^a t^{x-1} \, dt = \lim_{\varepsilon \to 0} \frac{a^x - \varepsilon^x}{x} \quad \text{when} \quad x \neq 0,$$

$$= \lim_{\varepsilon \to 0} \ln(a/\varepsilon) \quad \text{when} \quad x = 0,$$

and therefore tends to a finite limit only when $x > 0$.] This integral for $\Gamma(x)$ always converges at the upper limit, and in fact eqn. (3.22) shows that, when x is an integer,

$$\Gamma(x) = (x-1)!. \tag{3.33}$$

The factorial function $x!$ is *defined* for all $x > -1$ by the equation

$$x! = \Gamma(x+1) = \int_0^\infty t^x \, e^{-t} \, dt \tag{3.34}$$

and, since $n! = n(n-1) \ldots 2.1$ when n is an integer, is a generalisation of the elementary definition of the factorial expression.

This concept of generalising an elementary idea occurs frequently in mathematics but any such generalisation must contain the elementary idea as a special case.

3. *The Laplace transform.* We define the Laplace transform, $L\{f(t)\}$, of a function $f(t)$ as the function $F(p)$ given by the equation

$$L\{f(t)\} = F(p) = \int_0^\infty e^{-pt} f(t) \, dt. \tag{3.35}$$

At this stage we take p to be real and positive and assume that the definite integral in eqn. (3.35) converges. [The integral in eqn. (3.35) converges if $f(t) = O(e^{ct})$ as $t \to \infty$, and $p > c$ where c is a real number, i.e. the Laplace transform of $f(t)$ exists if $f(t)$ is of "exponential order". In fact, by making p sufficiently large, the Laplace transform of $g(t)$ exists provided that $e^{-pt} g(t) = O(e^{-at})$, where $a > 0$, for large t.] Note that from a function $f(t)$ of the variable t we obtain, by applying the Laplace transformation, a new function $F(p)$ of p, which is the Laplace transform of $f(t)$.

Example 1. $\quad L\{1\} = \int_0^\infty e^{-pt} \, dt = \left[-\frac{1}{p} e^{-pt} \right]_0^\infty = \frac{1}{p}.$

Example 2.
$$L\{e^{-at}\} = \int\limits_0^\infty e^{-pt} e^{-at}\, dt = \int\limits_0^\infty e^{-(p+a)t}\, dt$$

$$= \left[-\frac{1}{(p+a)}\, e^{-(p+a)t} \right]_0^\infty = \frac{1}{p+a}, \quad p+a > 0.$$

Example 3.
$$L\{\sin \omega t\} = \int\limits_0^\infty e^{-pt} \sin \omega t\, dt$$

$$= \left[\frac{-e^{-pt}(p \sin \omega t + \omega \cos \omega t)}{p^2+\omega^2} \right]_0^\infty = \frac{\omega}{p^2+\omega^2}.$$

Example 4.
$$L\{\cos \omega t\} = \int\limits_0^\infty e^{-pt} \cos \omega t\, dt$$

$$= \left[\frac{e^{-pt}(\omega \sin \omega t - p \cos \omega t)}{p^2+\omega^2} \right]_0^\infty = \frac{p}{p^2+\omega^2}.$$

We give below two illustrative examples of functions defined by special relations.

Example 1. It is given that, for all x, y,

$$f(x)f(y) = f(x+y),$$

where $f(x)$ is differentiable and $f(0) \neq 0$. Write down the results of differentiating the above identity partially with respect to x and y, and deduce that $f(x) = e^{ax}$, where a is a constant.

Differentiating partially w.r. to x and y in turn, we obtain

$$f'(x)f(y) = f'(x+y), \quad f(x)f'(y) = f'(x+y).$$

By division we find

$$\frac{f'(x)}{f(x)} = \frac{f'(y)}{f(y)}.$$

Putting $y = 0$ in this relation we have $\dfrac{f'(x)}{f(x)} = \text{constant} = a$, say.

Hence
$$f(x) = Ae^{ax},$$

where A is a second constant. Substitution in the original equation now gives $A^2 = A$ so that $A = 0$ or 1. But $f(0) \neq 0$, i.e. $A \neq 0$, and hence $f(x) = e^{ax}$. These results include the special case $a = 0$.]

Example 2. Assuming that the functions $\theta(x)$, $\phi(x)$ can be defined uniquely by the equations

$$\theta''(x) = \theta(x), \qquad \theta(0) = 0, \qquad \theta'(0) = 1, \tag{1}$$

$$\phi''(x) = \phi(x), \qquad \phi(0) = 1, \qquad \phi'(0) = 0, \tag{2}$$

and without assuming the properties of the exponential or hyperbolic functions, prove that

(i) $\theta'(x) = \phi(x)$ and $\phi'(x) = \theta(x)$,

(ii) $\phi^2(x) - \theta^2(x)$ is constant,

(iii) $\phi(x)\phi(a-x) + \theta(x)\theta(a-x)$ is independent of x,

(iv) $\phi(x+y) = \phi(x)\phi(y) + \theta(x)\theta(y)$.

Multiplying eqns. (1) and (2) by $\theta'(x)$, $\phi'(x)$ respectively and and integrating w.r. to x from 0 to x, we find

$$\{\theta'(x)\}^2 = \{\theta(x)\}^2 + 1, \tag{3}$$

$$\{\phi'(x)\}^2 = \{\phi(x)\}^2 - 1, \tag{4}$$

so that
$$\{\theta'(x)\}^2 + \{\phi'(x)\}^2 = \{\theta(x)\}^2 + \{\phi(x)\}^2. \tag{5}$$

Again, multiplying eqns. (1) and (2) by $\phi'(x)$, $\theta'(x)$ respectively, adding and integrating over the same range as before we have

$$\int_0^x \{\theta''(x)\,\phi'(x) + \theta'(x)\,\phi''(x)\}\ \mathrm{d}x = \int_0^x \{\theta(x)\,\phi'(x) + \theta'(x)\,\phi(x)\}\ \mathrm{d}x,$$

i.e.
$$\left[\theta'(x)\phi'(x)\right]_0^x = \left[\theta(x)\phi(x)\right]_0^x,$$

which gives
$$\theta'(x)\phi'(x) = \theta(x)\phi(x). \tag{6}$$

From eqns. (5) and (6),

$$\{\theta'(x) \pm \phi'(x)\}^2 = \{\theta(x) \pm \phi(x)\}^2 .$$

Taking square roots of these equations we have

$$\theta'(x) + \phi'(x) = \theta(x) + \phi(x), \tag{7}$$

$$\theta'(x) - \phi'(x) = -\theta(x) + \phi(x), \tag{8}$$

the ambiguities of sign on taking the square roots having been resolved by considering the case where $x = 0$. From eqns. (7) and (8) we obtain results (i).

Result (ii) follows at once on replacing $\theta'(x)$ in eqn. (3) by $\phi(x)$.

Since

$$\frac{\mathrm{d}}{\mathrm{d}x}\{\phi(x)\,\phi(a-x) + \theta(x)\,\theta(a-x)\}$$

$$= \phi'(x)\phi(a-x) - \phi(x)\phi'(a-x) + \theta'(x)\theta(a-x) - \theta(x)\theta'(a-x)$$

$$= \theta(x)\phi(a-x) - \phi(x)\theta(a-x) + \phi(x)\theta(a-x) - \theta(x)\phi(a-x)$$

$$= 0,$$

it follows that the function in (iii) is independent of x. In fact putting $x = 0$ this function is equal to $\phi(a)$,

i.e. $$\phi(x)\phi(a-x)+\theta(x)\theta(a-x) = \phi(a).$$

Putting $a = x+y$ now gives result (iv).

Exercises 3 : 11

1. Verify, by integration, the Laplace transforms given in the following table:

	$f(t)$	$L\{f(t)\}$
1	1	$\dfrac{1}{p}$
2	t^n, n an integer $\geqslant 0$	$\dfrac{n!}{p^{n+1}}$
3	e^{at}, $a < p$	$\dfrac{1}{p-a}$
4	$t^n e^{at}$, $a < p$, n an integer $\geqslant 0$	$\dfrac{n!}{(p-a)^{n+1}}$
5	$\sin \omega t$	$\dfrac{\omega}{p^2+\omega^2}$
6	$\cos \omega t$	$\dfrac{p}{p^2+\omega^2}$
7	$t \sin \omega t$	$\dfrac{2\omega p}{(p^2+\omega^2)^2}$
8	$t \cos \omega t$	$\dfrac{1}{p^2+\omega^2}-\dfrac{2\omega^2}{(p^2+\omega^2)^2} = \dfrac{p^2-\omega^2}{(p^2+\omega^2)^2}$
9	$\sinh at$	$\dfrac{a}{p^2-a^2}$
10	$\cosh at$	$\dfrac{p}{p^2-a^2}$
11	$\sin(\omega t+\alpha)$	$\dfrac{p \sin \alpha+\omega \cos \alpha}{p^2+\omega^2}-$
12	$\cos(\omega t+\beta)$	$\dfrac{p \cos \beta-\omega \sin \beta}{p^2+\omega^2}$

2. The Gamma function $\Gamma(x)$, $x > 0$, is defined by

$$\Gamma(x) = \int_0^\infty t^{x-1} e^{-t} \, dt.$$

If n is a positive integer, evaluate

(i) $\Gamma(n+1)$,

(ii) $\int_0^\infty x^n e^{-2x} \, dx$,

(iii) $\Gamma(8/3)/\Gamma(2/3)$ and

(iv) $\Gamma(3/2)$ given that $\int_0^\infty e^{-x^2} \, dx = \frac{1}{2}\sqrt{\pi}$.

(v) Express $\Gamma(x+h) - 2\Gamma(x) + \Gamma(x-h)$, where h is positive and smaller than x, as an integral, and show that it is positive. What does this tell you about the shape of the graph of $y = \Gamma(x)$ for positive x?

3. Given that $\qquad \phi(\lambda) = \int_0^\pi \ln(1 - 2\lambda \cos x + \lambda^2) \, dx$,

prove that $\qquad \phi(\lambda) = \phi(-\lambda) = \frac{1}{2}\phi(\lambda^2)$.

Deduce that, if $|\lambda| < 1$, $\phi(\lambda) = 0$; and if $|\lambda| > 1$, $\phi(\lambda) = 2\pi \ln |\lambda|$.

4. The *beta-function* is defined by

$$B(p, q) = \int_0^1 x^{p-1}(1-x)^{q-1} \, dx.$$

(i) Show that

$$B(p, q+1) = \frac{q}{p} B(p+1, q).$$

Hence or otherwise show that, if p and q are positive integers,

$$B(p, q) = \frac{(p-1)!\,(q-1)!}{(p+q-1)!}$$

(ii) Show that

$$B(p, q) = 2 \int_0^{\pi/2} \cos^{2p-1}\theta \, \sin^{2q-1}\theta \, d\theta.$$

Hence or otherwise show that

$$B(p, q) = B(q, p).$$

5. If $\phi(x) = \int_0^x e^{-t^2} \, dt$, and given that $\phi(\infty) = \frac{1}{2}\sqrt{\pi}$, prove the following results:

(i) $\qquad \phi(x) = x - \frac{1}{3} x^3 + \frac{1}{5.2!} x^5 - \frac{1}{7.3!} x^7 + \cdots,$

(ii) $\phi(x) = \dfrac{1}{2}\sqrt{\pi} + \displaystyle\int_{\infty}^{x} e^{-t^2}\, dt,$

(iii) $\displaystyle\int_{\infty}^{x} e^{-t^2}\, dt = -\dfrac{1}{2x} e^{-x^2} - \dfrac{1}{2}\int_{\infty}^{x} \dfrac{1}{t^2}\, e^{-t^2}\, dt.$

Hence, or otherwise, deduce that

(iv) $\phi(x) = \dfrac{1}{2}\sqrt{\pi} - e^{-x^2}\left(\dfrac{1}{2x} - \dfrac{1}{2^2 x^3} + \dfrac{3}{2^3 x^5} - \cdots\right).$

Prove also that

(v) $(2n+1)\displaystyle\int_{0}^{x} t^{2n}\phi(t)\, dt = x^{2n+1}\phi(x) - \dfrac{1}{2} n!\left\{1 - e^{-x^2}\sum_{r=0}^{n}\dfrac{x^{2r}}{r!}\right\},$

where n is a positive integer.

6. If

$$F(x) = e^{2x}\int_{0}^{x} e^{-2t}f(t)\, dt - e^{x}\int_{0}^{x} e^{-t}f(t)\, dt,$$

prove that

    (i) $\quad F(0) = 0,$

    (ii) $\quad F'(0) = 0,$

    (iii) $\quad F''(x) - 3F'(x) + 2F(x) = f(x).$

7. The function $f(x)$ is defined by

$$f(x) = \int_{0}^{x} \dfrac{dt}{1+t^2}, \qquad a = \lim_{x\to\infty} f(x) = \int_{0}^{\infty} \dfrac{dt}{1+t^2}.$$

By considering $f(x) - f(y)$ and changing the variable in the integrand, show that

$$f(x) - f(y) = f\left(\dfrac{x-y}{1+xy}\right).$$

Prove further that (i) $f(x) + f(1/x) = a$, (ii) $f(1) = \tfrac{1}{2}a$, (iii) $f(\sqrt{3}) = \tfrac{2}{3}a$.

Miscellaneous Exercises III

1. Integrate w.r. to x the following expressions:

(i) $x\sin x\sin 2x$,   (ii) $\dfrac{x+1}{x^2+4x+6}$,   (iii) $\dfrac{\sqrt{(1-x^2)}}{x^2}$,

(iv) $\dfrac{1}{x^3+3x-4}$,   (v) $\dfrac{1}{\sqrt{(x+a)} - \sqrt{(x+b)}}$,

(vi) $\dfrac{5x^3 - 16x^2 + 11x - 8}{(x^2+1)(x-2)^2}$.

2. Evaluate the following definite integrals:

(i) $\displaystyle\int_{\frac{1}{2}}^{1} \frac{\sin^{-1} x}{x^3}\, dx$,

(ii) $\displaystyle\int_{0}^{\pi/3} \frac{dx}{\cos x(1+\cos x)}$,

(iii) $\displaystyle\int_{0}^{1} \frac{x^3\, dx}{1+x+x^2}$,

(iv) $\displaystyle\int_{0}^{\pi/4} \tan^3 x\, dx$,

(v) $\displaystyle\int_{1}^{e} x^3 (\ln x)^2\, dx$,

(vi) $\displaystyle\int_{0}^{1} \frac{\sqrt{(1-x^2)}}{4-x^2}\, dx$,

(vii) $\displaystyle\int_{0}^{\frac{1}{2}} e^{2x} \sin \pi x\, dx$,

(viii) $\displaystyle\int_{0}^{\pi/2} \frac{(1+\cos x+\sin x)^2}{1+\cos x}\, dx$,

(ix) $\displaystyle\int_{1}^{\infty} \frac{x\, dx}{(x^2+2)^2 \sqrt{(x^2-1)}}$,

(x) $\displaystyle\int_{0}^{\frac{3}{2}} \sqrt{(x^2+3x)}\, dx$,

(xi) $\displaystyle\int_{0}^{\frac{1}{2}} \frac{\sin^{-1} x\, dx}{(1-x^2)^{\frac{3}{2}}}$,

(xii) $\displaystyle\int_{0}^{\pi/2} \cosh x \cos x\, dx$,

(xiii) $\displaystyle\int_{1}^{2} \frac{(x^2+1)\, dx}{x(2x+1)}$.

3. Prove the results:

(i) $\displaystyle\int_{0}^{1} \frac{(3x+5)\, dx}{x^2+x+1} = \frac{3}{2} \ln 3 + \frac{7\pi \sqrt{3}}{18}$,

(ii) $\displaystyle\int_{0}^{\pi/4} \sec^3 \theta\, d\theta = \tfrac{1}{2} [\sqrt{2} + \ln (1+\sqrt{2})]$,

(iii) $\displaystyle\int_{0}^{4} \frac{\sqrt{(2x+1)}\, dx}{\sqrt{(2x+1)}+2} = 4 \ln \frac{5}{3}$,

(iv) $\displaystyle\int_{0}^{\infty} \frac{x^2(x+1)}{(x^2+1)^3}\, dx = \frac{(\pi+4)}{16}$,

(v) $\displaystyle\int_{0}^{1} \frac{dx}{(1+x) \sqrt{(1+x^2)}} = \frac{1}{\sqrt{2}} \ln (1+\sqrt{2})$.

4. If a is positive, prove that the value of $\displaystyle\int_{-1}^{+1} \frac{dx}{\sqrt{(1-2ax+a^2)}}$ is 2 if $a < 1$, but that the value is $2/a$ if $a > 1$.

5. Prove that $\int\limits_{ra}^{(r+1)a} f(x)\,dx = \int\limits_0^a f(x+ra)\,dx$. If $f(x+a) = c\,f(x)$, where a and c are constants, prove that $f(x+ra) = c^r f(x)$ when r is an integer. Deduce that, if n is a positive integer and c is not equal to unity

$$(1-c)\int\limits_0^{na} f(x)\,dx = (1-c^n)\int\limits_0^a f(x)\,dx.$$

State the corresponding result when $c = 1$.

6. Show that $\int\limits_a^b f(x)\,dx = \int\limits_a^b f(a+b-x)\,dx$. Hence, or otherwise, evaluate

$$\int\limits_{\pi/n}^{(n-1)\pi/n} x \sin^3 x\,dx.$$

7. Show that $\int\limits_0^{\pi/2} \ln \sin x\,dx = \int\limits_0^{\pi/2} \ln \cos x\,dx = \tfrac12 \int\limits_0^{\pi/2} \ln \sin 2x\,dx - \tfrac14\pi \ln 2$.

Deduce that $\int\limits_0^{\pi/2} \ln \sin x\,dx = -\tfrac12\pi \ln 2$.

8. If $I_n = \int\limits_0^\theta \dfrac{\sin (2n-1)\theta}{\sin \theta}\,d\theta$ find $I_n - I_{n-1}$. Hence show that, if n is a

positive integer, $\int\limits_0^{\pi/2} \dfrac{\sin (2n-1)\theta}{\sin \theta}\,d\theta = \dfrac{\pi}{2}$ and $\int\limits_0^{\pi/2} \dfrac{\sin^2 n\theta}{\sin^2 \theta}\,d\theta = \dfrac{n\pi}{2}$.

9. Find the angle x such that $5+4 \cos \theta + 3 \sin \theta = 10 \cos^2 \tfrac12(\theta - x)$. Hence, or otherwise, prove that

$$\int\limits_0^\pi \dfrac{d\theta}{(5+4 \cos \theta + 3 \sin \theta)^{\frac12}} = \dfrac{2}{\sqrt{10}} \ln \left(\dfrac{13+4 \sqrt{10}}{3} \right).$$

10. (i) Prove that $\int \dfrac{(1-x^2)\,dx}{x^3 + kx^2 + x}$ can be evaluated by means of the substitution $w = x + x^{-1}$.

(ii) Prove that

$$\int \dfrac{(1-x^2)\,dx}{x^3 + kx^2 - x} \quad \text{and} \quad \int \dfrac{(1+x^2)\,dx}{x^4 + kx^2 + 1}$$

can be evaluated by means of the substitution $v = x - x^{-1}$.

(iii) Find

$$\int \dfrac{(1+x)^2\,dx}{(1+x^2)^2}.$$

11. If $I_n = \int x^n \cos x\,dx$, show that

$$I_n = x^n \sin x + nx^{n-1} \cos x - n(n-1)I_{n-2}.$$

Evaluate $\int\limits_0^{\pi/4} x^4 \cos 2x \, dx$.

12. If $f(m, n) = \int\limits_0^1 t^{m-1}(1-t)^{n-1} \, dt$ where m, n are positive, show that

$$f(m+1, n) + f(m, n+1) = f(m, n),$$
$$n f(m+1, n) = m f(m, n+1)$$

and express $f(m+1, n)$ and $f(m, n+1)$ in terms of $f(m, n)$. Show, also, that if n is a positive integer,

$$f(m, n) = \frac{(n-1)!}{m(m+1) \dots (m+n-1)}.$$

13. If $I_n = \int\limits_0^x \frac{t^n \, dt}{\sqrt{(1+t^2)}}$, prove that, for $n > 1$,

$$n I_n + (n-1)I_{n-2} = x^{n-1} \sqrt{(1+x^2)},$$

and show that

$$\int\limits_0^1 \frac{t^3 \, dt}{\sqrt{(1+t^2)}} = \frac{1}{3}(2-\sqrt{2}).$$

14. Find $f(x)$ if $\cosh\left\{\int f(x) \, dx\right\} = f(x)$.

15. If
$$I = \int\limits_0^\pi \frac{x \cos^2 x \sin x}{\sqrt{(1+3\cos^2 x)}} \, dx,$$

show that

$$I = \frac{\pi}{2} \int\limits_0^\pi \frac{\cos^2 x \sin x}{\sqrt{(1+3\cos^2 x)}} \, dx,$$

and hence evaluate I.

16. Prove that

$$\int\limits_0^{\pi/3} \sqrt{(\cos 2x - \cos 4x)} \, dx = \tfrac{1}{2}\sqrt{6} - \tfrac{1}{4}\sqrt{2} \ln(2+\sqrt{3}).$$

17. If n is a positive integer greater than 1, and if

$$S_n = \int\limits_0^{\frac{1}{2}\pi} t^n \sin t \, dt, \qquad C_n = \int\limits_0^{\frac{1}{2}\pi} t^n \cos t \, dt,$$

prove that

$$S_n = \frac{n\pi^{n-1}}{2^{n-1}} - n(n-1)S_{n-2},$$

$$C_n = \frac{\pi^n}{2^n} - n(n-1)C_{n-2}. \qquad \text{(Continued overleaf)}$$

Calculate the area between the two curves

$$y = 4x^4 \sin x \quad \text{and} \quad y = \pi^2 x^2 \sin x$$

for the range $0 \leqslant x \leqslant \frac{1}{2}\pi$.

18. Prove that, if $a > 0$,

$$\int_0^{\frac{1}{2}\pi} \frac{1 - a \cos \theta}{1 - 2a \cos \theta + a^2} \, d\theta = \pi - \cot^{-1} a \quad \text{or} \quad -\cot^{-1} a,$$

according as $a < 1$ or $a > 1$, where the principal value of $\cot^{-1} a$ is taken. Evaluate the integral when $a = 1$.

19. If $\qquad P_n(x) = \dfrac{1}{2^n n!} \dfrac{d^n}{dx^n} \{(x^2 - 1)^n\},$

prove, by integration by parts, that

$$\int_{-1}^{1} P_m(x) P_n(x) \, dx = 0 \quad \text{if} \quad m \neq n,$$

$$= \frac{2}{2n+1} \quad \text{if} \quad m = n.$$

20. The functions $u(x)$ and $v(x)$ satisfy the equations

$$u'' + u = 0, \quad u(0) = 0, \quad u'(0) = 1,$$
$$v'' + v = 0, \quad v(0) = 1, \quad v'(0) = 0.$$

Show, without using the trigonometrical or exponential functions, that

$$u' = v, \quad v' = -u, \quad u^2 + v^2 = 1,$$
$$u(a+b) = u(a) v(b) + v(a) u(b).$$

21. Express

$$y = \frac{4}{(1-x)^2 (1-x^2)}$$

in partial fractions. Deduce that $\left(\dfrac{1}{n!} \dfrac{d^n y}{dx^n} \right)_{x=0}$ is equal to $(n+2)^2$ when n is even, and $(n+1)(n+3)$ when n is odd.

22. The functions $L_n(x)$ are defined by

$$L_n(x) = e^x \frac{d^n}{dx^n} (x^n e^{-x}),$$

$n = 0, 1, 2, \ldots$ Show that $L_n(x)$ is a polynomial (a *Laguerre polynomial*) of degree n, that the coefficient of x^n is $(-1)^n$ and that $L_n(0) = n!$.

By substituting for $L_n(x)$, but not for $L_m(x)$, and integrating by parts, show that

$$\int_0^\infty L_m(x) L_n(x) e^{-x} \, dx = \begin{cases} 0 & (n > m \geqslant 0), \\ (n!)^2 & (m = n). \end{cases}$$

CHAPTER IV

GEOMETRY OF TWO DIMENSIONS

4 : 1 Introduction

The behaviour of functions and physical systems can usually be illustrated by means of geometrical figures. If sets of numerical results are represented graphically, relationships which are not otherwise obvious may be indicated. For these reasons alone a knowledge of geometrical techniques is important. Moreover, the geometry of plane figures is the basis of much advanced mathematics and acts as a guide to the development of physical ideas. This chapter falls into two broad sections; the first section is concerned with the application of calculus to the geometrical investigation of curves and the second with more detailed consideration of an important class of curves, the conic sections. Emphasis is placed on the methods and techniques which may be used in the solution of problems other than those given here.

4 : 2 Gradient, tangent and normal

In Chapter I we introduced the equation of a straight line in the form

$$ax + by + c = 0 \tag{4.1}$$

and saw that the angle ψ between the line and the positive direction of the x-axis is given by $\tan \psi = -a/b$. We call $\tan \psi$ the *gradient* of the line.

The derivative of a function $y = f(x)$ was defined in § 2 : 1 as $\lim_{\delta x \to 0} \delta y/\delta x$. This has an immediate interpretation in terms of the geometry of the curve $y = f(x)$. For any given value of δx, the ratio $\delta y/\delta x$ is the gradient of the chord PQ, see Fig. 4.1(a). (In diagrams it is customary to represent δx as positive but in fact

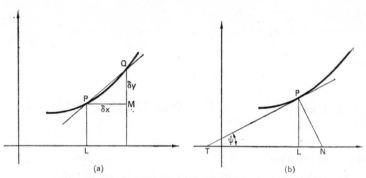

FIG. 4.1. The tangent as the limiting case of a chord.

δx may be negative. The existence of the limit dy/dx implies that the same value is obtained when $\delta x \to 0$ through either positive or negative values.) The state of affairs when the limit is reached is shown in Fig. 4.1(b) where Q coincides with P and the chord has become the *tangent* at P. The gradient of the tangent is therefore

$$\tan \psi = \frac{dy}{dx} = f'(x). \tag{4.2}$$

If $ax + by + c = 0$, then y is a continuous function of x and $dy/dx = -a/b = $ constant. Hence eqn. (4.1) represents a curve with a constant direction, i.e. a straight line. This proves that a linear equation represents a straight line.

The *normal* to a curve at any point P is the line through P perpendicular to the tangent at P. The gradient of the normal PN in Fig. 4.1(b) is

$$\tan \left(\psi + \frac{1}{2}\pi \right) = -\cot \psi = \frac{-1}{dy/dx}.$$

The segments TL, LN of the x-axis in Fig. 4.1(b) are called the *sub-tangent* and *sub-normal* respectively.

If we take the coordinates of P in Fig. 4.1(b) to be (x_0, y_0) and denote the value of dy/dx when $x = x_0$ by $(dy/dx)_0 = f'(x_0)$, the equation of the tangent line TP is

$$y - y_0 = f'(x_0)(x - x_0), \tag{4.3}$$

where x and y are the current coordinates of the equation. It is frequently useful to regard the tangent as a line which intersects the curve in two coincident points or as having *two point contact* with the curve.

The equation of the normal PN is

$$(x-x_0)+f'(x_0)(y-y_0) = 0, \qquad (4.4)$$

this being the equation of the line through P perpendicular to the tangent at P.

Example 1. Find the tangent at the point $P(x_0, y_0)$ on the conic

$$ax^2+2hxy+by^2+2gx+2fy+c = 0. \qquad (1)$$

Here $dy/dx = -(ax+hy+g)/(hx+by+f)$.
Therefore the required tangent is

$$(y-y_0) = -(x-x_0)\frac{(ax_0+hy_0+g)}{(hx_0+by_0+f)}$$

which reduces to

$$(ax_0+hy_0+g)x+(hx_0+by_0+f)y = ax_0^2+2hx_0y_0+by_0^2+gx_0+fy_0. \quad (2)$$

Since P lies on the conic, (x_0, y_0) satisfies eqn. (1) and the r.h. side of eqn. (2) takes the value $-(gx_0+fy_0+c)$. Then the equation of the tangent may be rearranged to its standard form

$$ax_0x+by_0y+h(xy_0+x_0y)+g(x+x_0)+f(y+y_0)+c = 0. \qquad (3)$$

Example 2. If a curve is given parametrically in the form $x = f(t), y = g(t)$, the equations of the tangent and normal are, from eqns. (4.3) and (4.4),

$$\{y-g(t)\}f'(t) = \{x-f(t)\}g'(t),$$
$$\{x-f(t)\}f'(t)+\{y-g(t)\}g'(t) = 0$$

respectively.

Exercises 4 : 2

1. Show that the equation of the normal to the curve

$$\left(\frac{x}{a}\right)^n+\left(\frac{y}{b}\right)^n = 2$$

at the point (a, b) is

$$\frac{x-a}{b} = \frac{y-b}{a}.$$

2. Find the equations of the tangents and normals to the curve $y^2 = 3x^2-x^5$ at its points of intersection with the line $x = 1$.

3. A point P has co-ordinates $(2, 3)$; verify that it lies on the curve $x(7x^2 - y^3) = 2$. Find the equation of the tangent at P and determine whether it passes above or below the origin.

4. If $y = (x^2 + 1)e^{-x}$ prove that $dy/dx \leqslant 0$ for all values of x and sketch the curve $y = (x^2 + 1)e^{-x}$.

5. Find the coordinates of the point of intersection K, other than the origin, of the parabolas $y^2 = 4ax$ and $2x^2 = ay$. Show that the parabolas intersect at K at an angle $\tan^{-1}\left(\frac{3}{5}\right)$.

6. A straight line is drawn from the origin to touch the curve $y = \sin x$ at a point where $2\pi < x < 5\pi/2$. Show that α, the value of x at the point of contact, satisfies

$$\sin \alpha = \alpha \cos \alpha.$$

7. The parametric equations of a curve are

$$x = a(2 \cos \theta - \cos 2\theta), \quad y = a(2 \sin \theta - \sin 2\theta).$$

Obtain the equations of the tangent and the normal at the point where $\theta = \frac{1}{2}\pi$.

8. Show that the equation of the tangent at the point t on the curve

$$x = a \cos^3 t, \quad y = a \sin^3 t$$

is

$$x \sin t + y \cos t - a \sin t \cos t = 0.$$

Prove that the locus of intersection of tangents at right angles to one another is the curve whose equation in polar coordinates can be expressed in the form $2r^2 = a^2 \cos^2 2\theta$.

9. Show that the equation of the normal to the parabola $y^2 = 4ax$ at the point $(at^2, 2at)$ is

$$y + tx - 2at - at^3 = 0.$$

Show that the locus of the intersection of perpendicular-normals to the above parabola is the parabola $y^2 = a(x - 3a)$.

10. Show that the equation of the chord joining the points $(at_1^2, 2at_1)$, $(at_2^2, 2at_2)$ of the parabola $y^2 = 4ax$ can be expressed in the form $(t_1 + t_2)y - 2x = 2at_1t_2$.

The points P, Q are variable points on the parabola such that PQ passes through the fixed point $(4a, 0)$. Show that PQ subtends a right angle at the vertex $(0, 0)$ of the parabola and that the locus of the mid-point of PQ is the parabola $y^2 = 2ax - 8a^2$.

11. Find the equation of the tangent to the parabola $y^2 = 4ax$ at the point $(at^2, 2at)$.

P, Q are variable points on the parabola such that the tangents at P and Q are perpendicular. Show that the locus of the mid-point of PQ is the parabola $y^2 = 2a(x - a)$.

12. Find the equations of the tangent and the normal to the hyperbola $xy = c^2$ at the point $(ct, c/t)$.

The chord LM of this hyperbola subtends a right angle at a third point N of the hyperbola. Show that the tangent at N is perpendicular to LM.

13. Show that the line $ax+by+c = 0$ is a tangent to the hyperbola $xy = k^2$ if and only if $c^2 - 4abk^2 = 0$.

14. The curve whose equation is

$$y = e^x(ax^3+bx^2+cx+d)$$

if such that it is parallel to the x-axis at $x = 0$, 1 and 2, and cuts the y-axis at $y = -7$. Determine a, b, c, d and sketch the curve.

15. Find the gradient of the curve $y^x = x^2 - 1$ at the point at which $x = 3$.

4 : 3 Points of inflexion

In Fig. 4.2 the gradient at a point of the curve decreases, i.e. $d^2y/dx^2 < 0$, as the point moves from Q_1 to P but, as the point moves from P to Q_2, the gradient increases, i.e., $d^2y/dx^2 > 0$.

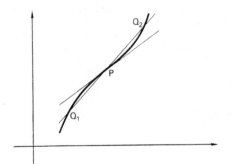

FIG. 4.2. A point of inflexion.

Since the direction of the tangent is changing continuously, $d^2y/dx^2 = 0$ at P. Such a point P at which d^2y/dx^2 vanishes, having opposite signs on the two sides of P, is called a *point of inflexion*. Note that, near a point of inflexion, the curve crosses its tangent. If d^2y/dx^2 has the same sign on each side of P, the curve does not have an inflexion at P and the curve does not cross the tangent there. In fact points of inflexion occur where dy/dx has maximum or minimum values. [See § 5 : 6.]

If the line Q_1PQ_2 in Fig. 4.2 is rotated in the clockwise sense about P, both Q_1 and Q_2 move along the curve and finally coincide with P. The tangent at an inflexion is said to have *3 point contact* with the curve. We generalise this idea to the case of n *point contact* of two curves, in which n points of intersection of the curves coincide. For example, the curve $y = x^5$ and the line $y = 0$ have 5 point contact at the origin.

It must be emphasised that the curve $y = f(x)$ has an inflexion at $x = x_0$ only if $f''(x_0) = 0$, whatever the value of $f'(x_0)$. [This condition is necessary but not sufficient for an inflexion at $x = x_0$.]

Exercises 4:3

1. Find the x-coordinates of the points of inflexion on the curves

(i) $$y = 3x^5 + 5x^4 - 20x^3 + 2x + 7,$$

(ii) $$y = 3x^5 - 10x^4 + 10x^3 + 6x + 4.$$

2. By considering the derivative of the function

$$f(x) = \sin x \tan x - 2 \ln \sec x$$

prove that $f(x)$ steadily increases as x increases from 0 to $\frac{1}{2}\pi$. Show also that the graph of the function has no inflexion between these limits.

3. Prove that $y = x^n e^{-x}$ has points of inflexion at two positive values of x when $n > 1$. Show that the product of the two values of y at these points of inflexion is

$$n^n(n-1)^n e^{-2n}.$$

4. Find the values of x at which the curve $y = 1/(1+x^2)$ has points of inflexion and show that the curve $y = 1/(1+x^2) + a + bx$ has points of inflexion for the same values of x.

By putting $x + \frac{1}{2} = z$, or otherwise, find the values of x at which the curve $y = x^3/(1+x+x^2)$ has points of inflexion.

5. Show that the points of inflexion of the curve

$$(1+x^2)y + x - 1 = 0$$

lie on the line

$$x + 4y = 3.$$

4:4 The arc length of a curve

The length of an arc of a plane curve requires careful definition. Suppose that $P_1, P_2, \ldots, P_n$ are points on the finite arc AB of a given plane curve and that they lie between A and B, i.e., a point moving along the curve from A to B passes through the points $P_1, P_2, \ldots, P_n$ in turn, see Fig. 4.3. Then, provided that the ratio of the lengths of the greatest and least of the chords $AP_1, P_1P_2, \ldots, P_nB$ is of order unity, the sum of the lengths of the $n+1$ chords $AP_1, P_1P_2, \ldots, P_nB$ is a first approximation to the length of the arc AB. If $n \to \infty$, so that the number of intermediate points $P_1, P_2, \ldots, P_n$ is increased without limit and the length of each chord tends to zero, we define the length of the arc AB to be the limiting value of the sum of the lengths of these chords.

If the neighbouring points R, S on the curve $f(x, y) = 0$ have coordinates (x, y), $(x+\delta x, y+\delta y)$ and the distances along the

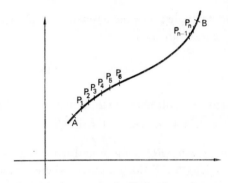

FIG. 4.3. A curve as the limit of a polygon.

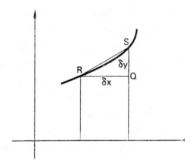

FIG. 4.4.

curve of R, S from some fixed point on the curve are s, $s+\delta s$ respectively, cf. Fig. 4.4, then to the first order the length of the chord RS is equal to the length δs of the arc RS.

$$\therefore \quad (\delta s)^2 = (\delta x)^2 + (\delta y)^2 + \text{terms of higher order in } \delta x \text{ and } \delta y. \quad (4.5)$$

Dividing eqn. (4.5) by δx and letting $\delta x \to 0$ gives

$$\left(\frac{\mathrm{d}s}{\mathrm{d}x}\right)^2 = 1 + \left(\frac{\mathrm{d}y}{\mathrm{d}x}\right)^2 = 1 + \tan^2 \psi = \sec^2 \psi. \quad (4.6)$$

Similarly

$$\left(\frac{\mathrm{d}s}{\mathrm{d}y}\right)^2 = 1 + \left(\frac{\mathrm{d}x}{\mathrm{d}y}\right)^2 = 1 + \cot^2 \psi = \operatorname{cosec}^2 \psi.$$

$$\therefore \quad \frac{\mathrm{d}x}{\mathrm{d}s} = \pm \cos \psi, \quad \frac{\mathrm{d}y}{\mathrm{d}s} = \pm \sin \psi.$$

If ψ is an acute angle and s increases with x and y, the positive signs must be chosen in each case and

$$\frac{\mathrm{d}x}{\mathrm{d}s} = \cos \psi, \quad \frac{\mathrm{d}y}{\mathrm{d}s} = \sin \psi. \tag{4.7}$$

This is the usual convention adopted. Equations (4.7) may also be derived from Fig. 4.4 in which $\lim_{\delta x \to 0} S\hat{R}Q = \psi$, by noting that $\cos S\hat{R}Q = \delta x/\delta s$, $\sin S\hat{R}Q = \delta y/\delta s$ and letting $\delta x \to 0$.

If s is the arc length AP along a curve, where A is a fixed point and P an arbitrary point on the curve, and ψ is the inclination of the tangent at P to a given direction, usually but not always parallel to Ox, it is often possible to find a relation between s and ψ. This relation is called the *intrinsic equation* of the curve; s and ψ are *intrinsic coordinates*. Intrinsic equations are of little use in determining the intersections of two curves but are useful in dealing with the curvature properties of a single curve, cf. § 4 : 5. The method of obtaining the cartesian equation of a curve from the intrinsic equation is illustrated in § 4 : 7.

If $\mathrm{d}s/\mathrm{d}x > 0$, then eqn. (4.6) implies that the length of the arc AB of the curve $y = f(x)$ between the points A, B at which $x = x_1$, x_2 respectively is $\displaystyle\int_{x_1}^{x_2} \sqrt{\left\{1 + \left(\frac{\mathrm{d}y}{\mathrm{d}x}\right)^2\right\}}\,\mathrm{d}x$. If the curve is given parametrically and A, B have parameters t_1, t_2 respectively, then the length of the arc is $\displaystyle\int_{t_1}^{t_2} \sqrt{(\dot{x}^2 + \dot{y}^2)}\,\mathrm{d}t$, provided that $\dot{x} \geqslant 0$ over the range of integration.

Example 1. Find the length of the curve $y = -\ln(1 - x^2)$ from the origin to the point where $x = x_1 (0 < x_1 < 1)$.

$$\mathrm{d}y/\mathrm{d}x = 2x/(1 - x^2) > 0 \quad \text{for} \quad 0 < x < 1.$$

Therefore the required arc length

$$= \int_0^{x_1} \sqrt{\left[1+\left\{\frac{2x}{(1-x^2)}\right\}^2\right]}\, dx = \int_0^{x_1} \sqrt{\left\{\frac{(1+x^2)^2}{(1-x^2)^2}\right\}}\, dx$$

$$= \int_0^{x_1} \frac{1+x^2}{1-x^2}\, dx = \int_0^{x_1} \left(-1+\frac{2}{1-x^2}\right) dx = \ln\left(\frac{1+x_1}{1-x_1}\right)-x_1.$$

Example 2. Calculate the length from $x = 0$ to $x = a\pi$ of the curve, the *cycloid*, whose parametric equations are $x = a(\theta - \sin \theta)$, $y = a(1 - \cos \theta)$.

$$\dot{x} = a(1-\cos \theta) > 0 \quad \text{for} \quad 0 < \theta < \pi.$$

Therefore the required arc length $= \int_0^\pi \sqrt{\{a^2(1-\cos \theta)^2 + a^2 \sin^2 \theta\}}\, d\theta$

$$= a \int_0^\pi \sqrt{\{2(1-\cos \theta)\}}\, d\theta = 2a \int_0^\pi \sin\left(\tfrac{1}{2}\theta\right) d\theta = 4a.$$

Exercises 4 : 4

1. Show that the length of the arc of the parabola $x = at^2$, $y = 2at$ between the limits $t = -1$ and $t = 1$ is

$$2a[\sqrt{2}+\ln(1+\sqrt{2})].$$

2. Find the area of the region bounded by two arcs of the parabolas $y^2 = x$, $x^2 = y$, and show that the perimeter of this region is

$$\tfrac{1}{2}\ln(2+\sqrt{5})+\sqrt{5}.$$

3. The coordinates of a point on a curve are given by the equations

$$x = a(u-\tanh u), \quad y = a \operatorname{sech} u$$

where u is a variable parameter. Prove that the arc s of the curve, measured from a suitable point (to be specified), is given by

$$s = a \ln \cosh u.$$

4. Prove that the curve $x = a \cos^3 t$, $y = 2a \sin^3 t$ has length $28a/3$.

5. Prove that the length of the arc of the curve

$$y = (x+1)(x+2)-\tfrac{1}{8}\ln(2x+3)$$

between the points for which $x = 1$ and $x = 2$, respectively, is

$$6+\tfrac{1}{8}\ln \tfrac{7}{5}.$$

6. Sketch the curve whose parametric equations are

$$x = t^2, \quad y = (t-1)^2.$$

(*Continued overleaf*)

Calculate

    (i) the area bounded by this curve and the chord $x = 1$,

    (ii) the length of the curve between the points where $t = 0$ and $t = 1$.

4:5 Curvature

The direction of a curve at any point is determined by the gradient $dy/dx = \tan \psi$. The *curvature*, which we denote by $\varkappa$, measures the rate of change of direction of the curve w.r. to arc length and is defined by

$$\varkappa = \frac{d\psi}{ds}. \tag{4.8}$$

If we consider the circle of radius a with its centre at $(0, a)$, see Fig. 4.5, the arc length OP is $a\psi$, and the intrinsic equation of the

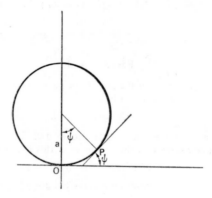

Fig. 4.5. The curvature of a circle.

circle is $s = a\psi$. Hence $d\psi/ds = 1/a = \varkappa$ and the curvature of a circle is the same at every point of its circumference. For this reason the *radius of curvature* of a curve at a point is defined to be

$$\varrho = \frac{1}{|\varkappa|} \tag{4.9}$$

and is the radius of the circle having the same curvature as the curve at that point. If a distance $PC = \varrho$ is marked off along the normal at a point P of the curve on the concave side of the curve, the point C so obtained is called the *centre of curvature* of the curve at P.

Since
$$\frac{dy}{dx} = \tan \psi,$$

$$\frac{d^2y}{dx^2} = \sec^2 \psi \cdot \frac{d\psi}{dx} = \sec^2 \psi \cdot \frac{d\psi}{ds} \cdot \frac{ds}{dx} = \varkappa \sec^3 \psi.$$

But $\sec \psi = \pm(1 + \tan^2 \psi)^{\frac{1}{2}} = \pm \left\{1 + \left(\frac{dy}{dx}\right)^2\right\}^{\frac{1}{2}}.$

$$\therefore \frac{1}{\varrho} = \left| \frac{d^2y/dx^2}{\{1 + (dy/dx)^2\}^{\frac{3}{2}}} \right|. \tag{4.10}$$

For a curve given parametrically in terms of the parameter t, eqns. (2.12) and (4.10) give

$$\frac{1}{\varrho} = \left| \frac{\dot{x}\ddot{y} - \ddot{x}\dot{y}}{(\dot{x}^2 + \dot{y}^2)^{\frac{3}{2}}} \right|. \tag{4.11}$$

The coordinates (x_c, y_c) of the centre of curvature at the point (x_0, y_0) of the curve $f(x, y) = 0$ are given by

$$x_c = x_0 - \varkappa_0^{-1} \sin \psi_0, \quad y_c = y_0 + \varkappa_0^{-1} \cos \psi_0, \tag{4.12}$$

where $\varkappa$, from (4.8), may be negative and $-\frac{1}{2}\pi \leqslant \psi_0 \leqslant \frac{1}{2}\pi$.

Example 1. Find the curvature and coordinates of the centre of curvature of the curve $4ay^2 = 27(x - 2a)^3$ at the point $P(7a/3, a/2)$.

Using the notation $y_n = d^n y/dx^n$,

$$8ayy_1 = 81(x - 2a)^2 \quad \text{giving} \quad (y_1)_P = \tfrac{9}{4},$$

$$8ayy_2 + 8ay_1^2 = 162(x - 2a) \quad \text{giving} \quad (y_2)_P = \frac{27}{8a}.$$

$$\therefore \varkappa = \frac{216}{97^{\frac{3}{2}}a} = \frac{1}{\varrho_P}.$$

$$\tan \psi = \frac{9}{4}, \quad \sin \psi = \frac{9}{\sqrt{97}}, \quad \cos \psi = \frac{4}{\sqrt{97}}.$$

$$\therefore x_c = -\frac{41a}{24}, \quad y_c = \frac{62a}{27}.$$

Example 2. Find the radius of curvature at the point θ of the cycloid $x = a(\theta - \sin \theta)$, $y = a(1 - \cos \theta)$.

$$\dot{x} = a(1 - \cos \theta); \quad \ddot{x} = a \sin \theta.$$

$$\dot{y} = a \sin \theta; \quad \ddot{y} = a \cos \theta.$$

$$\therefore \varrho = |4a \sin (\tfrac{1}{2}\theta)|.$$

Example 3. If dy/dx is small, then eqn. (4.10) gives $1/\varrho = d^2y/dx^2$ approximately; use of the binomial theorem [eqn. (5.13)] indicates that the error in using this approximation is of order $d^2y/dx^2 . (dy/dx)^2$. This result is used in the solution of problems involving the bending of beams.

We now investigate curvature from another viewpoint. Suppose P_1, P_2 are two neighbouring points on a curve at which the tangents to the curve make angles ψ and $\psi + \delta\psi$ with Ox; the normals at P_1, P_2 to the curve meet at K, see Fig. 4.6. Then $P_1\hat{K}P_2 = \delta\psi$

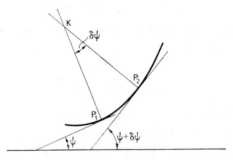

FIG. 4.6. The centre of curvature as the intersection of consecutive normals.

and, to the first order, the chord $P_1P_2 = \delta s$. The sine rule applied to the triangle P_1KP_2 gives $P_1K = (P_1P_2 \sin P_1\hat{P}_2K)/\sin \delta\psi$. Hence when $\delta\psi \to 0$, i.e., as P_2 approaches P_1 so that $P_1\hat{P}_2K \to \frac{1}{2}\pi$ and

$$\frac{P_1P_2}{\sin \delta\psi} \to \frac{ds}{d\psi},$$

then $P_1K \to \varrho$. Therefore in the limit the point K is the centre of curvature of the curve at P_1. This shows that we may consider the centre of curvature of a curve as the limit of the point of intersection of consecutive normals. The locus of the centre of curvature of a curve is called the *evolute* of that curve.

Example. The normal to the parabola $x = at^2$, $y = 2at$ at the point t is $tx + y - 2at - at^3 = 0$. The intersection of this line with the normal at t_1 is the point $\{a(2 + t^2 + tt_1 + t_1^2), -att_1(t_1 + t)\}$.
Therefore the centre of curvature at t is the point $\{a(2 + 3t^2), -2at^3)\}$.
Therefore the evolute of the parabola $x = at^2$, $y = 2at$ is the curve $27ay^2 = 4(x - 2a)^3$.

If C is the centre of curvature at a point P of a curve, then the circle with centre C and radius $CP = \varrho$, the radius of curvature at P, is called the *circle of curvature* at P. Suppose that P, Q, R, are three neighbouring points on a curve and A is the centre of the circle defined by the points P, Q, R, i.e., A is the point of inter-section of the perpendicular bisectors SA, TA, of the chords PQ, QR, (Fig. 4.7). Then, as Q and R approach P, the lines SA, TA become consecutive normals to the curve and A becomes the

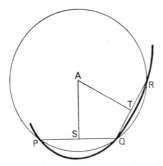

FIG. 4.7. The circle of curvature has three-point contact.

centre of curvature at P. This implies that the circle of curvature at P has three-point contact with the curve at P.

The above property of the circle of curvature forms the basis of *Newton's method* of finding the radius of curvature. Suppose the curve under consideration passes through the origin and has the axis Ox as tangent there, see Fig. 4.8. Let P be the point (x, y) on the curve and C the centre of the circle, of radius r, which passes through P and touches Ox at O. Then, if Q is the point in which the ordinate through P cuts the circle again and N is the foot of this ordinate, the geometry of the circle gives $ON^2 = NP \cdot NQ$ or $x^2 = y(2r - y)$. Therefore $r = \frac{1}{2}(y + x^2/y)$. Letting both x and $y \to 0$ by making P move along the curve to O, the circle becomes the circle of curvature at O and r becomes ϱ in the limit. Therefore

$$\varrho = \left| \frac{1}{2} \lim_{x \to 0} \left(\frac{x^2}{y} \right) \right|. \tag{4.13}$$

This is Newton's formula. If the curve does not pass through the origin or does not touch the x-axis there, suitable translation of the origin and/or rotation of the axes as given in § 4 : 10 may be used.

Example. The radius of curvature of the parabola $x^2 = 4ay$ at the origin is $2a$.

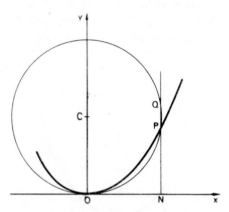

Fig. 4.8. Illustrating Newton's method for the radius of curvature.

Exercises 4 : 5

1. Prove that the radius of curvature at the point $(a, 0)$ on the curve whose equation is $y^2 = (a^3 - x^3)/x$ is $3a/2$.

2. Show that the radius of curvature at the point t on the curve

$$x = 2a \sin t + a \sin 2t, \quad y = 2a \cos t + a \cos 2t$$

is

$$\{8a \cos (t/2)\}/3.$$

3. Show that for the curve given by the equations

$$x = a(1 - \cos t), \quad y = at \quad (a > 0),$$

$$\varrho = \pm a \sec t (1 + \sin^2 t)^{\frac{3}{2}}.$$

Find the coordinates of the centre of curvature at the point $t = \pi/3$.

4. Find the radius of curvature and the coordinates of the centre of curvature of the curve $y = k \ln (x/a)$ at the point where it is met by the x-axis. (Take $k > 0, a > 0$.)

5. Find the coordinates of the centre of curvature at the point $(2, 4)$ on the parabola

$$y^2 = 4(x + 2).$$

6. O is the point $(0, 0)$ and P is the point $(3a/2, 3a/2)$ on the curve $3ay^2 = 2x^3$. If r is the radius of curvature at P and s is the length of the arc OP, prove that $2r = 9s + 4a$.

7. The parametric equations of a curve are

$$x = a(\cos \theta + \theta \sin \theta), \quad y = a(\sin \theta - \theta \cos \theta),$$

where θ is the parameter and a is a constant.

Find the radius of curvature, ϱ, in terms of θ, and the coordinates of the centre of curvature. Show that the centre of curvature lies on a circle of radius a.

8. If a curve is parametrically defined by $x = a \cos^3 \theta$, $y = a \sin^3 \theta$ and the arc is measured from the point defined by $\theta = 0$, show that $s = (3a/2) \sin^2 \theta$, $\tan \psi = -\tan \theta$, $\varrho^3 = 27axy$.

9. The parametric equations of a curve are $x = c \ln \tan (\tfrac{1}{2}\theta)$, $y = c \operatorname{cosec} \theta$. Show that the radius of curvature is given by y^2/c.

10. A curve is given parametrically by $x = e^t \cos t$, $y = e^t \sin t$.

Show that the tangent at any point t makes an angle $(t + \pi/4)$ with the x-axis, and that the radius of curvature at t is $\sqrt{2}e^t$.

Show that the evolute is the parent curve turned through a right angle.

11. Find the radius of curvature of the curve

$$4x^2 + 4xy + y^2 - 6x - 8y = 0,$$

at the origin.

12. Find the radius of curvature of the ellipse $x^2/a^2 + y^2/b^2 = 1$ at the point $(0, b)$.

13. Trace the curve $y^2 = x(x-1)^2$.

Find the equation of the tangent to this curve at the point $P(\tfrac{1}{4}, \tfrac{3}{8})$ and the coordinates of the point where this tangent meets the curve again.

By using Newton's method, or otherwise, find the radius of curvature of this curve at the origin.

14. A curve has parametric equations

$$\left.\begin{array}{l} x = n \cos t + \cos nt \\ y = n \sin t - \sin nt \end{array}\right\} \quad (n > 1).$$

Show that the radius of curvature at the point with parameter t is

$$\frac{4n \sin \{(n+1)t/2\}}{(n-1)}.$$

15. Prove that the centre of curvature of the rectangular hyperbola $xy = c^2$ at an arbitrary point $P(ct, c/t)$ is outside the square bounded by the lines $x = \pm 2c$, $y = \pm 2c$.

16. Find the radius of curvature at the origin, of the curve

$$y = 2x + 3x^2 - 2xy + y^2 + 2y^3,$$

and show that the circle of curvature at the origin has equation

$$3(x^2 + y^2) = 5(y - 2x).$$

17. The length of the perpendicular from the origin to the tangent at a point P of the curve $x^{\frac{2}{3}} + y^{\frac{2}{3}} = a^{\frac{2}{3}}$ is p, and the radius of curvature at P is ϱ. Prove that $\varrho = 3p$.

4 : 6 Envelopes

If a *family* of lines is such that each line is at a fixed distance p from the origin and hence touches the circle $x^2 + y^2 = p^2$, this circle is called the envelope of the family of lines $x \cos \alpha + y \sin \alpha = p$. Different values of the parameter α give different members

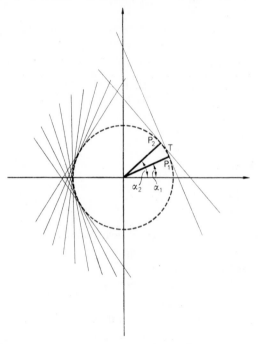

FIG. 4.9. A circle enveloped by a family of straight lines.

of the family. If the two members of the family with parameters α_1 and α_2 and touching the circle at P_1, P_2 intersect in the point T, then as $\alpha_2 \to \alpha_1$ the intersection T tends to the point ($p \cos \alpha_1$, $p \sin \alpha_1$), i.e., to coincidence with P_1. This result may be clearly seen by reference to Fig. 4.9. We can, therefore, say that the envelope of this family of lines is the locus of intersection of consecutive members of the family. This is a special case of a property of envelopes or enveloping curves.

The idea of the envelope of a family need not be confined to straight lines. A family of curves $f(x, y, \alpha) = 0$, where α is the parameter which determines different members of the family, in general, envelopes a curve. The envelope is obtained by eliminating α from the two equations

$$f(x, y, \alpha) = 0, \qquad \frac{\partial f}{\partial \alpha} = f_\alpha(x, y, \alpha) = 0. \qquad (4.14)$$

The proof of this result is given in Vol. 2, § 1 : 5.

Example. The envelope of the family of parabolas $y = x \tan \alpha - \dfrac{gx^2}{2V^2 \cos^2 \alpha}$ is the parabola $x^2 = \dfrac{2V^2}{g} \left[\dfrac{V^2}{2g} - y \right]$. Only the points on and inside the surface obtained by revolving this *bounding parabola* about the vertical may be hit by a projectile fired from O with speed V.

Since the evolute of a curve is the intersection of consecutive normals of that curve, we see that the evolute is the envelope of the normals to a curve. For example the evolute of the parabola $x = at^2$, $y = 2at$ is the envelope of the family of lines $tx + y - 2at - at^3 = 0$.

The evolute has a property which is of some practical importance. If a flexible thread ACP is wound around a curve S_1 so that it is in contact with S_1 from A to C and then lies along the tangent at C with CP straight, then, as the thread is unwound, P traces out a curve S_2 which is such that S_1 is the evolute of S_2. This may give a convenient method of designing the profiles of curves. Further, by choosing the initial length of the straight section CP to have different values, the different curves S_2 so obtained all have the same evolute S_1.

Exercises 4 : 6

1. Prove that the equation

$$2yt = x + (t^2 - 1)a, \qquad (1)$$

where a and t are parameters, represents a family of parallel straight lines when t is fixed and a is variable, and write down the equation of that straight line which passes through the origin.

When a is fixed and t is variable, prove that equation (1) represents a family of tangents to the parabola $y^2 = a(x - a)$.

When a and t both vary, find the relation which must hold between a and t in order that equation (1) shall represent the family of tangents to the circle $x^2 + y^2 = 1$.

2. Show that the evolute of the rectangular hyperbola $x = ct$, $y = c/t$ is the curve

$$(x + y)^{\frac{2}{3}} - (x - y)^{\frac{2}{3}} = (4c)^{\frac{2}{3}} .$$

3. Find the evolute of the ellipse $x = a \cos \varphi$, $y = b \sin \varphi$.

4. Find the envelope, as θ varies, of the straight line whose equation is

$$x \cos^3 \theta + y \sin^3 \theta = a, \qquad (a > 0).$$

Sketch this envelope, and find the radius of curvature at one of the points of the curve nearest to the origin.

5. (i) A family of curves is represented by $At^2 + 2Bt + C = 0$, where A, B and C are functions of x and y. Show that the equation of the envelope of this family is given by the condition for equal roots in the quadratic.

(ii) Determine the envelope of the family of circles

$$x^2 + y^2 - ax \cos \phi - by \sin \phi = 0$$

either by using the substitution $\tan (\phi/2) = t$ and applying the result of (i), or otherwise. Sketch the envelope for $a = 3$, $b = 1$.

4:7 The loaded cable: intrinsic equations

The curve in which a loaded cable hangs illustrates the use of the work of the previous sections. Consider, Fig. 4.10, a cable carrying a load w per unit length; P_1 and P_2 are the points with intrinsic coordinates (s, ψ), $(s + \delta s, \psi + \delta \psi)$ at which the tensions are T and $T + \delta T$ respectively. Then horizontal and vertical resolutions for the equilibrium of the element $P_1 P_2$ give

$$(T + \delta T) \cos (\psi + \delta \psi) - T \cos \psi = 0,$$
$$(T + \delta T) \sin (\psi + \delta \psi) - T \sin \psi = w \, \delta s.$$

Dividing each of these equations by δs and letting $\delta s \to 0$ gives

$$\frac{\mathrm{d}}{\mathrm{d}s} (T \cos \psi) = 0, \qquad \frac{\mathrm{d}}{\mathrm{d}s} (T \sin \psi) = w. \qquad (4.15)$$

The first of these equations implies that $T \cos \psi = T_0$ where T_0 is

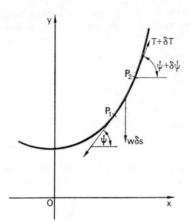

FIG. 4.10. A loaded flexible cable.

constant. Then the second equation may be written

$$\frac{d}{ds}(T \sin \psi) = \frac{d}{d\psi}(T_0 \tan \psi)\frac{d\psi}{ds} = \frac{T_0}{\varrho}\sec^2 \psi = w,$$

i.e.

$$T_0 \sec^2 \psi = w\varrho. \tag{4.16}$$

This is the equation satisfied by any flexible cable subject to a vertical loading w per unit length of cable. The loading w is usually given as a function of position. Two cases of particular importance are given below. [See also Vol. 3, pp. 45–67.]

Example 1. *A uniform flexible cable hanging freely; $w = $ constant.*

Writing $T_0 = wc$, we find

$$\varrho = \frac{ds}{d\psi} = c \sec^2 \psi; \qquad s = c \tan \psi + \text{constant}.$$

Also

$$\frac{dx}{d\psi} = \frac{dx}{ds}\cdot\frac{ds}{d\psi} = \cos \psi \cdot c \sec^2 \psi = c \sec \psi.$$

$$\therefore x = c \ln (\sec \psi + \tan \psi) + \text{constant}.$$

Similarly,

$$\frac{dy}{d\psi} = \frac{dy}{ds}\cdot\frac{ds}{d\psi} = \sin \psi \cdot c \sec^2 \psi = c \sec \psi \tan \psi.$$

$$\therefore y = c \sec \psi + \text{constant}.$$

Choosing $s = 0$ where $\psi = 0$, i.e. where the cable is horizontal, and cartesian axes with Ox horizontal and the lowest point of the cable at the point $(0, c)$, all the constants of integration vanish and we have

$$s = c \tan \psi, \quad x = c \ln (\sec \psi + \tan \psi), \quad y = c \sec \psi.$$

The relation for x gives

$$e^{x/c} = \sec \psi + \tan \psi, \quad e^{-x/c} = \sec \psi - \tan \psi.$$

$$\therefore y = c \sec \psi = c \cosh (x/c),$$

$$s = c \tan \psi = c \sinh (x/c),$$

and the cable hangs in the form of a *catenary*. The reader may easily verify the formulae $y^2 = c^2 + s^2$, $T = wy$.

This example illustrates the technique for the derivation of the cartesian equation from the intrinsic equation of a curve. For, if

$$s = f(\psi), \quad \text{then} \quad \frac{dx}{d\psi} = \frac{dx}{ds}\frac{ds}{d\psi} = f'(\psi) \cos \psi.$$

Similarly,

$$\frac{dy}{d\psi} = f'(\psi) \sin \psi.$$

Integration gives x and y as functions of ψ and elimination of ψ between these gives y as a function of x.

Example 2. *Uniform horizontal loading;* $w = W \cos \psi$ where W is constant.

In this case eqn. (4.16) gives $ds/d\psi = c_1 \sec^3 \psi$ where $c_1 = T_0/W$. Hence $dx/d\psi = c_1 \sec^2 \psi$, $dy/d\psi = c_1 \sec^2 \psi \tan \psi$.

Choosing cartesian axes so that $x = 0$, $y = 0$ where $\psi = 0$, we find $x = c_1 \tan \psi$, $y = \frac{1}{2}c_1 \tan^2 \psi$ and therefore the cable hangs in the shape of the parabola $2c_1 y = x^2$. This is the approximate shape of the cables of a suspension bridge which carries a straight horizontal road.

Exercises 4 : 7

1. Find the parametric equations of the curve, the *cycloid*, whose intrinsic equation is $s = 4a \sin \psi$, given that $x = 0 = y$ when $\psi = 0$.

2. Find the intrinsic equation of the parabola $x = at^2$, $y = 2at$, given that $s = 0$ where $t = 0$.

3. Find the intrinsic equation of the *epicycloid*

$$x = 3a \cos \theta - a \cos 3\theta, \quad y = 3a \sin \theta - a \sin 3\theta,$$

given that $s = 0$ where $\psi = 0$.

4. The tangent PQ at a point $P(x, y)$ on a curve C makes an angle ψ with the x-axis and intersects it in Q. The point $(0, 1)$ lies on C and the length

$PQ = 1$ for all points. Show that the radius of curvature is $\cot \psi$, and that

$$x = \cos \psi + \ln \tan \tfrac{1}{2}\psi, \quad y = \sin \psi$$

are parametric equations for C.

5. Determine the cartesian equation of the curves for which $\varkappa = \cos^2 \psi$.

4 : 8 Polar coordinates

We now discuss briefly techniques for obtaining the geometrical properties of curves whose equations are given in polar coordinates. The direction of the tangent at P to the curve $r = f(\theta)$

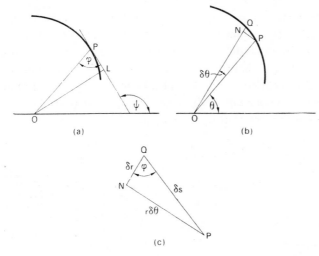

FIG. 4.11. The direction of the tangent in polar coordinates.

is given by the angle φ between the radius vector OP and the tangent PL, Fig. 4.11(a). We obtain the direction of the tangent by taking two neighbouring points $P(r, \theta)$ and $Q(r + \delta r, \theta + \delta\theta)$, Figs. 4.11(b) and 4.11(c), and letting Q tend to coincidence with P. Since $ON = r \cos \delta\theta$,

$$QN = r + \delta r - r \cos \delta\theta = \delta r + O\{(\delta\theta)^2\}.$$

$$\therefore \ \tan \varphi = \lim_{\delta\theta \to 0} \frac{PN}{NQ} = \lim_{\delta\theta \to 0} \left\{ \frac{r\delta\theta}{\delta r} + O\left(\frac{(\delta\theta)^2}{\delta r} \right) \right\}.$$

$$\therefore \ \tan \varphi = \frac{r \, d\theta}{dr} = \frac{r}{dr/d\theta}. \tag{4.17}$$

Also, if δs denotes the arc length PQ,

$$\delta s = \sqrt{\{(\delta r)^2 + (r\delta\theta)^2\}} + O\{(\delta\theta)^2\}.$$

$$\therefore \quad \frac{ds}{dr} = \pm\left\{1 + r^2\left(\frac{d\theta}{dr}\right)^2\right\}^{\frac{1}{2}} = \pm\sec\varphi. \tag{4.18}$$

When φ is acute, as shown in the figures,

$$\frac{dr}{ds} = \cos\varphi, \quad r\frac{d\theta}{ds} = \sin\varphi. \tag{4.19}$$

The *pedal*, or *p-r*, equation of the curve $r = f(\theta)$ relates the perpendicular distance $p = OL$ of the tangent at (r, θ) from the pole O with the radius vector $r = OP$. Since $p = r\sin\varphi$, elimination of θ and φ between this equation, $r = f(\theta)$ and eqn. (4.17) gives the pedal equation. The pedal equation is of use in finding the curvature of a curve whose polar equation is given. For, differentiating the equation $p = r\sin\varphi$ w.r. to r,

$$\frac{dp}{dr} = \sin\varphi + r\cos\varphi\,\frac{d\varphi}{dr}$$

$$= r\frac{d\theta}{ds} + r\frac{dr}{ds}\frac{d\varphi}{dr} = r\frac{d(\theta+\varphi)}{ds} = r\frac{d\psi}{ds} = \frac{r}{\varrho}.$$

$$\therefore \quad \varrho = \frac{r}{dp/dr}. \tag{4.20}$$

Example 1. By writing $x = r\cos\theta$, $y = r\sin\theta$ the equations of the straight line $x\cos\alpha + y\sin\alpha = p$ and the circle $x^2 + y^2 - ax = 0$ are expressed in the forms $r\cos(\theta-\alpha) = p$, $r = a\cos\theta$ respectively.

Example 2. Since $p/r = \sin\varphi$ and $\tan\varphi = r\,d\theta/dr$, then $r^2/p^2 = \operatorname{cosec}^2\varphi = 1 + \cot^2\varphi$;

$$\therefore \quad \frac{1}{p^2} = \frac{1}{r^2} + \frac{1}{r^4}\left(\frac{dr}{d\theta}\right)^2.$$

Example 3. In the *cardioid* $r = a(1 - \cos\theta)$, $\tan\varphi = \tan(\tfrac{1}{2}\theta)$. Therefore $\varphi = \tfrac{1}{2}\theta$. Also $p = r\sin\tfrac{1}{2}\theta$ and, since $r = 2a\sin^2(\tfrac{1}{2}\theta)$, $r^3 = 2ap^2$ is the pedal equation. Then $\varrho = \tfrac{2}{3}\sqrt{(2ar)}$.

If φ is an acute angle, so that ds/dr and $dr/d\theta$ are both positive, eqn. (4.18) can be expressed in the form

$$\frac{ds}{d\theta} = \left\{ \left(\frac{dr}{d\theta} \right)^2 + r^2 \right\}^{\frac{1}{2}}.$$

Hence in this case the arc length l of the curve $r = f(\theta)$ between the points for which $\theta = \alpha$ and $\theta = \beta$ is given by

$$l = \int_\alpha^\beta \left[\left(\frac{dr}{d\theta} \right)^2 + r^2 \right]^{\frac{1}{2}} d\theta = \int_\alpha^\beta [\{f'(\theta)\}^2 + \{f(\theta)\}^2]^{\frac{1}{2}} d\theta. \quad (4.21)$$

Example. Find the length of the perimeter of the cardioid $r = a(1 + \cos\theta)$.

Figure 6.8, p. 363, shows that the required perimeter l is twice the arc ABO.

$$\therefore l = 2 \int_0^\pi \sqrt{\{a^2 \sin^2\theta + a^2(1 + \cos\theta)^2\}} \, d\theta$$

$$= 2a \int_0^\pi \sqrt{\{2(1 + \cos\theta)\}} \, d\theta = 4a \int_0^\pi \cos(\tfrac{1}{2}\theta) \, d\theta = 4a \left[2 \sin(\tfrac{1}{2}\theta) \right]_0^\pi = 8a.$$

Exercises 4 : 8

1. Show that, in the curve $r^2 = a^2 \sec\theta$, angle φ is given by $\tan\varphi = 2 \cot\theta$.

2. Sketch the curve $r = 1 + 2\cos\theta$, which consists of two loops. Show that its p-r equation referred to the origin O is $r^4 = p^2(3 + 2r)$ and find an expression for ϱ. If the initial line cuts the loops at A and B, show that the radii of curvature at A and B are in the ratio 27:5.

3. A point moves so that the product of its distances from two fixed points, A and B, is constant and equal to $3c^2$, where $c = \tfrac{1}{2}AB$. By taking the midpoint of AB as pole, show that the polar equation of the locus of the point can be expressed in the form

$$r^4 - 2c^2r^2 \cos 2\theta - 8c^4 = 0.$$

Find the p-r equation of the curve, and hence show that its curvature at any point is $(3r^4 - 8c^4)/(6c^2r^3)$.

4. Sketch the curve $r = a\cos^2\theta$, showing that it consists of two loops. Show that the length of one loop is

$$a \frac{[2\sqrt{3} + \ln(2 + \sqrt{3})]}{\sqrt{3}}.$$

5. Show that the *p-r* equation of the ellipse $x^2/a^2 + y^2/b^2 = 1$ is

$$\frac{a^2 b^2}{p^2} = a^2 + b^2 - r^2 .$$

Show also that the *p-r* equation of the hyperbola $x^2/a^2 - y^2/b^2 = 1$ is

$$\frac{a^2 b^2}{p^2} = r^2 - a^2 + b^2 .$$

6. Sketch the curve whose equation in polar coordinates is $r = 1 + \cos 2\theta$. Prove that the length of the curve corresponding to $0 \leqslant \theta \leqslant 2\pi$ is

$$8 + \frac{4}{\sqrt{3}} \ln (2 + \sqrt{3}).$$

4:9 Curve sketching

The previous sections of this chapter have been primarily concerned with the detailed properties of a curve at a point. Some problems necessitate a clear idea of the shape of a curve as a whole. This is best obtained from a *sketch* which exhibits the major features of the curve. It is usually impracticable to find this shape by plotting a large number of points on the curve. Each individual problem must be treated on its merits, but we enumerate below some techniques which are of general use in curve sketching. The equation of the curve is $f(x, y) = 0$, where we take $f(x, y)$ to be a polynomial in x and y, though many of the devices listed can be used when $f(x, y)$ involves transcendental functions also. First we give the equations of 6 curves to be used as illustrative examples and sketched in Fig. 4.12.

1. $ay^2 = x(a^2 - x^2), \qquad a > 0.$
2. $a^2 y^2 = x^2(a^2 - x^2), \qquad a > 0.$
3. $y = (x-a)(x-b)^2(x-c), \qquad 0 < a < b < c.$
4. $ay^2 = (x-a)^2(4a-x), \qquad a > 0.$
5. $y^2 = \dfrac{x}{(x-a)(x-b)}, \qquad 0 < a < b.$
6. $y^3 - 2xy^2 - x^2 y + 2x^3 + 3x^2 + 6y^2 + 7x = 0.$

We suggest investigation of the following points.

(i) *Symmetry about the axes.* If the equation $f(x, y) = 0$ is unaltered when x is replaced by $-x$, then y is an even function of x

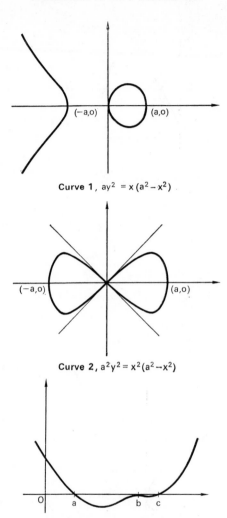

Curve 1, $ay^2 = x(a^2 - x^2)$

Curve 2, $a^2y^2 = x^2(a^2 - x^2)$

Curve 3, $y = (x-a)(x-b)^2(x-c)$

FIG. 4.12. Sketches of curves.

and the curve is symmetrical about Oy. Similarly, replacing y by $-y$ can indicate symmetry about Ox.

Curves 1, 4, 5 are symmetrical about Ox; curve 2 is symmetrical about Ox and Oy. The remaining curves have no symmetry of this kind.

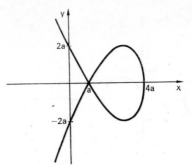

Curve 4, $ay^2 = (x-a)^2(4a-x)$

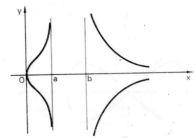

Curve 5, $y^2 = \dfrac{x}{(x-a)(x-b)}$

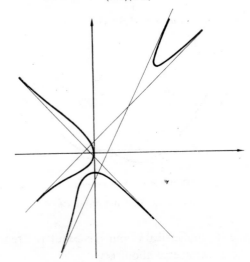

Curve 6, $y^3 - 2xy^2 - x^2y + 2x^3 + 3x^2 + 6y^2 + 7x = 0$

FIG. 4.12.

(ii) *Intersection with the axes.* Determine the points where the curve crosses Ox and also find the directions in which it does so. This may be done either by finding the sign of dy/dx at each such point or by noting whether y changes from positive to negative as x increases through the point or vice versa. Similar methods are used for intersections with the y-axis. A repeated root of even order indicates that the axis touches the curve. A repeated root of odd order indicates that the curve has an inflexion on the axis which is a tangent there. This test also shows whether the curve lies above or below Ox or to the left or right of Oy.

Curve 3 is such that $y > 0$ for $x < a$, and $y < 0$ for $a < x < b$; it crosses Ox at $x = a$ downwards to the right. Also y has a double zero when $x = b$; hence Ox is a tangent at $x = b$. Since $y < 0$ for $b < x < c$, the curve remains below Ox. It crosses Ox again at $x = c$ and thereafter $y > 0$ for $c < x$. The curve cuts Oy where $y = ab^2c$. These facts alone suffice to give the general shape of this curve.

(iii) *Excluded regions.* The equation should be examined to see if there is any range of values of x for which y cannot have real values, and vice versa. There are no points of the curve with coordinates inside such ranges.

Curve 1 is restricted to lie within the two regions for which $x \leqslant -a$ and $0 \leqslant x \leqslant a$. Curve 2 lies within the rectangle bounded by the lines $x = a$, $x = -a$, $y = \frac{1}{2}a$, $y = -\frac{1}{2}a$. [The latter result is obtained by noting that the equation, expressed as a quadratic in x^2, is

$$(x^2)^2 - a^2x^2 + a^2y^2 = 0.$$

If x^2 is to be real $(a^2)^2 \geqslant 4a^2y^2$.]

Curve 4 must lie to the left of the line $x = 4a$.
Curve 5 lies entirely in the regions $0 \leqslant x \leqslant a$ and $b \leqslant x$.

(iv) *Behaviour at infinity.* Where the equation permits large values of $|x|$ or $|y|$ the terms of the highest degree are dominant and give an approximation to the shape of the curve [see also test (vii)].

Curve 1 is similar in shape to $ay^2 = -x^3$ at large distances from the origin.

(v) *Behaviour near the origin.* If the curve passes through the origin it resembles the curve (or straight lines) obtained by neglecting all the terms except those of lowest degree. Usually these give the equations of one or more straight lines which are tangents at the origin. But if the terms of next lowest degree are included, a curve simpler than the one being investigated will be obtained.

Curve 6 gives $7x = 0$ when we neglect all except 1st degree terms. Therefore $x = 0$ is the tangent at the origin. If we include the next lowest degree terms we obtain

$$3x^2 + 6y^2 + 7x = 0.$$

We shall see later that this represents an ellipse (symmetrical about the x-axis) lying to the left of the origin. Only that part of the ellipse close to the origin is an approximation to the curve. Curve 2 resembles $x^2 = y^2$ near the origin. This gives two tangents $x = y$ and $x = -y$ which cross at the origin.

Curves 1 and 5 each have $x = 0$ as tangent at the origin. Near the origin these curves resemble respectively $ay^2 = a^2 x$ and $aby^2 = x$. These are both parabolas lying to the right of Oy.

If it is required, similar information about the behaviour of the curve at a point (x_0, y_0) other than the origin can be obtained by choosing new coordinate axes having this point as origin, cf. §4:10.

(vi) *Singular points.* A singular point on a curve is a point at which dy/dx is indeterminate (taking the form $0/0$).

Classification of singular points at the origin. When the origin lies on the curve, the equation of the curve must be of the form

$$(a_1 x + a_2 y) + (b_1 x^2 + b_2 xy + b_3 y^2)$$
$$+ (c_1 x^3 + c_2 x^2 y + c_3 xy^2 + c_4 y^3) + \ldots = 0,$$

where the a's, b's, etc., are constants. If at least one of a_1, a_2 is non-zero, then the origin O is an ordinary point on the curve, the tangent there having equation $a_1 x + a_2 y = 0$. If $a_1 = a_2 = 0$ then the origin is a singular point of the curve. Further, if not all of b_1, b_2, b_3 are zero this singular point is a *double point* of the curve. Similarly if $a_1 = a_2 = b_1 = b_2 = b_3 = 0$ and not all of c_1, c_2, c_3, c_4 are zero the curve has a *triple point* at O, etc. When the curve has a double point at O, it behaves near O like the pair of straight lines

$$b_1 x^2 + b_2 xy + b_3 y^2 = 0.$$

1. If these lines are real and distinct the curve has two distinct branches through O and the double point is a *node*.

2. If these lines are real and coincident,

i.e. if $b_1x^2 + b_2xy + b_3y^2 \equiv k(\beta_1x + \beta_2y)^2$,

the curve has in general a single tangent at the origin and the curve has a *cusp* there if it does not continue through the origin, and has a *tacnode* if the curve does continue through the origin.

3. If the lines are imaginary, then the origin is an *isolated point*. An isolated point is a point P whose coordinates satisfy the equation of the curve but which is such that there are no other points of the curve in the vicinity of P. (See Vol. 2, § 5 : 6.) For example, the curve $y^2 = x^2(x-a)$, where $a > 0$, has an isolated point at the origin. The various cases are illustrated in Fig. 4.13.

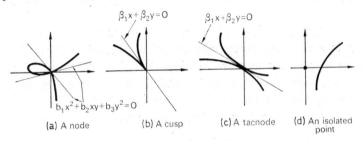

(a) A node   (b) A cusp   (c) A tacnode   (d) An isolated point

FIG. 4.13. Types of singular points.

Singular points can be located by obtaining dy/dx in the form $f(x)/g(x)$, without cancellation of common factors, and finding the common roots of $f(x) = 0$, $g(x) = 0$. If the point (h, k) is a singular point, it can be investigated most easily by choosing new coordinate axes with this point as origin. (See § 4 : 10.)

Example. Curve 2 (Fig. 4.12) has a node at O.

The curve $ay^2 = x^3$, $a > 0$, has a cusp at O.

The curve $a^2(x+y)^2 = x^2y^2$, $a > 0$, has a tacnode at O. [See Fig. 4.14(a).] Its equation can be written $xy = \pm a(x+y)$. The + sign corresponds to a hyperbola with asymptotes $x = a$, $y = a$; the − sign to a similar hyperbola with asymptotes $x = -a$, $y = -a$. The tacnode at the origin has $x + y = 0$ as tangent.

The curve $a^2y^2 = x^2(x^2 - 4a^2)$, $a > 0$, has an isolated point at O. [See Fig. 4.14(b).]

(vii) *Asymptotes.* An asymptote is a tangent line whose point of contact with the curve is an infinite distance from the origin,

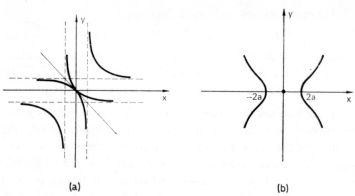

FIG. 4.14. (a) The curve $a^2(x+y)^2 = x^2y^2$. (b) The curve $a^2y^2 = x^2(x^2-4a^2)$.

i.e. "a tangent at infinity". A curve of the nth degree may have up to n real asymptotes with directions parallel to the straight lines whose equations are obtained by taking the terms of the highest degree in $f(x, y)$ and equating them to zero. The equations of the asymptotes themselves are obtained by making approximations in the equation of the curve.

The curve 6 has terms of the highest degree

$$y^3 - 2xy^2 - x^2y + 2x^3 = (y-x)(y+x)(y-2x)$$

showing that the asymptotes are parallel to the lines $y-x = 0$, $y+x = 0$, $y-2x = 0$. Choosing for illustration that asymptote parallel to $y-2x = 0$, we write the equation of the curve in the form

$$y = 2x - \frac{3x^2 + 6y^2 + 7x}{y^2 - x^2}. \tag{4.22}$$

For points of the curve near this asymptote $y \approx 2x$; therefore the last fraction on the r.h.s. is a correcting term to the above approximate value. Hence substituting the approximate value $y = 2x$ in the small correcting term of eqn. (4.22) we obtain

$$y \approx 2x - \frac{27x^2 + 7x}{3x^2} = 2x - 9 + O\left(\frac{1}{x}\right).$$

This means that, for large values of $|x|$ in the region near the line $y = 2x$, this line is a first approximation, and that $y = 2x - 9$ is a second approximation to the equation of the curve. To find the next approximation we write the equation of the curve

$$y = 2x - 9 - \frac{12x^2 - 3y^2 + 7x}{y^2 - x^2}.$$

In the correcting term we put the approximate value $y = 2x - 9$ so that

$$y \approx 2x - 9 - \frac{115x - 243}{3x^2 - 36x + 81} \cdot$$

Since $|x|$ is large we take only the first member in the numerator and the denominator of the correction term giving

$$y \approx 2x - 9 - \frac{115}{3x} \cdot$$

This shows that for large positive values of x the curve lies just below its asymptote $y = 2x - 9$, and for large negative values of x it lies just above this asymptote. A similar investigation for the other asymptotes leads to the results

$$y \approx x + \frac{9}{2} + \frac{325}{8x}, \qquad y \approx -x - \frac{3}{2} - \frac{55}{24x} \cdot$$

The reader should see from these equations how the curve lies with respect to the other asymptotes

$$2y - 2x = 9, \qquad 2y + 2x = -3.$$

This investigation of the behaviour of a curve near its asymptotes is an example of an *iterative* (or step by step) process. (See § 5 : 9.)

Curve 5 may be written in the form

$$x^2y^2 - (a+b)xy^2 + aby^2 - x = 0.$$

The directions of its asymptotes (if any) are therefore either $x = 0$ or $y = 0$. To proceed further we remember that the curve is symmetrical about Ox and is excluded from the region $a \leqslant x \leqslant b$. Hence the curve must approach $x = a$ from the left both for positive and negative y, and approach $x = b$ from the right. The equation in x for a given y (i.e. the intersections of the curve and $y =$ constant) is a quadratic in x. If the line $y =$ constant is an asymptote the corresponding root must be infinite; hence $y^2 = 0$. (At least one root of a quadratic equation tends to ∞ if the first coefficient tends to zero.) The x-axis is a double asymptote which the curve approaches from both above and below.

(viii) *Intersections with the asymptotes.* Any finite points in which the curve cuts the asymptotes, and if convenient the direction in which it cuts them should be determined. The fact that two of the intersections of the asymptote and the curve are at infinity makes the solution simpler. Since curve 6 is a cubic curve, there is only one other intersection with each asymptote so that the equations reduce to linear equations. The asymptote $y = 2x - 9$ cuts curve 6 in the point $\left(\dfrac{243}{115}, -\dfrac{549}{115} \right) \cdot$

The asymptote $y = 0$ cuts curve 5 only at the origin and the asymptotes $x = a$ and $x = b$ do not cut the curve at any finite points.

(ix) *Gradient of the curve.* It is usually possible to find dy/dx in terms of x, y, and therefore the gradient at known points on the curve may be found, as well as those points where dy/dx vanishes (tangent horizontal) or becomes infinite (tangent vertical).

Curve 1 has horizontal tangents at $x = \pm a/\sqrt{3}$ and a vertical tangent at $y = 0$ [the origin, see section (v)]. Curve 2 has

$$\frac{dy}{dx} = \frac{(a^2 - 2x^2)y}{(a^2 - x^2)x}.$$

This gives horizontal tangents at $x = \pm a/\sqrt{2}$. At the origin dy/dx is indeterminate. [The curve crosses itself at the origin, see section (v).]

For curve 5

$$2y\frac{dy}{dx} = \frac{1}{(a-b)}\left\{\frac{b}{(x-b)^2} - \frac{a}{(x-a)^2}\right\}.$$

Hence dy/dx vanishes if $x = \pm\sqrt{ab}$. Negative values of x are excluded. Further, since $a < \sqrt{(ab)} < b$ and $a < x < b$ is an excluded region, this curve has no horizontal tangents.

(x) *The use of polar coordinates.* Sketching a curve from its polar equation is not very practicable unless the equation is in the form $r = f(\theta)$. Then the shape is usually given by plotting and determining the maximum and minimum values of r as θ varies (see § 5 : 6) and any excluded sectors.

Example. Putting $x = r\cos\theta$ and $y = r\sin\theta$ in the equation for curve 2 gives the polar form

$$r^2 = a^2\cos 2\theta\sec^4\theta.$$

Since $\cos 2\theta$ is negative for $\frac{1}{4}\pi < \theta < \frac{3}{4}\pi$ and again for $\frac{5}{4}\pi < \theta < \frac{7}{4}\pi$ the curve is confined to two right angled sectors which include the positive and negative halves of the x-axis.

In tracing a curve (passing through the origin) from its equation in polar coordinates the direction of the tangent to the curve at the origin is given by the (limiting) value of θ which makes $r \to 0$. Also many curves can be seen, from their equations, to lie inside a circle, or some other simple curve; if the given curve and the circle have points in common at which the curves each have a unique tangent, they must *touch* at these points for they cannot cross. [See Examples 1, 2 following.]

Example 1. Sketch the curve $r = a \cos 3\theta$.

Since $-1 \leqslant \cos 3\theta \leqslant 1$, this curve, C_1, lies entirely inside the circle $r = a$ and these curves touch at points for which $3\theta = -2\pi$, 0, 2π. (For the values $\theta = -\pi/3$, $+\pi/3$, $r = -a$; this gives points coinciding with those already obtained.)

For values $\theta = -5\pi/6$, $-\pi/2$, $-\pi/6$, $\pi/6$, $\pi/2$, $5\pi/6$, r vanishes showing that there are three directions for the tangents at O, viz.

$$(\pi/6, \; -5\pi/6), \quad (\pi/2, \; -\pi/2), \quad (5\pi/6, \; -\pi/6).$$

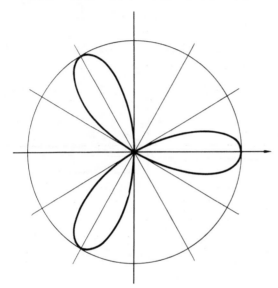

FIG. 4.15. The curve $r = a \cos 3\theta$.

As θ runs from $-\pi$ to $+\pi$ the whole curve is traced twice, once with $r > 0$, viz.

$$-5\pi/6 < \theta < -\pi/2, \quad -\pi/6 < \theta < \pi/6, \quad \pi/2 < \theta < 5\pi/6,$$

and once with $r < 0$, viz.

$$-\pi < \theta < -5\pi/6, \quad -\pi/2 < \theta < -\pi/6, \quad \pi/6 < \theta < \pi/2, \quad 5\pi/6 < \theta < \pi.$$

The curve C_1 is shown in Fig. 4.15.

Example 2. Sketch the curve $r^2 = a^2 \cos 3\theta$.

A fundamental difference between this curve, C_2, and the curve $r = a \cos 3\theta$, C_1, of Example 1 above, is that for the curve C_2 those values of θ for which $\cos 3\theta < 0$ give no real values for r. The tangents at the origin and the points of contact with the circle $r = a$ are the same for both curves. For positive $\cos 3\theta$, $r = a(\cos 3\theta)^{\frac{1}{2}}$ on curve C_2; since $(\cos 3\theta)^{\frac{1}{2}} \geqslant \cos 3\theta$ the value of r for specified θ is greater on curve C_2 than on C_1 and the points of C_2 lie outside the curve C_1 except for those for which $r = 0$ or a. Curve C_2 is shown in Fig. 4.16.

The equation of C_2 can be written

$$r^2 = a^2(4\cos^3\theta - 3\cos\theta) = a^2\cos\theta(4\cos^2\theta - 3) = a^2\cos\theta(\cos^2\theta - 3\sin^2\theta),$$

i.e. $$r^5 = a^2 r\cos\theta(r^2\cos^2\theta - 3r^2\sin^2\theta) = a^2 x(x^2 - 3y^2)$$

or $$(x^2 + y^2)^5 = a^2 x^2(x^2 - 3y^2)^2.$$

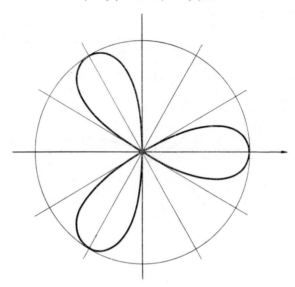

Fig. 4.16. The curve $r^2 = a^2\cos 3\theta$.

Equating the terms of this equation with the lowest powers of x, y, we see that curve C_2 behaves near the origin like

$$x^2(x^2 - 3y^2)^2 = 0,$$

i.e. $$x = 0, \quad x = \sqrt{3}y, \quad x = -\sqrt{3}y.$$

These are the tangents at the origin obtained from the earlier polar equation. [The previous example reduces to

$$(x^2 + y^2)^2 = ax(x^2 - 3y^2)$$

in cartesian coordinates.]

We now give, in illustration of the techniques described above, some rather more difficult examples.

Example 1. Sketch the curve $(x^2+y^2)^2 = 16\,axy^2$, $a > 0$.

In cases such at this it is most convenient to convert to polar coordinates, the polar equation of this curve being

$$r^3(r-16a\cos\theta\sin^2\theta) = 0.$$

Since the pole ($r = 0$) lies on the curve

$$r = 16a\cos\theta\sin^2\theta = 16a\cos\theta(1-\cos^2\theta), \qquad (1)$$

we need sketch this latter curve only. Note the following points.

(i) The curve, C, is symmetrical about Ox and so we need consider the range $0 \leqslant \theta \leqslant \pi$ only.

(ii) r is positive for $0 < \theta < \pi/2$, r is negative for $\pi/2 < \theta < \pi$.

(iii) *Near* the pole, $\cos\theta\sin^2\theta$ is *nearly* zero and as $\theta \to 0$, $\pm\pi/2$ or π, $r \to 0$; hence the tangents at the pole lie in the directions given by these values of θ. In fact near O, the curve behaves like $xy^2 = 0$.

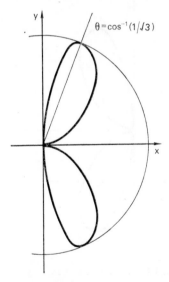

FIG. 4.17. The curve $(x^2+y^2)^2 = 16axy^2$.

(iv) The curve has no real asymptotes.

(v) Since $dr/d\theta = 16a\sin\theta(3\cos^2\theta-1)$, (see § 5:2), r increases as θ increases from 0 to $\cos^{-1}(1/\sqrt{3})$, has a maximum $32a/(3\sqrt{3})$ when $\theta = \cos^{-1}(1/\sqrt{3})$, then decreases to a minimum $-32a/(3\sqrt{3})$ when $\theta = -\cos^{-1}(1/\sqrt{3})$ and then increases to zero as θ increases to π.

Remembering that a negative r for $\theta = \alpha$ on C is equivalent to a point $(|r|, \pi+\alpha)$ on C we see that the loops of the curve are described twice as θ

increases from 0 to 2π. In fact the curve C touches the circle $r = 32a/(3\sqrt{3})$ at the point where $\theta = \pm\cos^{-1}(1/\sqrt{3})$. The curve is shown in Fig. 4.17. [The fact that there is no curve for $x < 0$ can be seen from the given cartesian equation, which for $x < 0$ would imply either $y^2 < 0$ or $(x^2 + y^2)^2 < 0$.]

Example 2. Sketch the curve whose equation, in cartesian coordinates, is

$$x^4 - 2xy^2 + y^4 = 0. \tag{1}$$

The highest order terms, $x^4 + y^4$, in this equation have no real factors and so the curve has no real asymptotes. In fact, regarding eqn. (1) as a quadratic in y^2 and solving, we find

$$y^2 = x\{1 \pm \sqrt{(1 - x^2)}\}. \tag{2}$$

There is therefore no curve for $x < 0$ as is otherwise clear from eqn. (1), [for if $x < 0$ then the sum of three positive terms is zero which cannot be so].

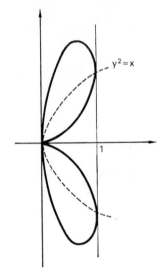

Fig. 4.18. The curve $x^4 - 2xy^2 + y^4 = 0$.

Equation (2) also implies that there is no curve for $x > 1$. Also the curve is symmetric about Ox and so henceforth we consider the case $y \geqslant 0$ only. The curve has tangents $x = 0$, $y = 0$ (twice) at the origin, one part of the curve in the first quadrant lies above the parabola $y^2 = x$, the other lies below $y^2 = x$.

Further, since

$$2y\frac{dy}{dx} = 1 \pm \frac{1 - 2x^2}{\sqrt{(1 - x^2)}}, \tag{3}$$

$dy/dx \to \mp\infty$ as $x \to 1$ and so the tangent at $(1, 1)$ is the line $x = 1$. Also the upper branch of that part of the curve which lies in the first quadrant has a maximum at $(\sqrt{3}/2, 3\sqrt{3}/4)$, whereas $dy/dx > 0$ on the lower branch in the first quadrant and this branch has no stationary points. The curve is shown in Fig. 4.18.

Example 3. Find the coordinates, in terms of t, of the point (other than the origin) in which the line $y = tx$ meets the curve $x^3 + y^3 = 2axy$, $a > 0$. Hence sketch the portion of the curve in the first quadrant.

The coordinates are easily found to be

$$x = \frac{2at}{1+t^3}, \quad y = \frac{2at^2}{1+t^3}, \tag{1}$$

and that part of the curve in the first quadrant is given parametrically by eqns. (1) as t increases from 0 to ∞. [Note that the only real asymptote of the curve is parallel to the line $x+y = 0$ and is, in fact, the line $x+y = -\frac{2}{3}a$. The curve does not go off to infinity in the first quadrant as is clear from eqns. (1) since $t > 0$ for points in the first quadrant.]

Since
$$\frac{dy}{dx} = \frac{t(2-t^3)}{1-2t^3},$$

(i) the x-axis, $t = 0$, touches the curve at the origin;

(ii) when $t = 2^{-\frac{1}{3}}$, dy/dx is infinite and the tangent is vertical, i.e. the tangent is parallel to Oy at $\left(2^{\frac{5}{3}}a/3, 2^{\frac{4}{3}}a/3\right)$;

(iii) y has a maximum (considered as a function of x) when $t = 2^{\frac{1}{3}}$, i.e. at the point $\left(2^{\frac{4}{3}}a/3, 2^{\frac{5}{3}}a/3\right)$.

(iv) $dy/dx \to \infty$ as $t \to \infty$ so that the y-axis is the tangent as the curve approaches the origin again.

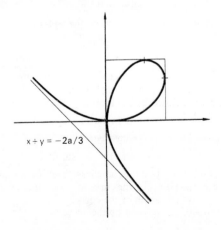

$x + y = -2a/3$

FIG. 4.19. The curve $x^3 + y^3 = 2axy$.

[Results (i) and (iv) are obvious from the fact that near the origin the curve behaves like $xy = 0$.]

The required portion of the curve is shown in Fig. 4.19. [The remainder of the curve, with it sole real asymptote $x+y = -2a/3$ is also shown.]

Exercises 4 : 9

Sketch the curves:

1. $ay^2 = x^2(x+b);$ $a > 0,$ $b > 0.$

2. $y^2 = \dfrac{x}{x^2-4}$.

3. $y = \dfrac{x(1+x)}{x^2-x+1}$.

4. Show that, for all real values of k other than zero, the line $y = k$ meets the curve

$$y(x-3)(x+1) = ax+b$$

in real points, if b lies between $-3a$ and a.

Sketch the curve in the cases

(i) $a = -3,$ $b = 7;$ (ii) $a = +3,$ $b = 7.$

5. Make a rough sketch of the hyperbola $16x^2 - 9y^2 - 32x = 0$ and find the radius of curvature at the origin.

6. Sketch the curve

$$y^2 = \frac{x^2(1-x)^2}{3+x}$$

and find the angle between the tangents at the origin.

7. Sketch the graph of the curve given by the equation

$$y^2(1-x)(x-2) = x^2,$$

and prove that the area between the curve and its asymptotes is 3π.

8. Sketch the curve $y^2 = ax^2(a-x)/(3a+x)^2$ and show that the acute angle between the tangents at the origin is $\tan^{-1}(3/4)$.

Show that the area enclosed by the loop is

$$4(10 - 9 \ln 3)a^2/3.$$

9. A curve is given by the parametric equations

$$x = a \sin 4t, \quad y = b \sin t,$$

where $a > 0$ and $b > 0$. Show that the curve is symmetrical about both axes of coordinates, and find the points of the curve at which the tangent is parallel to the x-axis. Draw a rough sketch of the curve.

Prove that the total area enclosed by the curve is

$$\frac{16}{15} ab(1 + \sqrt{2}).$$

10. Sketch the curve $ay^2 = x^2(x+a)$ where $a > 0$.

Find the equations of the tangents to the curve at the origin. Show that the radius of curvature of the curve at the point

$$\left(\frac{-a}{2}, \frac{a}{2\sqrt{2}}\right) \quad \text{is} \quad \frac{27a}{40}.$$

11. Sketch the curve $3ay^2 = x(x-a)^2$, where $a > 0$.
Show that

$$\frac{dy}{dx} = \pm\frac{(3x-a)}{2\sqrt{(3ax)}}$$

and, hence or otherwise, show that the perimeter of the loop of the curve is $4a/\sqrt{3}$.

12. Sketch the curve $r^2 = 2a^2 \cos 2\theta$.

If A and B are the points $(a, 0)$, $(-a, 0)$ and P is an arbitrary point on this curve, prove that $PA \cdot PB = a^2$.

13. The two curves with equations

$$6x^2+y^2 = 35 \quad \text{and} \quad y = \frac{1}{x^2}$$

have four real points in common, of which one is that with coordinates $(1+\sqrt{2}, 3-2\sqrt{2})$. Find the coordinates of the other three.

Sketch the two curves in the same diagram and hence or otherwise show that the inequality

$$\sqrt{(35-6x^2)} > \frac{1}{x^2}$$

is valid when x lies in one or other of two intervals, the sum of whose lengths is 4.

14. Sketch the hyperbola

$$y = \frac{x}{x-2}$$

and write down the equation of its mirror image in the y-axis.
Find the values of x for which

(a) $\dfrac{x}{x-2} > \dfrac{x}{x+2}$;   (b) $\dfrac{x^2}{x^2-2} > \dfrac{x^2}{x^2+2}$.

15. Sketch the graph of the function

$$y = \frac{x^2+2x+2}{x+1}$$

showing the asymptotes and the way in which the graph approaches its asymptotes.

16. Sketch the curve $y^2 = x^2(x-c)$ for $c = 1, 0, -1$. Find the area enclosed by the loop in the case $c = -1$.

17. Sketch the curve

$$y = \frac{(x-1)(x-4)}{(x-2)(x-3)}.$$

(Continued overleaf)

Prove that the normals to the curve at the points where it meets the x-axis meet on the asymptote parallel to that line.

18. Sketch the curve

$$6y^2 = x(x-y)(x-3y);$$

find its asymptotes and indicate them on your sketch.

19. Sketch the curve

$$x^5+y^5 = 5ax^2y^2 \qquad (a > 0).$$

By writing $y = tx$ prove that the area of the loop is $5a^2/2$.

20. Sketch the curve

$$r(1-2\cos\theta) = 3a\cos 2\theta,$$

and find the equations of its asymptotes.

4 : 10 Translation and rotation of axes

In many geometrical figures the axes of coordinates have no direct connection with the figure; the axes are introduced as a means of representing the geometrical points and properties in terms of variables, x, y, and equations. The properties are unaltered if different axes are used, although the equations and representations of these properties are altered. Nevertheless, the position of the origin and the directions of the axes are at our disposal and success in the solution of any particular problem in coordinate geometry frequently lies in a suitable choice of axes. To sum up "Fit the axes to the problem and not the problem to the axes".

To find the law of transformation of coordinates for a change of origin without change of direction of the axes, i.e. for a *translation of the axes*, we use two sets Oxy and $A\xi\eta$, Fig. 4.20(a). An arbitrary point P has coordinates (x, y) referred to Oxy and (ξ, η) referred to $A\xi\eta$. Clearly the transformation is

$$x = x_A+\xi, \quad y = y_A+\eta, \tag{4.23}$$

where (x_A, y_A) are the coordinates of A referred to the axes Oxy.

Example 1. Translation of the origin to the point $(2, 1)$ transforms the equation of the ellipse

$$x^2+3xy+2y^2-7x-10y+8 = 0 \quad \text{into} \quad \xi^2+3\xi\eta+2\eta^2-4 = 0.$$

Example 2. If A_1, A_2 are the points (x_1, y_1), (x_2, y_2) respectively, find the coordinates of the point P dividing the line A_1A_2 in the ratio $l:m$.

Referred to axes $A_1\xi\eta$ the coordinate of A_2 are x_2-x_1, y_2-y_1 and P has

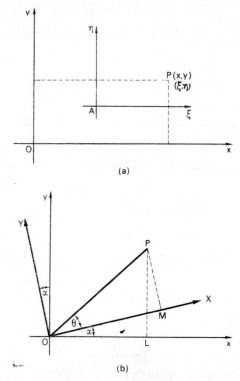

FIG. 4.20. (a) Translation of axes. (b) Rotation of axes.

coordinates $\xi = l(x_2-x_1)/(l+m)$, $\eta = l(y_2-y_1)/(l+m)$. Transferring to axes Oxy by (4.23), P has coordinates

$$x = \frac{lx_2+mx_1}{l+m}, \quad y = \frac{ly_2+my_2}{l+m}.$$

If we regard $m/l = t$ as variable, then the position of P varies along the straight line through A_1A_2 and hence

$$x = \frac{x_2+tx_1}{1+t}, \qquad y = \frac{y_2+ty_1}{1+t}$$

are the parametric equations of the straight line through A_1A_2. Eliminating t between these equations we obtain a linear relation between x and y, thereby proving that a straight line must have a linear equation.

We now develop formulae relating coordinates referred to axes in different directions but with a common origin. Suppose we have two sets of axes Oxy, OXY, where OXY are obtained from Oxy by a rotation through a positive angle α. Let P be an arbitrary point whose coordinates are (x, y), (X, Y) referred to the respective axes, Fig. 4.20(b). Since

$$x = OL = OP \cos(\theta + \alpha), \quad y = PL = OP \sin(\theta + \alpha),$$
$$X = OM = OP \cos\theta, \qquad Y = PM = OP \sin\theta,$$
$$x = OP \cos\theta \cos\alpha - OP \sin\theta \sin\alpha = X \cos\alpha - Y \sin\alpha,$$
$$y = OP \sin\theta \cos\alpha + OP \cos\theta \sin\alpha = X \sin\alpha + Y \cos\alpha. \quad (4.24)$$

Equations (4.24) may be solved to give

$$X = x \cos\alpha + y \sin\alpha,$$
$$Y = -x \sin\alpha + y \cos\alpha. \qquad (4.25)$$

For an alternative derivation of these formulae for the change in coordinates consequent on a *rotation of the axes* the reader should consult § 7 : 3, p. 420.

Example. $S = ax^2 + 2hxy + by^2$ transforms into

$$S = a'X^2 + 2h'XY + b'Y^2, \quad \text{where}$$
$$a' = a \cos^2\alpha + 2h \sin\alpha \cos\alpha + b \sin^2\alpha,$$
$$b' = a \sin^2\alpha - 2h \sin\alpha \cos\alpha + b \cos^2\alpha,$$
$$h' = h \cos 2\alpha + \tfrac{1}{2}(b - a) \sin 2\alpha.$$

The reader should verify that $a + b = a' + b'$, $ab - h^2 = a'b' - h'^2$, i.e., that $a + b$, $ab - h^2$ are each *invariant* under a rotation of axes. Similarly,

$$x^2 + y^2 = X^2 + Y^2$$

is invariant under rotation.

---

4 : 11 The area of a triangle

We now determine the area of the triangle ABC whose vertices A, B, C are the points (x_1, y_1), (x_2, y_2), (x_3, y_3) referred to the axes Oxy. The specification of a triangle automatically includes the sense of rotation around the triangle. Either we may enumerate the vertices by ABC, BAC, etc., or we may say the triangle is the area contained by the lines AB, AC or by the lines CA, CB, etc. The usual convention is to take a counter clockwise rotation in the plane as a positive rotation; right handed axes are such that

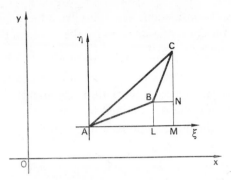

Fig. 4.21. The area of a triangle.

a positive rotation takes the direction Ox into that of Oy through the positive quadrant.

In Fig. 4.21, ABC is a positive rotation and we take the area ABC to be a positive area whereas the area ACB is taken to be a negative area. Introducing axes $A\xi$, $A\eta$ through A parallel to Ox, Oy the coordinates of A, B, C are given by the following table

	Oxy	$A\xi\eta$
A	(x_1, y_1)	$(0, 0)$
B	(x_2, y_2)	$(\xi_2, \eta_2) = (x_2 - x_1, y_2 - y_1)$
C	(x_3, y_3)	$(\xi_3, \eta_3) = (x_3 - x_1, y_3 - y_1)$

From the figure we see that

$$\varDelta ABC + \tfrac{1}{2}\xi_2\eta_2 + \tfrac{1}{2}(\xi_3 - \xi_2)(\eta_3 - \eta_2) + \eta_2(\xi_3 - \xi_2) = \tfrac{1}{2}\xi_3\eta_3.$$

$$\therefore \quad \varDelta ABC = \tfrac{1}{2}(\xi_2\eta_3 - \xi_3\eta_2)$$

or

$$\varDelta ABC = \tfrac{1}{2}(x_2 - x_1)(y_3 - y_1) - \tfrac{1}{2}(x_3 - x_1)(y_2 - y_1). \quad (4.26)$$

4 : 12 The general equation of the second degree

In engineering and physics, curves whose equations are of the second degree are of common occurrence. These curves are known as conic sections or more simply as conics. We first derive

some results of considerable generality from the general equation
which, with the conventional form for the choice of coefficients, is

$$S = ax^2 + 2hxy + by^2 + 2gx + 2fy + c = 0. \qquad (4.27)$$

The methods used here are illustrative of the general techniques
for obtaining geometrical information. The standard forms of the
various types of conic are obtained by special choice of the position of the origin and directions of the coordinate axes.

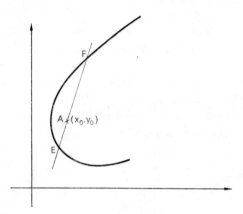

FIG. 4.22.

We first consider the intersections E, F of the curve with an
arbitrary straight line passing through the point $A(x_0, y_0)$, see
Fig. 4.22. It is convenient to use the parametric form of the equation of the straight line passing through A in the form

$$x = x_0 + ls, \quad y = y_0 + ms. \qquad (4.28)$$

The distance s from A to (x, y) is the parameter and l, m are the
cosines of the angles made by the line with the coordinate axes
$(l^2 + m^2 = 1)$. Substitution into the equation of the conic gives
the quadratic for s, whose roots are the distances AE, AF, i.e.

$$(al^2 + 2hlm + bm^2) s^2 + 2(lX_0 + mY_0) s + S_0 = 0, \qquad (4.29)$$

where

$$X_0 = ax_0 + hy_0 + g, \quad Y_0 = hx_0 + by_0 + f, \qquad (4.30)$$
$$S_0 = ax_0^2 + 2hx_0y_0 + by_0^2 + 2gx_0 + 2fy_0 + c.$$

We define the *centre* of the curve as the point C such that any chord through C is bisected at C. Let A coincide with C; then the roots of eqn. (4.29) are equal and opposite (i.e. $AE = -AF$) for all directions of the line and

$$lX_0+mY_0 = 0, \qquad (4.31)$$

for all values of l, m. This is only true if $X_0 = 0 = Y_0$, i.e. if

$$ax_0+hy_0+g = 0 = hx_0+by_0+f. \qquad (4.32)$$

Hence the centre of the conic must be at the intersection of the lines

$$\frac{1}{2}\frac{\partial S}{\partial x} \equiv ax+hy+g = 0, \quad \frac{1}{2}\frac{\partial S}{\partial y} \equiv hx+by+f = 0. \quad (4.33)$$

Note that there is no centre to the curve if $ab-h^2 = 0$, i.e., if the terms of the second degree in S form a perfect square.

The asymptotes of the conic $S = 0$ are parallel to the straight lines given by

$$ax^2+2hxy+by^2 = 0. \qquad (4.34)$$

Equations (4.23) imply that a translation of axes does not affect the second-degree terms in the equation of a conic; choosing the origin at the centre merely removes the first degree terms, and alters the term independent of x and y. Using x, y as current coordinates with the origin at the centre of the curve we may write the equation of the conic in the form

$$ax^2+2hxy+by^2+S_0 = 0. \qquad (4.35)$$

Three cases arise according as $ab-h^2 < 0$, $ab-h^2 > 0$ or $ab-h^2 = 0$.

Case (i) $ab-h^2 < 0$. Since the terms of the second degree have real factors the curve has two real asymptotes. The use of the results of § 4 : 10 for rotation of axes shows that the equation can be put into the form

$$a'X^2-b'Y^2+S_0 = 0, \qquad (4.36)$$

where $a'-b' = a+b$ and $ab-h^2 = -a'b'$. The angle of rotation is given by $\tan 2\alpha = 2h/(a-b)$.

A central conic whose terms of the second degree have real factors is a *hyperbola*. The general conic is a hyperbola if the terms of the second degree have real factors, i.e. $ab - h^2 < 0$. This implies the existence of a centre ($ab \neq h^2$). The properties of the hyperbola are discussed further in § 4 : 14.

Case (ii) $ab - h^2 > 0$. This condition implies that the terms of second degree are a *definite* form (cf. § 1 : 6), positive if $a > 0$, negative if $a < 0$. (Hence if a and S_0 of eqn. (4.35) have the same sign there are no real points on the curve.) There are no asymptotes to the curve, and rotation of axes transforms the equation to

$$a'X^2 + b'Y^2 + S_0 = 0, \qquad (4.37)$$

where a' and b' have the same sign, $a' + b' = a + b$ and $ab - h^2 = a'b'$. Again the angle of rotation is given by $\tan 2\alpha = 2h/(a - b)$. The form (4.37) shows that the distance of the point (X, Y) from the origin never vanishes or becomes infinite; the curve is therefore oval in shape. This is an *ellipse*, for which the test in the general form is the absence of real factors for the terms of second degree, i.e. $ab - h^2 > 0$, a condition which also implies the existence of a centre. The ellipse is discussed in detail in § 4 : 13.

One point of general importance is worth emphasising. Whenever a quadratic form $ax^2 + 2hxy + by^2$ is such that $ab - h^2 \neq 0$ it is always possible to find a pair of orthogonal axes, i.e. *principal axes*, for which the form reduces to the sum or difference of two squares. This is a result which is of frequent occurrence in mathematics.

Case (iii) $ab - h^2 = 0$. In this case the terms of the second degree form a perfect square and the curve has no centre. The curve is a *parabola*. The reader is probably familiar with the general shape of this curve. We indicate briefly here how to show that the curve has this shape.

Since the terms of the second degree form a perfect square, we may write the equation as

$$S = (px + qy)^2 + 2gx + 2fy + c = 0. \qquad (4.38)$$

(There is no asymptote parallel to $px + qy = 0$.) Since

$$2gx + 2fy + c \leqslant 0$$

for all points on the curve, we conclude that the curve lies wholly on one side of some straight line. This follows because the sign of the perpendicular distance from (x, y) to $2gx+2fy+c = 0$ can have only a negative sign. The method introduced on page 220 can be used to show the following properties:

1. An arbitrary line drawn in a certain direction cuts the curve once only. Any line drawn from a point on the curve in this special direction is a *diameter*, but an arbitrary line drawn in any other direction cuts the curve in two points which are real, coincident or imaginary.

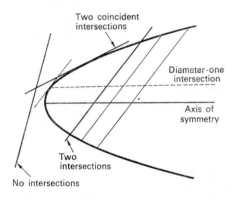

Two coincident
intersections

Diameter-one
intersection

Axis of
symmetry

Two
intersections

No intersections

FIG. 4.23. Intersections of a line and a parabola.

2. The mid-points of all chords parallel to a fixed direction lie on one diameter. The chords are parallel to the tangent line at the end of the diameter.

3. There is one diameter which is perpendicular to the chords which it bisects. This diameter is therefore an axis of symmetry.

These properties, whose proofs are left as examples for the reader, are illustrated in Fig. 4.23 and indicate that the curve has the shape shown there. Since there is only one diameter which bisects chords at right angles, this diameter is perpendicular to the tangent at its end. This is the only point where the tangent and corresponding diameter are perpendicular and is the *vertex*.

The final conclusion is therefore that the general equation of the second degree—and consequently *any* equation of the second degree—must represent one of the three types of curve, ellipse, parabola or hyperbola.

Example 1. Prove statement 1 above.

Let $S = (px+qy)^2+2gx+2fy+c = 0$ represent the parabola.
Draw the line

$$x = x_0+ls, \quad y = y_0+ms$$

through $A\ (x_0, y_0)$. From eqn. (4.29) the intersections are given by

$$s^2(pl+qm)^2+2s(lX_0+mY_0)+S_0 = 0.$$

This has two roots for s, real or imaginary, as long as $pl+qm$ does not vanish. The values of l, m which make this vanish, and give only one root for s, are $l/q = m/(-p) = 1/\sqrt{(p^2+q^2)}$ and so the equation of a diameter is

$$\frac{(x-x_0)}{q} = \frac{(y-y_0)}{-p}$$

or

$$p(x-x_0)+q(y-y_0) = 0. \tag{1}$$

Example 2. Find the equation of the axis of symmetry of the parabola

$$(px+qy)^2+2gx+2fy+c = 0.$$

Let (x_0, y_0) lie on the diameter $p(x-x_0)+q(y-y_0) = 0$ and be the mid-point of the chord

$$x = x_0+ls, \quad y = y_0+ms, \tag{2}$$

[different l, m from those of Example 1]. The intersections of the chord and parabola are given by the roots of

$$s^2(pl+qm)^2+2s(lX_0+mY_0)+S_0 = 0.$$

Since (x_0, y_0) is the mid-point of the chord the sum of these roots is zero and

$$lX_0+mY_0 = 0.$$

The gradient of the chord (2) is m/l. If the chord is perpendicular to the diameter (1), then

$$\frac{-X_0}{Y_0} = \frac{m}{l} = \frac{q}{p}.$$

$$\therefore \ pX_0+qY_0 = 0.$$

But from eqn. (4.30) $X_0 = p(px_0+qy_0)+g$, $Y_0 = q(px_0+qy_0)+f$. Hence x_0, y_0 satisfy the equation

$$(p^2+q^2)\,(px+qy)+pg+qf = 0.$$

This is therefore the equation of the axis of symmetry.

Example 3. A, B, C, D are four points on a conic whose equation is $S = 0$. The lines AB, CD have equations $L = 0$, $M = 0$ respectively. Show that the equation $S+\lambda LM = 0$ represents a conic passing through A, B, C and D. Show also that if $B = C$ then the equation $S+\lambda LM = 0$ represents a conic through A and D touching the conic $S = 0$ at B.

Show that there are exactly two parabolas touching the circle $x^2+y^2 = 1$ at the point $(1, 0)$ and passing through the points $(0, 1)$ and $(-1, 0)$. Show also that the axes of these two parabolas are perpendicular.

The equation $S+\lambda LM = 0$, being of the second degree in x and y, represents a conic. Further, this equation is satisfied identically when $S = 0 = L$ and therefore this conic passes through A and B. Similarly, it passes through C and D. If $B = C$, i.e. the points B and C coincide, then two of the points at which the conics $S = 0$ and $S+\lambda LM = 0$ meet coincide, i.e. the conics touch one another.

Notes. (i) If $A = B$, so that L is a tangent to S at A, then the two conics touch at A.

(ii) If in addition $B = C$, the conics have three point contact (and therefore cross) at A. By suitable choice of λ and the coefficients in the equation $M = 0$, we can make $S+\lambda LM = 0$ the equation of a circle (determined by 3 points only) and this will be the circle of curvature of S at A.

(iii) If finally all four points A, B, C, D coincide so that $L = M$ and both are the tangent at A, the conics $S = 0$, $S+\lambda L^2 = 0$ have four point contact at A.

To continue the given problem, the equation of the family of conics touching the circle $x^2+y^2 = 1$ at $(1, 0)$ and passing through the points $(0, 1)$ and $(-1, 0)$ is

$$x^2+y^2-1+\lambda(x-1)(x-y+1) = 0.$$

For this conic to be a parabola the second-degree terms $(1+\lambda)x^2+\lambda xy+y^2$, must form a perfect square, i.e.

$$\lambda^2-4(1+\lambda) = \lambda^2-4\lambda-4 = 0.$$

This quadratic equation has two real roots λ_1, $\lambda_2 = 2\pm\sqrt{8}$, and so there are two (and only two) real parabolas in the family. Further, see Example 2 above, their axes are parallel to the lines

$$y-\sqrt{(1+\lambda_1)}x = 0, \quad y-\sqrt{(1+\lambda_2)}x = 0,$$

and for the stated values of λ_1, λ_2 these lines are perpendicular.

Exercises 4 : 12

1. Identify the type of conic represented by each of the following equations and where appropriate find its centre:

(i) $\qquad\qquad x^2-6xy-7y^2-2x+4y-1 = 0.$

(ii) $\qquad 13x^2-18xy+36y^2+2x+4y-2 = 0.$

(iii) $\qquad\quad x^2+6xy+9y^2+3x+2y+4 = 0.$

(iv) $\qquad\quad x^2-4xy+5y^2+2x-8y-6 = 0.$

2. Find the coordinates of the centre of the conic whose equation is

$$3x^2 + 8xy + 6y^2 - 14x - 20y - 26 = 0.$$

Also obtain the equations of the tangent and the normal to this conic at the point (2, 3).

3. Prove that the condition for the equation

$$ax^2 + 2hxy + by^2 + 2gx + 2fy + c = 0$$

to represent a pair of straight lines (a degenerate form of hyperbola) is

$$abc + 2fgh - af^2 - bg^2 - ch^2 = 0.$$

[*Hint*. The coordinates of the centre satisfy the eqn. $S = 0$ and

$$S \equiv x(ax + hy + g) + y(hx + by + f) + (gx + fy + c).]$$

4. Use the method of § 4:12 to prove that the equation of the tangent to the curve $S = 0$ at the point (x_0, y_0) is

$$axx_0 + h(xy_0 + x_0y) + byy_0 + g(x + x_0) + f(y + y_0) + c = 0.$$

[*Hint*. Choose A (x_0, y_0) to be on the curve and find the ratio m/l which gives two roots $s = 0$ for the quadratic equation. Use the identity of Qu. 3.]

5. Prove that the general equation (4.38) for a parabola can be put in the form

$$(p^2 + q^2)(px + qy + \lambda)^2 = 2(pf - qg)(qx - py + \mu),$$

where $px + qy + \lambda = 0$ is the equation of the axis of symmetry. Find μ. What does the line $qx - py + \mu = 0$ represent?

6. A number of chords of the parabola (4.38) are drawn with a fixed gradient m/l. Find the equation of the diameter through their mid-points.

4:13 The properties of the ellipse

In § 4 : 12 we saw that, after moving the origin to the centre of the curve $S = 0$ and rotating the axes through a suitable angle, the equation of an ellipse takes the form

$$a'X^2 + b'Y^2 + S_0 = 0.$$

If X and Y are real, a' and S_0 (and b' and S_0) must have opposite signs. We therefore consider the equation of the ellipse in the *standard form*

$$\frac{x^2}{a^2} + \frac{y^2}{b^2} = 1 \tag{4.39}$$

(a and b here are different from those in previous sections). The ellipse is an oval shaped curve symmetrical about both axes, Fig. 4.24. In the *standard form* it is assumed that $a > b$; $2a$ and $2b$

are the major and minor axes respectively. If the circle $x^2+y^2 = a^2$ (the *auxiliary circle*) is drawn on the same figure the ordinate of the ellipse for an arbitrary x is b/a times the ordinate of the circle at the same value of x. The ellipse can be obtained from the circle by orthogonal projection. If the plane of the circle makes an angle β with that of the ellipse then $b = a \cos \beta$.

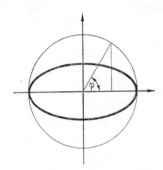

Fig. 4.24. The ellipse and its auxiliary circle.

The *eccentricity* of the ellipse is defined by

$$e = \sin \beta$$

or

$$b^2 = a^2(1-e^2), \qquad 0 \le e \le 1. \tag{4.40}$$

If $e = 0$ the ellipse is a circle; if $e = 1$ the ellipse degenerates into a segment of a straight line.

The most celebrated property of the ellipse is the *focus-directrix* property. In Fig. 4.25, O is the centre of the ellipse (S, S' are foci) and

$$OS = OS' = ae,$$
$$OA = OA' = a,$$
$$OL = OL' = \frac{a}{e}.$$

Then for any point P on the ellipse the focus-directrix property states

$$SP = ePM, \tag{4.41}$$

where PM is perpendicular to the *directrix* which is the line through L perpendicular to the major axis. The point S is a *focus* of the ellipse. Similarly the point S' and the line $L'M'$ are a second focus and a second directrix respectively. The coordinate axes Ox, Oy are chosen to coincide with the major and minor axes OA, OB respectively. It is easy to show that the focus-directrix definition (4.41) leads to the standard eqn. (4.39) of the curve [after use of eqn. (4.40)].

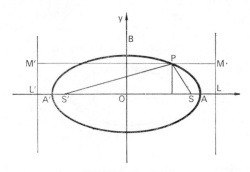

FIG. 4.25. The ellipse with its foci and directrices.

If P is (x, y) then $PM = a/e - x$ and $PM' = a/e + x$.

$$SP = a - ex, \quad S'P = a + ex.$$
$$\therefore \quad SP + S'P = 2a. \tag{4.42}$$

This is another important property of the ellipse, i.e. the sum of the focal distances is constant, equal to the major axis $A'A$.

If the coordinates are given in the form

$$x = a \cos \varphi, \quad y = b \sin \varphi$$

then φ is the eccentric angle shown in Fig. 4.24. It gives the equation of the ellipse in parametric form.

Example 1. The equations of the tangent and normal to the ellipse at the point $(a \cos \varphi, b \sin \varphi)$ are respectively

$$bx \cos \varphi + ay \sin \varphi = ab, \quad ax \sin \varphi - by \cos \varphi = (a^2 - b^2) \sin \varphi \cos \varphi.$$

Example 2. The normal at P bisects the angle between the focal distances SP and $S'P$.

Let P be the point $(a \cos \varphi, b \sin \varphi)$, then the focal distances are

$$SP = a(1 - e \cos \varphi) \quad \text{and} \quad S'P = a(1 + e \cos \varphi).$$

The equation of the normal is $ax \sin \varphi - by \cos \varphi = a^2 e^2 \sin \varphi \cos \varphi$; this cuts the x-axis in the point $R(ae^2 \cos \varphi, 0)$. Hence the distances from R to the foci are

$$SR = ae(1 - e \cos \varphi) \quad \text{and} \quad S'R = ae(1 + e \cos \varphi).$$

$$\therefore \quad \frac{SP}{SR} = \frac{S'P}{S'R}.$$

This means that PR divides the base of the triangle SPS' in the same ratio as the sides SP and $S'P$. Hence PR bisects the angle SPS'.

Example 3. Define conjugate diameters of an ellipse and prove that $y = mx$ and $y = m'x$ are conjugate diameters of the ellipse

$$\frac{x^2}{a^2} + \frac{y^2}{b^2} = 1 \quad \text{if} \quad mm' = \frac{-b^2}{a^2}.$$

Chords parallel to one diameter are bisected by the *conjugate* diameter. Let the set of chords be $y = mx + c$, where c is a variable parameter. The ends of the chord are given by

$$\frac{x^2}{a^2} + \frac{(mx + c)^2}{b^2} = 1$$

or

$$x^2(a^2m^2 + b^2) + 2a^2mcx + a^2(c^2 - b^2) = 0.$$

If (x_1, y_1) are the coordinates of the mid-point then x_1 is half the sum of the roots of this quadratic. Therefore

$$x_1 = \frac{-a^2mc}{a^2m^2 + b^2} \quad \text{and} \quad y_1 = mx_1 + c = \frac{b^2c}{a^2m^2 + b^2}.$$

Eliminating c between these equations gives the locus of the mid-points. It is

$$y_1 = \frac{-b^2x_1}{a^2m} = m'x_1.$$

$$\therefore \quad mm' = \frac{-b^2}{a^2}.$$

Exercises 4 : 13

1. Give the geometrical meaning of the eccentric angle of a point on the ellipse

$$\frac{x^2}{a^2} + \frac{y^2}{b^2} = 1.$$

A rod of length l slides with its ends A and B on rectangular axes Ox and Oy respectively and P is a point on the rod such that $AP:PB = \lambda:\mu$, where $\lambda > \mu$. Prove that the locus of P is an ellipse and find the eccentricity. Find the lengths of the axes and position of the foci in the case when $\lambda:\mu = 3:1$.

2. If N and N' are the feet of the perpendiculars drawn from the foci S and S' respectively to any tangent of the ellipse, prove that $SN \cdot S'N' = b^2$.

3. Prove that the line $lx + my + n = 0$ touches the ellipse $x^2/a^2 + y^2/b^2 = 1$ if $a^2l^2 + b^2m^2 = n^2$.

Lines are drawn through the origin perpendicular to the tangents from a point P to the above ellipse. If the lines are conjugate diameters of the ellipse, prove that P lies on the curve

$$a^2x^2 + b^2y^2 = a^4 + b^4.$$

4. By rotating the axes through a certain angle θ, prove that the equation $13x^2 - 10xy + 13y^2 = 72$ represents an ellipse. Find θ and the lengths of the semi-axes of the ellipse.

5. Prove that any two conjugate diameters of an ellipse form with either directrix a triangle whose orthocentre is at the corresponding focus.

6. Prove that the equation of the tangent to the ellipse $b^2x^2 + a^2y^2 = a^2b^2$ at any point P on it can be expressed in the form $x \cos \alpha + y \sin \alpha = p$, where

$$p^2 = a^2 \cos^2 \alpha + b^2 \sin^2 \alpha.$$

Hence show that the product of the perpendiculars from the two foci to a tangent is constant.

Show also that the locus of the intersection of pairs of perpendicular tangents is a circle (the director circle).

7. Prove that conjugate diameters of the ellipse $b^2x^2 + a^2y^2 = a^2b^2$ are obtained by orthogonal projection of perpendicular diameters of a circle of radius a.

4 : 14 The properties of the hyperbola

By a suitable choice of axes the general equation of the hyperbola can be reduced to the form

$$a'X^2 - b'Y^2 + S_0 = 0.$$

The *standard form* of the equation is taken as

$$\frac{x^2}{a^2} - \frac{y^2}{b^2} = 1, \ a, b > 0. \tag{4.43}$$

There is an "excluded region" $|x| < a$. The asymptotes are $x/a \pm y/b = 0$. The curve approaches $x/a - y/b = 0$ from below for positive values of x and from above for negative x, and approaches the asymptote $x/a + y/b = 0$ from above for positive x. There are no (real) points with horizontal tangents: there are vertical tangents at $x = \pm a$. The curve has two symmetrical branches as shown in Fig. 4.26.

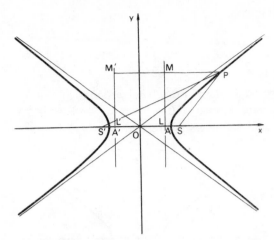

FIG. 4.26. The hyperbola and its foci and directrices.

The hyperbola has eccentricity e defined by

$$b^2 = a^2(e^2-1), \quad e > 1 \qquad (4.44)$$

and cannot be defined by orthogonal projection.

As before,

$$OS = OS' = ae,$$
$$OA = OA' = a,$$
$$OL = OL' = \frac{a}{e}.$$

The focus-directrix property is

$$SP = ePM. \qquad (4.45)$$

The hyperbola has a second focus S' and second directrix $L'M'$ as for the ellipse. The focus-directrix property leads to eqn. (4.43) when OA is taken as the x-axis.

For the hyperbola the focal distances SP and $S'P$ satisfy the relation

$$SP - S'P = \pm 2a \qquad (4.46)$$

(the positive sign gives one branch and the negative sign the other branch).

A parametric form for the hyperbola is

$$x = \pm a \cosh u, \quad y = b \sinh u \qquad (-\infty < u < \infty)$$

each sign giving one branch. An alternative parametric form is

$$x = \frac{a}{2}\left(t+\frac{1}{t}\right), \quad y = \frac{b}{2}\left(t-\frac{1}{t}\right).$$

With this the left-hand branch corresponds to $-\infty < t < 0$ and the right-hand branch to $0 < t < \infty$. (See Fig. 4.27.)

(The two parameters are related by $t = e^u$.)

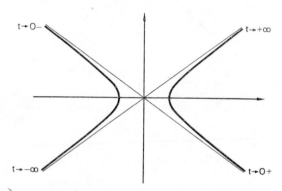

FIG. 4.27. The hyperbola $x = \frac{1}{2}a(t+1/t)$, $y = \frac{1}{2}b(t-1/t)$.

An important hyperbola is one whose asymptotes are perpendicular, i.e.

$$x^2 - y^2 = a^2.$$

This has eccentricity $e = \sqrt{2}$, and the perpendicular lines $x \pm y = 0$ as asymptotes. If the axes are rotated through an angle $\frac{1}{4}\pi$, the new coordinates are

$$\xi = \frac{x+y}{\sqrt{2}}, \quad \eta = \frac{x-y}{\sqrt{2}}$$

and the equation of the curve becomes

$$2\xi\eta = a^2.$$

This is the equation of a *rectangular hyperbola* which has the coordinate axes as its asymptotes.

Exercises 4 : 14

1. Show that perpendicular tangents to the hyperbola $x^2/a^2 - y^2/b^2 = 1$ intersect on the circle (*director circle*) $x^2 + y^2 = a^2 - b^2$.

2. Show that the locus of the foot of the perpendicular from the origin to a tangent to the rectangular hyperbola $x = ct$, $y = c/t$ is the curve

$$(x^2 + y^2)^2 = 4c^2 xy.$$

3. Show that the angle between the asymptotes of a hyperbola is

$$2 \tan^{-1} \{ \sqrt{(e^2 - 1)} \}.$$

4. The coordinates of a point P are given parametrically in terms of a real variable t by the relations

$$x = a + b \cosh t + c \sinh t, \quad y = p + q \cosh t + r \sinh t.$$

Show that, in general, the locus of P is one branch of a hyperbola.

Prove that $q^2 - r^2 = c^2 - b^2$ is the condition that the hyperbola should be rectangular.

5. Prove that the intersection of two tangents to the parabola $x = at^2$, $y = 2at$ which make an angle of $45°$ with each other lies on the rectangular hyperbola

$$x^2 - y^2 + 6ax + a^2 = 0.$$

Find the centre and the equations of the asymptotes of this hyperbola.

6. Prove that the circle with centre at the point $(0, c)$ which touches the hyperbola

$$x^2 - y^2 = 1$$

has radius $\sqrt{(1 + \tfrac{1}{2}c^2)}$.

Prove that tangents can be drawn to this circle from the origin provided $c^2 > 2$, and that they then touch the circle at points which lie, for varying c, on the curve

$$x^4 - y^4 = 2y^2.$$

7. Show that the radius of curvature at any point (x_1, y_1) of the rectangular hyperbola $x^2 - y^2 = a^2$ is $(x_1^2 + y_1^2)^{\frac{3}{2}}/a^2$ numerically and that the corresponding centre of curvature is the point

$$\left(\frac{2x_1^3}{a^2}, \quad -\frac{2y_1^3}{a^2} \right).$$

4 : 15 The properties of the parabola

The parabola has no centre and therefore its standard form is referred to axes whose origin is at the vertex, such that Ox is the axis of symmetry and Oy is the tangent at the vertex. With these axes the equation is

$$y^2 = 4ax. \tag{4.47}$$

The parametric form of the equation for this parabola is

$$x = at^2, \quad y = 2at. \tag{4.48}$$

The point $(a, 0)$ is the *focus* and the line $x = -a$ is the *directrix*; unlike the ellipse and hyperbola the parabola has only one focus

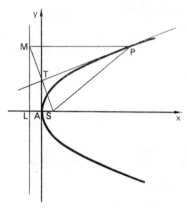

FIG. 4.28. The parabola in the standard position.

and one directrix, see Fig. 4.28. The eccentricity for *all* parabolas is $e = 1$. Also

$$\begin{aligned}
SP^2 &= (at^2-a)^2+4a^2t^2 \\
&= a^2(t^2+1)^2, \\
PM &= a(t^2+1) \\
\therefore \quad SP &= PM.
\end{aligned}$$

This is frequently given as the defining property of the parabola.

An important property of the parabola is its reflecting property. This may be proved as follows.

At P,

$$x = at^2, \quad y = 2at, \quad \frac{dx}{dt} = 2at, \quad \frac{dy}{dt} = 2a, \quad \frac{dy}{dx} = \frac{1}{t}.$$

The equation of the tangent at P is therefore

$$y-2at = \frac{1}{t}(x-at^2),$$

or

$$x - ty + at^2 = 0.$$

This cuts the y-axis at $T(0, at)$ which is the mid-point of MS where M is $(-a, 2at)$ and S is $(a, 0)$. Since PMS is an isosceles triangle $(SP = PM)$ the tangent PT bisects the base, and therefore the angle SPM. A ray of light leaving S and striking the parabola at P would therefore be reflected in the direction MP. This is true no matter how far P is along the parabola.

Exercises 4 : 15

All the following exercises refer to the parabola $x = at^2$, $y = 2at$.

1. Prove that the locus of intersection of perpendicular tangents is the directrix (the line $x = -a$).

2. The tangents at the points P and Q on the parabola meet at R, and the normals at P and Q meet at K. If K lies on the line $y = -a$, prove that R lies on the rectangular hyperbola $xy = a^2$.

3. P is a point on the parabola, S is the focus and PM is the perpendicular from P to the directrix of the parabola. Show that the tangent at P to the parabola bisects SM and that the centre of curvature C at the point P is such that

$$PC^2 = \frac{4SP^3}{a}.$$

4. P is a point on the parabola with vertex A and focus S. If the tangent at P meets the axis of the parabola in T, and if N is the mid-point of PT, prove that SN is perpendicular to PT.

Prove also that the locus of N is the tangent at A.

5. P is a point on the parabola with vertex A and focus S. If PA meets the directrix in Z, prove that the tangent at P is parallel to SZ.

6. Perpendiculars PM, QN, on to any tangent of the parabola are drawn from fixed points P, Q on the axis equidistant from the focus. Prove that $PM^2 - QN^2$ is constant for all tangents.

7. Find the equation of the chord joining the two points $P(at^2, 2at)$, $Q(at'^2, 2at')$ on the parabola, and prove that $t' = -1/t$ if the chord passes through the focus.

PSQ is a focal chord of a parabola whose focus is S and whose vertex is A. PA and QA are produced to meet the directrix in R and T respectively. Prove that RST is a right angle.

8. If the normals at the points $P(at_1^2, 2at_1)$ and $Q(at_2^2, 2at_2)$ on the parabola meet on the curve at the point $R(aT^2, 2aT)$, prove that t_1 and t_2 are the roots of the equation

$$t^2 + tT + 2 = 0.$$

(Continued overleaf)

Show that the mid-point N of the chord PQ is on the parabola $y^2 = 2ax+4a^2$ and that the distance of N from the line $x = -a$ is greater than $3a$.

4:16 The polar equation of a conic

The polar equation of a conic section is most easily obtained from the focus-directrix property using the focus as origin: the simplest form occurs with the major axis along the initial line, Fig. 4.29.

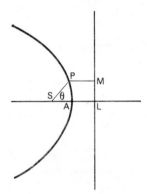

FIG. 4.29. A conic in polar coordinates.

From the focus-directrix property

$$r = SP = ePM.$$

Also $\qquad\qquad SL = r \cos \theta + PM.$

Let $l = eSL$, then the equation of the conic is

$$\frac{l}{r} = 1 + e \cos \theta. \tag{4.49}$$

The ends of the major axis are the points where $\theta = 0, \pi$. (If $e > 1$, we take the minus sign below.)

$$\therefore \quad \pm 2a = \frac{l}{1+e} + \frac{l}{1-e} = \frac{2l}{1-e^2}.$$

$$\therefore \quad l = \pm a(1-e^2).$$

The quantity $2l$ is the *latus rectum* which is the chord ($\theta = \frac{1}{2}\pi$) through the focus at right angles to the major axis.

For an ellipse $e < 1$, $l = a(1-e^2)$.

For a parabola $e = 1$, $l = 2a$ (of standard form).

For a hyperbola $e > 1$, $l = a(e^2-1)$.

The modifications necessary in these forms if the orientation of the curves is altered may easily be worked out by the reader.

The equations of tangent lines are seldom obtained, or of much significance, in polar coordinates. The direction of the curve (or its tangent line) at any point is obtained through the angle between the tangent line and the radius vector.

If we differentiate eqn. (4.49) we get

$$\frac{l}{r^2}\frac{\mathrm{d}r}{\mathrm{d}\theta} = e\sin\theta.$$

But

$$\left(\frac{l}{r}-1\right) = e\cos\theta$$

$$\therefore\ \left(\frac{l}{r}-1\right)^2 + \frac{l^2}{r^4}\left(\frac{\mathrm{d}r}{\mathrm{d}\theta}\right)^2 = e^2,$$

i.e.

$$l^2\left[\frac{1}{r^2}+\frac{1}{r^4}\left(\frac{\mathrm{d}r}{\mathrm{d}\theta}\right)^2\right] - \frac{2l}{r} + 1 = e^2$$

or

$$\frac{2l}{r}+e^2-1 = \frac{l^2}{p^2}, \qquad (4.50)$$

[see § 4 : 8, Example 2].

This is the pedal equation of a conic referred to its focus as pole. By differentiating this we get

$$\frac{-2l^2}{p^3}\frac{\mathrm{d}p}{\mathrm{d}r} = \frac{-2l}{r^2}, \quad \text{i.e.} \quad \frac{r}{\mathrm{d}p/\mathrm{d}r} = \frac{lr^3}{p^3}.$$

Therefore $$\varrho = \frac{lr^3}{p^3}$$

is the radius of curvature of a conic at any point.

4:17 Some special curves

In this chapter we have introduced several curves by name, viz. the catenary, the cardioid and the conics. Here we give brief accounts by means of examples of two other important curves.

Example 1. *The cycloid*

A circular disc of radius a rolls in a plane without slipping on a straight line Ox of the plane. Find the parametric equations of the locus of a marked point P of the disc, originally in contact with O.

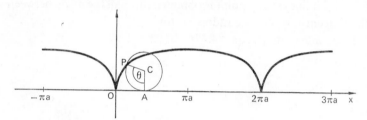

FIG. 4.30. The cycloid $x = a(\theta - \sin\theta)$, $y = a(1 - \cos\theta)$.

The condition of no slipping implies that arc AP = distance OA (Fig. 4.30). When the disc has rotated through the angle θ the coordinates of P are

$$x = OA - CP \sin\theta = a(\theta - \sin\theta),$$
$$y = AC - CP \cos\theta = a(1 - \cos\theta).$$

Some properties of this curve are derived in Example 2, p. 185, and a sketch of the curve for $-\pi \leqslant \theta \leqslant 3\pi$ is given in Fig. 4.30.

Example 2. A circle, of radius a and centre C, rolls on the outside of a fixed circle of radius $4a$ and centre O. A marked point P on the rolling circle is initially in contact with a marked point A on the fixed circle. Taking rectangular cartesian axes Oxy with the x-axis along OA, show that the locus of P is the *epicycloid* given by the equations

$$x = a(5\cos\theta - \cos 5\theta), \quad y = a(5\sin\theta - \sin 5\theta),$$

where θ is the angle AOC. Sketch this epicycloid.

Prove that the length of the arc AP of the epicycloid is $s = 10a \sin^2\theta$ for $0 \leqslant \theta \leqslant \pi/2$ and calculate, in terms of θ, the angle ψ which the tangent at P to the epicycloid makes with Ox. By calculating $\mathrm{d}s/\mathrm{d}\psi$ or otherwise, show that the radius of curvature of the epicycloid at P is $|(10\,a \sin 2\theta)/3|$.

Show also that the velocity of P is $\{10a \sin (2\theta)\}\, \mathrm{d}\theta/\mathrm{d}t$ along PD, where D is the point of the rolling circle furthest from O.

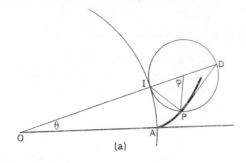

(a)

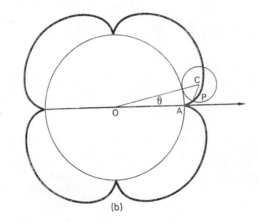

(b)

Fig. 4.31. The epicycloid $x = a(5 \cos \theta - \cos 5\theta)$, $y = a(5 \sin \theta - \sin 5\theta)$.

With reference to Fig. 4.31(a), the condition for rolling is

$$\text{arc } IP = \text{arc } IA, \quad \text{i.e.} \quad 4a\theta = a\phi,$$

so that $\phi = 4\theta$. The coordinates of P are

$$x = OI \cos \theta + CP \cos (\pi - \phi - \theta) = a(5 \cos \theta - \cos 5\theta),$$

$$y = OI \sin \theta - CP \sin (\pi - \phi - \theta) = a(5 \sin \theta - \sin 5\theta).$$

The locus of P is sketched in Fig. 4.31(b).

The locus of a marked point on a circle which rolls on the *outside* of a fixed circle is called an *epicycloid*. In our case this locus is a closed curve; P retraces its path after one complete revolution. However, an epicycloid is only a closed curve if the ratio of the radii of the fixed and moving circles is a rational number. The locus of a point on a circle rolling *inside* a fixed circle is called a *hypocycloid*.

For $0 \leqslant \theta \leqslant \pi/2$,

$$\left(\frac{ds}{d\theta}\right)^2 = \left(\frac{dx}{d\theta}\right)^2 + \left(\frac{dy}{d\theta}\right)^2$$

$$= 25a^2 \{(\sin\theta - \sin 5\theta)^2 + (\cos\theta - \cos 5\theta)^2\}$$

$$= 25a^2 \{2 - 2(\cos 5\theta \cos\theta + \sin 5\theta \sin\theta)\}$$

$$= 50a^2(1 - \cos 4\theta) = 100a^2 \sin^2 2\theta.$$

Therefore

$$\frac{ds}{d\theta} = 10a \sin 2\theta,$$

$$s = \int_0^\theta 10a \sin 2\theta \, d\theta$$

$$= 5a(1 - \cos 2\theta) = 10a \sin^2\theta.$$

Also

$$\tan\psi = \frac{dy}{d\theta} \Big/ \frac{dx}{d\theta} = \frac{\cos\theta - \cos 5\theta}{\sin 5\theta - \sin\theta} = \tan 3\theta.$$

Hence $\psi = 3\theta$. It follows that

$$\varrho = \left|\frac{ds}{d\psi}\right| = \left|\frac{1}{3}\frac{ds}{d\theta}\right| = \left|\frac{(10a \sin 3\theta)}{3}\right|.$$

For the motion of the disc, I is the instantaneous centre, see Vol 3, § 4:7, and therefore P is moving perpendicular to PI, i.e. along PD since angle $IPD = \pi/2$. The speed of P is

$$\frac{ds}{dt} = \frac{ds}{d\theta}\frac{d\theta}{dt} = 10a \sin 2\theta \frac{d\theta}{dt}.$$

[This result may also be derived by noting that the angular velocity of the moving circle is $\omega = 5 \, d\theta/dt$ and that the veclocity of P is $\omega \, IP$. See § 5: 8.]

Exercises 4 : 17

1. A disc of radius b rolls on the outside of a fixed disc of radius $a - b$ $(a > b > 0)$. The motion takes place in one plane, and a point on the rolling disc at a distance c from its centre traces out a curve. Show that, if $ac < b^2$, the curve has no points of inflexion.

2. A circular disc of radius a is maintained in a vertical plane and rolls without slipping along a straight line on a horizontal plane. A point fixed on the disc at distance $b(< a)$ from its centre traces out the curve C. Find the curvature of C at its highest and lowest points, and find also the height of the points at which the curvature is zero.

Miscellaneous Exercises IV

1. Find the point of contact of the tangent to the curve $3y^2 = (x+2)^3$ which makes an acute angle α with the x-axis, such that $\tan \alpha = 3/2$, and find the radius of curvature of the curve at this point.

2. Sketch one arch of the cycloid $x = a(\theta - \sin \theta)$, $y = a(1 - \cos \theta)$ and show that ϱ at any point is $4a \sin (\theta/2)$.

Find the coordinates of the centre of curvature in terms of θ.

3. Prove that for the cardioid $r = a(1 + \cos \theta)$,

(i) the tangent at the point (r, θ) makes an angle

$$\frac{\pi}{2} + \frac{3\theta}{2}$$

with the initial line;

(ii) the perpendicular p from the pole on to the tangent at (r, θ) is given by $2ap^2 = r^3$.

4. A circle of radius a rolls inside a fixed circle of radius $3a$. Show that, referred to axes through the centre of the fixed circle, the parametric equations to the curve C described by a point P on the circumference of the rolling circle may be expressed in the form

$$x = 2a \cos \theta + a \cos 2\theta,$$
$$y = 2a \sin \theta - a \sin 2\theta.$$

Find the angle ψ which the tangent to C at P makes with the axis of x, and show that, if A is the point of contact of the two circles, AP is the normal to C at P.

By calculating $ds/d\psi$, or otherwise, show that the radius of curvature at P is numerically equal to $8a \sin (3\theta/2)$, and that the centre of curvature is the point K on PA produced such that $AK = 3PA$.

5. Prove that the line $lx + my + n = 0$ touches the curve

$$x^4 + y^4 = a^4 \quad \text{if} \quad l^{\frac{4}{3}} + m^{\frac{4}{3}} = \left(\frac{n}{a}\right)^{\frac{4}{3}}.$$

Prove also that the radius of curvature of the curve at its points of intersection with the lines $y = \pm x$ is $2^{\frac{1}{4}} a/3$.

6. P is a point on a circle of radius a which rolls along the x-axis, and I is the point of contact. If θ is the angle subtended by PI at the centre of the circle, show that the equations of the path described by P are

$$x = a(\theta - \sin \theta), \quad y = a(1 - \cos \theta).$$

Find the equation of the tangent at P and prove that it passes through the extremity of the diameter through I.

Prove that the radius of curvature at P is $2PI$ and lies along PI.

7. From the point P, (x, y), on the curve given by

$$x = c \ln (\sec \psi + \tan \psi) \quad \text{and} \quad y = c \sec \psi,$$

PN is drawn perpendicular to the *x*-axis, and the tangent *PT* cuts the *x*-axis at *T* and *NQ* is perpendicular to *PT*. Prove that the coordinates, (X, Y), of *Q* are

$$X = x - c \sin \psi, \qquad Y = c \cos \psi.$$

Hence, or otherwise, prove that *QN* is a tangent to the locus of *Q*, and that *P* is the centre of curvature corresponding to the point *Q*.

8. *PQ* is a diameter of a circle which rolls, without slipping, on a fixed straight line. If *P* was initially in contact with the line at *O*, obtain the parametric equations of the loci of *P* and *Q*, taking the line as *x*-axis, the perpendicular to it through *O* as *y*-axis and the angle θ through which *PQ* has turned as parameter.

Prove that (i) the tangents at *P* and *Q* to their respective loci intersect at the other end of the diameter through the point of contact of the circle with the line, (ii) if *s* and *S* are the lengths of the arcs described by *P* and *Q* respectively,

$$\frac{s}{S} = \tan \frac{\theta}{4}.$$

9. Prove that if

$$x^{\frac{2}{3}} + y^{\frac{2}{3}} = a^{\frac{2}{3}},$$

then

$$\varrho = 3(axy)^{\frac{1}{3}}.$$

Find the coordinates of the centre of curvature at the point (x_1, y_1) of the curve in the second quadrant.

10. Prove that the circle of curvature at the point $\theta = \pi/6$ on the astroid $x = a \cos^3 \theta$, $y = a \sin^3 \theta$ touches the *y*-axis.

11. If $x = a(t + \sin t)$, $y = a \cos t$, and *s* is the arc of the curve measured from the point where $t = 0$, prove that

$$\varrho^2 + s^2 = 16a^2.$$

12. Find the area and the perimeter of the region bounded by the two parabolas $y^2 = 4(x - 1)$ and $y^2 = -4(x - 3)$.

13. Prove that the straight line $lx + my + n = 0$ touches the hyperbola $b^2 x^2 - a^2 y^2 = a^2 b^2$ if $a^2 l^2 - b^2 m^2 = n^2$.

The circle $x^2 + y^2 - 2ky + c = 0$ cuts one asymptote of the hyperbola in the distinct points *P*, *P'*; and the other in *Q*, *Q'*; where *P* and *Q* are on the same side of the *y*-axis. If *PQ* is a tangent to the hyperbola, prove that the circle must pass through the foci of the hyperbola.

14. Assuming the focus-directrix definition of an ellipse, show that its equation can be put in the form

$$\frac{x^2}{a^2} + \frac{y^2}{b^2} = 1.$$

Tangents are drawn to an ellipse of eccentricity *e* from a point on a concentric circle. Prove that the chord of contact of the tangents touches a concentric coaxial ellipse of eccentricity $e \sqrt{(2 - e^2)}$.

15. Find the equation of the normal to the hyperbola $b^2 x^2 - a^2 y^2 = a^2 b^2$ at the point (x', y') on the curve.

If A is a fixed point (h, k), not lying on the hyperbola, prove that, in general, four normals can be drawn from A to the hyperbola, and that their feet all lie on the curve

$$(a^2 + b^2)xy - b^2kx - a^2hy = 0.$$

Prove that this curve is a rectangular hyperbola, and find its asymptotes.

16. Prove that the equation of the chord joining points with eccentric angles φ and ψ on the ellipse

$$b^2x^2 + a^2y^2 = a^2b^2$$

is

$$bx \cos \tfrac{1}{2}(\varphi + \psi) + ay \sin \tfrac{1}{2}(\varphi + \psi) = ab \cos \tfrac{1}{2}(\varphi - \psi).$$

PFQ and $PF'Q'$ are two focal chords of an ellipse, the foci being F, F', and the eccentric angles of Q and Q' are φ and φ'. Show that the ratio $\tan \tfrac{1}{2}\varphi : \tan \tfrac{1}{2}\varphi'$ is constant for all positions of P.

17. Show that the orthocentre of a triangle inscribed in the hyperbola $x = kt, y = k/t$ lies on the curve.

P_1, P_2, P_3, P_4 are four points on the hyperbola. H_1 is the orthocentre of the triangle $P_2P_3P_4$ and H_2, H_3, H_4 are the orthocentres of the other three triangles defined by three of the points P_1, P_2, P_3, P_4. Show that if P_1, P_2, P_3, P_4 lie on the circle

$$x^2 + y^2 + 2gx + 2fy + c = 0,$$

then H_1, H_2, H_3, H_4 are also concyclic.

18. Show that the pair of straight lines joining the origin to the points of intersection of the conic

$$ax^2 + 2hxy + by^2 = 1 \quad \text{and the circle} \quad x^2 + y^2 = r^2 \quad \text{has equation}$$

$$\left(a - \frac{1}{r^2}\right)x^2 + 2hxy + \left(b - \frac{1}{r^2}\right)y^2 = 0.$$

Deduce that the semi-axes of this conic are r_1, r_2 where r_1^2 and r_2^2 are the roots of the quadratic equation in u

$$\left(a - \frac{1}{u}\right)\left(b - \frac{1}{u}\right) - h^2 = 0.$$

19. Show that the conic

$$x^2 - 6xy - 7y^2 - 2x + 4y - 1 = 0$$

is a hyperbola, and find its centre and the equation of each axis and each asymptote.

20. Obtain the equation of the conic

$$x^2 + 4xy + y^2 - 6(x + y) + 9 = 0$$

referred to its centre as origin. Also obtain the equation of its major axis.

21. A diameter of the conic

$$2x^2 + xy + 3y^2 = 6x + 7y + 44$$

is parallel to the line $y = 2x$. Find where this diameter, produced if necessary, meets the y-axis.

22. Prove that the latus rectum of the parabola
$$9x^2 + 6xy + y^2 + 2x + 3y + 4 = 0$$
is $7\sqrt{10}/100$.

23. If k is chosen so that the parabola
$$x^2 = 4k(y - 3c)$$
touches the parabola
$$y^2 = x,$$
find k in terms of c. Find also the coordinates of the point of contact P of the two parabolas.

V is the vertex of the first parabola and the tangent at P to the parabolas meets the y-axis at T. Show that T trisects OV, where O is the origin.

24. Chords are drawn through the focus of the parabola P_1 whose equation is $y^2 = 4ax$; show that their mid-points lie on a parabola P_2 coaxial with P_1, and find its focus and directrix.

Parabolas P_3, P_4, ..., P_n, ... are derived in a similar way from P_2, P_3, ..., P_{n-1}, ... respectively. Show that their foci tend to the point $(2a, 0)$ as limit. What is the limiting position of their directrices?

25. Find the equation of the normal at the point with parameter t on the rectangular hyperbola $x = ct$, $y = c/t$. Show that, if the normals at the points t_1, t_2, t_3, t_4 are concurrent, then $t_1 t_2 t_3 t_4 = -1$ and the line joining any two of the four points is perpendicular to the line joining the other two.

26. Prove that the equation of the tangent to the curve $r = 1/f(\theta)$ at the point $\theta = \alpha$ is
$$\frac{1}{r} = f(\alpha) \cos (\theta - \alpha) + f'(\alpha) \sin (\theta - \alpha).$$

Hence, or otherwise, find the equations of the tangents to the conic $l/r = 1 + e \cos \theta$ at the extremities of the latus rectum through the origin.

27. Sketch for *positive* values of x the graphs of each of the following functions

(i) $y = e^{(x-1)/x^2}$,

(ii) $y = \dfrac{1}{x} - 1 + \ln x$.

Indicate carefully in each case the behaviour of the function and its derivative both for very large and for very small positive values of x, and the positions of any stationary points there may be.

28. Sketch the curves $y = f(x)$, $y = f'(x)$, for a function $f(x)$ for which
$$f'(0) < 0, \quad f''(x) \geqslant 0;$$
$$\frac{f(x)}{x} \to 1 \quad \text{as} \quad x \to +\infty$$
in the range $x \geqslant 0$.

29. Sketch the curves

(i) $\qquad\qquad y^2(b^2 + x^2) = x^2(b^2 - x^2), \qquad b > 0,$

(ii) $\qquad\qquad y^2 + 2(x^2 - 2)xy + x^4 = 0,$

(iii) $\qquad\qquad a(x^2 - y^2) = y^3 \qquad (a > 0).$

CHAPTER V

APPLICATIONS OF DIFFERENTIATION

5 : 1 Convergence of series

One of the most important applications of differentiation considered in this chapter concerns infinite series. We give first an elementary discussion of the convergence of infinite series.

A series is made up of terms $u_1, u_2, u_3, \ldots, u_n, \ldots$ so that

$$s_n = u_1 + u_2 + u_3 + \ldots + u_n$$

is the sum of the first n terms. If the sequence s_n tends to a finite limit s as $n \to \infty$, i.e. $\lim_{n \to \infty} s_n = s$, the infinite series is *convergent* and its *sum* is s. If $s_n \to \pm\infty$ as $n \to \infty$, the series is *divergent*; if s_n neither tends to a limit nor diverges to $\pm\infty$, the series *oscillates*. [See § 1 : 8.]

Example. Consider the geometric series

$$s_n = a + ar + ar^2 + \ldots + ar^{n-1} = a\frac{(1 - r^n)}{(1 - r)},$$

if $r \neq 1$. Without loss of generality we take $a > 0$.

We determine $\lim_{n \to \infty} s_n$ by using the results of Example 3, p. 54.

If $|r| < 1$, $\lim_{n \to \infty} s_n = a/(1 - r)$ and the series converges to this value.

If $r = 1$, $s_n = na$ and the series diverges.

If $r = -1$, $s_{2n} = 0$, $s_{2n+1} = a$ and the series oscillates between 0 and a.

If $r > 1$, s_n increases indefinitely with n and the series diverges.

If $r < -1$, s_n oscillates unboundedly, i.e. $|s_n|$ increases indefinitely.

We conclude that the geometric series converges if and only if $|r| < 1$.

A first test for the convergence of any infinite series is obtained by direct application of the definition of convergence. If a number

s exists such that $|s - s_n|$ can be made as small as we please by taking n large enough, the series converges to the sum s; this test applies whether the terms are positive or negative. The forms of the remainder in Taylor's and Maclaurin's theorems (discussed in § 5 : 4) are well adapted for this test by providing a formula for $R_n = s - s_n$ which must tend to zero if the series is to converge to s.

A second test is derived by comparison with the geometric series $\sum_{p=1}^{\infty} ar^{p-1}$. We need consider only positive values of r. If a series of positive terms $\sum_{p=1}^{\infty} u_p$ is such that (apart from a finite number of terms at the beginning) its terms are each less than the corresponding terms of a convergent geometric series then, by the definition of convergence given above, $\sum_{p=1}^{\infty} u_p$ must converge also. Similarly, if the terms of the series $\sum_{p=1}^{\infty} u_p$ are correspondingly greater than those of a divergent geometric series, then the series $\sum_{p=1}^{\infty} u_p$ diverges. This leads to the *ratio test*:

"An infinite series, whose terms u_n are such that

$$\lim_{n \to \infty} \left| \frac{u_{n+1}}{u_n} \right| = l,$$

is *convergent* if $l < 1$, is *divergent* if $l > 1$."

If $l = 1$ the series may converge or diverge; more elaborate tests are required in this case. Usually, if $l = 1$ and the series converges, it does so very slowly and a large number of terms must be taken to give a good approximation to the sum; such series are of little value for numerical computation. The ratio test will not find the sum of a series; it can only indicate convergence or divergence. It should be noted that, if $\sum_{p=1}^{\infty} u_p$ converges, then $u_n \to 0$ as $n \to \infty$. [See Example 3, p. 247.]

A series which contains positive and negative terms is *absolutely convergent* if $\sum_{1}^{\infty} |u_p|$ is convergent, i.e. if the sum of the moduli of the terms converges. If a series is absolutely convergent, then it is convergent. If a series with positive and negative terms is convergent but the series $\sum_1^\infty |u_p|$ is divergent, $\sum_1^\infty u_p$ is said to be *conditionally convergent*.

Example 1. The series for e^x is convergent for all values of x.

$$e^x = \sum_0^\infty \frac{x^p}{p!} \quad \text{so that} \quad \frac{u_{n+1}}{u_n} = \frac{x}{n} .$$

Therefore $\lim\limits_{n \to \infty} \left| \dfrac{u_{n+1}}{u_n} \right| = \lim\limits_{n \to \infty} \dfrac{|x|}{n} = 0 \quad$ for all x.

Therefore by the ratio test the series is convergent.

Example 2. The series $\sum\limits_1^\infty \dfrac{1}{p(p+1)}$ converges to the sum 1.

Since

$$\frac{1}{p(p+1)} = \frac{1}{p} - \frac{1}{p+1} ,$$

$$s_n = \sum_1^n \frac{1}{p(p+1)} = \left(\frac{1}{1} - \frac{1}{2} \right) + \left(\frac{1}{2} - \frac{1}{3} \right) + \ \cdots \ + \left(\frac{1}{n} - \frac{1}{n+1} \right)$$

$$= 1 - \frac{1}{n+1} .$$

Therefore

$$\lim_{n \to \infty} s_n = \lim_{n \to \infty} \left(1 - \frac{1}{n+1} \right) = 1.$$

Therefore directly from the definition of convergence the series converges to the sum 1.

Example 3. Show that the condition $a_n \to 0$ is necessary but not sufficient for the convergence of the series $\sum\limits_1^\infty a_n$.

If the series converges, then, by the general principle of convergence, given any $\varepsilon > 0$, $\exists$ a number $N(\varepsilon)$ such that

$$|s_n - s_m| < \varepsilon \quad \text{for} \quad m, n > N(\varepsilon)$$

and in particular $|s_n - s_{n-1}| = |a_n| < \varepsilon$ and so a necessary condition for convergence is that $a_n \to 0$ as $n \to \infty$.

That the condition is not sufficient for convergence is clearly shown by the *counter example*

$$s_k = \sum_{n=1}^k n^{-\frac{1}{2}} \tag{1}$$

in which the nth term tends to zero as $n \to \infty$ but, since every term on the right-hand side of (1) except the last exceeds $n^{-\frac{1}{2}}$,

$$s_k > k \cdot k^{-\frac{1}{2}} = k^{\frac{1}{2}} \quad \text{for} \quad k > 1. \tag{2}$$

Inequality (2) implies that, given any positive p, $s_{p^2} > p$ and hence the series $\sum_1^\infty n^{-\frac{1}{2}}$ diverges although the nth term tends to zero.

Many of the infinite series which occur in mathematics and physics consist of terms $u_n(x)$ which are functions of a variable x. In such cases, if a series converges, its sum $s(x)$ will in general be a function of x also. A problem of major importance is to determine whether $\Sigma u_n'(x) = s'(x)$, i.e. whether such an infinite series may be differentiated term by term. We *quote* results which cover the most important type of series, the power series

$$f(x) = \sum_0^\infty a_p x^p = a_0 + a_1 x + a_2 x^2 + \ldots + a_n x^n + \ldots .$$

Application of the tests for convergence usually shows that this series is absolutely convergent when $|x| < R$ where R is a positive number (which may be infinite) called the "radius of convergence" of the series. In this case two theorems of pure mathematics state that

(i) $$f'(x) = \sum_0^\infty p a_p x^{p-1},$$

(ii) $$\int_0^x f(t)\, dt = \sum_0^\infty a_p \frac{x^{p+1}}{(p+1)},$$

whenever $|x| < R$. This means that a power series may be differentiated or integrated term by term when $|x| < R$.

Example 1. If $|x| < 1$, then the geometric progression $\sum_0^\infty x^p$ converges

$$\therefore \quad (1-x)^{-1} = \sum_0^\infty x^p \quad \text{for} \quad |x| < 1.$$

Differentiating, $(1-x)^{-2} = \sum_0^\infty p x^{p-1}$ for $|x| < 1$.

By the ratio test this last series is absolutely convergent for $|x| < 1$ and so, differentiating again,

$$2(1-x)^{-3} = \sum_0^\infty p(p-1)x^{p-2}, \quad \text{etc.}$$

Example 2. If $|x| < 1$, then $1 - x^2 + x^4 - \ldots + (-1)^n x^{2n} + \ldots = (1+x^2)^{-1}$.
Integrating gives

$$\int_0^x \frac{\mathrm{d}t}{1+t^2} = \tan^{-1} x = x - \frac{x^3}{3} + \frac{x^5}{5} - \ldots + \frac{(-1)^n x^{2n+1}}{(2n+1)} + \ldots$$

$$\text{for} \quad |x| < 1.$$

Finally we give a test for convergence known as the *integral test*. "If $f(x)$ is a function of x which is positive and continuous for all $x > 1$ and steadily decreases as x increases, then $\sum_{r=1}^\infty f(r)$ and $\int_1^\infty f(x)\,\mathrm{d}x$ both converge or both diverge."

Since $f(r) > f(x) > f(r+1)$ for $r < x < r+1$ where r is a positive integer,

$$\int_r^{r+1} f(r)\,\mathrm{d}x > \int_r^{r+1} f(x)\,\mathrm{d}x > \int_r^{r+1} f(r+1)\,\mathrm{d}x,$$

i.e.

$$f(r) > \int_r^{r+1} f(x)\,\mathrm{d}x > f(r+1).$$

Therefore, by addition,

$$\sum_1^{n-1} f(r) > \int_1^n f(x)\,\mathrm{d}x > \sum_1^{n-1} f(r+1) = \sum_2^n f(r).$$

Letting $n \to \infty$ we have the required result.
We note that the sequence u_n, where

$$u_n = \sum_{r=1}^{n-1} f(r) - \int_1^n f(x)\,\mathrm{d}x,$$

is an increasing sequence. But

$$u_n - f(1) + f(n) = \sum_{r=2}^n f(r) - \int_1^n f(x)\,\mathrm{d}x < 0.$$

Hence u_n is bounded above and therefore tends to a limit. [See p. 54.]

Example 1. $\sum_{1}^{\infty} \frac{1}{n^\alpha}$ converges if $\int_{1}^{\infty} \frac{dx}{x^\alpha}$ converges. This integral takes the value

$$\lim_{N \to \infty} \left(\frac{N^{1-\alpha} - 1}{1 - \alpha} \right) \quad \text{if} \quad \alpha \neq 1, \quad \lim_{N \to \infty} (\ln N) \quad \text{if} \quad \alpha = 1.$$

Clearly the integral is only convergent if $\alpha > 1$. Hence $\sum_{1}^{\infty} \frac{1}{n^\alpha}$ is convergent if and only if $\alpha > 1$. In particular the series $\sum_{1}^{\infty} \frac{1}{n}$ diverges.

Further, by the above result, it follows that

$$\sum_{r=1}^{n-1} \frac{1}{r} - \int_{1}^{n} \frac{1}{x} \, dx = \sum_{r=1}^{n-1} \frac{1}{r} - \ln n$$

tends to a finite limit. In fact we can write

$$\lim_{n \to \infty} \left\{ \sum_{r=1}^{n-1} \frac{1}{r} - \ln n \right\} = \gamma$$

where γ is a finite constant, called *Euler's constant*.

Example 2. The convergence of the series with positive and negative terms

$$\sum_{1}^{\infty} \frac{-1)^{n-1}}{n} = 1 - \frac{1}{2} + \frac{1}{3} - \frac{1}{4} + \frac{1}{5} - \ \cdots$$

is investigated as follows.

Since $s_{2m} = \left(1 - \frac{1}{2}\right) + \left(\frac{1}{3} - \frac{1}{4}\right) + \left(\frac{1}{5} - \frac{1}{6}\right) + \ \ldots + \left(\frac{1}{2m-1} - \frac{1}{2m}\right)$ and

$s_{2m+2} = s_{2m} + \left(\frac{1}{2m+1} - \frac{1}{2m+2}\right)$, the sequence of "partial" sums $s_2, s_4,$ $s_6, \ldots, s_{2m}, \ldots$ is an increasing sequence of numbers. We may also write

$$s_{2m} = 1 - \left(\frac{1}{2} - \frac{1}{3}\right) - \left(\frac{1}{4} - \frac{1}{5}\right) - \ \cdots \ - \left(\frac{1}{2m-2} - \frac{1}{2m-1}\right) - \frac{1}{2m} < 1.$$

This is true for all values of m. Therefore any member of the sequence $s_2, s_4,$ $s_6, \ldots, s_{2m}, \ldots$ is greater than its predecessors but is less than unity. This is sufficient to prove that $\lim_{m \to \infty} s_{2m} = l_1$, where $0 < l_1 \leqslant 1$. [See p. 54.] Similarly we can prove that s_{2m+1}, the sum of an odd number of terms, forms a decreasing sequence and also tends to a limit l_2, where $0 < l_2 \leqslant 1$. Finally, we prove that these two limits are the same. Since

$$s_{2m+1} = s_{2m} + \frac{1}{2m+1},$$

$$\therefore \quad \lim_{m \to \infty} (s_{2m+1} - s_{2m}) = \lim_{m \to \infty} \frac{1}{2m+1} = 0,$$

i.e. $$l_1 = l_2.$$

The reader should note that it is difficult to give general rules for handling conditionally convergent series. In fact, by taking the terms in a different order the series can be made to converge to any value.

Example 3. Discuss the convergence of the series

(i) $\displaystyle\sum_{n=2}^{\infty} \frac{n}{\sqrt{(n^3-4)}}$,   (ii) $\displaystyle\sum_{n=1}^{\infty} \frac{\sqrt{n}}{n^2-2}$,   (iii) $\displaystyle\sum_{n=1}^{\infty} \frac{(\frac{1}{2}n)^n}{n!}$,   (iv) $\displaystyle\sum_{n=1}^{\infty} \frac{1}{n} \sin \frac{2n\pi}{3}$.

(i) Each term exceeds the corresponding term of the series $\Sigma n^{-\frac{1}{2}}$. This latter series diverges by the integral test and so the given series diverges. [It is easy to show that, if Σv_n is a series of positive terms and $\displaystyle\lim_{n \to \infty} \frac{u_n}{v_n}$ is a finite non-zero number, then the series Σu_n and Σv_n both converge or both diverge.]

(ii) The nth term is comparable with $n^{-\frac{3}{2}}$ and $\Sigma n^{-\frac{3}{2}}$ converges. Hence the given series converges.

(iii) The ratio test gives

$$\frac{u_{n+1}}{u_n} = \frac{1}{2}\left(1 + \frac{1}{n}\right)^n.$$

As $n \to \infty$, $\left(1 + \dfrac{1}{n}\right)^n \to e$, (see p. 272), and so $u_{n+1}/u_n \to e/2 > 1$. By the ratio test, the series diverges.

(iv) The series is

$$\frac{\sqrt{3}}{2}\left(\frac{1}{1} - \frac{1}{2} + \frac{1}{4} - \frac{1}{5} + \frac{1}{7} - \frac{1}{8} + \frac{1}{10} - \frac{1}{11} + \cdots\right).$$

It is easy to show, by the method used in Example 2 above, that this series converges.

Exercises 5 : 1

Test the following series (Σu_n), with u_n as stated, for convergence or divergence:

1. $\dfrac{x^n}{n^2}$.

2. $\dfrac{\sin nx}{n(n+1)}$.   3. $\dfrac{n}{(n+1)(n+2)}$.

4. $n(n+1)\left(\dfrac{x}{a}\right)^n$, $a > 0$.   5. $n!x^n$.   6. $\dfrac{1}{n \ln n}$.

7. If $t_n = \displaystyle\sum_{r=1}^{n} \frac{1}{r(r+1)}$ and $s_n = \displaystyle\sum_{r=1}^{n} \frac{1}{r(r+2)}$,   prove that

$$\lim_{n \to \infty} \frac{s_n}{t_n} = \frac{3}{4}.$$

8. Show by integrating a suitable geometric progression that

$$\ln(1+x) = \sum_{1}^{\infty} (-1)^{n-1} \frac{x^n}{n} \quad \text{for} \quad |x| < 1.$$

9. If $a > 0$, and the inverse functions are interpreted as acute angles, prove that

$$\tan^{-1}(1+a) - \tan^{-1} a = \cot^{-1}(1+a+a^2).$$

Hence prove that, if n is a positive integer,

$$\cot^{-1} 3 + \cot^{-1} 7 + \cot^{-1} 13 + \cdots + \cot^{-1}(1+n+n^2) = \cot^{-1}(1+2/n),$$

and deduce that the infinite series $\sum_{n=1}^{\infty} \cot^{-1}(n^2)$ converges.

10. Express $\sin 3x$ in terms of $\sin x$ and find the sum to n terms and to infinity of the series whose rth term is $3^{r-1} \sin^3(\theta/3^r)$.

11. (i) If $r > 0$, show that $\tan^{-1}(1/2r^2) = \tan^{-1}(2r+1) - \tan^{-1}(2r-1)$.
Hence find the value of $\sum_{r=1}^{\infty} \tan^{-1}(1/2r^2)$.

(ii) Sum the series

$$\sum_{r=1}^{n} \frac{r}{(r+4)(r+5)(r+6)}.$$

12. (i) Show that $\tanh \alpha + \coth \alpha = 2 \coth 2\alpha$. Hence evaluate

$$\sum_{r=1}^{n} \frac{1}{2^r} \tanh\left(\frac{x}{2^r}\right).$$

(ii) Sum the series

$$\sum_{r=1}^{\infty} \frac{(r+1)^2}{r!}.$$

13. Prove that

$$\sum_{n=1}^{99} \frac{1}{\sqrt{n} + \sqrt{(n+1)}} = 9.$$

Prove that $\sum_{r=1}^{100} \frac{1}{\sqrt{n}} > 10$.

14. Find the real values of x for which the following series are *convergent*:

(i) $$x - \frac{x^3}{3} + \frac{x^5}{5} - \frac{x^7}{7} + \cdots,$$

(ii) $$1 - \frac{3x^2}{2!} + \frac{5x^4}{4!} - \frac{7x^6}{6!} + \cdots,$$

(iii) $\sum_{n=1}^{\infty} n^{-1}(x/2)^n$,   (iv) $\sum_{n=1}^{\infty} \frac{x^n}{\sqrt{n}}$,   (v) $\sum_{n=1}^{\infty} 2^{-n} \cos nx$.

15. Determine whether the following series are convergent or divergent:

(i) $\sum_{n=0}^{\infty} \frac{2n-1}{n^2-2}$,   (ii) $\sum_{n=0}^{\infty} \frac{n+1}{n^3-2}$,

(iii) $\sum_{n=1}^{\infty} \frac{2n-1}{3n+2}$,   (iv) $\sum_{n=1}^{\infty} \frac{n+3}{2n^2+5}$,   (v) $\sum_{n=1}^{\infty} n \cdot 3^{-n}$,

(vi) $\sum_{n=1}^{\infty} \frac{(-1)^n}{n^2}$,   (vii) $\sum_{n=1}^{\infty} \frac{(-1)^n}{\sqrt{n}}$.

16. If $\sum_{n=1}^{\infty} v_n$ is a convergent series of positive terms and $0 < u_n < kv_n$ for all values of n, where k is a positive constant, prove that $\sum_{n=1}^{\infty} u_n$ is convergent. State the corresponding theorem for divergent series.

(i) Determine whether the series Σt_n is convergent or not when

(a) $t_n = \dfrac{\ln(n+1) - \ln n}{n}$,   [see eqn. (5. 12)],

(b) $t_n = \dfrac{(1+1/n)^n}{3n}$,   [see Example 4, p. 272].

(ii) For what range of values of θ is $\sum_{n=1}^{\infty} \frac{\cosh n\theta}{2^n}$ convergent?

17. If $f(x)$ is a positive decreasing function of x prove that

$$f(n+1) < \int_{n}^{n+1} f(x)\,dx < f(n)$$

and deduce that $\sum_{n=1}^{\infty} \left\{ f(n) - \int_{n}^{n+1} f(x)\,dx \right\}$ is convergent.

Using this result with $f(x) = 1/x$, prove the following results:

(i) If $F(N) = \sum_{n=1}^{N} \frac{1}{n} - \ln N$, prove that $F(N)$ is a decreasing sequence. Conclude that $F(N)$ tends to a limit as N tends to infinity.

(ii) If $s(n) = 1 + \frac{1}{2} + \frac{1}{3} + \ldots + \frac{1}{n}$, show that, for any fixed positive integer k,

$$\lim_{n \to \infty} \frac{s(n)}{s(kn)} = 1 \quad \text{and} \quad \lim_{n \to \infty} \frac{s(n)}{s(n^k)} = \frac{1}{k}.$$

(iii) $\lim_{n \to \infty} \left\{ \frac{1}{n+1} + \frac{1}{n+2} + \ldots + \frac{1}{2n} \right\} = \ln 2$.

5 : 2 Inequalities

We now consider the application of differentiation to inequalities using geometrical ideas. If the derivative $f'(x)$ of a function $f(x)$ is continuous and $f'(x) > 0$ in the interval $a \le x \le b$, then $f(x)$ is increasing at every point of the interval. In this case $f(x)$ is a *strictly monotonic increasing* function of x. This is represented graphically by the fact that the curve $y = f(x)$ rises throughout the whole interval, Fig. 5.1(a).

If $f'(x) \geqslant 0$ in the interval $a \leqslant x \leqslant b$, i.e. $f'(x)$ may vanish at some points, $f(x)$ is said to be *monotonic increasing*, Fig. 5.1(b).

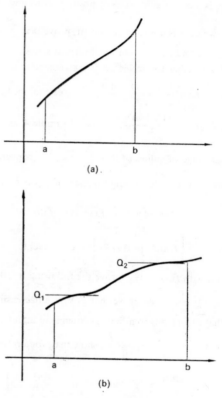

FIG. 5.1. (a) A strictly monotonic increasing function. (b) A monotonic increasing function.

In this case the curve $y = f(x)$ never descends at any point. If x_1 and x_2 are any two points of the interval such that $x_1 < x_2$, the ordinate at Q_2, Fig. 5.1(b), must be at least as high as the ordinate at Q_1. In particular the curve neither falls below its starting level, $f(a)$, nor rises above its finishing level, $f(b)$. All these results are embodied in the formal statement:

"If $f'(x) \geqslant 0$ for all x in the interval $a \leqslant x \leqslant b$, and $a < x_1 < x_2 < b$, then

$$f(a) \leqslant f(x_1) \leqslant f(x_2) \leqslant f(b)."$$

In the latter series of inequalities the "equal" signs do *not* hold for a *strictly* monotonic increasing function. The corresponding results if $f'(x) \leqslant 0$ for all x in the range $a \leqslant x \leqslant b$ are

$$f(a) \geqslant f(x_1) \geqslant f(x_2) \geqslant f(b),$$

and may be derived from the previous case by considering the function $-f(x)$ which is an increasing function.

Example 1. If $f(x) = x - \ln(1+x)$,

$$f'(x) = 1 - \frac{1}{1+x} = \frac{x}{1+x} \geqslant 0 \text{ for all } x \geqslant 0.$$

Therefore $f(x)$ never falls below its starting value $f(0)$.
Therefore $x - \ln(1+x) \geqslant f(0) = 0$, for $x \geqslant 0$.
Similarly $f'(x) = \dfrac{x}{1+x} \leqslant 0$ for $-1 \leqslant x \leqslant 0$.

Therefore $f(x)$ never falls below its finishing value $f(0)$.
Therefore $x - \ln(1+x) \geqslant 0$ for $-1 \leqslant x \leqslant 0$.

Example 2. Show that $1 - \dfrac{x^2}{2} \leqslant \cos x \leqslant 1 - \dfrac{x^2}{2} + \dfrac{x^4}{24}$.

Consider $f(x) = \cos x - 1 + \dfrac{x^2}{2}$.

$$f'(x) = x - \sin x, \quad f''(x) = 1 - \cos x.$$

Therefore $f''(x) \geqslant 0$ for all x and, since $f'(0) = 0$, $f'(x) \geqslant 0$ for $x \geqslant 0$. But $f(0) = 0$.

Therefore $f(x) \geqslant 0$ for $x \geqslant 0$.

Therefore $1 - \dfrac{x^2}{2} \leqslant \cos x$ for $x \geqslant 0$.

Similarly considering $g(x) = 1 - \dfrac{x^2}{2} + \dfrac{x^4}{24} - \cos x$,

$$g^{(4)}(x) = 1 - \cos x \geqslant 0 \quad \text{and, since} \quad g'''(0) = 0, \quad g'''(x) \geqslant 0 \text{ for } x \geqslant 0.$$

Proceeding in this way we find $g(x) \geqslant 0$ which is the other part of the result for $x \geqslant 0$. Since we are dealing with even functions the result holds for negative values of x also.

Example 3. A function $f(x)$ exists for $x \geqslant 2$ and k is fixed and positive. Prove that

   (i) if $\dfrac{\mathrm{d}}{\mathrm{d}x}\{xf(x)\} \leqslant -kf(x)$, then $f(x) \leqslant Ax^{-1-k}$,

   (ii) if $\dfrac{\mathrm{d}}{\mathrm{d}x}\{xf(x)\ln x\} \leqslant -kf(x)$, then $f(x) \leqslant Bx^{-1}(\ln x)^{-1-k}$,

where A and B are independent of x.

(i) In this case

$$\frac{\mathrm{d}}{\mathrm{d}x}\{xf(x)\} \leqslant -\frac{kxf(x)}{x}$$

or, since $x > 0$,

$$\frac{1}{xf(x)}\frac{\mathrm{d}\{xf(x)\}}{\mathrm{d}x} \leqslant -\frac{k}{x},$$

i.e.

$$\frac{\mathrm{d}}{\mathrm{d}x}\ln\{xf(x)\} \leqslant -\frac{k}{x} = \frac{\mathrm{d}}{\mathrm{d}x}\ln(x^{-k}). \tag{1}$$

But, if $\psi'(x) \leqslant \phi'(x)$ for $x > 2$, then

$$\frac{\mathrm{d}}{\mathrm{d}x}\{\psi(x)-\phi(x)\} \leqslant 0 \quad \text{for} \quad x > 2,$$

i.e. $\psi(x)-\phi(x)$ is a decreasing function of x and so $\psi(x)-\phi(x) \leqslant f(2)-\phi(2)$ $= A$, say, for $x \geqslant 2$. Using this result in inequality (1) we have

$$\ln\{xf(x)\}-\ln(x^{-k}) \leqslant \ln A,$$

i.e. $\qquad\qquad f(x)/x^{-1-k} \leqslant A,$

or $\qquad\qquad f(x) \leqslant Ax^{-1-k}.$

Similarly,

$$\frac{\mathrm{d}}{\mathrm{d}x}\{xf(x)\ln x\} \leqslant -kf(x)$$

implies that

$$\frac{\mathrm{d}}{\mathrm{d}x}\{xf(x)\ln x\} \leqslant -\frac{kxf(x)\ln x}{x\ln x}$$

or $\qquad\qquad \dfrac{\mathrm{d}}{\mathrm{d}x}\ln\{xf(x)\ln x\} \leqslant -\dfrac{k}{x\ln x},$

which implies

$$\ln\{xf(x)\ln x\}-k\{\ln\ln x\} \leqslant \ln B, \text{ say,}$$

or $\qquad\qquad \ln\left\{\dfrac{xf(x)\ln x}{(\ln x)^k}\right\} \leqslant \ln B,$

i.e. $\qquad\qquad f(x) \leqslant Bx^{-1}(\ln x)^{-1-k}.$

In some cases the theory of maxima and minima may be of value. Thus, if the greatest and least values of $f(x)$ are M, m respectively in the range $[a, b]$ then

$$m \leqslant f(x) \leqslant M \quad \text{for} \quad a \leqslant x \leqslant b.$$

[See also § 5 : 6 for a detailed discussion of maxima and minima.]

Example 1. Prove by differentiation, or otherwise, that

$$xy \leqslant e^{x-1} + y \ln y$$

for all real x and all positive y. When does the sign of equality hold?

Consider the function $f(x) = xy - e^{x-1}$, regarded as function of x. Then

$$f'(x) = y - e^{x-1}$$

so that $f(x)$ has a maximum when

$$x = 1 + \ln y. \tag{1}$$

This maximum value is $y \ln y$. Hence

$$xy - e^{x-1} \leqslant y \ln y$$

which is equivalent to the required result. Equality holds only when x is given by eqn. (1).

––––––––––––––––––

Example 2. By considering the stationary value of the function $x - \ln x$, show that, for $x > 0$.

$$\ln x \leqslant x - 1.$$

Deduce that, if $a_1, a_2, \ldots, a_n$ are positive numbers and $A = \dfrac{1}{n} \sum_{1}^{n} a_r$ then

$$\sum_{r=1}^{n} \ln \left(\frac{a_r}{A} \right) \leqslant \left(\sum_{r=1}^{n} \frac{a_r}{A} \right) - n = 0.$$

Hence deduce that

$$\frac{a_1 + a_2 + \cdots + a_n}{n} \geqslant (a_1 a_2 \cdots a_n)^{1/n}.$$

Prove that if u, v, w are positive quantities and $u + v + w = 1$, then

$$\frac{1}{u^2} + \frac{1}{v^2} + \frac{1}{w^2} \geqslant 27.$$

If $f(x) = x - \ln x$, then $f'(x) = (x-1)/x$ and clearly $f(x)$ has a minimum, unity, when $x = 1$. Therefore $x - \ln x \geqslant 1$, i.e. $\ln x \leqslant x - 1$ for $x > 0$.

Using this result for each of the quantities a_1/A, a_2/A, $\ldots$, where $A = \left(\sum_{r=1}^{n} a_r \right) \Big/ n$, and adding we find

$$\sum_{r=1}^{n} \ln \left(\frac{a_r}{A} \right) \leqslant \sum_{r=1}^{n} \left(\frac{a_r}{A} - 1 \right) = \left(\sum_{r=1}^{n} \frac{a_r}{A} \right) - n = \frac{nA}{A} - n = 0.$$

It follows that

$$\ln\left(\frac{a_1 a_2 \cdots a_n}{A^n}\right) \leqslant 0,$$

i.e.

$$a_1 a_2 \cdots a_n \leqslant A^n$$

or

$$(a_1 a_2 \cdots a_n)^{1/n} \leqslant \frac{a_1 + a_2 + \cdots a_n}{n}. \tag{1}$$

The quantities on the left-hand and right-hand sides of eqn. (1) are called the geometric mean and the arithmetic mean respectively of the n positive numbers a_r. Hence the geometric mean of n positive numbers cannot exceed their arithmetic mean.

Now

$$\frac{1}{u^2} + \frac{1}{v^2} + \frac{1}{w^2} = \frac{u^2 v^2 + v^2 w^2 + w^2 u^2}{u^2 v^2 w^2},$$

and by the above result

$$u^2 v^2 + v^2 w^2 + w^2 u^2 \geqslant 3(u^4 v^4 w^4)^{\frac{1}{3}}.$$

Also

$$1 = (u + v + w) \geqslant 3(uvw)^{\frac{1}{3}}.$$

$$\therefore \quad \frac{1}{u^2} + \frac{1}{v^2} + \frac{1}{w^2} \geqslant \frac{3}{(uvw)^{\frac{2}{3}}} \geqslant \frac{3}{3^{-2}} = 27.$$

Exercises 5 : 2

1. Prove that

(i) $a(1-a) \leqslant \frac{1}{4}$ for all values of a,

(ii) if $b \leqslant c \leqslant 1$, then $b(1-c) \leqslant \frac{1}{4}$.

(iii) $x\, e^{1-x} \leqslant 1$ for all values of x.

2. If $0 < x < 1$, prove that

$$x + \frac{x^2}{2} + \frac{x^3}{3} + \cdots + \frac{x^n}{n} < \ln\left(\frac{1}{1-x}\right) < x + \frac{x^2}{2} + \cdots + \frac{x^{n-1}}{n-1} + \frac{x^n}{n(1-x)}.$$

3. Prove that $2^n > n^2$ for $n > 4$.

4. Show that, if $x > 0$,

$$x - \tfrac{1}{3}x^3 + \tfrac{1}{5}x^5 > \tan^{-1} x > x - \tfrac{1}{3}x^3.$$

5. Show that, if $x > 0$, $\ln(1+x) > x/(1+x)$. Show also that, if $x > 0$,

$$x - \tfrac{1}{2}x^2 < \ln(1+x) < x - \tfrac{1}{2}x^2 + \tfrac{1}{3}x^3.$$

6. If n is a positive integer and x is a positive variable, prove by differentiation that

$$\frac{(n+1+x)^{n+1}}{(n+x)^n}$$

is an increasing function of x.

Deduce that

(i) $\left(1+\dfrac{\sin x-\tan x}{n+1+\tan x}\right)^{n+1} < \left(1+\dfrac{\sin x-\tan x}{n+\tan x}\right)^n$ if $0 < x < \dfrac{1}{2}\pi$.

(ii) $(2n)^{2n+1} < (2n-1)^n\,(2n+1)^{n+1}$ $(n = 1, 2, \ldots)$.

7. Expressing $\ln(1+x)$ as $\displaystyle\int_1^{1+x}\dfrac{du}{u}$ prove that, for $x > 0$,

$$\ln(1+x) < x$$

and $x-\dfrac{x^2}{2} < \ln(1+x)$.

(*Hint*: $1-u^2 < 1$ so that $1-u < \dfrac{1}{1+u}$ if $u > 0$.)

8. Prove that, if $0 < x < 1$,

$$e^x < 1+x+\tfrac{3}{4}x^2.$$

9. If $f(x) = x^2+\ln\cos x$, compute $f'(x)$ and $f''(x)$. For $0 < x < \pi/4$ show that

$$0 < f'(x) < x$$

and

$$0 < f(x) < x^2/2.$$

10. Show that $f(x) = \sin x \tan x-2\ln\sec x$ increases steadily as x increases from 0 to $\tfrac{1}{2}\pi$. Show also that the curve $y = f(x)$ has no inflexion in this range. Sketch the curve $y = f(x)$ for $0 \leqslant x < \tfrac{1}{2}\pi$.

11. Show that, if $x > 0$, $a > 0$, and $x \neq a$,

(i) $rx^{r-1}(x-a) > x^r-a^r > ra^{r-1}(x-a)$ $(r > 1)$,

(ii) $rx^{r-1}(x-a) < x^r-a^r < ra^{r-1}(x-a)$ $(0 < r < 1)$.

Deduce that

$$\dfrac{N^{r+1}+r}{r+1} < \sum_1^N n^r < \dfrac{(N+1)^{r+1}-1}{r+1}   (0 < r).$$

12. Prove that $0 < \ln(1+x)-\dfrac{2x}{2+x} < \dfrac{1}{12}x^3$, for $x > 0$.

13. Prove that $(3\cos\theta+\sec\theta)^2 \geqslant 12$ for all real values of θ.

14. Show that, when x is positive,

$$\dfrac{1}{x} > \ln(1+x)-\ln x > \dfrac{1}{1+x}.$$

Deduce that $\left(1+\dfrac{1}{x}\right)^x$ increases, and $\left(1+\dfrac{1}{x}\right)^{x+1}$ decreases, as x increases $(x > 0)$.

5 : 3 The mean-value theorem and linear approximations

If a function $f(x)$ has a derivative at all points within the interval $a < x < b$, its graph is a smooth curve starting at height $f(a)$ and finishing at height $f(b)$. It is clear from a figure that the tangent to the curve is parallel to the chord joining the points $\{a, f(a)\}$, $\{b, f(b)\}$ at least one point inside the interval, (see Fig. 5.2). In fact

$$f'(\xi) = \frac{f(b) - f(a)}{b - a}, \qquad (5.1)$$

where $a < \xi < b$. This is the *mean value theorem*.

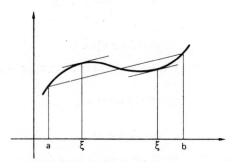

FIG. 5.2. Illustrating the mean value theorem.

If $f(a) = f(b) = 0$ this result means that there is at least one value $x = \xi (a < \xi < b)$ for which the derivative vanishes; or we may say that at least one zero of $f'(x)$ separates two zeros of $f(x)$. In this form the theorem is known as *Rolle's theorem*. This result is one of such importance in calculus that a proof which simply appeals to a figure is not strictly sufficient. Usually in books on analysis a proof of Rolle's theorem is given first and the mean value theorem is then deduced. An alternative form of eqn. (5.1) is obtained by writing $b = a + h$ to give

$$f(a + h) = f(a) + hf'(a + \theta h), \qquad (5.2)$$

where $0 < \theta < 1$. Reference to Fig. 5.2 suggests that, although the actual value of θ is not known, this value depends not only on the function $f(x)$ but also upon the values of a and b (or h).

Many functions commonly occurring in physics and engineering arise from differential equations; when numerical values are required in a particular problem, the value of some function $y = f(x)$ and one or more of its derivatives may be known for a single value of x only. To estimate values of the function at neighbouring points we can use eqn. (5.2). Suppose that $f''(x)$ exists for points of the curve near $x = a$, then

$$f(a+h) = f(a)+hf'(a+\theta_1 h) = f(a)+h[f'(a)+\theta_1 hf''(a+\theta_2 h)],$$

where $0 < \theta_2 < \theta_1 < 1$.

$$\therefore \quad f(a+h) = f(a)+hf'(a)+O(h^2). \qquad (5.3)$$

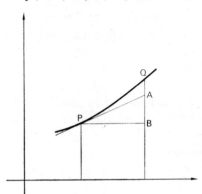

FIG. 5.3. Illustrating δy and $\mathrm{d}y$.

Provided h is small we may neglect the term $O(h^2)$ in eqn. (5.3) and obtain an estimate for $f(a+h)$. This is equivalent to replacing the curve by its tangent at P, see Fig. 5.3, and also gives a geometrical interpretation of the differential of a function (introduced in § 2 : 9). Taking P and Q to be the points (x, y) and $(x+\delta x, y+\delta y)$ respectively then $PB = h = \delta x$ and $QB = \delta y$. The tangent at P meets the ordinate QB at A and therefore the differential $\mathrm{d}y = f'(x)\,\delta x = PB \tan A\hat{P}B = AB$. The error made in using differentials, or in replacing the curve by its tangent, is $\theta_1 h^2 f''(a+\theta_2 h)$; a knowledge of $f''(x)$ will therefore give an estimate of this error.

In many cases the value of a function, $f(x)$, may be known at a number of neighbouring points whereas $f'(x)$ is unknown, e.g. the values $f(x)$ at P and Q in Fig. 5.3 may be known. To estimate the values of $f(x)$ for points lying between P and Q we replace the curve by the chord PQ and estimate $f(x)$ from points on this line. (Figure 5.3 suggests that, in general, the errors will be of the same order as that made by using A instead of Q.) The more closely the chord approaches the curve the more accurate the estimates will be, but, if the points P, Q are widely separated or the gradient of the curve is altering rapidly in the neighbourhood, the estimates are unlikely to be accurate. The commonest use of this method, which is a form of *linear interpolation*, occurs with tabulated functions such as logarithms, sines, cosines, etc. In the tables the values of a function are given at convenient intervals over a range of the independent variable. For example, five-figure sine tables do not list the value of $\sin 35°16'20''$ but an estimate of this can be obtained by adding $\frac{1}{3}$ of the difference between $\sin 35°16'$ (0·57738) and $\sin 35°17'$ (0·57761) to the former, giving 0·57746. It should be noted that the accuracy of a result derived by linear interpolation cannot exceed the accuracy of the tables from which it is derived. Figures 5.2 and 5.3 also indicate that the errors made in estimates using linear interpolation lie on the concave side of the curve, whereas those made using the mean value theorem lie on the convex side of the curve. If it is possible to use both methods, then a very good approximation may be found by averaging. (It is assumed that the points P and Q of Fig. 5.3 are close together.)

An account of the general theory of interpolation is given in § 5 : 11.

Example. Using the figures given below obtain estimates of the values of $\sin 20° 15'$ and $\cos 20° 15'$.

$\theta°$	20°12′	20°21′
$\sin \theta°$	0·34530	0·34775
$\cos \theta°$	0·93849	0·93759

If $y = \sin x°$, then $dy = (\pi/180) \cos x° \, dx$. In this case $x = 20°12'$ and $dx = \frac{1}{20}$. Therefore $dy = (\pi/180) \times 0·93849 \times \frac{1}{20} = 0·00082$, and (using the differential method), $\sin 20°15' = 0·34530 + 0·00082 = 0·34612$.

If $y = \cos x°$, then $dy = -(\pi/180) \sin x° \, dx$. In this case $x = 20°12'$ and $dx = \frac{1}{20}$. Therefore $dy = -(\pi/180) \times 0·34530 \times \frac{1}{20} = -0·00030$, and $\cos 20°15' = 0·93849 - 0·00030 = 0·93819$.

The calculation can also be made by working backwards, so to speak. The calculation for $\sin 20°15'$ uses $dy = (\pi/180) \cos x° \, dx$ where $dx = -\frac{1}{10}$ and $x = 20°21'$. Therefore $dy = -(\pi/180) \times 0.93759 \times \frac{1}{10} = -0.00164$ and $\sin 20°15' = 0.34775 - 0.00164 = 0.34611$.

For comparison we make the approximation using (linear) interpolation. We find

$$\sin 20°15' = 0.34530 + \tfrac{1}{3}(0.34775 - 0.34530) = 0.34612,$$

$$\cos 20°15' = 0.93849 + \tfrac{1}{3}(0.93759 - 0.93849) = 0.93819.$$

Values given in the tables for the sine and cosine are respectively 0.34612 and 0.93819.

Exercises 5 : 3

Values of the exponential function are given in the following table:

x	-1.0	-0.5	0	0.5	1.0
e^x	0.3679	0.6065	1	1.6487	2.7183

1. Starting from the values of e^{-1}, $e^{-0.5}$, e^0, $e^{0.5}$ use the mean value theorem to obtain estimates for e^x when $x = -0.75, -0.25, 0.25, 0.75$. Obtain also an estimate of the error in each result.

2. Use the mean value theorem to obtain similar estimates for the same set of values of e^x starting from $e^{-0.5}$, e^0, $e^{0.5}$, e^1 respectively. Are the values given by this method nearer to the true values than those given by exercise 1? Give reasons.

3. Obtain estimates for the same set of quantities by using linear interpolation in each of the intervals $(-1, -0.5)(-0.5, 0)$ $(0, 0.5)$ $(0.5, 1)$.

4. By taking the average of the results of questions 1 and 3 check the accuracy of your estimates by showing that the values so obtained form a geometric series whose common ratio is $e^{0.5}$ approximately.

5 : 4 Taylor's and Maclaurin's theorems

Taylor's theorem enables the value of a function $f(x)$ at points near $x = a$ to be estimated from the values of $f(a)$ and of the derivatives of $f(x)$ at $x = a$. The theorem also provides an estimate of the error made in a polynomial approximation to a function. Maclaurin's theorem is a special case of Taylor's theorem with $a = 0$ and gives an expansion of a function "about the origin", i.e. for points near $x = 0$. Taylor's theorem is a generalisation of the mean value theorem. Our proof consists in inventing suitable functions to which to apply Rolle's theorem and is essentially that given by Hardy.

Suppose $f(x)$ is a function which has derivatives of orders up to and including the nth at all points within an interval $a < x < b$. First we introduce a function

$$F_n(x) = f(b) - f(x) - (b-x)f'(x) - \frac{(b-x)^2}{2!}f''(x) - \ldots$$

$$- \frac{(b-x)^{n-1}}{(n-1)!}f^{(n-1)}(x),$$

so that

$$F_n(b) = 0, \quad F_n'(x) = -\frac{(b-x)^{n-1}}{(n-1)!}f^{(n)}(x).$$

Next we introduce a function $\varphi(x)$ to which we can apply Rolle's theorem, viz.

$$\varphi(x) = F_n(x) - \frac{(b-x)^n}{(b-a)^n}F_n(a).$$

Clearly $\varphi(a) = \varphi(b) = 0$ and differentiation gives

$$\varphi'(x) = F_n'(x) + \frac{n(b-x)^{n-1}}{(b-a)^n}F_n(a)$$

$$= \frac{n(b-x)^{n-1}}{(b-a)^n}\left[F_n(a) - \frac{(b-a)^n}{n!}f^{(n)}(x)\right].$$

By Rolle's theorem $\varphi'(x)$ must vanish for at least one value $x = \xi$, where $a < \xi < b$. The factor $(b-x)^{n-1}$ cannot vanish for $x = \xi$.

$$\therefore \quad F_n(a) = \frac{(b-a)^n}{n!}f^{(n)}(\xi). \tag{5.4}$$

Substitution of the full value of $F_n(a)$ into eqn. (5.4) gives

$$f(b) = f(a) + (b-a)f'(a) + \frac{(b-a)^2}{2!}f''(a) + \ldots$$

$$+ \frac{(b-a)^{n-1}}{(n-1)!}f^{(n-1)}(a) + R_n, \tag{5.5}$$

where $R_n = \dfrac{(b-a)^n}{n!}f^{(n)}(\xi)$ and $a < \xi < b$. This is the generalisation of eqn. (5.2) and is one form of *Taylor's theorem*.

Other forms which are often quoted and are more useful in certain problems are obtained simply by a change of notation, e.g.

$$f(a+h) = f(a)+hf'(a)+\frac{h^2}{2!}f''(a)+ \ldots +\frac{h^{n-1}}{(n-1)!}f^{(n-1)}(a)$$

$$+\frac{h^n}{n!}f^{(n)}(a+\theta h), \qquad (5.6)$$

where $0 < \theta < 1$. Here h can take any value such that $0 \le h \le b-a$. Another form is

$$f(x) = f(a)+(x-a)f'(a)+\frac{(x-a)^2}{2!}f''(a)+ \ldots$$

$$+\frac{(x-a)^{n-1}}{(n-1)!}f^{(n-1)}(a)+\frac{(x-a)^n}{n!}f^{(n)}(\xi), \qquad (5.7)$$

where $a < \xi < x \le b$. It is possible, by modification of the proof, to obtain alternative forms for the remainder term R_n.

Maclaurin's theorem is obtained from eqn. (5.7) by choosing $a = 0$. The full statement of the theorem is as follows. If $f(x)$ is a function which has derivatives of all orders up to and including the nth in an interval $0 < x < b$, then

$$f(x) = f(0)+xf'(0)+\frac{x^2}{2!}f''(0)+ \ldots$$

$$+\frac{x^{n-1}}{(n-1)!}f^{(n-1)}(0)+R_n, \qquad (5.8)$$

where $R_n = \frac{x^n}{n!}f^{(n)}(\xi)$ and $0 < \xi < x < b$. The modification in the statement of the theorem to cover negative values of b is left to the reader.

The expansions (5.7) and (5.8) and equivalent forms are only valid when the left-hand side is evaluated for points which lie *within* the range for which $f(x)$ has the required derivatives; the point about which the expansion is made may either be an internal point or an end point of this range.

Example 1. Maclaurin's theorem may be used to verify Newton's formula [eqn. (4.13)] for the curvature of a curve touching Ox at the origin. For, using the suffix zero to denote the value at the origin, Maclaurin's theorem gives

$$y = (y)_0 + x\left(\frac{dy}{dx}\right)_0 + \frac{1}{2}x^2\left(\frac{d^2y}{dx^2}\right)_0 + O(x^3).$$

In this case $(y)_0 = 0 = (dy/dx)_0$.

$$\therefore \left(\frac{d^2y}{dx^2}\right)_0 = \lim_{x \to 0}\left[\frac{2y}{x^2} + O(x)\right] = \lim_{x \to 0}\left(\frac{2y}{x^2}\right).$$

$$\therefore (\varrho)_0 = \frac{\left[1 + \left(dy/dx\right)_0^2\right]^{\frac{3}{2}}}{|(d^2y/dx^2)_0|} = \left|\lim_{x \to 0}\left(\frac{x^2}{2y}\right)\right|.$$

Example 2. Taylor's theorem may be used to investigate limits of the form

$$\lim_{x \to a}\left[\frac{f(x)}{g(x)}\right], \quad \text{where} \quad f(a) = 0 = g(a).$$

Writing $x = a + h$ and using Taylor's theorem gives

$$\lim_{x \to a}\left[\frac{f(x)}{g(x)}\right] = \lim_{h \to 0}\left[\frac{f(a+h)}{g(a+h)}\right] = \lim_{h \to 0}\left[\frac{hf'(a) + h^2\dfrac{f''(a)}{2!} + h^3\dfrac{f'''(a)}{3!} + \cdots}{hg'(a) + h^2\dfrac{g''(a)}{2!} + h^3\dfrac{g'''(a)}{3!} + \cdots}\right].$$

Clearly if $f^{(p)}(a)$, $g^{(q)}(a)$ are the first non-vanishing derivatives at $x = a$ of $f(x)$, $g(x)$ respectively, then the limit takes the value 0 if $p > q$, $f^{(p)}(a)/g^p(a)$ if $p = q$, $\pm\infty$ if $p < q$. This is *l'Hôpital's rule*.

For example, $\displaystyle\lim_{x \to a}\left[\frac{x^2\ln x - a^2\ln a}{x^2 - a^2}\right] = \lim_{x \to a}\left[\frac{2x\ln x + x}{2x}\right] = \ln a + \frac{1}{2}$.

Exercises 5 : 4

Find the following limits:

1. $\displaystyle\lim_{x \to a}\left[\frac{\cosh x - \cosh a}{\sinh x - \sinh a}\right]$.

2. $\displaystyle\lim_{x \to a}\left[\frac{1}{\sin x - \sin a} - \frac{1}{(x-a)\cos a}\right]$.

3. $\displaystyle\lim_{x \to 0}\left[\frac{\ln(1+ax)}{\ln(1+bx)}\right]$.

4. $\displaystyle\lim_{x \to 0}\left[\frac{\sin x - x}{x\cos x - x}\right]$.

5 : 5 Expansions in power series

Many of the important functions of mathematics may be expressed as infinite power series by means of Maclaurin's or Taylor's theorems. We give here examples of this application of the theorems.

(i) *The exponential function.* From the definition of $\exp(x)$, given in § 2 : 4, $f(x) = \exp(x) = f'(x) = f''(x) = \ldots$.

Hence $f(0) = f'(0) = f''(0) = \ldots = 1$ and Maclaurin's theorem gives

$$f(x) = \exp(x) = 1 + x + \frac{x^2}{2!} + \ldots + \frac{x^{n-1}}{(n-1)!} + R_n,$$

where $R_n = \frac{x^n}{n!} \exp(\xi)$. The derivatives of $\exp(x)$ exist and are continuous for all x. Therefore $\exp(\xi)$ is finite and, since $\lim\limits_{n \to \infty} x^n/n! = 0$ for all x, $R_n \to 0$ as $n \to \infty$ and the series converges to $\exp(x)$ for all x.

We may use Taylor's theorem to prove the index law for the exponential function. In this case $f(a) = f'(a) = f''(a) = \ldots$ and Taylor's theorem (5.6) gives

$$f(a+x) = \exp(a+x)$$
$$= \exp(a)\left[1 + x + \frac{x^2}{2!} + \ldots + \frac{x^{n-1}}{(n-1)!}\right] + R_n,$$

where $R_n = \frac{x^n}{n!} \exp(a+\xi)$. As before, for any finite value of x, $R_n \to 0$ as $n \to \infty$ and the infinite series converges.

$$\therefore \quad \exp(a+x) = \exp(a) \cdot \left(1 + x + \frac{x^2}{2!} + \ldots\right) = \exp(a) \cdot \exp(x).$$

This agrees with the use of the notation $\exp(x) = e^x$ where the variable x appears as an index.

(ii) *The trigonometric functions.* Suppose $f(x) = \sin x$. Then by definition, eqns. (1.1), (1.2),

$$\sin x = x - \frac{x^3}{3!} + \frac{x^5}{5!} - \frac{x^7}{7!} + \ldots$$
$$+ \frac{(-1)^n x^{2n+1}}{(2n+1)!} + \ldots \quad \text{for all } x. \quad (5.9)$$

Similarly

$$\cos x = 1 - \frac{x^2}{2!} + \frac{x^4}{4!} - \frac{x^6}{6!} + \ldots$$
$$+ \frac{(-1)^n x^{2n}}{(2n)!} + \ldots \quad \text{for all } x. \quad (5.10)$$

We may apply Taylor's theorem to $\sin(a+x)$ in which case $f(a) = \sin a$, $f'(a) = \cos a$, $f''(a) = -\sin a$, etc., and therefore

$$\sin(a+x) = \sin a + x\cos a - \frac{x^2}{2!}\sin a - \frac{x^3}{3!}\cos a$$

$$+ \frac{x^4}{4!}\sin a + \ldots + R_n.$$

As before, $R_n \to 0$ as $n \to \infty$ for all finite x, and hence

$$\sin(a+x) = \sin a\left(1 - \frac{x^2}{2!} + \frac{x^4}{4!} - \ldots\right)$$

$$+ \cos a\left(x - \frac{x^3}{3!} + \frac{x^5}{5!} - \ldots\right),$$

i.e.

$$\sin(a+x) = \sin a\cos x + \cos a\sin x.$$

Similarly $\cos(a+x) = \cos a\cos x - \sin a\sin x$.

(iii) *The logarithm function.* If $f(x) = \ln(1+x)$ where $x > 0$, then

$$f'(x) = (1+x)^{-1}, \quad f''(x) = -(1+x)^{-2}, \ldots,$$

$$f^{(n)}(x) = (-1)^{n-1}(n-1)!\,(1+x)^{-n}.$$

$$\therefore \ f(0) = 0, \quad f'(0) = 1, \quad f''(0) = -1,$$

$$f'''(0) = 2!, \ldots, \quad f^{(n)}(0) = (-1)^{n-1}(n-1)!$$

and Maclaurin's theorem gives

$$\ln(1+x) = x - \frac{x^2}{2} + \frac{x^3}{3} - \frac{x^4}{4} + \ldots + \frac{(-1)^{n-2}x^{n-1}}{(n-1)} + R_n,$$

where $R_n = (-1)^n x^n / \{n(1+\xi)^n\}$ and $\xi \geqslant 0$. Hence $|R_n| \leqslant x^n/n$ and tends to zero as $n \to \infty$ provided $0 \leqslant x \leqslant 1$.

The form of the remainder used above is unsuitable for negative x and we investigate the logarithmic series for negative x by a different method. Integrating the geometric series

$$1 + t + t^2 + \ldots + t^{n-1} = \frac{1-t^n}{1-t}$$

gives

$$\int_0^x \frac{dt}{1-t} = \int_0^x (1+t+t^2+ \ldots +t^{n-1})\,dt + \int_0^x \frac{t^n\,dt}{1-t},$$

where $0 \leqslant x < \delta < 1$. Hence

$$-\ln(1-x) = x + \frac{x^2}{2} + \frac{x^3}{3} + \ldots + \frac{x^n}{n} + R_n$$

where

$$R_n = \int_0^x \frac{t^n\,dt}{1-t}.$$

In this integral

$$(1-t)^{-1} < (1-\delta)^{-1}$$

since

$$0 \leqslant x < \delta < 1.$$

Hence

$$R \leqslant (1-\delta)^{-1} \int_0^x t^n\,dt = \frac{x^{n+1}}{(n+1)(1-\delta)}.$$

Therefore $\lim_{n \to \infty} R_n = 0$. Therefore the series is convergent and

$$\ln(1-x) = -x - \frac{x^2}{2} - \frac{x^3}{3} - \ldots - \frac{x^n}{n} - \ldots \quad \text{for} \quad 0 \leqslant x < 1.$$

This, combined with the result obtained from Maclaurin's theorem, shows that

$$\ln(1+x) = x - \frac{x^2}{2} + \frac{x^3}{3} - \ldots = \sum_{n=1}^{\infty} \frac{(-1)^{n-1} x^n}{n} \quad (5.11)$$

for $-1 < x \leqslant 1$.
Combining the series for $\ln(1+x)$ and $\ln(1-x)$ we find

$$\ln(1+x) - \ln(1-x) = \ln\left(\frac{1+x}{1-x}\right)$$

$$= 2\left\{x + \frac{x^3}{3} + \frac{x^5}{5} + \ldots + \frac{x^{2n+1}}{2n+1} + \ldots\right\}.$$

Writing $x = 1/(2p+1)$ gives

$$\ln\left(1+\frac{1}{p}\right) = 2 \sum_{n=0}^{\infty} \frac{1}{(2n+1)(2p+1)^{2n+1}} \quad (5.12)$$

if $p > 0$. The series on the right-hand side of eqn. (5.12) is rapidly convergent and hence is suitable for computation.

(iv) *The binomial series*. To obtain this series we use a method which is of importance in the solution of differential equations by means of power series.

If $z = (1+x)^k$ where k is a real number, then

$$(1+x)\frac{\mathrm{d}z}{\mathrm{d}x} = kz$$

and $z = 1$ when $x = 0$. We assume that, for $|x| < \varrho$,

$$z_1 = \sum_{p=0}^{\infty} a_p x^p,$$

an absolutely convergent power series which may be differentiated. Then

$$(1+x)\frac{\mathrm{d}z_1}{\mathrm{d}x} = a_1 + (2a_2 + a_1)x + (3a_3 + 2a_2)x^2 + \ldots$$

$$+ \{(n+1)a_{n+1} + na_n\} x^n + \ldots,$$
$$kz_1 = k(a_0 + a_1 x + a_2 x^2 + \ldots + a_n x^n + \ldots).$$

Equating like powers of x gives the set of equations

$$ka_0 = a_1,$$
$$ka_1 = 2a_2 + a_1,$$
$$ka_2 = 3a_3 + 2a_2,$$
$$\ldots \quad \ldots$$
$$\ldots \quad \ldots$$
$$ka_n = (n+1)a_{n+1} + na_n,$$
$$\ldots \quad \ldots$$

The solution of these equations is

$$a_1 = ka_0,$$
$$a_2 = k(k-1)\frac{a_0}{2!},$$
$$a_3 = k(k-1)(k-2)\frac{a_0}{3!},$$
$$\ldots \quad \ldots$$
$$\ldots \quad \ldots$$
$$a_n = k(k-1)(k-2)\ldots(k-n+1)\frac{a_0}{n!},$$
$$\ldots \quad \ldots$$

Also $z_1 = 1$ when $x = 0$ if $a_0 = 1$. The ratio test shows that the series is absolutely convergent if $|x| < 1$. The above analysis shows that we have found an infinite series whose sum z_1 satisfies the differential equation. Now, it can be proved that there is only *one* solution of the differential equation for which $z = 1$ when $x = 0$. Hence $\varrho = 1$, $z = z_1$ and we have the *binomial theorem*

$$(1+x)^k = 1+kx+\frac{k(k-1)x^2}{2!}+\frac{k(k-1)\,(k-2)x^3}{3!}+ \cdots$$
$$+\frac{k(k-1)\,(k-2)\,\cdots\,(k-n+1)x^n}{n!}+ \cdots, \qquad (5.13)$$

for $|x| < 1$. When $|x| \geqslant 1$ the series is of no interest unless k is a positive integer in which case it terminates.

Example 1. The expansion of $u = (x+a)^k$.
If $|x/a| < 1$, we write

$$u = a^k \left(1+\frac{x}{a}\right)^k$$
$$= a^k \left[1+k\left(\frac{x}{a}\right)+\frac{k(k-1)}{2!}\left(\frac{x}{a}\right)^2+\frac{k(k-1)\,(k-2)}{3!}\left(\frac{x}{a}\right)^3+ \cdots\right],$$

i.e. we obtain an expansion in ascending powers of (x/a).
If $|x/a| > 1$, we write

$$u = x^k \left(1+\frac{a}{x}\right)^k$$
$$= x^k \left[1+k\left(\frac{a}{x}\right)+\frac{k(k-1)}{2!}\left(\frac{a}{x}\right)^2+\frac{k(k-1)\,(k-2)}{3!}\left(\frac{a}{x}\right)^3+ \cdots\right],$$

i.e. we obtain an expansion in ascending powers of (a/x).

Example 2. Express
$$f(x) = \frac{2x-1}{(1-x)^2\,(2-x)}$$

as a sum of partial fractions and hence obtain the expansion of $f(x)$ in ascending powers of x, giving the term in x^n. For what ranges of values of x is the expansion valid?

The partial fractions are easily found to be given by

$$f(x) = \frac{3}{2-x}-\frac{3}{1-x}+\frac{1}{(1-x)^2}\,.$$

Therefore by the binomial theorem

$$f(x) = \frac{3}{2}\left(1-\frac{x}{2}\right)^{-1} - 3(1-x)^{-1} + (1-x)^{-2}$$

$$= \frac{3}{2}\sum_0^\infty \left(\frac{x}{2}\right)^n - 3\sum_0^\infty x^n + \sum_0^\infty (n+1)x^n .$$

The coefficient of x^n is $3/2^{n+1}+n-2$ and since the radii of convergence of the series are 2, 1, 1, the expansion is valid for $|x| < 1$.

Example 3. Write down the expansion of $\ln [1+(1/n)]$ in ascending powers of $1/n$ and show that, if n is a large positive number,

$$\left(1+\frac{1}{n}\right)^n = e\left(1-\frac{1}{2n}+\frac{11}{24n^2}-\frac{7}{16n^3}\right) \qquad \text{approximately.}$$

$$\ln\left(1+\frac{1}{n}\right) = \frac{1}{n} - \frac{1}{2n^2} + \frac{1}{3n^3} - \cdots + \frac{(-1)^{r-1}}{rn^r} + \cdots .$$

$$\therefore \ n\ln\left(1+\frac{1}{n}\right) = 1 - \frac{1}{2n} + \frac{1}{3n^2} - \frac{1}{4n^3} + O\left(\frac{1}{n^4}\right) .$$

$$\therefore \ \left(1+\frac{1}{n}\right)^n = \exp\left[1 - \frac{1}{2n} + \frac{1}{3n^2} - \frac{1}{4n^3} + O\left(\frac{1}{n^4}\right)\right]$$

$$= e\cdot\exp\left[-\frac{1}{2n} + \frac{1}{3n^2} - \frac{1}{4n^3} + O\left(\frac{1}{n^4}\right)\right]$$

$$= e\left[1 + \left(-\frac{1}{2n} + \frac{1}{3n^2} - \frac{1}{4n^3}\right) + \frac{1}{2!}\left(-\frac{1}{2n} + \frac{1}{3n^2}\right)^2 \right.$$

$$\left. + \frac{1}{3!}\left(-\frac{1}{2n}\right)^3 + O\left(\frac{1}{n^4}\right)\right],$$

leading to

$$\left(1+\frac{1}{n}\right)^n = e\left(1 - \frac{1}{2n} + \frac{11}{24n^2} - \frac{7}{16n^3}\right) + O\left(\frac{1}{n^4}\right),$$

which implies the required result.

Example 4. Show that $\qquad \lim_{n\to\infty}\left(1+\frac{x}{n}\right)^n = e^x .$

Here we use a theorem of pure mathematics which states that if

$$\lim_{t\to a}\{\ln f(t)\} = k, \qquad \text{then} \qquad \lim_{t\to a}\{f(t)\} = e^k .$$

In our case $\lim_{n\to\infty}\left\{\ln\left(1+\frac{x}{n}\right)^n\right\} = \lim_{n\to\infty}\left\{n\ln\left(1+\frac{x}{n}\right)\right\}$

$$= \lim_{n\to\infty}\left\{n\left[\frac{x}{n} + O\left(\frac{x^2}{n^2}\right)\right]\right\} = x.$$

Hence the result follows and establishes the alternative definition of e^x stated in § 2 : 4. Similarly, $\lim\limits_{n \to \infty} \left\{ \left(1 + \dfrac{1}{n} \right)^{nx} \right\} = e^x$.

Example 5. Find $\qquad \lim\limits_{x \to 0} \left\{ \dfrac{a \sin bx - b \sin ax}{x^3} \right\}$.

Expanding the numerator as a power series in x gives

$$a \sin bx - b \sin ax = a \left\{ bx - \frac{1}{3!} (bx)^3 + O(x^5) \right\} - b \left\{ ax - \frac{1}{3!} (ax)^3 + O(x^5) \right\}$$

$$= ab(a^2 - b^2) \frac{x^3}{6} + O(x^5).$$

Therefore the required limit is $ab(a^2 - b^2)/6$.

Example 6. To find the power series for $\cos^2 x$ we express it in the form $\frac{1}{2}(1 + \cos 2x)$, and use the power series for $\cos 2x$ in the form $\sum\limits_{0}^{\infty} (-1)^n (2x)^{2n}/(2n)!$

Example 7. (i) Find $\qquad \lim\limits_{\theta \to \pi/2} \dfrac{\sin (\theta \cos \theta)}{\cos (\theta \sin \theta)}$.

(ii) Show that $\dfrac{3 \sin 2\phi}{2(2 + \cos 2\phi)} = \phi$ approximately if ϕ is small, and estimate the order of magnitude of the error for small values of ϕ.

(i) We write $\theta = \pi/2 - \psi$ and require

$$l = \lim_{\psi \to 0} \frac{\sin \{(\pi/2 - \psi) \cos (\pi/2 - \psi)\}}{\cos \{(\pi/2 - \psi) \sin (\pi/2 - \psi)\}} = \lim_{\psi \to 0} \frac{\sin \{(\pi/2 - \psi) \sin \psi\}}{\cos \{(\pi/2 - \psi) \cos \psi\}}$$

$$= \lim_{\psi \to 0} \frac{\sin \{\pi\psi/2 + O(\psi^2)\}}{\cos \{\pi/2 - \psi + O(\psi^2)\}} = \lim_{\psi \to 0} \frac{\sin \{\pi\psi/2 + O(\psi^2)\}}{\sin \{\psi + O(\psi^2)\}}$$

$$= \lim_{\psi \to 0} \frac{\pi\psi/2 + O(\psi^2)}{\psi + O(\psi^2)} = \frac{\pi}{2}.$$

(ii) Using the series expansions for $\sin x$, $\cos x$ we have

$$\frac{3 \sin 2\phi}{2(2 + \cos 2\phi)} = \frac{3\{2\phi - [(2\phi)^3/3!] + O(\phi^5)\}}{2\{2 + 1 - [(2\phi)^2/2!] + O(\phi^4)\}}$$

$$= \frac{\phi\{1 - (2\phi^2/3) + O(\phi^4)\}}{1 - (2\phi^2/3) + O(\phi^4)} = \phi + O(\phi^5).$$

Example 8. If $y = f(x) = [x + \sqrt{(1 + x^2)}]^{\frac{1}{2}}$, show that

$$(1 + x^2) \frac{d^2y}{dx^2} + x \frac{dy}{dx} - \frac{1}{4} y = 0.$$

Differentiate this equation n times by Leibniz's theorem and deduce that

$$f^{(n+2)}(0) = (\tfrac{1}{4} - n^2) f^{(n)}(0).$$

Hence find the expansion of y in ascending powers of x.

$$\frac{dy}{dx} = \frac{1 + x/\sqrt{(1+x^2)}}{2[x + \sqrt{(1+x^2)}]^{\frac{1}{2}}} = \frac{y}{2\sqrt{(1+x^2)}}. \tag{1}$$

$$\therefore \quad (1+x^2)\left(\frac{dy}{dx}\right)^2 = \frac{1}{4} y^2.$$

Differentiating and cancelling $2\,dy/dx$ gives

$$(1+x^2)\frac{d^2y}{dx^2} + x\frac{dy}{dx} - \frac{1}{4} y = 0.$$

Leibniz's theorem gives

$$(1+x^2)f^{(n+2)}(x) + 2nx f^{(n+1)}(x) + n(n-1) f^{(n)}(x) + x f^{(n+1)}(x)$$
$$+ n f^{(n)}(x) - \tfrac{1}{4} f^{(n)}(x) = 0.$$

Putting $x = 0$ gives

$$f^{(n+2)}(0) = (\tfrac{1}{4} - n^2) f^{(n)}(0). \tag{2}$$

But $f(0) = 1$ and eqn. (1) gives $f'(0) = \tfrac{1}{2}$.

Then eqn. (2) gives

$$f^{2p}(0) = 1 \cdot \tfrac{1}{4} \cdot (\tfrac{1}{4} - 2^2) \; \cdots \; \{\tfrac{1}{4} - (2p-2)^2\} = a_{2p},$$
$$f^{2p+1}(0) = \tfrac{1}{2} \cdot (\tfrac{1}{4} - 1^2) \cdot (\tfrac{1}{4} - 3^2) \; \cdots \; \{\tfrac{1}{4} - (2p-1)^2\} = b_{2p+1}.$$

Hence

$$[x + \sqrt{(1+x^2)}]^{\frac{1}{2}} = \sum_{p=0}^{\infty} \frac{a_{2p}}{(2p)!} x^{2p} + \sum_{p=0}^{\infty} \frac{b_{2p+1}}{(2p+1)!} x^{2p+1}, \tag{3}$$

valid for $|x| < 1$ since the radius of convergence of each of the series of eqn. (3) is unity.

Example 9. Maclaurin's theorem can be used to obtain series solutions of certain differential equations subject to prescribed conditions when $x = 0$. In illustration we first derive the power series for $\sin x$ which we define as that solution of the equation

$$f''(x) + f(x) = 0 \tag{1}$$

for which $f(0) = 0$, $f'(0) = 1$.

Differentiating eqn. (1) n times and putting $x = 0$, we find

$$f^{n+2}(0) = -f^n(0).$$

It follows that

$$f^{2r+1}(0) = (-1)^r f'(0) = (-1)^r,$$
$$f^{2r}(0) = (-1)^r f(0) = 0.$$

The series expansion for $f(x)$ is therefore

$$x - \frac{x^3}{3!} + \frac{x^5}{5!} - \cdots + \frac{(-1)^r x^{2r+1}}{(2r+1)!} + \cdots.$$

Similarly we can derive the series for $\cos x$ when defined as that solution of eqn. (1) for which $f(0) = 1$, $f'(0) = 0$.

Example 10. We obtain that solution $y = f(x)$ of *Airy's equation* $d^2y/dx^2 - xy = 0$ for which $f(0) = 0$, $f'(0) = 1$.

Differentiating Airy's equation $(n+1)$ times by Leibniz's theorem, we find

$$f^{(n+3)}(x) - x f^{(n+1)}(x) - (n+1) f^n(x) = 0$$

so that

$$f^{(n+3)}(0) = (n+1) f^n(0), \qquad (n \geqslant 0).$$

But, putting $x = 0$ in Airy's equation, we have $f''(0) = 0$. Hence

$$f^{(3r)}(0) = 0, \quad f^{(3r+2)}(0) = 0, \quad f^{(3r+1)}(0) = 2.5 \ldots (3r-1).$$

$$\therefore \ f(x) = x + \frac{2x^4}{4!} + \frac{2.5x^7}{7!} + \cdots + \frac{2.5 \ldots (3r-1)x^{3r+1}}{(3r+1)!} + \cdots.$$

Exercises 5 : 5

1. Prove that $\tan x = x + \frac{x^3}{3} + \frac{2x^5}{15} + \frac{17x^7}{315} + \cdots$ (x being an acute angle).

(i) Hence prove that

$$\ln \sec x = \frac{x^2}{2} + \frac{x^4}{12} + \frac{x^6}{45} + \cdots$$

When $x = 0.1$, show that $1 + \ln \sec x - \cosh x$ is approximately 4.2×10^{-6}.

(ii) Deduce the expansion of $\tan^2 x$ as far as the term in x^6. Hence show that $\sec^2 x$ differs from $27/(3-x^2)^3$ by about $x^6/135$ when x is small.

2. Find the values of a and b if the expansion of

$$\frac{1+ax}{1+bx} \ln (1+x)$$

in powers of x contains no term in x^2 and no term in x^3, and show that the coefficient of x^4 is $-\frac{1}{36}$.

3. By combining expansions of trigonometric and exponential functions, or otherwise, sum the series

(i)

$$1 + \frac{x^4}{4!} + \frac{x^8}{8!} + \frac{x^{12}}{12!} + \cdots,$$

(ii)

$$\frac{x^3}{3!} + \frac{x^7}{7!} + \frac{x^{11}}{11!} + \cdots.$$

4. By using Maclaurin's theorem, or otherwise, show that

$$\ln (\sec x + \tan x) = x + \frac{x^3}{6} + \frac{x^5}{24} + \ldots .$$

Hence, or otherwise, prove that

$$\lim_{x \to 0} \left[\frac{\ln (\sec x + \tan x) - 2 \sin x + x \cos x}{x^5} \right] = \frac{1}{15} .$$

5. Expand $e^x \cos x$ by Maclaurin's theorem, giving the first five terms.

6. If $y = e^{\tan^{-1} x}$ where $\tan^{-1} x$ lies between $-\pi/2$ and $+\pi/2$, show that $(1 + x^2) (dy/dx) = y$, and, by successive differentiation of this equation, obtain, using Maclaurin's theorem, the expansion of y in ascending powers of x as far as the term in x^5.

Deduce that

$$\lim_{x \to 0} \left[\frac{e^{\tan^{-1} x} - e^x \left(1 - \frac{x^3}{3} \right)}{x^5} \right] = \frac{1}{5} .$$

7. If $y = \dfrac{\ln (1 + x)}{1 + x}$ show that

$$D_0^{n+1} y + (2n + 1) D_0^n y + n^2 D_0^{n-1} y = 0,$$

where

$$D_0^n y \equiv \left(\frac{d^n y}{dx^n} \right)_{x=0} .$$

Hence, or otherwise, obtain the series expansions for y as far as the term in x^3.

8. An approximation to $(1 - x)^{-2}$ is obtained by using the first n terms of the binomial expansion. By differentiating the geometrical progression

$$1 + x + x^2 + \ldots + x^{n-1} + x^n = \frac{1 - x^{n+1}}{1 - x} ,$$

prove that the error in the approximation is

$$\frac{(n+1)x^n - nx^{n+1}}{(1-x)^2} .$$

9. Express $\dfrac{4x - 5}{(1 - x)^2 (3x + 2)}$ as a sum of partial fractions. Hence determine the coefficient of x^n in the expansion of this expression in a series of ascending powers of x, and state the range of values of x for which the expansion holds.

10. Show that there is a range of values of x for which the function

$$(1 + x + x^2 + x^3)^{-2}$$

has an expansion $\sum_{r=0}^{\infty} c_r x^r$, where the coefficients c_r are independent of x. Prove that

(i) $$2c_{4r} = 2c_{4r+2} = -c_{4r+1} \quad \text{and} \quad c_{4r+3} = 0,$$

(ii) $$\sum_{r=0}^{\infty} \frac{1}{2^{2r}} c_{2r} = \frac{64}{45} .$$

11. Find

(i) $\quad\quad \lim_{x \to 0} \{x^{1/x}\},$ (ii) $\quad \lim_{x \to 0} \left\{ \left(\frac{1+x}{1-x} \right)^{1/x} \right\}.$

12. Evaluate the limits of the following expressions (a and b being positive):

(i) $\quad\quad \sqrt[n]{(a^n + b^n)},$ as $\quad n \to \infty;$

(ii) $\quad\quad \dfrac{1}{x^2} - \operatorname{cosec}^2 x,$ as $\quad x \to 0;$

(iii) $\quad\quad \dfrac{\ln b - \ln x}{b - x},$ as $\quad x \to b;$

(iv) $\quad\quad (1-x)^{-3} \int_1^x \ln (3t - 3t^2 + t^3)\, dt,$ as $\quad x \to 1;$

(v) $\quad\quad \dfrac{5^x - 4^x}{3^x - 2^x},$ as $\quad x \to 0;$

(vi) $\quad\quad xe^{-n^2 x}$ as $\quad x \to \infty;$

(vii) $\quad\quad x \sin (\pi/x)$ as $\quad x \to \infty;$

(viii) $\quad\quad \dfrac{x^2 + 2 \cos x - 2}{x^4}$ as $\quad x \to 0.$

13. Determine the constants a and b so that $(1 + a \cos 2x + b \cos 4x)/x^4$ may have a finite limit as $x \to 0$, and find the value of the limit.

14. Find

(i) $\quad \lim_{n \to \infty} \left(1 + \dfrac{2}{n} \right)^{1/n},$ (ii) $\quad \lim_{x \to 0} \dfrac{x \sin^2 x}{\sin 2x - 2 \sin x},$

(iii) $\quad \lim_{x \to \pi/2} \dfrac{\cos x}{\cos 3x},$ (iv) $\quad \lim_{n \to \infty} n(\sqrt{(n^2 + 1)} - n),$

(v) $\quad \lim_{x \to 0} \dfrac{1 - 2^x}{\sin x},$ (vi) $\quad \lim_{x \to \infty} (3x^2 - 1)e^{-x},$

(vii) $\quad \lim_{x \to 0} \dfrac{x \sinh x}{1 - \cos x},$ (viii) $\quad \lim_{x \to \infty} \left(\dfrac{x+2}{x+1} \right)^x.$

15. Obtain the first four terms of the expansions of (i) $e^x \cos (x + \alpha)$ where α is constant, (ii) $\ln (1 + \sin x)$.

16. Determine the successive derivatives of $f(x)$ at $x = 0$, given that

$$\frac{df(x)}{dx} = x + f(x), \quad f(0) = 0,$$

and give the value of $f^{(n)}(0)$ for $n > 1$.

Hence show that the solution of the differential equation

$$\frac{dy}{dx} = x + y,$$

satisfying $y = 0$ when $x = 0$, is

$$y = e^x - 1 - x,$$

and check your result by solving the equation by some other method. [See Vol. 2, § 1 : 4.]

17. If $y = \sin(2m+1)\theta$, where m is a positive integer, and $x = \sin\theta$, show that

$$(1-x^2)\left(\frac{dy}{dx}\right)^2 = (2m+1)^2(1-y^2).$$

Hence prove that, if n is a positive integer or zero,

$$(1-x^2)\left(\frac{d^{n+2}y}{dx^{n+2}}\right) - (2n+1)x\frac{d^{n+1}y}{dx^{n+1}} + \{(2m+1)^2 - n^2\}\frac{d^n y}{dx^n} = 0,$$

and deduce that

$$\sin(2m+1)\theta = (2m+1)\left[\sin\theta - \frac{(2m+1)^2 - 1^2}{3!}\sin^3\theta\right.$$
$$\left. + \frac{\{(2m+1)^2 - 1^2\}\{(2m+1)^2 - 3^2\}}{5!}\sin^5\theta - \ldots\right].$$

18. The *Bessel function of order zero* satisfies the equation

$$x\frac{d^2 J}{dx^2} + \frac{dJ}{dx} + xJ = 0,$$

together with the conditions that $J = 1$ when $x = 0$, and all its derivatives exist at $x = 0$.

Differentiate the equation n times, and show that

$$\frac{d^{n+1}J}{dx^{n+1}} = -\frac{n}{n+1}\frac{d^{n-1}J}{dx^{n-1}} \quad \text{when} \quad x = 0 \quad (n \geqslant 1).$$

Derive the Maclaurin series for $J(x)$, and calculate the range of values of x for which the series converges.

19. A function $u(x)$ is such that

$$(1-x^2)u'(x) = xu(x) + 1 \quad (|x| < 1).$$

If $u(0) = 0$, show that the Maclaurin expansion of $u(x)$ as far as the term involving x^5 is

$$x + \tfrac{2}{3}x^3 + \tfrac{8}{15}x^5.$$

20. The function $y(x)$ satisfies

$$dy/dx = 2xy + 1 \tag{1}$$

with $y(0) = 0$.

Find the relationship between $y^{(n)}(0)$ and $y^{(n-2)}(0)$ and hence find the Maclaurin expansion of y, giving the general terms of odd and even order.

Show that

$$y(x) = e^{x^2}\int_0^x e^{-t^2}\,dt$$

satisfies eqn. (1).

21. If $y = \sin(a \sin^{-1} x)$, and $y_n = \mathrm{d}^n y/\mathrm{d}x^n$, show that

    (i) $(1-x^2)y_2 - xy_1 + a^2 y = 0$,

    (ii) $(1-x^2)y_{n+2} - (2n+1)xy_{n+1} + (a^2 - n^2)y_n = 0$.

Hence determine a relationship between y_{n+2} and y_n when $x = 0$. By considering the Maclaurin expansion of y, and writing $x = \sin t$, prove the identity

$$\sin 5t = 5 \sin t - 20 \sin^3 t + 16 \sin^5 t.$$

5 : 6 Maxima and minima

The determination of maxima and minima is of great importance in physical problems; e.g. the most economical use of material frequently involves an investigation of the minima of some function. Further, the nature and stability of the equilibrium

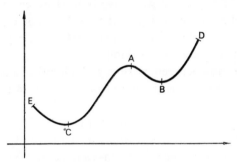

FIG. 5.4.

states of mechanical and physical systems are often determined by finding the conditions under which some function, e.g. potential energy, strain energy, entropy, has a maximum or a minimum. In this section we determine the conditions under which a function of one variable has maxima and minima.

Roughly speaking $f(x)$ has a *maximum* at $x = a$ if its graph has a local maximum at that point, i.e., if the ordinate at $x = a$ is higher than any other ordinate in the immediate neighbourhood. Similarly $f(x)$ has a minimum at $x = b$ if the ordinate at $x = b$ is lower than any other ordinate in the immediate neighbourhood. In Fig. 5.4 the point A is at a maximum of $f(x)$ whereas B and C are at minima. Formally a maximum is defined as follows: *The function $f(x)$ has a maximum, $f(a)$, at $x = a$ if a positive constant*

δ *can be found such that* $f(x) < f(a)$ *for* $|x-a| < \delta$, $x \neq a$. It is immaterial if δ is small, provided it is different from zero so that there are points on the curve $y = f(x)$ on *both* sides of $x = a$ below the level of A. Similarly, $f(x)$ *has a minimum at* $x = b$ *if a positive constant* δ' *can be found such that* $f(x) > f(b)$ *for* $|x-b| < \delta'$, $x \neq b$. In this case there must be points on both sides of B above the level of B.

It is necessary to distinguish between *greatest value* and maximum and between *least value* and minimum. If the curve of Fig. 5.4 is defined only between E and D, then D gives the greatest value of $f(x)$ although D is not at a maximum. In Fig. 5.4 C gives the least value of $f(x)$ as well as being a minimum. However, the least value of $f(x)$ could well have been at an end point of the range of definition of $f(x)$; e.g. the bending moment in a beam clamped at one end may have its greatest value, but not a maximum as defined here, at the clamp.

Discrimination between maxima and minima of a *differentiable* function may be effected by use of one or other of the following tests.

(a) At a point P to the left of A, Fig. 5.4, the gradient of the curve, i.e. $f'(x)$, is positive whereas to the right of A, at Q, this gradient is negative. Since $f'(x)$ is taken to be continuous, *if $x = a$ gives a maximum of $f(x)$, then $f'(x)$ must change from positive when $x < a$, through zero when $x = a$, to negative for $x > a$.* Similarly, *if $x = b$ gives a minimum of $f(x)$, then $f'(x)$ must change from negative when $x < b$, through zero when $x = b$, to positive for $x > b$.*

A point where $f'(x)$ vanishes, irrespective of other conditions imposed [e.g. change in sign of $f'(x)$], is a *stationary* point and may be neither a maximum nor a minimum.

(b) Suppose the function $f(x)$ is expanded about $x = a$ by Taylor's theorem. Then

$$f(x)-f(a) = (x-a)f'(a) + \frac{(x-a)^2}{2!}f''(a)$$

$$+ \frac{(x-a)^3}{3!}f'''(a) + \dots \qquad (5.14)$$

Since we need only be concerned with numerically small values of $(x-a)$, the dominant or largest term on the right-hand side of eqn. (5.14) is the first, namely $(x-a)f'(a)$. But this changes sign as $(x-a)$ changes sign and hence the condition $f(x) < f(a)$ for a maximum cannot be fulfilled unless $f'(a) = 0$. This is a necessary condition for a maximum at $x = a$. The dominant term on the right-hand side of eqn. (5.14) is now $\frac{1}{2}(x-a)^2 f''(a)$ whose sign is determined by $f''(a)$. Hence, if $f''(a) < 0$, then $f(x)-f(a) < 0$ for $(x-a)$ sufficiently small. Therefore $f'(a) = 0$, $f''(a) < 0$ are sufficient conditions for a maximum.

However, $f''(a)$ may itself vanish. In this case the dominant term on the right-hand side of eqn. (5.14) will be that term of the Taylor series corresponding to the derivative of lowest order which does not vanish at $x = a$. If this derivative is of odd order (i.e. the third, fifth, etc.), there can be no maximum of $f(x)$ at $x = a$. On the other hand, if the first non-vanishing derivative at $x = a$ is of even order (i.e. second, fourth, etc.), and has a negative sign, $f(x) < f(a)$ for $(x-a)$ sufficiently small and $f(x)$ has a maximum at $x = a$. Similar tests hold for a minimum.

To sum up, *sufficient conditions for a maximum at $x = a$ are:*

(i) $f'(a) = 0$,

(ii) $f^{(2m)}(a) < 0$, *all lower-order derivatives vanishing at $x = a$.*

Sufficient conditions for a minimum at $x = b$ are

(i) $f'(b) = 0$,

(ii) $f^{(2m)}(b) > 0$, *all lower-order derivatives vanishing at $x = b$.*

It must be emphasised that, if the first non-vanishing derivative (higher order than the first) of $f(x)$ at $x = a$ is of *odd* order, then $f(x)$ does *not* have a maximum or minimum although it is said to be stationary. In practice it is not always convenient to find these higher-order derivatives and in these circumstances method (a) is usually more convenient.

If $f(x)$ is continuous then the maxima and minima of $f(x)$ occur alternately, a fact which is of particular importance in investigations of stability.

If $f'(x)$ is undefined at $x = a$, see Fig. 5.5, then $f(x)$ may have a maximum or minimum there.

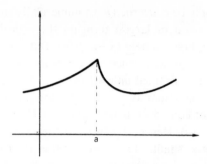

Fig. 5.5. Illustrating a maximum where $f'(x)$ is undefined.

Example 1. If q and r are real, find the condition that the equation $x^3 + qx + r = 0$ has three real roots.

This problem is best solved by investigating the maximum and minimum of the cubic curve $y = x^3 + qx + r$. We first examine the more general case of the equation

$$f(x) \equiv ax^3 + bx^2 + cx + d = 0 \qquad (a > 0).$$

Consider the curve $y = f(x)$. Its stationary points are given by $\mathrm{d}y/\mathrm{d}x = 0$, i.e. $3ax^2 + 2bx + c = 0$. If this has complex roots, $\mathrm{d}y/\mathrm{d}x$ is always positive and $f(x)$ can have only one real zero. If the stationary points are real at $x = \alpha$, $x = \beta \ (\alpha < \beta)$, then

$$\frac{\mathrm{d}y}{\mathrm{d}x} = 3a(x-\alpha)(x-\beta).$$

The tests of § 5:6 show that at $x = \alpha$ there is a maximum, at $x = \beta$ a minimum. The shape of the curve $y = f(x)$ is then as in Fig. 5.6. Here we have shown the maximum at $x = \alpha$ above Ox and the minimum at $x = \beta$ below Ox, in which case $f(x)$ has three real zeros. It is clear that if the minimum at $x = \beta$ is above the axis, i.e. if $f(\beta) > 0$ (and $a > 0$), there is only one real zero.

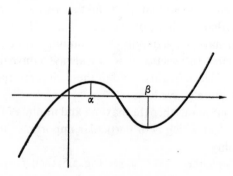

Fig. 5.6. A cubic curve.

For similar reasons there is only one real zero if $f(\alpha) < 0$. If there are three real zeros they are separated by $x = \alpha$ and $x = \beta$ and $f(\alpha) \cdot f(\beta) < 0$. It is probably easier to use these geometrical methods and ideas to investigate a given cubic equation than to rely upon formulae, which may be complicated. This result that the zeros of $f(x)$ are separated by the zeros of $f'(x)$ *provided that $f'(x)$ is continuous*, is a useful general result for locating the zeros of $f(x)$.

For the equation $x^3 + qx + r = 0$ the turning points are given by $3x^2 + q = 0$; therefore for real turning points $q < 0$. Further in this case $f(\alpha) \cdot f(\beta) = r^2 + 4q^3/27$. Therefore the condition for three real roots is $4q^3 + 27r^2 < 0$. (This ncludes the condition $q < 0$.)

Example 2. Find the values of x for which the function

$$y = \frac{x^3 - x^2 + 4}{x^3 + x^2 + 4}$$

is stationary and discuss the character of these stationary points.

Investigate the number of real roots of the equation

$$x^3(a-1) + x^2(a+1) + 4(a-1) = 0$$

for different values of a.

Since $y = 1 - \dfrac{2x^2}{x^3 + x^2 + 4}$, $\dfrac{dy}{dx} = \dfrac{2x(x^3 - 8)}{(x^3 + x^2 + 4)^2}$, and so y has two real stationary points:

when $x = 0$,   a maximum $y = 1$;

when $x = 2$,   a minimum $y = \frac{1}{2}$.

Also y is undefined (infinite) when $x^3 + x^2 + 4 = 0$ and this equation has one real root $x = -2$ and so the line $x = -2$ is an asymptote. As $x \to \infty$, $y \to 1 - 0$; as $x \to -\infty$, $y \to 1 + 0$ and so the line $y = 1$ is an asymptote. The graph of y is shown in Fig. 5.7.

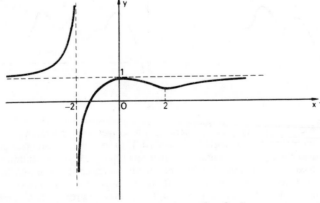

FIG. 5.7. The graph $y = \dfrac{x^3 - x^2 + 4}{x^3 + x^2 + 4}$.

The roots of the given equation occur at the intersections of the given curve and the line $y = a$. The following cases arise:

(i) If $a > 1$, there is one real root only and this lies in the interval $(-\infty, -2)$.

(ii) If $a = 1$, there are two roots $x = 0$. In this case the equation reduces to the quadratic $x^2 = 0$.

(iii) If $1 > a > \frac{1}{2}$, there are three real roots, one in $(-2, 0)$, one in $(0, 2)$ and one in $(2, \infty)$.

(iv) If $a = \frac{1}{2}$, there are three real roots, one in $(-2, 0)$ and two coincident at $x = 2$.

(v) If $a < \frac{1}{2}$, there is one real root only and it lies in $(-2, -1)$.

Example 3. If $P(x)$ is a polynomial in x, discuss the number of (real) roots of $P'(x) = 0$ lying between two successive roots of $P(x) = 0$. Discuss also the number of roots of $P(x) = 0$ lying between two successive roots of $P'(x) = 0$.

If
$$P_n(x) = 1 + x + \frac{x^2}{2!} + \ldots + \frac{x^n}{n!},$$

prove that the equation $P_n(x) = 0$ has no root when n is even and one when n is odd.

Between successive roots of the equation $P(x) = 0$, say at $x = a, b$, the graph of $y = P(x)$ must lie either entirely above or entirely below the x-axis. For illustration we consider the case when the graph lies above the x-axis. Since $P(x)$ is a polynomial the graph is continuous, and in the range (a, b) there may be a number of maxima, minima or inflexions with horizontal tangents; possible cases are illustrated in Fig. 5.8(a), (b).

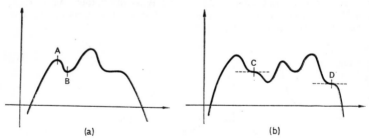

(a)   (b)

Fig. 5.8.

Since the curve is continuous there must be *at least* one maximum (or one minimum if the curve lies below the x-axis). If there is more than one maximum, then maxima and minima must alternate—for the curve is continuous. These maxima and minima may be separated by points of inflexion with horizontal tangents, e.g. as shown at C or D in Fig. 5.8(b). Now each maximum or minimum must arise at a root of $P'(x) = 0$ but it may be a repeated root. Each inflexion with a horizontal tangent, such as C or D, is also a root of $P'(x) = 0$ and these points give repeated roots. (See § 4:3.) For each maximum or minimum the first non-vanishing derivative of $P(x)$ is of even order; the corresponding zero of $P'(x)$ is either simple or a repeated root of odd order. Thus each maximum or minimum corresponds to an *odd* number of roots of $P'(x)$ $= 0$. There must be an odd number of maxima or minima in (a, b), so that, in the absence of inflexions, there must be an odd number of roots of $P'(x) = 0$ between $x = a$ and $x = b$.

If there is an inflexion, the first non-vanishing derivative of $P(x)$ has odd order. Consequently the corresponding zero of $P'(x)$ is a repeated zero of even order. Now whether there are inflexions in (a, b) or not there must be at least one maximum (or minimum); consequently there can be only an odd number of roots of $P'(x) = 0$ between the successive roots a and b of $P(x) = 0$.

In the special case quoted the first two polynomials are

$$P_1(x) = 1 + x, \qquad P_2(x) = 1 + x + x^2/2!,$$

and the equation $P_1(x) = 0$ has one real root $x = -1$, whereas the equation $P_2(x) = 0$ has no real root. To prove the required result by induction we *assume* that the equation $P_{2r-1}(x) = 0$ has one real root and that the equation $P_{2r}(x) = 0$ has no real roots. We use this assumption to prove that the equation $P_{2r+1}(x) = 0$ has one real root and the equation $P_{2r+2}(x) = 0$ has none. (We know our assumption is true for $r = 1$.)

A polynomial equation of odd order must have at least one real root. Now $P_{2r+1}'(x) = P_{2r}(x)$ and $P_{2r}(x)$ has no real zeros and the derivative of $P_{2r+1}(x)$ must have the same sign, positive for all values of x. Therefore, $P_{2r+1}(x)$ is a strictly increasing function running from $-\infty$ through zero to $+\infty$ as x increases from $-\infty$ to $+\infty$.

Now $P_{2r+2}'(x) = P_{2r+1}(x)$ and, since $P_{2r+1}(x)$ has only one zero, the equation $P_{2r+2}(x) = 0$ either has two roots, lying on either side of the zero of $P_{2r+1}(x)$, or it has none. The value $x = \alpha$ which makes $P_{2r+1}(x)$ vanish must give the *minimum* value of $P_{2r+2}(x)$.

But $$P_{2r+2}(x) = P_{2r+1}(x) + x^{2r+2}/(2r+2)!$$

∴ $$P_{2r+2}(\alpha) = 0 + \alpha^{2r+2}/(2r+2)! > 0.$$

Hence $P_{2r+2}(x)$ has no zeros, its graph lying entirely above the x-axis. Thus we have deduced the result for $P_{2r+1}(x)$ and $P_{2r+2}(x)$ from that for $P_{2r-1}(x)$ and $P_{2r}(x)$. We know the result is true for $r = 1$ and it therefore follows, by induction, for all positive integers r.

Example 4. A cylinder is inscribed in a cone of height h. If the volume of the cylinder is a maximum, show that its height is $h/3$.

Show further that when the height of the cylinder is $h/2$, its curved surface area is a maximum.

Let x be the height of the cylinder and α the semi-vertical angle of the cone. Then the radius of the cylinder is $(h-x) \tan \alpha$. Therefore the volume, V, of the cylinder is given by

$$V = \pi x(h-x)^2 \tan^2 \alpha.$$
$$\frac{dV}{dx} = \pi[h^2 - 4hx + 3x^2] \tan^2 \alpha,$$

i.e.

$$\frac{dV}{dx} = \pi(h - 3x)(h - x)\tan^2\alpha.$$

Hence, when V is stationary, $x = \frac{1}{3}h$ and since dV/dx changes from positive to negative as x increases through $\frac{1}{3}h$ this gives the maximum of V. In fact $V_{max} = (4\pi h^3 \tan^2\alpha)/27$. The stationary point where $x = h$ is of no physical interest.

The curved surface area $S = 2\pi x(h - x)\tan\alpha$.

$$\therefore \quad \frac{dS}{dx} = 2\pi(h - 2x)\tan\alpha,$$

and,

$$\frac{d^2S}{dx^2} = -4\pi\tan\alpha.$$

Therefore $x = \frac{1}{2}h$ gives the maximum of S and $S_{max} = \frac{1}{2}\pi h^2\tan\alpha$.

Example 5. Find the point in the first quadrant at which the tangent to the curve $r^2 = a^2\cos 2\theta$ is parallel to Ox.

We need the point at which y is stationary. In general, if $r = f(\theta)$, we need the stationary points of $y = r\sin\theta = f(\theta)\sin\theta = F(\theta)$, say.

In this case $F(\theta) = a\sin\theta\cos^{\frac{1}{2}} 2\theta$.

$$\therefore \quad F'(\theta) = a\left(\cos\theta\cos^{\frac{1}{2}} 2\theta - \sin\theta\frac{\sin 2\theta}{\cos^{\frac{1}{2}} 2\theta}\right),$$

i.e.

$$F'(\theta) = a\frac{\cos 3\theta}{\cos^{\frac{1}{2}} 2\theta}.$$

Therefore the required points occur where $\cos 3\theta = 0$, so that $\theta = \pi/6$ is the only point in the first quadrant. More detailed examination shows that this gives a maximum value of y.

Example 6. If $x_1, x_2, \ldots, x_n$ are a set of n numbers find the value of x for which

$$s = \sqrt{\left[\sum_{r=1}^{n}(x - x_r)^2\right]}$$

is least.

We find the minimum value of

$$s^2 = \sum_{r=1}^{n}(x - x_r)^2,$$

$$\frac{d(s^2)}{dx} = 2\sum_{r=1}^{n}(x - x_r) = 2\left(nx - \sum_{r=1}^{n}x_r\right),$$

$$\frac{d^2(s^2)}{dx^2} = 2n.$$

Therefore the minimum value of s^2 occurs when $x = \bar{x} = \dfrac{\left(\sum\limits_{r=1}^{n} x_r\right)}{n}$. This result is of importance in statistics.

Example 7. If r_1 and r_2 are the focal distances of a point on an ellipse of major axis $2a$, find the greatest and least values of $r_1 r_2^2$. Distinguish between the cases where the eccentricity e is greater or less than $\frac{1}{3}$.

Since $r_1 + r_2 = 2a$ we require the greatest and least values of

$$f(r_2) = r_2^2(2a - r_2) \text{ considered as a function of } r_2.$$

$$\frac{df}{dr_2} = 4ar_2 - 3r_2^2 = r_2(4a - 3r_2).$$

$$\frac{d^2f}{dr_2^2} = 4a - 6r_2.$$

The only stationary value of $f(r_2)$ of physical interest occurs when $r_2 = 4a/3$ But in an ellipse of eccentricity e, r_2 can only vary between $a(1-e)$ and $a(1+e)$. Therefore, if $e < \frac{1}{3}$, $df/dr_2 > 0$ for $a(1-e) \leqslant r_2 \leqslant a(1+e)$, i.e. $f(r_2)$ is a strictly increasing function of r_2 and hence the least and greatest values of f are $a^3(1-e)^2(1+e)$ and $a^3(1-e)(1+e)^2$ respectively.

If $e \geqslant \frac{1}{3}$, then r_2 can attain the value $4a/3$ and since d^2f/dr_2^2 is negative there, f takes its maximum and greatest value $32a^3/27$. In this case f takes its least value when $r_2 = a(1-e)$, i.e. the least value is $a^3(1-e)^2(1+e)$ as before.

Example 8. In the transport by sea of a certain cargo, the cost per day is $A + Bv^n$, where A, B and n are positive constants ($n > 1$) and v is the speed, which is uniform. If T is the cost of transport over a given distance, show that there is an optimum value of v (for which T is a minimum). Prove that

$$\frac{T}{T_0} = \frac{(n-1)v_0}{nv} + \frac{1}{n}\left(\frac{v}{v_0}\right)^{n-1},$$

where v_0 is the optimum speed and T_0 the minimum cost.

If $n = 2$, find the limits between which v/v_0 must lie in order that the cost shall be within 10% of the minimum.

Let l be the distance of a specific journey. Then the time in days to cover this distance is l/v (we take v as the distance covered per day).

$$\therefore \quad T = \frac{l}{v}[A + Bv^n] = l\left[\frac{A}{v} + Bv^{n-1}\right].$$

$$\therefore \quad \frac{dT}{dv} = l\left[-\frac{A}{v^2} + (n-1)Bv^{n-2}\right] = \frac{l}{v^2}[(n-1)Bv^n - A].$$

Clearly when $v = v_0 = \left[\dfrac{A}{(n-1)B}\right]^{1/n}$, T is a minimum since dT/dv changes from negative to positive as v passes through v_0. There are no other physically realisable stationary values of T.

Since $A = (n-1)Bv_0^n$ we have

$$T = \frac{Bl}{v}\left[(n-1)\,v_0^n + v^n\right] \text{ and the minimum cost } T_0 = Blnv_0^{n-1}.$$

$$\therefore \quad \frac{T}{T_0} = \frac{(n-1)v_0}{nv} + \frac{1}{n}\left(\frac{v}{v_0}\right)^{n-1}.$$

If $n = 2$, $\dfrac{T}{T_0} = \dfrac{v_0}{2v} + \dfrac{v}{2v_0}$. In this case for T to lie within 10% of T_0 we must have

$$\frac{v_0}{2v} + \frac{v}{2v_0} < \frac{110}{100}\,;$$

i.e.

$$5v^2 - 11v_0 v + 5v_0^2 < 0;$$

i.e.

$$\frac{11 - \sqrt{21}}{10} < \frac{v}{v_0} < \frac{11 + \sqrt{21}}{10}\,; \qquad (\text{See } \S\,1:6)$$

i.e.

$$0\cdot64 v_0 < v < 1\cdot56 v_0 \text{ approximately.}$$

Example 9. Show that the curve

$$y = f(x) = a\,e^{-kx}\sin(nx+\beta),$$

where a, k, n, β are positive constants, is contained between the curves $y = \pm a e^{-kx}$. Show also that

$$f'(x) = pa\,e^{-kx}\cos(nx+\beta+\theta),$$

where $p = \sqrt{(n^2+k^2)}$, $\theta = \tan^{-1}(k/n)$. Deduce that all the maxima of $f(x)$ lie on the curve $y = (an/p)e^{-kx}$ and the minima of $f(x)$ lie on the curve $y = -(an/p)\,e^{-kx}$.

Since $\sin(nx+\beta) \leqslant 1$ for all x it follows that

$$a e^{-kx}\sin(nx+\beta) \leqslant a e^{-kx}$$

for all x, equality holding when $nx+\beta = 2r\pi$, where $r = 0,\ \pm1,\ \pm2,\ldots$. It follows that the curves $y = f(x)$, $y = a\,e^{-kx}$ have common points [at $x = (2r\pi-\beta)/n$, $y = a\exp\{-k(2r\pi-\beta)/n\}$] but do not cross. Hence the curves touch at these points. [*Note* that these points are *not* maxima for the curve $y = f(x)$ since the slopes at these points must be the same as the corresponding slopes of $y = a e^{-kx}$, i.e. negative.] Similarly, the curve $y = f(x)$ touches the curve $y = -a e^{-kx}$ where $\sin(nx+\beta) = -1$, i.e. where $x = \{(2s+1)\pi-\beta\}/n$, $s = 0,\ \pm1,\ \pm2,\ldots$.
    Since

$$f'(x) = a e^{-kx}\{n\cos(nx+\beta) - k\sin(nx+\beta)\}$$
$$= a\sqrt{(n^2+k^2)}\,e^{-kx}\{\cos\theta\cos(nx+\beta) - \sin\theta\sin(nx+\beta)\},$$

where θ is the acute angle $\tan^{-1}(k/n)$,

$$f'(x) = pae^{-kx}\cos(nx+\beta+\theta)$$

as stated. Hence the maxima of $f(x)$ occur where

$$nx+\beta+\theta = (2r+\tfrac{1}{2})\pi, \quad r = 0, \pm1, \pm2, \ldots$$

At these points $\sin(nx+\beta) = \cos\theta = n/p$ and $y = (an/p)e^{-kx}$, i.e. the maxima of $f(x)$ lie on the stated curve. Similarly, the minima of $f(x)$ lie on the curve $y = -(an/p)e^{-kx}$.

The curve is shown on Fig. 5.9.

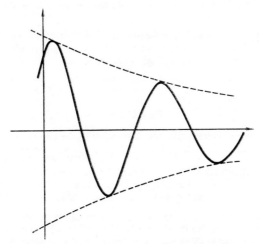

Fig. 5.9. The curve $y = ae^{-kx}\sin(mx+\beta)$.

Example 10. Sketch the curve

$$y = \tfrac{1}{2}a\{\sin(m+n)x+\sin(m-n)x\}, \tag{1}$$

where $m/n \gg 1$.

The equation of this curve can be written

$$y = a\sin mx\cos nx \tag{2}$$

and clearly (using arguments similar to those of Example 9 above) touches the curves $y = a\cos nx$, $y = a\sin mx$, but not, in general, at stationary points of any of these curves. However, since $m/n \gg 1$, we can consider the given curve from a different point of view by regarding eqn. (2) as representing a rapidly varying harmonic function $\sin mx$ with a slowly varying amplitude factor $a\cos nx$. The period $2\pi/m$ can be regarded as the period of the oscillations, the period $2\pi/n$ as the (much slower) period of amplitude variation.

Note that (1) is the result of combining two harmonic vibrations of equal

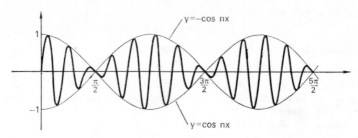

FIG. 5.10. The curve $y = a \sin mx \cos nx$, $m/n \gg 1$.

amplitudes but slightly differing frequencies and illustrates the mathematical background to the physical phenomenon of beats or amplitude modulation in electronics. The curve is sketched in Fig. 5.10.

Exercises 5 : 6

1. In the same diagram give rough sketches of the curves
$$y = e^{-kx}, \qquad y = e^{-kx} \sin x,$$
for positive values of x, where k is a positive constant.

Show that the points for which $e^{-kx} \sin x$ is a maximum lie on a curve whose equation is $y = Ae^{-kx}$, and find A in terms of k.

2. (i) The base of a tetrahedron $OABC$ is an equilateral triangle ABC of side x. If the distance from the vertex O to the middle point of each edge of the base is a fixed length b, show that the volume V of the tetrahedron is given by
$$24V = x^2(12b^2 - x^2)^{\frac{1}{2}}.$$
Hence show that, as x varies, the maximum volume of the tetrahedron is $\frac{2}{3}b^3$.

(ii) Find the maximum value of $(\ln x)/x$ and sketch the curve $xy = \ln x$

3. Determine the maxima and minima of the function
$$12x^5 - 15x^4 + 20x^3 - 330x^2 + 600x + 2$$
in the range $0 \leqslant x \leqslant 3$.

4. (i) Find all maxima and minima of
$$(x^4 + 5x^2 + 8x + 8)e^{-x}.$$

(ii) Find the minimum value of the function
$$a + b + c + x - 4(abcx)^{\frac{1}{4}},$$
where a, b, c are positive constants, and sketch the graph.

Hence, or otherwise, show that
$$a + b + c + d - 4(abcd)^{\frac{1}{4}} \geqslant a + b + c - 3(abc)^{\frac{1}{3}},$$
for any positive numbers a, b, c, d.

5. The coordinates of a fixed point P in the first quadrant are (a, b). Prove that the length of the shortest line through P, terminated by the axes, is $\left(a^{\frac{2}{3}} + b^{\frac{2}{3}}\right)^{\frac{3}{2}}$.

6. A sphere of radius a lies on a horizontal table. A thin hollow right circular cone is placed over the sphere so that it touches the sphere along a horizontal circle and its base rests on the table. Show that if the volume of the cone is a minimum its semi-vertical angle is $\sin^{-1} \frac{1}{3}$.

7. Sketch the graph of the curve

$$y = 4 \cos x - 3 \cos 2x$$

from $x = 0$ to $x = \pi$.

Find the values of x giving maximum and minimum values of the function in this range.

8. Find the lengths of the circular cylinders (i) of greatest volume (ii) of greatest curved surface area which can be inscribed in a sphere of radius r.

9. An open vessel consists of a hollow circular cylinder of internal radius r, depth h and thickness c, closed at one end by a circular disc of radius $(r+c)$ and thickness c. If the volume of the material is the fraction $61/64$ of the internal volume V prove that $64\pi c/V = 125/(r+c)^2 - 64/r^2$ and, for a constant c, find r and h when V is a minimum.

10. $ABCD$ is a square, of side $2a$, and a figure is formed by describing semicircles on AB, CD as diameters and outside the square. Show that the area of the maximum rectangle which can be inscribed in this figure so as to have two vertices on each semi-circle and a pair of opposite sides parallel to AD, BC is $3\sqrt{3}a^2$, and find the lengths of its sides.

11. The height and the circumference of a solid right circular cylinder together have a constant sum c. Express as a multiple of c the circumference of the cylinder whose total surface area is a maximum. Give evidence that your answer refers to a maximum area.

12. The total area S of a variable right circular cone, including the base, is constant. If r is the radius of the base, l the slant height and V the volume, prove that

$$V\frac{\mathrm{d}V}{\mathrm{d}r} = \frac{1}{9} \pi r^2 S(l - 3r).$$

Show that the greatest volume is $\frac{1}{3}\pi^{-\frac{1}{2}}(\frac{1}{2}S)^{\frac{3}{2}}$.

13. The coordinates of a point P on a curve are $x = a \cos^5 t$, $y = a \sin^5 t$, where t is a variable parameter. Prove that the greatest and least distances of P from the origin are a and $\frac{1}{4}a$ respectively.

14. Prove that an isosceles triangle of given perimeter and maximum area must be equilateral.

15. (i) Find the maximum and minimum values of y given by

$$y = (4x^2 - 2)e^{-x^2/2}.$$

(*Continued overleaf*)

(ii) The brightness of a small area varies inversely as the square of its distance r from the source of light, and directly as the cosine of the angle between r and the normal to the small area. Find at what height above the centre of a circle of radius a a light should be placed so that the brightness at the circumference should be greatest.

16. Discuss fully the stationary values of the function $(x-a)^2(x-1)$, (i) when $a < 1$, (ii) when $a > 1$ and (iii) when $a = 1$.

Make a clear sketch of the graph of the function in each case.

17. Prove that the function $\cos x + \sec x$ has a maximum value -2 and a minimum value 2. Draw a *rough* sketch of the graph of the function. Prove that the equation

$$\cos x + \sec x = 2\sin x$$

has no real roots.

Find all the real roots of the equation

$$\cos x + \sec x = 2\cos^n x$$

in the two cases (i) n an even positive integer, (ii) n an odd positive integer.

18. The equation of a plane curve is

$$y^3 + x^3 - 9xy + 1 = 0,$$

and (x_1, y_1) is a point on the curve at which the tangent is parallel to the x-axis. Prove that, at (x_1, y_1)

$$\frac{d^2y}{dx^2} = \frac{18}{27 - x_1^3}.$$

Prove also that the stationary values of y occur at the points for which

$$x = (27 \pm 3\sqrt{78})^{\frac{1}{3}}$$

and determine which of these gives a maximum value of y and which a minimum.

19. Discuss the turning points of $(2x+1)e^{-x^2}$.

20. Within a given circle of radius a a fixed point A is distant h from the centre. A variable chord PQ moves in such a way that $AP = AQ$. Show that there are two positions of PQ for which the area of the triangle APQ is numerically a maximum and that, if Δ_1 and Δ_2 denote these maximum areas,

$$\Delta_1\Delta_2 = \tfrac{1}{4}a(a^2 - h^2)^{3/2}.$$

21. A man standing in a field at a point A distant a from a straight road wishes to reach a point B on the road distant $\sqrt{(a^2+b^2)}$ from A; to do this he walks at speed V in a straight line to a point P on the road and then walks at speed $kV(k > 1)$ along the road to B. Show that the least time in which he can reach B is

$$\frac{1}{kV}[b + a\sqrt{(k^2-1)}],$$

provided $kb > \sqrt{(a^2+b^2)}$.

Find the corresponding time when $\sqrt{(a^2+b^2)} \geqslant kb$.

22. A solid consists of a box of height H and square base of side x, surmounted by a right pyramid of height h, the base of the pyramid coinciding with a square face of the box. Show that the volume V and surface area S of the solid are

$$V = x^2H + \tfrac{1}{3}x^2h,$$
$$S = x^2 + 4xh + x\sqrt{(x^2 + 4h^2)}.$$

If the surface area is fixed prove that the greatest volume is given by

$$36(3 + \sqrt{5})V^2 = S^3.$$

23. A sphere of radius a rests on a horizontal table. A thin hollow right circular cone, placed over the sphere, touches it along a horizontal circle, and the circular rim of the cone is on the table. Prove that the area of the curved surface of the cone is

$$\pi a^2 \frac{1 + \sin \theta}{\sin \theta(1 - \sin \theta)},$$

where 2θ is the vertical angle of the cone.

Deduce that this curved surface area is a minimum when $\theta = \sin^{-1}(\sqrt{2} - 1)$.

24. A cone of semi-vertical angle θ is inscribed in a sphere of radius a. Prove that the volume of the cone is

$$\tfrac{8}{3}\pi a^3 \sin^2 \theta \cos^4 \theta.$$

Prove that the cone of maximum volume that can be inscribed in a sphere of given radius has $8/27$ of the volume of the sphere.

Prove also that if the volume of the cone is a maximum the area of its curved surface is also a maximum and find this maximum area.

25. Show that the function

$$y = \frac{x^4 + 22x^2 + 9}{x(x^2 + 3)}$$

has a minimum at $x = 1$, and find all the maximum and minimum values of y.

Using a sketch graph, or otherwise, show how the number of real roots of the equation

$$x^4 - kx^3 + 22x^2 - 3kx + 9 = 0$$

depends on the value of the real number k.

26. Find the condition on the coefficients p, q, r for the equation $x^3 + 3px^2 + 3qx + r = 0$ to have a repeated root.

If this condition is satisfied and $q \neq p^2$, show that the repeated root is

$$(pq - r)/\{2(q - p^2)\}.$$

Find the third root.

27. Prove that the equation $x^3 - 3px^2 + 4q = 0$ has three real roots if p and q have the same sign and $p^6 > q^2$.

Show that in this case two roots will be positive or negative according as the sign of p is positive or negative. (It may be assumed that $p \neq 0$, $q \neq 0$.)

Solve the equation

$$x^3 - 6x^2 + 16 = 0.$$

28. Given that $k > 0$, $a > 0$, prove by considering the minimum value of the function $x^{-k} + (a-x)^{-k}$, that

$$\frac{1}{x^k} + \frac{1}{(a-x)^k} \geqslant \frac{2^{k+1}}{a^k} \quad \text{when} \quad 0 < x < a.$$

Deduce from this that, if $x > 0$, $y > 0$,

$$\frac{1}{x^k} + \frac{1}{y^k} \geqslant \frac{2^{k+1}}{(x+y)^k}.$$

29. The function $x(\pi - x)$ is approximated for $0 \leqslant x \leqslant \pi$ by the function $a \sin x$, the constant a being chosen so that

$$\int_0^\pi \{x(\pi - x) - a \sin x\}^2 \, dx$$

is a minimum. Find a.

5 : 7 Small increments and proportional errors

If $y = f(x)$ and δx, δy are corresponding small increments in x, y respectively, Taylor's theorem (5.5) may be expressed in the form

$$\delta y = f'(x)\,\delta x + \frac{(\delta x)^2}{2!} f''(x) + \frac{(\delta x)^3}{3!} f'''(x) + \dots. \quad (5.15)$$

In particular

$$\delta y \approx f'(x)\,\delta x, \quad (5.16)$$

the error being of order $(\delta x)^2$. This result can be used to determine the approximate error δy in the calculated value of y consequent upon a known error δx in the measured variable x. The *proportional* error in y is defined as $(\delta y)/y = [f'(x)/f(x)]\,(\delta x)$ and the *percentage* error as

$$\frac{100\,\delta y}{y} = \frac{100 f'(x)}{f(x)}\,\delta x.$$

Example 1. The height h of a tower BT is deduced from measurements of the angle of elevation $T\hat{A}B = x$ of the top T of the tower from a point A in the same horizontal plane as the base B of the tower; $AB = a$. If the angle x is slightly in error, find the error in the calculated value of h. (Assume a is known accurately.)

$$h = a \tan x.$$

$$\therefore \quad \delta h = \frac{dh}{dx}\,\delta x = a \sec^2 x\,\delta x.$$

We note that, if $\delta x > 0$, i.e. the angle x is too large, then $\delta h > 0$ and the height is overestimated.

Example 2. The range R of a projectile fired with velocity V at an angle of elevation α is $(V^2 \sin 2\alpha)/g$. If V and g are fixed show that the error in elevation required to make the shot fall short by the small quantity a at the maximum range D is $\pm (a/2D)^{\frac{1}{2}}$ radians.

R is clearly a maximum, D, when $\alpha = \frac{1}{4}\pi$ and $D = V^2/g$. From eqn. (5.15),

$$\delta R = \frac{2V^2 \cos 2\alpha \delta\alpha}{g} - \frac{4V^2 \sin 2\alpha (\delta\alpha)^2}{2g} + O\{(\delta\alpha)^3\}.$$

Therefore at $\alpha = \frac{1}{4}\pi$ and for $\delta R = -a$ we must have $-a = -2V^2(\delta\alpha)^2/g$ which gives the required result.

The use of logarithms is of value in the solution of problems of this type involving products of functions. For, if $y = u_1 u_2 \ldots u_n$, i.e. y is the product of n factors, then

$$\ln y = \ln u_1 + \ln u_2 + \ldots + \ln u_n. \tag{5.17}$$

But

$$\delta(\ln y) = \frac{d(\ln y)}{dy} \cdot \delta y = \frac{\delta y}{y} \tag{5.18}$$

and therefore, taking small increments of eqn. (5.17), we have

$$\frac{\delta y}{y} = \frac{\delta u_1}{u_1} + \frac{\delta u_2}{u_2} + \ldots + \frac{\delta u_n}{u_n}. \tag{5.19}$$

Example. The points A and B, at a distance a apart on a horizontal plane, are in line with the base C of a vertical tower and on the same side of C. The elevations of the top of the tower from A and B are observed to be α and β $(\alpha < \beta)$.

If the observations of the angles of elevation are uncertain by 4 minutes, show that the maximum possible percentage error in the calculated value of BC is approximately

$$\frac{\pi \sin (\alpha + \beta)}{27 \sin \alpha \cos \beta \tan (\beta - \alpha)}.$$

If h is the height of the tower and $BC = x$, then

$$h = x \tan \beta = (x + a) \tan \alpha.$$

$$\therefore \ x = \frac{a \tan \alpha}{(\tan \beta - \tan \alpha)} = a \sin \alpha \cos \beta \operatorname{cosec} (\beta - \alpha).$$

$$\therefore \ \ln x = \ln a + \ln \sin \alpha + \ln \cos \beta - \ln \sin (\beta - \alpha).$$

$$\therefore \ \frac{\delta x}{x} = \frac{\delta a}{a} + \frac{\cos \alpha \cdot \delta\alpha}{\sin \alpha} - \frac{\sin \beta \cdot \delta\beta}{\cos \beta} - \frac{\cos (\beta - \alpha) \cdot \delta(\beta - \alpha)}{\sin (\beta - \alpha)},$$

i.e. since $\delta a = 0$,

$$\frac{\delta x}{x} = [\cot \alpha + \cot (\beta - \alpha)] \, \delta\alpha - [\cot (\beta - \alpha) + \tan \beta] \, \delta\beta.$$

Clearly the proportional error is greatest when $\delta\alpha = -\delta\beta \,(= (4/60)\cdot(\pi/180)$ since the angles are uncertain by this amount in radians). Therefore the maximum possible percentage error is

$$100 \cdot \frac{4}{60} \cdot \frac{\pi}{180} \,[\cot\alpha + 2\cot(\beta-\alpha) + \tan\beta]$$

which reduces to

$$\frac{\pi\sin(\alpha+\beta)}{27\sin\alpha\cos\beta\tan(\beta-\alpha)}.$$

The mean value theorem for a function of two variables. Suppose that $u = f(x, y)$, where x, y are independent variables, see p. 99. Then $u + \delta u = f(x+\delta x, y+\delta y)$ so that

$$\delta u = f(x+\delta x, y+\delta y) - f(x, y)$$

or, by inserting and subtracting appropriate terms,

$$\delta u = f(x+\delta x, y+\delta y) - f(x, y+\delta y) + f(x, y+\delta y) - f(x, y).$$

Assuming that the partial derivatives f_x, f_y are continuous, the mean value theorem (5.2) then gives

$$f(x+\delta x, y+\delta y) - f(x, y+\delta y) = f_x(x+\theta_1\delta x, y+\delta y)\,\delta x,$$
$$f(x, y+\delta y) - f(x, y) = f_y(x, y+\theta_2\,\delta y)\,\delta y,$$

where $0 < \theta_1, \theta_2 < 1$. It follows that

$$\delta u = f_x(x+\theta_1\,\delta x, y+\delta y)\,\delta x + f_y(x, y+\theta_2\,\delta y)\,\delta y. \quad (5.20)$$

If now we assume that all the second-order partial derivatives of $f(x, y)$ exist and are continuous, we have by the above results

$$f_x(x+\theta_1\,\delta x, y+\delta y) = f_x(x, y) + f_{xx}(x+\theta_3\,\delta x, y+\delta y)\,\theta_1\,\delta x$$
$$+ f_{xy}(x+\theta_1\,\delta x, y+\theta_4\,\delta y)\,\delta y,$$
$$f_y(x, y+\theta_2\,\delta y) = f_y(x, y) + f_{yy}(x, y+\theta_4\,\delta y)\,\theta_2\,\delta y,$$

where $0 < \theta_3 < \theta_1 < 1$, $0 < \theta_4 < \theta_2 < 1$. Substitution in eqn. (5.20) then gives

$$\delta f = f_x(x, y)\,\delta x + f_y(x, y)\,\delta y + O\{(\delta x)^2\}. \quad (5.21)$$

This is a basic theorem of partial differentiation and is illustrated physically as follows:

Suppose $f(x, y)$ is a function of the rectangular cartesian coordinates x, y, and that A, B, C, D are neighbouring points (x, y), $(x+\delta x, y)$, $(x+\delta x, y+\delta y)$, $(x, y+\delta y)$ respectively in the

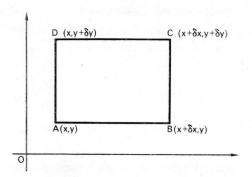

FIG. 5.11.

plane, Fig. 5.11. Then the difference in the values of f at the points A and C is

$$\delta f = f_C - f_A = (f_B - f_A) + (f_C - f_B).$$

But, if δx is small, the rate of change of f along the direction AB is approximately $(\partial f/\partial x)_A$ and so

$$f_B - f_A \approx \left(\frac{\partial f}{\partial x}\right)_A \delta x.$$

Similarly,

$$f_C - f_B \approx \left(\frac{\partial f}{\partial y}\right)_B \delta y$$

and

$$(\partial f/\partial y)_B = (\partial f/\partial y)_A + O(\delta x).$$

It follows that

$$\delta f \approx \left(\frac{\partial f}{\partial x}\right)_A \delta x + \left(\frac{\partial f}{\partial y}\right)_B \delta y.$$

[Later, Vol. 4, Chap. 1, it will be shown that the result is independent of the path A to C used in finding δf. Thus the same expression is found for δf using the path ADC or the path directly along AC.]

Note that, if x, y are each functions of an independent variable t, then eqn. (5.21), on dividing by δt and proceeding to the limit $\delta t \to 0$, implies that

$$\frac{df}{dt} = \frac{\partial f}{\partial x}\frac{dx}{dt} + \frac{\partial f}{\partial y}\frac{dy}{dt}. \tag{5.22}$$

The generalisation of the above result to n variables is as follows: If $f(x_1, x_2, \ldots, x_n)$ is a function of the n variables x_1, x_2, $\ldots, x_n$, then, corresponding to changes δx_1, δx_2, $\ldots, \delta x_n$ in $x_1, x_2, \ldots, x_n$ respectively, the change in f is δf, where

$$\delta f = \frac{\partial f}{\partial x_1} \delta x_1 + \frac{\partial f}{\partial x_2} \delta x_2 + \ldots + \frac{\partial f}{\partial x_n} \delta x_n. \qquad (5.23)$$

This result is of use in certain problems concerning small errors.

Example. A closed rectangular box with unequal sides a, b, c has its edges slightly altered in length by amounts δa, δb, δc respectively, so that both its volume and its surface area remain unchanged. Show that

$$\frac{\delta a}{a^2(c-b)} = \frac{\delta b}{b^2(a-c)} = \frac{\delta c}{c^2(b-a)}.$$

The volume $V = abc$.

$$\therefore \quad \frac{\delta V}{V} = \frac{\delta a}{a} + \frac{\delta b}{b} + \frac{\delta c}{c} = 0 \qquad (1)$$

since V is unchanged. The surface area $S = 2(ab+bc+ca)$,

$$\therefore \quad \delta S = \frac{\partial S}{\partial a} \delta a + \frac{\partial S}{\partial b} \delta b + \frac{\partial S}{\partial c} \delta c$$

$$= 2[(b+c)\,\delta a + (c+a)\,\delta b + (a+b)\,\delta c] = 0 \qquad (2)$$

since S is unchanged. Solution of (1) and (2) for δa, δb, δc gives the required result.

Exercises 5 : 7

1. The density ϱ of a body is calculated from its weights W_1 and W_2 in air and water respectively. Show that the proportional error due to errors δW_1, δW_2 is given by

$$\frac{\delta \varrho}{\varrho} = \frac{\delta W_2}{W_1 - W_2} - \frac{W_2 \, \delta W_1}{(W_1 - W_2)W_1}.$$

(Neglect the density of the air.)

2. The distances of a point and its image on the axis of a lens from the lens are x_1, x_2 respectively where $1/x_1 + 1/x_2 = 1/f$ and f is constant. Show that the longitudinal magnification of a small object is x_2^2/x_1^2.

3. The radius of a circular cylinder is calculated from the formula $V = \pi r^2 l$. If the measured volume is 2% too large and the measured length 1% too small calculate the percentage error in the calculated radius.

4. The points A and B, at a distance a apart on a horizontal plane, are in line with the base C of a vertical tower and on the same side of C. The elevations of the top of the tower from A and B are observed to be α and β ($\alpha < \beta$). Show that the height of the tower is $a \sin \alpha \sin \beta \operatorname{cosec} (\beta - \alpha)$.

If the maximum possible error in measuring the angles α and β is $d°$, show that the largest value of d which will ensure that the error in the calculated value of the height is less than 1%, is approximately

$$\frac{9 \sin \alpha \sin \beta \sin (\beta - \alpha)}{5\pi(\sin^2 \alpha + \sin^2 \beta)} .$$

5. The side BC of a triangle ABC is to be determined from measurements of the sides AB and AC and of the angle BAC. The measured values of the sides are liable to a small proportional error θ and the angle BAC to a small absolute error δA. Show that the calculated value of BC is liable to a proportional error $\theta + \{(bc/a^2) \sin A\} \delta A$.

The measured values of b, c, and A are 3, 5, and $60°$ respectively and are liable to errors of 1%, 1%, and $\frac{3}{4}\%$ respectively.

Show that the calculated value of a is liable to an error of approximately $1 \cdot 9\%$.

6. If $r^2 s = (s-a)(s-b)(s-c)$, where $2s = a+b+c$ and there is a small error δr in r due to small errors δa, δb δc in a, b, c respectively, prove that

$$\frac{2\,\delta r}{r} = \frac{\delta a}{2} \left[-\frac{1}{s} - \frac{1}{s-a} + \frac{1}{s-b} + \frac{1}{s-c} \right] + \text{two similar terms.}$$

The measured values of a, b, c are $2\,\mathrm{m}$, $5\,\mathrm{m}$, $5\,\mathrm{m}$, respectively, and the measurements are liable to errors of $0 \cdot 5$, $0 \cdot 25$, $0 \cdot 8$ per cent., respectively. Find the maximum possible error in the calculated value of the area of the incircle.

7. Show that the gradient of the curve $f(x, y) = 0$ at the point (x, y) is

$$-\frac{\partial f}{\partial x} \bigg/ \frac{\partial f}{\partial y} .$$

Show that the curves

$$x^3 - 3xy^2 = 2, \qquad 3x^2 y - y^3 = 11$$

intersect at the point $(2, 1)$ and find the angle between their tangents at this point.

8. If V is given by the formula

$$V = \tan x \cot y$$

and x and y are subject to small errors, show that

$$\frac{\delta V}{V} \approx \frac{2\,\delta x}{\sin 2x} - \frac{2\,\delta y}{\sin 2y}$$

where δx and δy are the errors in x and y and δV is the subsequent error in V.

9. The volume V of a right circular cone is to be computed from measurements of 12 cm for the base radius and 20 cm for the slant height. If there is a possible error in each of these measurements of $0 \cdot 06$ cm, show that the computed value for V could be in error by about $1 \cdot 2\%$.

10. If the area $\triangle$ of a triangle ABC is calculated from measurements of the sides a, b and the angle C prove that, if $C \neq \pi/2$,

$$\delta\triangle/\triangle \approx \delta a/a + \delta b/b + \cot C \, \delta C$$

where δa, δb, δC are the errors of measurement and $\delta\triangle$ the consequent error in $\triangle$.

5 : 8 Kinematics

Suppose a point (or particle) is moving along a straight line so that its distance at time t from a fixed point in the line is s. What do we mean by its speed at a point and how do we determine this speed? A suitable procedure is to measure the time δt the particle takes to cover an interval δs which includes the point. The ratio $\delta s/\delta t$ is the average speed of the particle over the interval and the shorter the interval the nearer the average speed will be to what we mean by the *speed at a point*. This means that we are, in effect, *defining* this speed v as a derivative, i.e. $v = \mathrm{d}s/\mathrm{d}t$.

If the particle is moving along a curve and s is the arc length from a fixed point on the curve, then $\mathrm{d}s/\mathrm{d}t$ is the speed of the particle along the curve. We have deliberately used the word "speed" rather than "velocity" because we wish to retain the word velocity to designate both speed and direction of motion. (Velocity is a *vector*.)

The acceleration f of a particle is also defined by a derivative, i.e. $f = \mathrm{d}v/\mathrm{d}t = \mathrm{d}^2s/\mathrm{d}t^2$. A very useful alternative form for the acceleration is obtained from the chain rule of differentiation

$$f = \frac{\mathrm{d}v}{\mathrm{d}t} = \left(\frac{\mathrm{d}v}{\mathrm{d}s}\right)\left(\frac{\mathrm{d}s}{\mathrm{d}t}\right) = v\left(\frac{\mathrm{d}v}{\mathrm{d}s}\right). \qquad (5.24)$$

The motion of a particle is frequently represented by a curve in which the distance is plotted against time. The gradient of the curve, being $\mathrm{d}s/\mathrm{d}t$, is the velocity; if the velocity is plotted against time the gradient is the acceleration.

Example. If a particle moves along a straight line with uniform acceleration f, then $\mathrm{d}v/\mathrm{d}t = f$.

Integrating gives $\qquad\qquad v = u + ft, \qquad\qquad\qquad (1)$
where u is the speed at $t = 0$. Then

$$\frac{\mathrm{d}s}{\mathrm{d}t} = u + ft.$$

Integrating again

$$s = s_0 + ut + \tfrac{1}{2}ft^2, \tag{2}$$

where s_0 is the displacement at $t = 0$. Eliminating t from eqns. (1) and (2) or integrating the equation $v\,dv/ds = f$ gives

$$v^2 = u^2 + 2f(s - s_0). \tag{3}$$

Equations (1), (2) and (3) are the formulae for uniformly accelerated motion in a straight line.

If a point P moving in a plane is joined by a straight line OP to a fixed origin O and OP makes an angle θ with a fixed direction in the plane, then $\omega = d\theta/dt$ is the *angular velocity* of the line OP. Also $d\omega/dt (= \omega\,d\omega/d\theta = d^2\theta/dt^2)$ is the angular acceleration of OP.

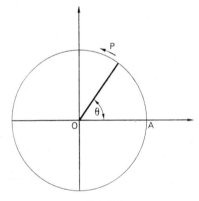

Fig. 5.12.

Suppose a particle P is moving in a plane and its coordinates at any instant are x, y. The derivatives $\dot{x} = dx/dt$, $\dot{y} = dy/dt$ are the components of the velocity of P parallel to Ox, Oy respectively. Similarly, $\ddot{x}$ and $\ddot{y}$ are the components of the acceleration of P.

Example. If P moves in a circle of radius a (Fig. 5.12), so that we may write $x = a \cos \theta$, $y = a \sin \theta$, then

$$\dot{x} = -a\dot{\theta} \sin \theta, \qquad \dot{y} = a\dot{\theta} \cos \theta,$$

$$\ddot{x} = -a\ddot{\theta} \sin \theta - a\dot{\theta}^2 \cos \theta, \qquad \ddot{y} = a\ddot{\theta} \cos \theta - a\dot{\theta}^2 \sin \theta.$$

If the particle P, in its circular motion, is on one of the axes, say with $\theta = 0$

the components of velocity are

$$\dot{x} = 0, \quad \dot{y} = a\dot{\theta},$$

and of acceleration,

$$\ddot{x} = -a\dot{\theta}^2, \quad \ddot{y} = a\ddot{\theta}.$$

The velocity therefore is along the circumference and of magnitude $a\dot{\theta}$. The acceleration has two components, one toward the centre of magnitude $a\dot{\theta}^2$, one along the circumference of magnitude $a\ddot{\theta}$. Stated thus the result applies to any position on the circle.

If a lamina is moving in a plane and a line AB drawn in the lamina makes an angle θ with a fixed line PQ in the plane (Fig. 5.13), then the angular velocity, ω, of the lamina is defined

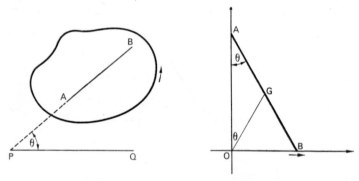

FIG. 5.13.   FIG. 5.14.

by $\omega = d\theta/dt$. Similarly the angular acceleration of the lamina is $d\omega/dt = d^2\theta/dt^2$. This definition gives a unique ω whatever lines are chosen in the lamina and in the plane. For if $A'B'$ is another line in the lamina, so that the angle α between AB and $A'B'$ is constant, $\varphi = \theta + \alpha$ and hence $\dot{\varphi} = d(\theta + \alpha)/dt = \dot{\theta}$ since $d\alpha/dt = 0$. Similarly ω is independent of the choice of line in the plane.

Example 1. A ladder AB is of length $2a$. The ends A, B rest against a vertical wall and on a horizontal floor respectively (Fig. 5.14). Calculate the horizontal and vertical upward components of the velocity and acceleration of G the mid-point of the ladder when B is moved away from O with uniform speed V.

Since $d(OB)/dt = d(2a \sin \theta)/dt = 2a\dot\theta \cos \theta = V$,

$$\therefore \quad a\ddot\theta \cos \theta - a\dot\theta^2 \sin \theta = 0.$$

$$\therefore \quad \dot\theta = \frac{V}{2a \cos \theta}, \quad \ddot\theta = \frac{V^2 \sec^2 \theta \tan \theta}{4a^2}.$$

The velocity components of G are $(a\dot\theta \cos \theta, -a\dot\theta \sin \theta) = (\tfrac{1}{2}V, -\tfrac{1}{2}V\tan \theta)$. The acceleration components of G are

$$(a\ddot\theta \cos \theta - a\dot\theta^2 \sin \theta, \; -a\ddot\theta \sin \theta - a\dot\theta^2 \cos \theta) = \left(0, \; -\frac{V^2}{4a} \sec^3 \theta\right).$$

Example 2. A boat B (or a trolley) is forced to move in a straight line BC and is hauled along by winding in a rope at a point A distance h from the line. Find the speed and acceleration of the boat when the rope is hauled in at constant speed v.

At any instant the length of rope is y and the distance BC is x (Fig. 5.15.) Then

$$y^2 = x^2 + h^2. \tag{1}$$

Differentiation gives $2y\dot y = 2x\dot x$,

$$\dot x = \frac{y\dot y}{x}. \tag{2}$$

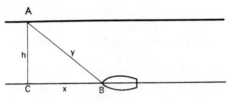

FIG. 5.15.

Note that $\dot x$ is numerically greater than $\dot y$. (If this problem is solved by resolution of velocities it must be remembered that the velocity of B is along BC. In fact $\dot y$ is the component along BA of the velocity of B.) But we are given that $\dot y = -v$.

$$\therefore \quad \dot x = -\frac{yv}{x}. \tag{3}$$

The negative sign indicates motion towards C. Differentiation of eqn. (3) gives the acceleration of B away from C

$$\ddot x = -\frac{v\dot y}{x} + \frac{yv\dot x}{x^2} = \frac{v^2}{x} - \frac{y^2 v^2}{x^3} = -\frac{(y^2 - x^2)v^2}{x^3} = -\frac{v^2 h^2}{x^3}. \tag{4}$$

Hence the acceleration of B is always towards C. Both speed and acceleration tend to infinity as B approaches C.

Example 3. *Connected rates of change.*

Here we demonstrate the technique by an illustrative example. A vessel whose walls are of negligible thickness has the form of an inverted right circular cone of semi-vertical angle $\pi/6$. Water is poured steadily into the vessel at the rate of 250 cm³/ min. Find the speed, in cm per minute, at which the water level is rising when the depth of water in the cone is 25 cm.

When the height of water in the vessel is x cm, the volume of this water is V cm³, where

$$V = \frac{1}{3}\pi x^3 \tan^2\left(\frac{\pi}{6}\right) = \frac{\pi x^3}{9}.$$

Therefore
$$\frac{dV}{dt} = \frac{dV}{dx}\frac{dx}{dt} = \frac{\pi x^2}{3}\frac{dx}{dt}.$$

In the given case, $dV/dt = 250$ cm³/min, and $x = 25$ cm so that the speed at which the water level is rising is

$$\frac{dx}{dt} = \frac{3\times250}{\pi\times(50)^2} = \frac{3}{10\pi} \quad \text{cm/min.}$$

Exercises 5 : 8

1. A particle moving along a straight line starts with a velocity of 4 m/s. At time t the acceleration of the particle is $(6t-8)$. Find:

(i) the distance the particle moves before first coming to instantaneous rest;

(ii) the time at which the particle returns to the starting point;

(iii) the greatest velocity of the particle in that interval.

2. A particle moving in a straight line has an acceleration at time t of $(6+6t)$. Between $t = 0$ s and $t = 3$ s the particle covers 243 m. Find its velocity when $t = 0$ s.

3. A particle moving in a straight line so that its velocity is directly proportional to the cube of the time for which it has been moving, has an acceleration of 12 m/s² after 1 s. Find how far it will move in the next second.

4. Water is poured into a trough of length l, whose cross section is an equilateral triangle of side a, at a rate k.

At what rate is the water rising in the trough when it is half full (i.e., half the volume of the trough is occupied by water)?

5. A lighthouse is distant a from the nearest point A of a straight shore-line, and the light revolves n times per minute. How fast is the patch of light travelling along the shore (i) at A, (ii) at distance x from A?

6. The horizontal velocity v of a point A is given by

$$v = V_0\{\sin pt + |\sin pt|\},$$

where V_0 and p are positive constants. Sketch the graphs of v and dv/dt from $t = 0$ to $t = 8\pi/p$.

If A is a point on one of the feet of a pedestrian whose average speed is U, find the ratio of V_0 to U.

7. The end P of a straight rod PQ describes with uniform angular velocity ω a circle of centre O while the end Q moves along a fixed line through O in the plane of the circle. The end R of an equal straight rod PR moves along the same fixed line through O; show that the velocities of the points Q and R are in the ratio $QO : OR$.

8. One extremity P of a rod PQ of length b moves with uniform speed $a\omega$ round the circumference of a circle of radius a and centre C, and the rod always passes through a fixed point A on the circumference. Find the components of the velocity of the point Q along and at right angles to the rod, and show that when Q is moving parallel to PC the angle φ between the rod and CA is given by $\cos \varphi = 2a/b$.

9. A crank OP rotates about a fixed centre O whilst the end B of the connecting rod PB is constrained to move along OB. If $P\widehat{O}B = \theta$, $P\widehat{B}O = \varphi$, prove that when the angular velocity of P is ω the linear velocity of the point B is

$$-OP \frac{\sin (\theta + \varphi)}{\cos \varphi} \omega.$$

If BP produced meets the perpendicular through O to the line OB at R, deduce that the velocity of B varies as OR.

10. A flywheel, whose centre is C, turns with constant angular velocity ω and a connecting rod AB, of length l, is attached to the flywheel at B, where $CB = r(< l)$. The end A of the connecting rod moves on a straight line through C. If φ is the angle which the rod makes with AC find a relation between φ and t and show that the angular acceleration of the rod can be expressed in the form $-(1 - r^2/l^2)\omega^2 \tan \varphi \sec^2 \varphi$.

11. OX, OY are two fixed perpendicular straight lines. A point P moves towards O along XO with uniform speed u and a point Q moves towards O along YO with uniform speed v. Prove that when $OP = a$ and $OQ = b$, P is approaching Q at the rate $V = (au + bv)/PQ$ and that PQ is rotating with angular speed $\Omega = (bu - av)/PQ^2$ and angular acceleration $2\Omega V/PQ$.

5 : 9 Approximate solution of equations

Unless a function $f(x)$ is a polynomial whose factors can be obtained explicitly, or is especially simple in form, the exact solutions of the equation $f(x) = 0$ cannot be found by any finite process. Consequently special methods must be adopted to find approximations to these solutions. Such methods are almost always numerical and often *iterative* (step by step). The aim of the method of *iteration* is to obtain a sequence of numbers

$x_0, x_1, x_2, \ldots, x_n, \ldots$, each member of the sequence being closer than its predecessors to the root being evaluated. A method is an iterative method when it relies upon the repetition of a single formula to obtain one member of the sequence from its predecessors, i.e. the sequence is generated from a formula which gives x_{n+1} in terms of x_n (and perhaps of $x_{n-1}, \ldots$, but such multiple recurrence relations will not be considered here). If the method is not strictly iterative in this sense but still provides a sequence of approximations, it is better described as a method of successive approximation. A satisfactory iterative process is self-correcting; a small error in the calculation of one member of the sequence will not prevent subsequent members calculated from the wrong one from converging to the exact root. An iterative method is usually very suitable for use on a computer because it consists of the repetition of the same sequence of calculations. Here we illustrate in detail three iterative methods, but there are many others.

Three factors are important in connection with any iterative process:

(i) Can the successive terms of the sequence be evaluated easily with the calculating tools available?
(ii) Does it converge to the required limit?
(iii) How rapidly does it converge?

We cannot say much, in general, about (i) because the labour involved depends upon the resources available. We can give one or two tests which show whether or not a given iterative formula converges, and, in any given case, we can investigate how rapidly the convergence takes place.

In our investigations we rely extensively on the use of graphical representations to give a clear understanding of what is taking place in each particular method.

1. The method of false position. This method is a development of the elementary technique for "locating" the root $x = \alpha$ of $f(x) = 0$ given in § 1 : 2. Two values $x = a$, $x = b$ are found for which $f(a)$, $f(b)$ have opposite signs [see Fig. 5.16(a), (b)]. The chord joining A and B cuts the x-axis at $x = x_1$, corresponding

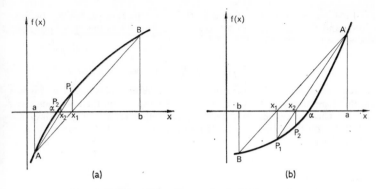

Fig. 5.16. Illustrating the method of false position.

to P_1 on the curve. The ordinate at P_1 must have a sign opposite
to one or other of those at A or B. (We assume that it is opposite
to that at A.) Now we join P_1 and A so that the chord cuts the
x-axis at $x = x_2$. Continuing in this way the process must converge to $x = \alpha$. By drawing suitable diagrams, with negative
gradient, the reader can see that the process converges in the
other possible cases also. Further, this process converges more
quickly the closer a is to the value α.

The analytical representation of the above is given by

$$\frac{b-x_1}{f(b)} = -\frac{x_1-a}{f(a)}.$$

[The minus sign is needed since $f(a)$, $f(b)$ have opposite signs.]
Solving for x_1 we find

$$x_1 = b - \frac{(b-a)f(b)}{f(b)-f(a)}$$

From this we deduce the recurrence formulae

$$x_{n+1} = x_n - \frac{f(x_n)}{\lambda_n}, \quad \lambda_n = \frac{f(x_n)-f(a)}{x_n-a}, \qquad (5.25)$$

where λ_n is the gradient of the chord joining P_n and A. This is the
method of false position.

Example. We solve the equation $x^5+x-1 = 0$ by the method of false
position.

First we note that $f(0) = -1$, $f(1) = 1$, $f(0.5) = -0.46875$. Because $f(0.5)$ and $f(1)$ differ in sign we take $a = 1$, $f(a) = 1$ as the "false position" to be used. In this case

$$\frac{1}{\lambda_n} = \frac{x_n - a}{f(x_n) - f(a)} = \frac{1 - x_n}{1 - f(x_n)}.$$

(The reversed order of numerator and denominator avoids negative numbers in the computation.) We start with $x_1 = 0.5$ and obtain the iterations given below. The last entries show that the correction term $-f(x_n)/\lambda_n$ does not affect the fourth decimal place. Hence the root is $x = 0.7549$ correct to four decimal places.

n	x_n	$f(x_n)$	$1/\lambda_n$	$-f(x_n)/\lambda_n$
1	0.5	−0.46875	0.34043	0.15957
2	0.65957	−0.21560	0.28005	0.06038
3	0.71995	−0.08662	0.25772	0.02233
4	0.74228	−0.03239	0.24964	0.00809
5	0.75036	−0.01176	0.24674	0.00290
6	0.75326	−0.00422	0.24570	0.00104
7	0.75430	−0.00151	0.24533	0.00037
8	0.75467	−0.00054	0.24520	0.00013
9	0.75480	−0.00019	0.24515	0.00005
10	0.75485	−0.00007	0.24513	0.00002

The above example shows, as is clear from Fig. 5.16, that λ_n does not vary much after the first few iterations and so can be given a constant value which is effectively the gradient of the line joining A to the position of the root.

We investigate the convergence of the method by using e_n to denote the difference $\alpha - x_n$. Since $f(\alpha) = 0$,

$$\alpha - x_{n+1} = e_{n+1} = \alpha - x_n + \frac{f(x_n)}{\lambda} = (\alpha - x_n) - \frac{f(\alpha) - f(x_n)}{\lambda_n}.$$

But, by the mean value theorem, $f(\alpha) - f(x_n) = (\alpha - x_n)f'(\xi_n)$, where $\alpha < \xi_n < x_n$, so that

$$e_{n+1} = \left\{ 1 - \frac{f'(\xi_n)}{\lambda_n} \right\} e_n = \mu_n e_n,$$

with $\mu_n = 1 - \dfrac{f'(\xi_n)}{\lambda_n}$. For the errors e_n to decrease, $|\mu_n|$ must be less than 1,

i.e.

$$0 < \frac{f'(\xi_n)}{\lambda_n} < 2$$

for sufficiently large values of n. Taking $f'(\xi_n) = f'(\alpha)$, a reasonable assumption when $\xi_n \approx \alpha$, this condition becomes

$$0 < \frac{f'(\alpha)}{\lambda_n} < 2.$$

This process is called a first-order process because in the relation $e_{n+1} = \mu_n e_n$ both errors occur to the first power.

2. The Newton–Raphson method. If x is an approximation to the root α of $f(x) = 0$ then, if $x + e = \alpha$, by Taylor's theorem

$$0 = f(x+e) = f(x) + e f'(x) + O(e^2).$$

Hence an approximate value for e is $-f(x)/f'(x)$. Thus we obtain an iteration formula

$$x_{n+1} = x - \frac{f(x_n)}{f'(x_n)}. \tag{5.26}$$

This (*Newton–Raphson*) formula replaces the λ_n of eqn. (5.25) by $f'(x_n)$. The graphical representation is shown in Fig. 5.17(a), (b).

The process is convergent, provided there is no horizontal tangent to the curve between A and P_1. If this is the case, the next intersection of the tangent with the axis will be further from the root than the stationary point.

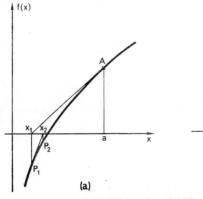
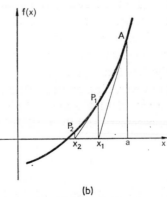

FIG. 5.17. Illustrating the Newton–Raphson method.

To investigate the convergence of the Newton–Raphson process we write $x_n = \alpha - e_n$. Then

$$f(x_n) = f(\alpha - e_n) = f(\alpha) - e_n f'(\alpha) + \tfrac{1}{2} e_n^2 f''(\alpha) + O(e_n^3),$$
$$f'(x_n) = f'(\alpha - e_n) = f'(\alpha) - e_n f''(\alpha) + O(e_n^2).$$
$$\therefore \quad \alpha - e_{n+1} = \alpha - e_n - \frac{f(\alpha) - e_n f'(\alpha) + \tfrac{1}{2} e_n^2 f''(\alpha) + O(e_n^3)}{f'(\alpha) - e_n f''(\alpha) + O(e_n^2)}.$$

Assuming that e_n is small, we deduce

$$e_{n+1} = e_n - e_n \left\{ 1 - \frac{1}{2} e_n \frac{f''(\alpha)}{f'(\alpha)} + O(e_n^2) \right\} \left\{ 1 - e_n \frac{f''(\alpha)}{f'(\alpha)} + O(e_n^2) \right\}^{-1}.$$

$$\therefore \quad e_{n+1} = e_n - e_n \left\{ 1 + \frac{1}{2} e_n \frac{f''(\alpha)}{f'(\alpha)} + O(e_n^2) \right\}.$$

$$\therefore \quad e_{n+1} = -\frac{f''(\alpha)}{2f'(\alpha)} e_n^2 + O(e_n^3)$$

$$\approx -\mu_n e_n^2,$$

where $\mu_n = f''(\alpha)/\{2 f'(\alpha)\}$. This shows that the method is a second-order process because of the second-degree factor e_n^2. This means that the errors decrease much more rapidly than with method 1 (the false position method). Furthermore, $|\mu_n|$ need not be less than 1 for convergence.

It might be thought that the Newton–Raphson formula is always preferable to the other, but this is not necessarily so because the Newton–Raphson method requires the evaluation of two functions $f(x_n)$ and $f'(x_n)$ at each iteration whereas the false position method, when λ_n is effectively constant, requires only one evaluation. Nevertheless, when the derivative is easily found the Newton–Raphson method is the more satisfactory procedure. However, if an approximation is sufficiently near the root for the curvature of the arc to be negligible, recalculation of $f'(x_n)$ is unnecessary and the modified formula

$$x_{n+1} = x_n - \frac{f(x_n)}{g}$$

may be used instead of the Newton–Raphson formula, g being the gradient of the tangent to the curve near x_n.

Example 1. The equation $x^2 = a$, $a > 0$.

The Newton–Raphson iterative formula with $f(x) = x^2 - a$, $f'(x) = 2x$ gives

$$x_{n+1} = \tfrac{1}{2}(x_n + a/x_n).$$

In illustration, considering the case when $a = 2$ and taking $x_1 = 1\cdot4$, we obtain the following sequence of approximations for $\sqrt{2}$.

$$x_1 = 1\cdot4, \qquad x_2 = \tfrac{1}{2}(1\cdot4 + 2/1\cdot4) = 1\cdot4143;$$
$$x_3 = \tfrac{1}{2}(1\cdot4143 + 2/1\cdot4143) = 1\cdot41421;$$
$$x_4 = \tfrac{1}{2}(1\cdot41421 + 2/1\cdot41421) = 1\cdot414214;$$
$$x_5 = \tfrac{1}{2}(1\cdot414214 + 2/1\cdot414214) = 1\cdot4142136;$$
$$x_6 = \tfrac{1}{2}(1\cdot4142136 + 2/1\cdot4142136) = 1\cdot41421360$$

Hence, $\sqrt{2} = 1\cdot414214$ correct to six places of decimals. Note that we add one additional decimal place at each approximation.

Example 2. Show graphically that the equation $e^x = 2 - x$ has only one real root. Verify that the root is approximately equal to $0\cdot4$ and find its value correct to four decimal places.

The graphs of e^x and $2 - x$ are shown in Fig. 5.18 and clearly intersect at one point only. Therefore there is only one real root of the equation. Fig. 5.18 indicates that this root is approximately $0\cdot4$.

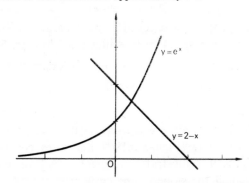

Fig. 5.18. Graphs of $y = e^x$ and $y = 2 - x$.

Let $f(x) = e^x + x - 2$. Then $f'(x) = e^x + 1$ and the Newton–Raphson formula gives

$$x_{r+1} = x_r - \frac{e^{x_r} + x_r - 2}{e^{x_r} + 1}.$$

Take $x_0 = 0\cdot4$.

Then $\quad x_1 = 0.4 - \dfrac{e^{0.4} + 0.4 - 2}{e^{0.4} + 1} = 0.4 + \dfrac{0.108}{2.492} = 0.434$ approximately.

$\therefore \quad x_2 = 0.434 - \dfrac{e^{0.434} + 0.434 - 2}{2.5}$ approximately.

$\qquad = 0.434 + .00888$

$\qquad = 0.44288$ approximately.

(The numerator is so small that we take the denominator to be 2·5.)
The calculation of x_3 does not affect the fifth place of decimals except in rounding off. In fact.

$$f(0.4428) = -0.00004 \quad \text{and} \quad f(0.4429) = +0.0001.$$

Hence correct to four places of decimals the root is 0·4429.

---

3. The solution of the equation $\phi(x) = x$. Many functions $f(x)$ are such that the equation $f(x) = 0$ can easily be written in the form

$$\phi(x) = x, \qquad (5.27)$$

where $\phi(x)$ is a well-behaved function in the neighbourhood of the root $x = \alpha$. The determination of α is equivalent to finding the intersection of the line $y = x$ and the curve $y = \phi(x)$.

Equation (5.27) can often be solved by the iteration formula

$$x_{n+1} = \phi(x_n). \qquad (5.28)$$

This process produces a series of points on a diagram either by a step-like path or a spiral path as illustrated in Figs. 5.19(i), (ii).

A_n is (x_n, x_n); P_n is (x_n, y_n), $y_n = \phi(x_n)$;

A_{n+1} is (x_{n+1}, x_{n+1}), $x_{n+1} = y_n$; P_{n+1} is (x_{n+1}, y_{n+1}),

$$y_{n+1} = \phi(x_{n+1});$$

etc. Clearly the procedure is convergent if the steps or the spiral approach the root. [Figure 5.19(i) illustrates covergent cases whereas Fig. 5.19(ii) illustrates divergent cases.] The method will be convergent if the slope of the curve $y = \phi(x)$ is numerically less than unity. To make the process approximate to the root when $|\phi'(\alpha)| > 1$ we would have to use the recurrence relation

$$x_n = \phi(x_{n+1}),$$

a relation which is inconvenient for practical use. Hence we deduce that the iteration is convergent if $|\phi'(\alpha)| < 1$. This condition

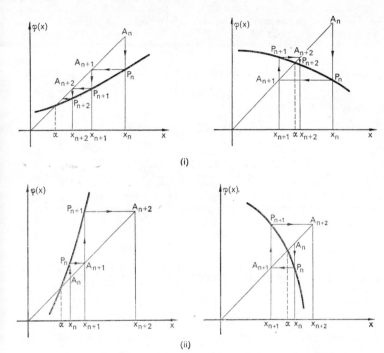

FIG. 5.19. Illustrating the iterative solution of the equation $\varphi(x) = x$.

is a sufficient condition, but the iteration may possibly converge if $|\phi'(\alpha)| = 1$, though it will converge very slowly.

The relation between consecutive errors in this method is

$$\alpha - e_{n+1} = \phi(\alpha - e_n) = \phi(\alpha) - e_n \phi'(\alpha) + O(e_n^2),$$

where $x_n = \alpha - e_n$. Therefore

$$e_{n+1} = e_n \phi'(\alpha) + O(e_n^2),$$

which shows that the iteration is a first-order process which converges more quickly the smaller the value of $\phi'(\alpha)$.

Since any iterative process provides a sequence of values $x_1, x_2, \ldots$ in which successive terms are related, usually, by an explicit formula, any of the tests for convergence of a sequence (not of a series) mentioned in § 1 : 8 can be applied.

Example. Find the real root of the equation

$$f(x) = x^5 + 5x - 1 = 0.$$

This equation has one positive root which lies in the interval $(0, 1)$ and no negative roots, since $f(0 \cdot 0) < 0, f(1) > 0$. Writing the equation in the form

$$x = \tfrac{1}{5} - \tfrac{1}{5}x^5$$

we determine the root from the iterative relationship

$$x_{n+1} = \tfrac{1}{5} - \tfrac{1}{5}x_n^5,$$

with $x_1 = 0 \cdot 5$. We find

x	$1 - x^5$	$0 \cdot 2(1 - x^5)$
0·5	0·96875	0·193750
0·193750	0·9997270	0·1999454
0·1999454	0·9996804	0·1999361
0·1999361	0·9996805	0·1999361

Further iterations do not affect the seventh place of decimals, so that the root, correct to seven places, is $0 \cdot 1999361$.

In some circumstances the approximate solution of an equation is wanted, not numerically, but in terms of some parameter in the coefficients. If this is small it is possible to solve the equation by obtaining the root as a power series in this parameter. Expansions by methods already explained (the binomial, exponential, sine series, or Taylor's or Maclaurin's theorems), or expansions by successive approximations may be used. The successive approximations in this case will include successively higher powers of the small parameter.

We illustrate the techniques in the following examples.

Example 1. If p/m is small find the numerically small root of the equation

$$x^3 - mx + p = 0.$$

We first write the equation in the form

$$x = \frac{p}{m} + \frac{x^3}{m}.$$

This is of the form $x = f(x)$ where the right-hand side is small. We may therefore substitute the approximate value $x_0 = 0$.

$$\therefore \quad x_1 = \frac{p}{m}.$$

Substituting again,

$$x_2 = \frac{p}{m} + \frac{1}{m} \cdot \frac{p^3}{m^3} = \frac{p}{m}\left(1 + \frac{p^2}{m^3}\right).$$

$$\therefore \quad x_3 = \frac{p}{m} + \frac{1}{m} \cdot \frac{p^3}{m^3}\left(1 + \frac{p^2}{m^3}\right)^3$$

$$= \frac{p}{m} + \frac{p^3}{m^4}\left(1 + \frac{3p^2}{m^3}\right) + O\left(\frac{p^7}{m^{10}}\right),$$

i.e.
$$x_3 = \frac{p}{m}\left(1 + \frac{p^2}{m^3} + \frac{3p^4}{m^6}\right).$$

Notice that each approximation adds another power of p^2/m^3 inside the bracket. No advantage is gained by expanding $(1 + p^2/m^3)^3$ to include more terms. The next approximation is

$$x_4 = \frac{p}{m} + \frac{p^3}{m^4}\left(1 + \frac{p^2}{m^3} + \frac{3p^4}{m^6}\right)^3$$

$$= \frac{p}{m}\left[1 + \frac{p^2}{m^3}\left(1 + \frac{p^2}{m^3} + \frac{3p^4}{m^6}\right)^3\right].$$

Here we must carry the expansion of $\left(1 + \dfrac{p^2}{m^3} + \dfrac{3p^4}{m^6}\right)^3$ as far as terms in $\dfrac{p^4}{m^6}$.

$$\left(1 + \frac{p^2}{m^3} + \frac{3p^4}{m^6}\right)^3 = 1 + \frac{3p^2}{m^3}\left(1 + \frac{3p^2}{m^3}\right) + \frac{3p^4}{m^6}\left(1 + \frac{3p^2}{m^3}\right)^2 + \cdots$$

$$= 1 + \frac{3p^2}{m^3} + \frac{12p^4}{m^6} + O\left(\frac{p^6}{m^9}\right).$$

$$\therefore \quad x_4 = \frac{p}{m}\left[1 + \frac{p^2}{m^3} + \frac{3p^4}{m^6} + \frac{12p^6}{m^9}\right].$$

Example 2. Find, as far as the term in ε^3, the solution, in ascending powers of ε, of the equation $\theta = \alpha + \varepsilon \sin \theta$, where ε is small.

$$\theta_0 = \alpha.$$
$$\theta_1 = \alpha + \varepsilon \sin \theta_0 = \alpha + \varepsilon \sin \alpha.$$
$$\theta_2 = \alpha + \varepsilon \sin \theta_1 = \alpha + \varepsilon \sin(\alpha + \varepsilon \sin \alpha),$$

i.e.
$$\theta_2 = \alpha + \varepsilon[\sin \alpha \cos(\varepsilon \sin \alpha) + \cos \alpha \sin(\varepsilon \sin \alpha)].$$

Retaining only terms of $O(\varepsilon)$ in the bracket, so that $\cos(\varepsilon \sin \alpha) = 1$ and $\sin(\varepsilon \sin \alpha) = \varepsilon \sin \alpha$, we have

$$\theta_2 = \alpha + \varepsilon \sin \alpha + \varepsilon^2 \sin \alpha \cos \alpha.$$

$$\therefore \quad \theta_3 = \alpha + \varepsilon[\sin \alpha \cos(\varepsilon \sin \alpha + \varepsilon^2 \sin \alpha \cos \alpha) + \cos \alpha \sin(\varepsilon \sin \alpha$$
$$+ \varepsilon^2 \sin \alpha \cos \alpha)],$$

and this gives θ as far as ε^3,

i.e.
$$\theta_3 = \alpha + \varepsilon \sin \alpha + \varepsilon^2 \sin \alpha \cos \alpha + \tfrac{1}{2}\varepsilon^3 \sin \alpha(3 \cos^2 \alpha - 1).$$

Note once more that we derive *one* additional term at each stage.

Example 3. A function y of x and λ is defined by the equation

$$y = x^2 + \lambda x^5 y^{-2}, \tag{1}$$

where λ is small. Assuming that y may be expressed in the form

$$p(x) + \lambda q(x) + \lambda^2 r(x) + \lambda^3 s(x) + \; \cdots,$$

find the functions $p(x)$, $q(x)$, $r(x)$ and $s(x)$.

A direct approach to this problem would be to substitute the given form for y into eqn. (1) thus:

$$p(x) + \lambda q(x) + \lambda^2 r(x) + \lambda^3 s(x) + \; \cdots \; = x^2 + \frac{\lambda x^5}{p(x) + \lambda q(x) + \lambda^2 r(x) + \lambda^3 s(x) + \; \cdots}$$

and then to expand the right-hand side as a power series in λ. Equating coefficients of like powers of λ gives equations to determine the unknown functions.

However, it is quicker and self-checking to use an iterative method, and to define a sequence of functions $y_1(x), y_2(x), \ldots, y_n(x), \ldots$ connected by the iterative relation

$$y_{n+1} = x^2 + \lambda x^5 y_n^{-2}.$$

Clearly
$$y_1 = x^2, \qquad y_2 = x^2 + \lambda x,$$

$$y_3 = x^2 + \frac{\lambda x^5}{(x^2 + \lambda x)^2} = x^2 + \lambda x \left(1 + \frac{\lambda}{x}\right)^{-2}$$

$$= x^2 + \lambda x - 2\lambda^2 + O(\lambda^3),$$

$$y_4 = x^2 + \frac{\lambda x^5}{(x^2 + \lambda x - 2\lambda^2)^2} = x^2 + \lambda x \left\{1 + \frac{\lambda}{x} - \frac{2\lambda^2}{x^2}\right\}^{-2}$$

$$= x^2 + \lambda x - 2\lambda^2 + \frac{7\lambda^3}{x} + O(\lambda^4).$$

$$\therefore \; p(x) = x^2, \quad q(x) = x, \quad r(x) = -2, \quad s(x) = 7/x.$$

Example 4. Find an approximation, as far as the term in ε^3, to the solution near $x = a$ of the equation

$$x = a + \varepsilon f(x),$$

where ε is small when compared with a and neither $f(x)$ nor any of its derivatives is large near $x = a$.

Writing $x = a + k$ so that k is small, we have

$$k = \varepsilon f(a + k).$$

To determine k as a power series in ε we use the iterative relation

$$k_{r+1} = \varepsilon f(a + k_r)$$

to determine a sequence of approximations $k_1, k_2 \ldots$ to k, using Taylor's theorem to expand $f(x + k_r)$ as a power series in k_r and taking care to obtain only one additional power of ε at each step.

Then

$$k_1 = \varepsilon f(a),$$

$$k_2 = \varepsilon f(a+k_1) = \varepsilon \{f(a)+k_1 f'(a)\}$$

$$= \varepsilon f(a)+\varepsilon^2 f(a) f'(a),$$

$$k_3 = \varepsilon f(a+k_2) = \varepsilon \{f(a)+k_2 f'(a)+\tfrac{1}{2}k_2^2 f''(a)\}$$

$$= \varepsilon f(a)+\varepsilon f'(a)\{\varepsilon f(a)+\varepsilon^2 f(a) f'(a)\}$$

$$+\frac{\varepsilon}{2} f''(a)\{\varepsilon^2 [f(a)]^2+O(\varepsilon^3)\}$$

$$= f(a)+\varepsilon^2 f'(a) f(a)+\varepsilon^3 \{f(a) [f'(a)]^2+\tfrac{1}{2} [f(a)]^2 f''(a)\}.$$

Exercises 5 : 9

1. By means of a sketch graph, or otherwise, show that the roots of the equation $x^3+3x^2-3 = 0$ are all real.

Find the positive root correct to three places of decimals.

2. By drawing the graphs of e^x-1 and $\ln(x+2)$, show that the equation $e^x-1 = \ln(x+2)$ has two, and only two, real roots. Find both the roots approximately, and, by using the Newton–Raphson formula, or any other method, find the larger root correct to two decimal places.

3. Obtain, graphically or otherwise, an approximation to the root of the equation $e^x+5x = 20$.

Calculate the value of the root correct to three significant figures.

4. When m is large show that the equation $x^3-mx+1 = 0$ has a small positive root given approximately by

$$x = \frac{1}{m}+\frac{1}{m^4}.$$

Find the smaller positive root of the equation $x^3-5x+1 = 0$, correct to 3 significant figures.

5. By considering the intersections of the parabola $y = x^2$ with a suitable circle, show that the equation

$$x^4-8x^2-24x+7 = 0$$

has only two real roots.

By means of the Newton–Raphson approximation, or otherwise, find correct to three significant figures the real root which lies between 3 and 4.

6. Show that the equation $x^4-2x = 1$ has two real roots and, by the method of iteration, or otherwise, show that their values, correct to three decimal places, are -0.475 and 1.395.

7. By means of a rough graph show that the equation $\tan x = 2x$ has an infinite number of real roots, and show further that the nth positive root is $(n+\tfrac{1}{2})\pi-y_n$, where to a first approximation $y_n = 1/(2n+1)\pi$.

8. If δ is small, prove that $x = 1/(8\delta)$ is an approximate solution of the equation

$$x + \delta = x \cosh \frac{1}{2x},$$

and find a closer approximation to the solution of this equation.

9. Show graphically, or otherwise, that the iterative process

$$x_{n+1} = 2/(x_n^2 + 3)$$

converges, from any initial value, to a root of the equation

$$x^3 + 3x - 2 = 0.$$

Using this or any other suitable process, calculate the root correct to three significant figures.

10. Show by a rough sketch that the equation $x = \coth x$ has two roots. Calculate the positive root correct to *two* significant figures, using the values of e^x provided below, and taking $x = 1$ as a first approximation, by the following methods:

(i) apply Newton's rule to $x \sinh x - \cosh x = 0$,
(ii) find a sequence $\{x_n\}$ such that $x_{n+1} = \coth x_n$.

For *either* process, illustrate graphically how it converges to the root.

x	1·0	1·1	1·2	1·3
e^x	2·72	3·00	3·32	3·67

11. Show that the equation

$$4x^3 + 6x^2 - 12x - 5 = 0$$

has three real roots, of which one is positive and two negative.

Calculate the positive root, correct to three significant figures.

12. The pulsatances ω of lateral vibrations of a uniform bar clamped at one end are given in terms of the roots of the equation

$$\cos \theta + \operatorname{sech} \theta = 0$$

by $\omega = a\theta^2$, where a is a constant.

Show graphically that the roots are approximately equal to successive odd multiples of $\pi/2$, and obtain the smallest root correct to three decimal places.

13. A curve $y = f(x)$ passes through the points $(a, -y_1)$ and (b, y_2) where y_1 and y_2 are both positive. If $f''(x)$ and $f'(x)$ do not vanish between $x = a$ and $x = b$ prove that a root of $f(x) = 0$ lies between

$$\frac{by_1 + ay_2}{y_1 + y_2} \quad \text{and} \quad b - \frac{y_2}{f'(b)}.$$

Find the positive root of the equation $x^3 - x - 4 = 0$ correct to four significant figures and prove that your solution has this accuracy.

14. If $y = a + x \ln y$, where x is small, prove that y is approximately equal to

$$a + x \ln a + \frac{x^2}{a} \ln a$$

and obtain the term in x^3 in the expansion.

5 : 10 Symbolic operators

In order that we can develop the techniques of numerical analysis we now introduce various operations which can be performed by symbolic operators.

1. The step operator E. The operation of choosing the next entry in a table is represented by

$$Ey_r = y_{r+1}. \tag{5.29}$$

Also

$$y_{r+2} = Ey_{r+1} = E^2 y_r, \dots, ; \qquad E^p y_r = y_{r+p}, \tag{5.30}$$

where p is an integer. This operator is linear, in the sense that

$$E(f_r + g_r) = Ef_r + Eg_r = f_{r+1} + g_{r+1}.$$

Further, the *inverse operator* which we denote by E^{-1} corresponds to a step in the opposite direction, viz. $E^{-1} y_r = y_{r-1}$. Therefore

$$EE^{-1} y_r = Ey_{r-1} = y_r, \quad E^{-1} Ey_r = E^{-1} y_{r+1} = y_r,$$

i.e.

$$EE^{-1} = 1 = E^{-1} E,$$

if we "cancel" the operand y_r. By definitions exactly similar to those of indices in elementary algebra we introduce fractional powers of E, in particular $E^{\frac{1}{2}}$, where

$$E^{\frac{1}{2}} E^{\frac{1}{2}} = E, \quad E^{\frac{1}{2}} E^{-\frac{1}{2}} = 1 = E^{-\frac{1}{2}} E^{\frac{1}{2}}, \quad E^{-\frac{1}{2}} E^{-\frac{1}{2}} = E^{-1}. \tag{5.31}$$

(In this work we interpret 1 as the identity operator.) Since two applications of $E^{\frac{1}{2}}$ correspond to the step from r to $r+1$, we interpret one application as corresponding to the step r to $r+\frac{1}{2}$ or $r+\frac{1}{2}$ to $r+1$. Thus

$$E^{\frac{1}{2}} y_r = y_{r+\frac{1}{2}}, \qquad E^{\frac{1}{2}} y_{r+\frac{1}{2}} = y_{r+1}.$$

Similarly,

$$E^{-\frac{1}{2}} y_r = y_{r-\frac{1}{2}}, \qquad E^{-\frac{1}{2}} y_{r-\frac{1}{2}} = y_{r-1}.$$

The values $y_{r+\frac{1}{2}}$, $y_{r-\frac{1}{2}}$ are to be associated with points halfway between x_{r+1}, x_r and x_r, x_{r-1} respectively.

2. The forward difference operator. We defined the first difference, which we have tentatively denoted by Δy, in § 1 : 9. This difference is called the forward difference belonging to y_r, and is written

$$\Delta y_r = y_{r+1} - y_r, \qquad (5.32)$$

because the difference is calculated *forward* from y_r. We now regard the Δ as symbolizing the operation of forming a forward difference at y_r and write

$$\Delta y_r = y_{r+1} - y_r = E y_r - y_r = (E-1)y_r,$$

and obtain the operator equation

$$\Delta = E - 1 \quad \text{or} \quad E = 1 + \Delta. \qquad (5.33)$$

Example. The second and third, etc., differences are given by

$$\Delta^2 = (E-1)^2 = E^2 - 2E + 1, \quad \Delta^2 y_r = (E^2 - 2E + 1)y_r = y_{r+2} - 2y_{r+1} + y_r,$$
$$\Delta^3 = E^3 - 3E^2 + 3E - 1, \qquad \Delta^3 y_r = y_{r+3} - 3y_{r+2} + 3y_{r+1} - y_{..}.$$

These results correspond to the formulae of pp. 58–59.

---

3. The backward difference operator ∇. We can also regard the difference $y_{r+1} - y_r$ as taken *backwards* from y_{r+1}. So we write

$$\nabla y_{r+1} = y_{r+1} - y_r \quad \text{or} \quad \nabla y_r = y_r - y_{r-1}. \qquad (5.34)$$

We regard ∇ as an operator and write the second of equations (5.34) as

$$\nabla y_r = y_r - E^{-1} y_r \quad \text{or} \quad \nabla = 1 - E^{-1}. \qquad (5.35)$$

Alternatively, we can obtain

$$\nabla y_{r+1} = \nabla E y_r = E y_r - y_r, \quad \text{or} \quad \nabla E = E - 1,$$

which leads to eqs. (5.35) after operation on the right by E^{-1}.

Example. If we operate on the second of eqs. (5.34) by E, we obtain

$$E(\nabla y_r) = \nabla y_{r+1}$$

(the operation of taking the succeeding first difference instead of the succeeding value of y).

$$\therefore \quad E \nabla y_r = \nabla y_{r+1} = y_{r+1} - y_r = E y_r - y_r.$$
$$\therefore \quad E \nabla = E - 1 = \nabla E.$$

This shows that the operators E, ∇ commute.

---

4. The central difference operator δ. There is a third possibility of regarding the difference $y_{r+1} - y_r$ as associated with y halfway between the tabulated values, instead of being taken either backwards or forwards. We represent this by

$$\delta y_{r+\frac{1}{2}} = y_{r+1} - y_r. \tag{5.36}$$

Using the operator E and regarding δ as an operator we can write, using $y_{r+\frac{1}{2}} = E^{\frac{1}{2}} y_r$,

$$\delta y_{r+\frac{1}{2}} = \delta E^{\frac{1}{2}} y_r = (E-1) y_r,$$

or

$$\delta E^{\frac{1}{2}} = E - 1 \tag{5.37}$$

from which we obtain, on operating with $E^{-\frac{1}{2}}$ on the right,

$$\delta = E^{\frac{1}{2}} - E^{-\frac{1}{2}}. \tag{5.38}$$

This is taken as the definition of the *central difference operator*.

Example. In a table the first differences are written in the intermediate positions and the second differences in the direct positions. Thus the second difference opposite y_r is obtained from $\delta y_{r+\frac{1}{2}} - \delta y_{r-\frac{1}{2}}$.

Therefore

$$\delta y_{r+\frac{1}{2}} - \delta y_{r-\frac{1}{2}} = \delta \left(y_{r+\frac{1}{2}} - y_{r-\frac{1}{2}} \right) = \delta \left(E^{\frac{1}{2}} - E^{-\frac{1}{2}} \right) y_r = \delta^2 y_r.$$

Also

$$\delta^2 = \left(E^{\frac{1}{2}} - E^{-\frac{1}{2}} \right)^2 = E - 2 + E^{-1}.$$

$$\therefore \quad \delta^2 y_r = (E - 2 + E^{-1}) y_r = y_{r+1} - 2y_r + y_{r-1}.$$

This latter expression agrees with the result of p. 59 for the entry in the second difference column opposite y_r.

---

5. The mean operator μ. The operation of taking the mean of two entries, viz. $\frac{1}{2}(y_{r+1} + y_r)$, should be associated with the half-way point and so the operator μ is given by

$$\mu y_{r+\frac{1}{2}} = \frac{1}{2}(y_{r+1} + y_r) \quad \text{or} \quad \mu y_r = \frac{1}{2}\left(\delta y_{r+\frac{1}{2}} + \delta y_{r-\frac{1}{2}} \right). \tag{5.39}$$

With the use of $E^{\frac{1}{2}}$, this leads to

$$\mu E^{\frac{1}{2}} = \frac{1}{2}(E + 1),$$

i.e.

$$\mu = \frac{1}{2}\left(E^{\frac{1}{2}} + E^{-\frac{1}{2}} \right). \tag{5.40}$$

This is the definition of the *"mean"* operator.

Example 1. Since
$$4\mu^2 = E + 2 + E^{-1},$$
and
$$\delta^2 = E - 2 + E^{-1},$$
therefore
$$\mu^2 = 1 + \tfrac{1}{4}\delta^2. \tag{5.41}$$
The latter is an important relation.

Example 2. From eqns. (5.38) and (5.40) we obtain
$$2\mu\delta = E - E^{-1}, \quad 2 + \delta^2 = E + E^{-1}.$$
$$\therefore \; E = 1 + \mu\delta + \tfrac{1}{2}\delta^2, \quad E^{-1} = 1 - \mu\delta + \tfrac{1}{2}\delta^2. \tag{5.42}$$

The manipulations of the above operators have been made as though they were real numbers. To justify these assumptions it should be shown that they all commute. They are all linear operators and it can be shown (see Exercises 5 : 10) that they do, in fact, all commute.

We now use these operators to derive some important formulae, and we shall, where necessary, use infinite series of the operators (cf. the use of the D operator in elementary differential equations, Vol. 2, Chap. II).

It should be emphasised that the numerical value of a difference is the same whether it is regarded as a forward, central or backward difference; the distinction is one of nomenclature and not of numerical value.

TABLE 5(a)

x	y	Δy	$\Delta^2 y$	$\Delta^3 y$	$\Delta^4 y$
-2	y_{-2}				
		Δ_{-2}			
-1	y_{-1}		Δ^2_{-2}		
		Δ_{-1}		Δ^3_{-2}	
0	y_0		Δ^2_{-1}		Δ^4_{-2}
		Δ_0		Δ^3_{-1}	
1	y_1		Δ^2_0		Δ^4_{-1}
		Δ_1		Δ^3_0	
2	y_2		Δ^2_1		
		Δ_2			
3	y_3				

TABLE 5(b)

x	y	∇y	$\nabla^2 y$	$\nabla^3 y$	$\nabla^4 y$
-2	y_{-2}				
		∇_{-1}			
-1	y_{-1}		∇^2_0		
		∇_0		∇^3_1	
0	y_0		∇^2_1		∇^4_2
		∇_1		∇^3_2	
1	y_1		∇^2_2		∇^4_3
		∇_2		∇^3_3	
2	y_2		∇^2_3		
		∇_3			
3	y_3				

TABLE 5(c)

x	y	δy	$\delta^2 y$	$\delta^3 y$	$\delta^4 y$
-2	y_{-2}				
		$\delta_{-\frac{3}{2}}$			
-1	y_{-1}		δ^2_{-1}		
		$\delta_{-\frac{1}{2}}$		$\delta^3_{-\frac{1}{2}}$	
0	y_0		δ^2_0		δ^4_0
		$\delta_{\frac{1}{2}}$		$\delta^3_{\frac{1}{2}}$	
1	y_1		δ^2_1		δ^4_1
		$\delta_{\frac{3}{2}}$		$\delta^3_{\frac{3}{2}}$	
2	y_2		δ^2_2		
		$\delta_{\frac{5}{2}}$			
3	y_3				

Tables 5(a)–(c) illustrate an abbreviated notation in which the y has been omitted from the difference terms, e.g. ∇_3 stands for the first-order backward difference ∇y_3; $\delta^3_{\frac{3}{2}}$ stands for the third-order central difference $\delta^3 y_{\frac{3}{2}} = \delta^2 y_2 - \delta^2 y_1 = \delta^2_2 - \delta^2_1$. The dotted [ines on the tables, following the suffix zero, go forwards, backwards or horizontally in the various cases corresponding to the type of difference used.

The relations between the operators are shown in Table 6 which gives each of the operators in terms of the others.

TABLE 6

	E	Δ	∇	δ	μ
E	E	$1+\Delta$	$(1-\nabla)^{-1}$	$1+\tfrac{1}{2}\delta^2$ $+\delta(1+\tfrac{1}{4}\delta^2)^{\frac{1}{2}}$	$2\mu^2+2\mu(\mu^2-1)^{\frac{1}{2}}$ -1
Δ	$E-1$	Δ	$\nabla(1-\nabla)^{-1}$	$\delta(1+\tfrac{1}{4}\delta^2)^{\frac{1}{2}}+\tfrac{1}{2}\delta^2$	$2\mu^2+2\mu(\mu^2-1)^{\frac{1}{2}}$ -2
∇	$1-E^{-1}$	$\Delta(1+\Delta)^{-1}$	∇	$\delta(1+\tfrac{1}{4}\delta^2)^{\frac{1}{2}}-\tfrac{1}{2}\delta^2$	$-2\mu^2+2\mu(\mu^2-1)^{\frac{1}{2}}$ $+2$
δ	$E^{\frac{1}{2}}-E^{-\frac{1}{2}}$	$\Delta(1+\Delta)^{-\frac{1}{2}}$	$\nabla(1-\nabla)^{-\frac{1}{2}}$	δ	$2(\mu^2-1)^{\frac{1}{2}}$
μ	$\tfrac{1}{2}\big(E^{\frac{1}{2}}$ $+E^{-\frac{1}{2}}\big)$	$(1+\tfrac{1}{2}\Delta)$ $\times(1+\Delta)^{-\frac{1}{2}}$	$(1-\tfrac{1}{2}\nabla)$ $\times(1-\nabla)^{-\frac{1}{2}}$	$(1+\tfrac{1}{4}\delta^2)^{\frac{1}{2}}$	μ

In order to obtain a value y_p from the value y_0 of a tabulated function we apply the operator E. Thus

$$y_p = E^p y_0 = (1+\Delta)^p y_0$$
$$= \left\{1+p\Delta+\binom{p}{2}\Delta^2+\binom{p}{3}\Delta^3+ \ldots +\binom{p}{m}\Delta^m+ \ldots\right\}y_0.$$
$$\therefore \ y_p = y_0+p\,\Delta y_0+\binom{p}{2}\Delta^2 y_0+\binom{p}{3}\Delta^3 y_0 + \ldots$$
$$+\binom{p}{m}\Delta^m y_0+ \ldots. \tag{5.43}$$

This formula is the *Gregory–Newton forward interpolation formula*.

At this stage it merely relates one entry in a table with another and the corresponding forward differences.

Example. If $p = 1$, $\quad y_1 = y_0+\Delta y_0 = y_0+(y_1-y_0) = y_1$.

If $p = 3$, $y_3 = y_0 + 3 \Delta y_0 + 3 \Delta^2 y_0 + \Delta^3 y_0$.

$$= y_0 + 3(y_1 - y_0) + 3(y_2 - 2y_1 + y_0) + (y_3 - 3y_2 + 3y_1 - y_0) = y_3.$$

Therefore, the formula, for integral values of p, is simply another version of the relations (1.31).

When p is not an integer the right-hand side of eqn. (5.43) becomes an infinite series of differences. However, when y is a polynomial function these differences are zero after a certain order, the formula involves only a finite number of (non-vanishing) terms and questions of convergence do not arise.

The justification of the formula when used with a non-polynomial function of necessity involves questions of convergence; this is the subject matter of more advanced numerical analysis and we do not discuss it here.

We can obtain a similar formula with backward differences. Thus, from $E = (1 - \nabla)^{-1}$, we obtain

$$y_p = E^p y_0 = (1 - \nabla)^{-p} y_0$$

$$= \left\{ 1 + p\nabla + \frac{p(p+1)}{2!} \nabla^2 + \cdots \right.$$

$$\left. + \frac{p(p+1) \cdots (p+m-1)}{m!} \nabla^m + \cdots \right\} y_0.$$

$$\therefore \ y_p = y_0 + p \nabla y_0 + \frac{p(p+1)}{2!} \nabla^2 y_0$$

$$+ \cdots + \frac{p(p+1) \cdots (p+m-1)}{m!} \nabla^m y_0 + \cdots. \quad (5.44)$$

This is the *Gregory–Newton backward interpolation formula*. Unless the higher order differences vanish, this is an infinite series whatever the value of p, and questions of convergence will arise unless y is a polynomial function.

Example. If $p = 1$, eqn. (5.44) gives

$$y_1 = y_0 + \nabla y_0 + \nabla^2 y_0 + \cdots + \nabla^m y_0 + \cdots.$$

This formula simply shows, for example, that any specified entry in the table of a polynomial is given by adding all the entries in the upward diagonal line immediately above that entry, provided this line is complete. The reader can check this from Table 8; it is approximately true for Table 9.

The corresponding formula involving central differences is more laborious to obtain because an expression with three terms has to be expanded. Starting from eqn. (5.42), viz. $E = 1 + \mu\delta + \frac{1}{2}\delta^2$, using eqn. (5.41), viz. $\mu^2 = 1 + \frac{1}{4}\delta^2$, and proceeding as before, we find

$$y_p = E^p y_0 = (1 + \mu\delta + \tfrac{1}{2}\delta^2)^p y_0.$$

We do not carry the expansion through in detail, for indirect methods are usually best, but indicate the form of the result and quote the answer which is

$$\left(1 + \mu\delta + \frac{1}{2}\delta^2\right)^p = 1 + \binom{p}{1}\left(\mu + \frac{1}{2}\delta\right)\delta + \binom{p}{2}\left(\mu + \frac{1}{2}\delta\right)^2\delta^2$$
$$+ \binom{p}{3}\left(\mu + \frac{1}{2}\delta\right)^3\delta^3 + \dots$$
$$= 1 + \binom{p}{1}\mu\delta + \binom{p}{1}\frac{\delta^2}{2} + \binom{p}{2}\left(\mu^2 + \mu\delta + \frac{1}{4}\delta^2\right)\delta^2$$
$$+ \binom{p}{3}\left(\mu^3 + \frac{3}{2}\mu^2\delta + \frac{3}{4}\mu\delta^2 + \frac{1}{8}\delta^3\right)\delta^3 + \dots.$$

If we remove even powers of μ by means of the relation (5.41) it is clear that all odd powers of δ have a factor μ in front, whereas even powers have no such factor. The early terms of the expansion are

$$\left(1 + \mu\delta + \frac{1}{2}\delta^2\right)^p = 1 + p\mu\delta + \frac{p^2}{2!}\delta^2 + \frac{p(p^2-1)}{3!}\mu\delta^3$$
$$+ \frac{p^2(p^2-1)}{4!}\delta^4 + \dots.$$

$$\therefore\ y_p = y_0 + \frac{p}{2}\left(\delta_{\frac{1}{2}} + \delta_{-\frac{1}{2}}\right) + \frac{p^2}{2!}\delta_0^2 + \frac{p(p^2-1)}{2\cdot 3!}\left(\delta_{\frac{1}{2}}^3 + \delta_{-\frac{1}{2}}^3\right)$$
$$+ \frac{p^2(p^2-1)}{4!}\delta_0^4 + \dots.$$

The complete formula is *Stirling's central difference interpolation formula* and is given by

$$y_p = y_0 + S_1\left(\delta_{\frac{1}{2}} + \delta_{-\frac{1}{2}}\right) + S_2\delta_0^2 + S_3\left(\delta_{\frac{1}{2}}^3 + \delta_{-\frac{1}{2}}^3\right) + S_4\delta_0^4 + \dots, \quad (5.45)$$

where

$$S_{2r+1} = \frac{1}{2}\left(\frac{p+r}{2r+1}\right), \quad S_{2r+2} = \frac{p}{2r+2}\left(\frac{p+r}{2r+1}\right). \quad (5.46)$$

We refer to these results in the next section.

Exercises 5 : 10

1. Verify, by algebraic manipulations, the relations given in Table 6.

2. From their definitions show that all the operations E, Δ, ∇, δ, μ, do commute with one another.

5 : 11 Interpolation

Tables of $\log_{10} x$ using five significant figures, often give the values of x by four figures only; the user has to *interpolate* to obtain the logarithm corresponding to the fifth figure of x (see § 5 : 3). This is a very common situation with tabulated functions; the value of the function is required for a point (i.e. a value of x) between two of the tabulated values. The related problem of *inverse interpolation* also occurs frequently; this is the process of finding an anti-logarithm. Since anti-logarithms are usually available in tables this difficulty arises more often in elementary practice with trigonometric functions. For example: the sine of a certain angle is 0·342 8; what is the angle? It happens that the figure 0·342 8 does not occur in four-figure tables. In this case inverse interpolation has to be used to find the angle. Here we shall be concerned chiefly with the question of direct interpolation and extend the methods and results of § 5 : 3.

The elementary method of interpolating, used, for example, with logarithms, is usually as follows.

Example. What is lg 1·3726?

(The notation "lg x" stands for $\log_{10} x$.)

The table gives

$$\text{lg } 1·372 = 0·137 \ 35, \quad \text{lg } 1·373 = 0·137 \ 67;$$
$$\text{difference} = 0·000 \ 32, \quad 0·6 \times \text{difference} = 0·000 \ 19.$$
$$\therefore \ \text{lg } 1·372 \ 6 = 0·137 \ 35 + 0·000 \ 19 = 0·137 \ 54.$$

This process is simple and can frequently be done in one's head. What exactly have we been doing in this case? We represent the process graphically thus, Fig. 5.20. The two ordinates at A, B have been joined by a straight line and the value y_p has been calculated from the formula

$$y_p = y_a + 0\cdot6(y_b - y_a).$$

In fact we have taken the expression

$$y_p = y_a + p\,\Delta y_a, \qquad (0 < p < 1) \tag{5.47}$$

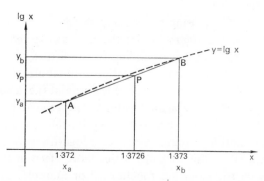

FIG. 5.20. Illustrating the process of linear interpolation.

to represent the logarithm between x_a and x_b. The expression in (5.47) is a polynomial in p of degree 1. The method just described is not, of course, accurate but may be sufficiently so if the interval (x_a, x_b) is sufficiently small. The system of interpolation discussed below is a generalisation of the elementary process given above. Essentially the method consists of finding a polynomial which takes the same values as the tabulated function for the given values of x; then we evaluate this polynomial for values of x not tabulated and take the values y_p so obtained as the values of the function required. In general, the greater the number of tabulated values we use in the construction of the polynomial the more accurately it fits the function. More advanced numerical analysis is concerned with finding the most convenient forms of polynomials to use in conjunction with the calculating tools available and the limits of error which may be incurred in the use of a certain polynomial. We hope the discussion given here will serve to introduce the reader to the methods in common use.

If we write y_0 for y_a in eqn. (5.47), then

$$y_p = y_0 + p\,\Delta y_0$$

is an example of the Gregory–Newton formula in which differences above the first are zero (a first-degree polynomial). When we discussed this formula we considered only integral values for p, but here we use non-integral values for p; this is typical of the process.

In eqn. (5.47) we used only two tabulated values and so were unable to construct a unique polynomial of degree greater than 1. However, if we use $k+1$ tabulated values of a function, we can construct a polynomial of degree k which fits at the tabulated values, and probably gives more accurate approximations for intermediate points.

The use of non-integral values for p in the Gregory–Newton formula (or Stirling's formula) leads, in principle, to infinite series. But, as we have seen, the higher order differences usually become small enough to be neglected beyond a certain order; consequently the approximation being used is a polynomial one.

A comparison of the three formulae (5.43) to (5.45) for the interpolation functions with Table 5(a)–(c) on p. 323 shows that the coefficients y_0, Δy_0, $\Delta^2 y_0$, ... lie on a forward (downward sloping) line in the table and consequently the forward formula should be used when the starting value y_0 is near the beginning of the table (otherwise the higher difference terms, which may not be negligible, are not available). Also, for best results, i.e. for a formula which converges rapidly, it is best to use values of p in the range $0 < p < 1$. Similarly, the Gregory–Newton backward formula is used when y_0 is near the bottom (forward) end of the table. Stirling's formula is best when y_0 is near the middle of the table with values of p in the range $-\frac{1}{4} < p < \frac{1}{4}$. It holds in the range $-\frac{1}{2} < p < \frac{1}{2}$ but the convergence may not be so rapid near the extremities of this range.

Example 1. The following table is constructed from Table 8:

x	y	δy	$\delta^2 y$	$\delta^3 y$	$\delta^4 y$
$-1\cdot0$	$3\cdot5280$				
		-32016			
$-0\cdot6$	$0\cdot3264$		25632		
		-6384		-16128	
$-0\cdot2$	$-0\cdot3120$		9504		6144
		$+3120$		-9984	
$+0\cdot2$	$0\cdot0000$		-480		6144
		2640		-3840	
$0\cdot6$	$0\cdot2640$		-4320		6144
		-1680		$+2304$	
$1\cdot0$	$0\cdot0960$		-2016		
		-3696			
$1\cdot4$	$-0\cdot2736$				

We use Newton's forward formula to obtain the value for $x = 0$. (This is the largest x for which this formula can be used.) The calculation is, with $p = 0\cdot5$, $y_0 = -0\cdot3120$,

$$
\begin{aligned}
y_p = \quad & y_0 && = -0\cdot3120 \\
& +\binom{p}{1}\Delta_0 && +0\cdot5\times0\cdot3120 \\
& +\binom{p}{2}\Delta_0^2 && +0\cdot125\times0\cdot0480 && = -0\cdot1980 \\
& +\binom{p}{3}\Delta_0^3 && -0\cdot0625\times0\cdot3840 \\
& +\binom{p}{4}\Delta_0^4 && -0\cdot0391\times0\cdot6144
\end{aligned}
$$

This value agrees exactly with the value for $x = 0$. Since the function is a polynomial of degree 4 it can be calculated exactly. The interpolation formulae give y as a function of p; since $x = x_0 + ph$ we can substitute for p and obtain the polynomial explicitly in x. We choose $x_0 = -0\cdot2$. Then

$$p = \frac{x+0\cdot2}{0\cdot4},$$

and the polynomial is

$$y_p = -0\cdot3120 + p\times0\cdot3120 - \tfrac{1}{2}p(p-1)\times0\cdot0480 - \tfrac{1}{6}p(p-1)(p-2)\times0\cdot3840$$
$$+ \tfrac{1}{24}p(p-1)(p-2)(p-3)\times0\cdot6144.$$

$$
\begin{aligned}
\therefore\ f(x) = & -0\cdot3120 + 0\cdot78(x+0\cdot2) - 0\cdot15(x^2 - 0\cdot04) \\
& - (x^3 - 0\cdot6x^2 - 0\cdot04x + 0\cdot024) \\
& + (x^4 - 1\cdot6x^3 + 0\cdot56x^2 + 0\cdot064x - 0\cdot024) \\
= & \ x^4 - 2\cdot6x^3 + 1\cdot01x^2 + 0\cdot884x - 0\cdot198.
\end{aligned}
$$

Example 2. The following table is constructed from Table 9 by rounding off to three decimal places;

x	y	δy	$\delta^2 y$	$\delta^3 y$	$\delta^4 y$	$\delta^5 y$
-1.0	2·718					
		-896				
-0.6	1·822		295			
		-601		-97		
-0.2	1·221		198		32	
		-403		-65		-11
$+0.2$	0·819		133		21	
		-270		-44		-6
0·6	0·549		89		15	
		-181		-29		
1·0	0·368		60			
		-121				
1·4	0·247					

(i) We use Newton's forward formula to interpolate in this table and find the value of the function for $x = -0.8$. For this value of x, $p = 0.5$ with $x_0 = -1.0$. $[-0.8 = x_0 + ph = -1.0 + 0.5 \times 0.4.]$

$$
\begin{aligned}
y_{-0.8} = \quad y_0 \quad &= \quad 2.718 \\
+ \binom{p}{1} \Delta_0 \quad &\quad -0.5 \times 0.896 \\
+ \binom{p}{2} \Delta_0^2 \quad &\quad -0.125 \times 0.295 \\
+ \binom{p}{3} \Delta_0^3 \quad &\quad -0.0625 \times 0.097 \quad = 2.223. \\
+ \binom{p}{4} \Delta_0^4 \quad &\quad -0.03916 \times 0.032 \\
+ \binom{p}{5} \Delta_0^5 \quad &\quad -0.02734 \times 0.011
\end{aligned}
$$

This value should be compared with the value 2·226 obtained from Table 9.
(ii) We use Newton's backward formula to interpolate in this table and

find the value of the function for $x = 1.2$. Again, $p = 0.5$.

$$
\begin{aligned}
y_{1\cdot2} = \quad y_0 \quad &= \quad 0.368 \\
+\binom{p}{1}\nabla_0 \quad & \quad -0.5\times0.181 \\
+\binom{p+1}{2}\nabla_0^2 \quad & \quad +0.375\times0.089 \\
+\binom{p+2}{3}\nabla_0^3 \quad & \quad -0.3225\times0.044 \quad = 0.299. \\
+\binom{p+3}{4}\nabla_0^4 \quad & \quad +0.2822\times0.012 \\
+\binom{p+4}{5}\nabla_0^5 \quad & \quad -0.2540\times0.011
\end{aligned}
$$

This compares with the value 0.301 obtained from Table 9.

(iii) Finally, we use the values in the middle of the table to obtain an interpolation for $x = 0.4$ by means of Stirling's formula.

$$
\begin{aligned}
y_{0\cdot4} = \quad y_0 \quad &= \quad 0.819 \\
+S_1\big(\delta_{\frac{1}{2}}+\delta_{-\frac{1}{2}}\big) \quad & \quad -0.25\times0.673 \\
+S_2\delta_0^2 \quad & \quad +0.125\times0.133 \\
+S_3\big(\delta_{\frac{1}{2}}^3+\delta_{-\frac{1}{2}}^3\big) \quad & \quad +0.0313+0.109 \quad = 0.671. \\
+S_4\delta_0^4 \quad & \quad -0.0078\times0.021 \\
+S_5\big(\delta_{\frac{1}{2}}^5+\delta_{-\frac{1}{2}}^5\big) \quad & \quad -0.0059\times0.017
\end{aligned}
$$

This should be compared with the value 0.670 given in Table 9.

In the use of the two Newton formulae here the table of values from which we worked is probably not sufficiently extensive to give the result correct to three places of decimals, for, if subsequent differences had been available they would probably have affected the last place. However, the later terms from Stirling's formula are much smaller. This illustrates the fact that, usually, Stirling's formula is more rapidly convergent than either of the Newton formulae.

Some practical points. A discrepancy between the value given by an interpolation function and the true value can arise from several sources. First, an error is introduced by "truncating" the series at, say, the mth difference and neglecting $(m+1)$th and higher differences. Second, errors are introduced by rounding-off; this occurs in the values of the function and causes oscillating errors in the differences, and it occurs in the individual terms of the formula and their sum.

It can be shown that the remainder term R_m which has been neglected by omitting higher order differences has the values

$h^{m+1} \begin{pmatrix} p \\ m+1 \end{pmatrix} f^{(m+1)} (\xi)$ in Newton's forward formula,

$h^{m+1} \begin{pmatrix} p+m \\ m+1 \end{pmatrix} f^{(m+1)} (\xi)$ in Newton's backward formula,

$h^{m+1} \ S_{m+1} \ f^{(m+1)} (\xi)$ (m odd) in Stirling's formula,

where ξ is some value of x lying in the range of x embraced by the table. Now the order of magnitude of the $(m+1)$th derivative is given by

$$h^{m+1} f^{(m+1)} (\xi) \approx \Delta_0^{m+1} \approx \delta_0^{m+1} \approx \nabla_0^{m+1} .$$

These considerations imply that the remainder R_m is of the same order of magnitude as the first neglected term of the series.

Example. In Newton's forward formula the coefficient of Δ_0^2 is $p(p-1)/2$, which has a maximum modulus in the range $0 \leqslant p \leqslant 1$ of $\frac{1}{8}$, for $p = \frac{1}{2}$.

$$\therefore \ |p(p-1) \Delta_0^2/2| \leqslant \tfrac{1}{8} |\Delta_0^2|. \tag{1}$$

Now any error less than $\frac{1}{2}$ unit of the smallest decimal place is negligible, for it cannot affect the last place. For (1) to be negligible for *any* value of p, $|\Delta_0^2|$ must be less than 4 units of the last decimal place. Hence, to use linear interpolation on a table, the interval h must be so chosen that the entries in the second difference column have a magnitude less than 4 units of the least decimal.

A similar calculation using Stirling's formula shows that higher values can be permitted when using central differences.

The effect of rounding errors varies both with m, the order giving negligible differences, and the value of p, and again the effect is smaller with central differences.

Exercises 5 : 11

1. A polynomial function is given by the following table:

x	0	1	2	3	4	5	6
f	0	3	14	39	84	155	258

Make a difference table and explain how the correctness of the arithmetic may be checked.

Use this table to find f when $x = 1 \cdot 5$ and when $x = 7$.

2. A fourth-degree polynomial is tabulated as follows:

x	0	0·1	0·2	0·3	0·4
y	1·0000	0·9208	0·6928	0·3448	−0·0752

x	0·5	0·6	0·7	0·8	0·9
y	−0·5000	−0·8452	−0·9992	−0·8432	−0·2312

Show from a difference table that there is an error and use the corrected table with the Stirling interpolation formula to find the value of y when $x = 0.45$.

3. Define the difference operators Δ and E and show that $\Delta \equiv E-1$
If y is a polynomial of fifth degree in x, show that

$$20y_3 = y_0 - 6y_1 + 15y_2 + 15y_4 - 6y_5 + y_6,$$

where $y_r = y(x_0+r)$, $r = 1, 2, \ldots, 6$.

Given that a polynomial of fifth degree has the values -12, -2, 1, 5, 3 and 0 corresponding to values 0, 1, 2, 4, 5 and 6 of x, evaluate the polynomial when $x = 3$ and $x = 3.5$.

4. A function is tabulated in the range $x_0 \leqslant x \leqslant x_n$ at equally spaced intervals h. If

$$f_p = f(x_p) = f(x_0+ph),$$

define the quantities Δf_p, Ef_p, where Δ is the forward difference operator and E is the shift operator. Hence, or otherwise, obtain the Newton–Gregory forward interpolation formula.

A function is tabulated below:

x	-1	0	1	2	3	4
$f(x)$	2	-2	2	26	106	302

Find a polynomial which fits these figures exactly.

5. When $\Delta f(x) = f(x+1) - f(x)$ and

$$x(x-1) \ldots (x-r+1) = x^{(r)},$$

prove that

$$\Delta x^{(r)} = rx^{(r-1)}.$$

Express $f(x) = x^4 + 2x$ in terms of $x^{(r)}$ and prove that $f(10) = 10020$, $\Delta f(10) = 4643$, $\Delta^2 f(10) = 1454$, $\Delta^3 f(10) = 276$, $\Delta^4 f(10) = 24$.

Use these values to construct a table of values of $f(x)$ for $x = 10, 11, 12, 13, 14, 15$. Show that there is a root of $x^4 + 2x = 23783$ in this range and estimate the root to one place of decimals.

6. Define the forward difference Δy_0 and show that

$$\Delta^3 y_0 = y_3 - 3y_2 + 3y_1 - y_0.$$

It is known that in the following table one value of y is incorrect, and that y is a cubic polynomial in x:

x	0	1	2	3	4	5	6	7
y	25	21	18	18	27	45	76	123

Construct a difference table for y and use it to locate and correct the wrong value.

By differentiating Bessel's formula

$$y_p = y_0 + p\delta y_{\frac{1}{2}} + \tfrac{1}{4}p(p-1)\,(\delta^2 y_0 + \delta^2 y_1)$$

$$+ \tfrac{1}{6}p(p-\tfrac{1}{2})\,(p-1)\,\delta^3 y_{\frac{1}{2}} + \ldots$$

with respect to p, show that the cubic polynomial y has a minimum value at $x = 7/3$.

7. Define the operators E, Δ, D and show that

$$\mathrm{E} = 1+\Delta, \quad h\mathrm{D} = \ln\,(1+\Delta).$$

Derive the formula for approximate differentiation

$$hy_1' = (-2y_0 - 3y_1 + 6y_2 - y_3)/6$$

by expanding $h\mathrm{DE}y_0$ in powers of Δ as far as Δ^3, and converting to function values.

5 : 12 Lagrangian interpolation

The interpolation formulae obtained so far require the differences, as well as the tabulated values, for a given function. The Lagrangian method provides an interpolation polynomial $I(x)$ which takes the tabulated values y_r at the values $x = x_r$. We write it in the form

$$I(x) = y_1 l_1(x) + y_2 l_2(x) + \ldots + y_r l_r(x) + \ldots + y_n l_n(x), \quad (5.48)$$

where the $l_r(x)$ are polynomials yet to be determined. In order that $I(x_r)$ shall have the value y_r for all the tabulated points the polynomials $l_r(x)$ must satisfy the conditions

$$y_r = y_1 l_1(x_r) + y_2 l_2(x_r) + \ldots + y_r l_r(x_r) + \ldots + y_n l_n(x_r).$$

$$\therefore \ l_1(x_r) = l_2(x_r) = \ldots = l_{r-1}(x_r) = l_{r+1}(x_r) = \ldots = l_n(x_r) = 0,$$

and

$$l_r(x_r) = 1, \quad (r = 1, 2, \ldots, n).$$

These may be summarised in the single relation

$$l_r(x_s) = \delta_{rs}, \quad (5.49)$$

where $\delta_{rs} = 1$ if $r = s$, $= 0$ otherwise. Since we wish $l_r(x)$ to vanish for the $n-1$ values of x at $x = x_1, x_2, \ldots, x_{r-1}, x_{r+1}, \ldots, x_n$ we can write it

$$l_r(x) = C(x-x_1)\,(x-x_2)\,\ldots\,(x-x_{r-1})\,(x-x_{r+1})\,\ldots\,(x-x_n).$$

By a suitable choice of C we make $l_r(x_r) = 1$ and obtain the form

$$l_r(x) = \frac{(x-x_1)(x-x_2) \ldots (x-x_{r-1})(x-x_{r+1}) \ldots (x-x_n)}{(x_r-x_1)(x_r-x_2) \ldots (x_r-x_{r-1})(x_r-x_{r+1}) \ldots (x_r-x_n)}.$$

(5.50)

This is a polynomial of degree $n-1$ when we are using n values of x_r, $(r = 1, 2, \ldots, n)$.

The interpolation polynomial $I(x)$, given in eqn. (5.48), assumes the required values even when the x_r are not uniformly spaced. Consequently, $I(x)$ can be used in these circumstances—when it is impossible to determine differences. The case of uniformly spaced values of x given by $x = x_0+ph$, where p replaces the variable x, is important. Under this transformation

$$(x-x_r)/(x_s-x_r) = (p-r)/(s-r) \text{ and so}$$

$$l_r(x) = \frac{(p-1)(p-2) \ldots (p-r+1)(p-r-1) \ldots (p-n)}{(r-1)(r-2) \ldots 1. \quad (-1) \ldots (r-n)}. \quad (5.51)$$

This shows that $l_r(x)$ has the same form for all values of x_0, h. This is an important property.

If $y_1 = y_2 = \cdots = y_n = 1$ in (5.48) $I(x)$ is a polynomial of degree $n-1$ which takes the value 1 for n values of x. Therefore $\sum_1^n l_r(x) \equiv 1$, for *all* values of x. This is a useful check in numerical work.

Example 1. We find by interpolation the value of lg cos 35·7° from the quoted values

$x°$	35·2	35·6	35·9
lg sin $x°$	$\bar{1}$·7607	$\bar{1}$·7650	$\bar{1}$·7682

The Lagrangian polynomials are

$$l_1(x) = \frac{(x-35·6)(x-35·9)}{(35·2-35·6)(35·2-35·9)}, \quad l_1(35·7) = \frac{(0·1)(-0·2)}{(-0·4)(-0·7)} = -\frac{1}{14},$$

$$l_2(x) = \frac{(x-35·2)(x-35·9)}{(35·6-35·2)(35·6-35·9)}, \quad l_2(35·7) = \frac{(0·5)(-0·2)}{(0·4)(-0·3)} = \frac{5}{6},$$

$$l_3(x) = \frac{(x-35·2)(x-35·6)}{(35·9-35·2)(35·6-35·2)}, \quad l_3(35·7) = \frac{(0·5)(0·1)}{(0·7)(0·3)} = \frac{5}{21}.$$

Since the entries differ only in the last two digits, we need only interpolate for these. The calculation is therefore

$$-7\times\tfrac{1}{14}+50\times\tfrac{5}{6}+82\times\tfrac{5}{21} = -0\cdot5+41\cdot7+19\cdot5 = 60\cdot7.$$

Hence log sin $35\cdot7° = \bar{1}\cdot7600+0\cdot0061 = \bar{1}\cdot7661.$
(The entry in four figure tables for lg sin $35\cdot7°$ is $\bar{1}\cdot7661$.)

Example 2. We use Lagrangian interpolation to evaluate tan $20\cdot1°$ and tan $20\cdot43°$ from the given table:

$x°$	20	20·2	20·4	20·6
tan $x°$	0·3640	0·3679	0·3719	0·3759

Since the table is given for equally spaced intervals of $0\cdot2°$ we can use the Lagrange polynomials in terms of p, where $x = 20+0\cdot2p$. The entries in the table correspond to $p = 0, 1, 2, 3$. The polynomials are

$$l_1 = \frac{(p-1)(p-2)(p-3)}{(-1)(-2)(-3)}, \qquad l_2 = \frac{p(p-2)(p-3)}{1\times(-1)(-2)},$$

$$l_3 = \frac{p(p-1)(p-3)}{2\times1\times(-1)}, \qquad l_4 = \frac{p(p-1)(p-2)}{3\times2\times1}.$$

To obtain the required values we need $p = 0\cdot5$ for the first. Hence

$$p = 0\cdot5, \quad l_1 = 0\cdot3125, \quad l_2 = 0\cdot9375, \quad l_3 = -0\cdot3125, \quad l_4 = 0\cdot0625.$$

We interpolate only the last two digits. The value then is

$$\tan 20\cdot1° = 0\cdot3600+40\times0\cdot3125+79\times0\cdot9375$$
$$+119\times(-0\cdot3125)+159\times(0\cdot0625)$$
$$= 0\cdot3659.$$

(This is also the value given in four figure tables.)

$$\text{For } p = 2\cdot15, \quad x = 20\cdot43, \quad \text{and}$$
$$l_1 = 0\cdot0911, \quad l_2 = -0\cdot1371, \quad l_3 = 1\cdot0508, \quad l_4 = 0\cdot0618.$$

This gives

$$\tan 20\cdot43° = 0\cdot3600+40\times0\cdot0911+79\times(-0\cdot1371)$$
$$+119\times1\cdot0508+159\times0\cdot0618$$
$$= 0\cdot3727.$$

(The value from four figure tables in $0\cdot3726$.)

It is clear from the last example that the values of l_1, l_2, l_3, l_4 do not depend upon the interval nor upon the tabulated function. Hence, when equal intervals of x are used the values of l_r can be determined as functions of p and depend only upon how many ordinates of the function are given. In the second example we used Lagrange functions for four point interpolation; they are:

$$l_1(p) = \tfrac{1}{6}(-p^3+6p^2+p-6), \quad l_2(p) = \tfrac{1}{2}(p^3-5p^2+6p),$$
$$l_3(p) = \tfrac{1}{2}(-p^3+4p^2-3p), \quad l_4(p) = \tfrac{1}{6}(p^3-3p^2+2p).$$

Many of these functions are tabulated for an odd number of points (3, 5 or 7) with the central value corresponding to $p = 0$, the tabulated entries corresponding to $p = -1\,(0\cdot1)\,1$ for three-point polynomials, and $p = -2\,(0\cdot1)\,2$ for five-point polynomials, etc.

The advantage of Lagrangian interpolation, with equal intervals, is that it does not require the evaluation of the differences, and the resulting calculations are relatively simple to perform. The method has the disadvantage that the degree of the polynomial to be used has to be decided at the start—it is one less than the number of ordinates used. With the use of differences each additional order of difference raises the degree of the polynomial by one and the process can be stopped at the desired accuracy and need not be estimated beforehand. The other advantage of Lagrangian interpolation is that it can be used with unequal intervals, though at the cost of considerable labour, in many cases.

Exercises 5 : 12

1. Use the Lagrange approximation formula to find the polynomial approximation of order 3 fitting the following data:

x	-1	0	2	3
$f(x)$	-2	-1	$+1$	$+4$

2. $x_1, \ldots, x_n$ are distinct numbers and, for $1 \leqslant r \leqslant n$, $p_r(x)$ is written for

$$(x-x_1) \ \cdots \ (x-x_{r-1})\,(x-x_{r+1}) \ \cdots \ (x-x_n).$$

By considering

$$\sum_{r=1}^{n} \alpha_r p_r(x),$$

for suitably chosen α_r, show that it is possible to find a polynomial of degree not exceeding $n-1$ which takes given values at $x_1, \ldots, x_n$.

Similarly, by considering

$$\sum_{r=1}^{n} (\beta_r x+\gamma_r)\,\{p_r(x)\}^2,$$

show that it is possible to find a polynomial of degree not exceeding $2n-1$

which takes given values at $x_1, \ldots, x_n$ and whose first derivative also takes given values at these points.

3. Obtain the coefficients A_r in Lagrange's four-point interpolation formula

$$p(a+\theta h) = A_{-1}p(a-h)+A_0 p(a)+A_1 p(a+h)+A_2 p(a+2h)$$

for a cubic polynomial, and show that, if fourth differences are negligible,

$$f(a+\tfrac{1}{2}h) = \tfrac{1}{16}\{-f(a-h)+9f(a)+9f(a+h)-f(a+2h)\}.$$

Evaluate $f(x)$ for $x = 3, 5, 7$ from the following table, and check your results by differencing at unit intervals.

x	0	2	4	6	8	10
$f(x)$	0·000	−0·450	−0·698	−0·791	−0·768	−0·664

4. Locate and correct the error in the tabulated values of y below. Then find y as a polynomial function of x.

x	−0·2	−0·1	0	0·1	0·2	0·3	0·4	0·5	0·6
y	−2·968	−3·041	−3·000	−2·839	−2·525	−2·133	−1·576	−0·875	−0·024

5 : 13 Numerical differentiation

The principle of interpolation is the use of a polynomial instead of the actual function tabulated, and in § 6 : 9 we obtain formulae for numerical integration by integrating the polynomial to give an estimate of a definite integral. Similarly, it seems reasonable to differentiate the polynomial to estimate the derivative of the function. In general, formulae for differentiation do not prove so accurate as those for integration. The reason for this is illustrated in Fig. 5.21. The approximating polynomial takes the same values as the function at the points $x = x_p = x_0+ph, p = \ldots, 0, 1, 2, \ldots$.

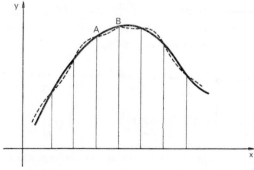

Fig. 5.21. Approximation to a function by means of a polynomial.

At other points the polynomial differs from the actual function; the figure shows that, although the differences may be small for the values of y between the tabulated points, and also for the integral (area under the curve), the gradients of the function and the polynomial may differ more markedly. The two curves will seldom have identical tangents. However, bearing this in mind, we obtain here one or two of the simpler formulae for derivatives. (This difference between differentiation and integration can be best explained by saying that differentiation is a sharpening process whereas integration is a smoothing process.)

Since $\qquad x_p = x_0 + ph, \quad$ when $\quad y_p = f(x_p),$

$$\frac{\mathrm{d}f}{\mathrm{d}x} = \frac{\mathrm{d}f}{\mathrm{d}p}\frac{\mathrm{d}p}{\mathrm{d}x}, \qquad y'_p = \frac{1}{h}\frac{\mathrm{d}f_p}{\mathrm{d}p}, \qquad (5.52)$$

where f_p stands for $f(x_0 + ph)$. In § 5 : 11 we obtained three formulae for f_p in terms of forward, backward and central differences. Any of these can be used in eqn. (5.52) to obtain a formula for y'_p. For example, using Newton's forward difference formula [eqn. 5.43)],

$$y'_p = \frac{1}{h}\left\{\Delta + \left(p - \frac{1}{2}\right)\Delta^2 + (3p^2 - 6p + 2)\frac{\Delta^3}{6} + \ldots\right\}f_0.$$

If we use linear interpolation, $\Delta^2 f_0 = 0$ and

$$y'_p = \frac{h}{1}\Delta f_0 = \frac{y_1 - y_0}{h}.$$

This gives the gradient of the chord joining the first two ordinates as the approximate gradient of the curve in this region. Using interpolation polynomials of higher degree gives a closer approximation. With a second degree polynomial

$$y'_p = \frac{1}{h}\left\{\Delta + \left(p - \frac{1}{2}\right)\Delta^2\right\}f_0 = \frac{y_1 - y_0}{h} + \left(p - \frac{1}{2}\right)\frac{y_2 - 2y_1 + y_0}{h}$$

$$= \frac{1}{h}\left\{\left(p - \frac{3}{2}\right)y_0 + 2(1 - p)y_1 + \left(p - \frac{1}{2}\right)y_2\right\},$$

etc. Similar formulae can be obtained from backward or central difference interpolation polynomials.

Example. From the central difference (Stirling's) formula we obtain

$$y_p' = \frac{1}{h}\left\{\frac{1}{2}\left(\delta_{-\frac{1}{2}}+\delta_{\frac{1}{2}}\right)+p\delta_0^2+\frac{3p^2-1}{12}\left(\delta_{-\frac{1}{2}}^3+\delta_{\frac{1}{2}}^3\right)+ \cdots\right\}.$$

The method may also be generalised to give formulae for second, or higher order, derivatives, but the calculations require the coefficients in the interpolation formulae to be multiplied out explicitly in terms of p before they can be differentiated. Since these coefficients are usually in a factorised form, this is often laborious, especially for higher orders.

It is also clear from Fig. 5.21 that the estimate of the derivative is not equally accurate at all points of the range. For example, the linear approximation is more likely to be accurate about halfway between two ordinates than at the ends (because the chord is more likely to be parallel to the tangent at a point between the ordinates than at the ordinates). This means that for some formulae values of p near $\frac{1}{2}$ are more accurate than values near $p = 0$. Also for ease of computation a series which is rapidly convergent is more useful, and certain formulae converge more rapidly for, say, $p = \frac{1}{2}$, than for $p = 0$.

Example. There is a formula, *Bessel's formula*, for interpolation

$$f_p = f_0+p\delta_{\frac{1}{2}}+\tfrac{1}{4}p(p-1)\left(\delta_0^2+\delta_1^2\right)+\tfrac{1}{12}p(p-1)(2p-1)\delta_{\frac{1}{2}}^3$$
$$+\tfrac{1}{48}(p+1)p(p-1)(p-2)\left(\delta_0^4+\delta_1^4\right)+ \cdots$$

in which the coefficients of differences of even order are symmetrical about the value $p = \frac{1}{2}$. Hence, as above, we obtain the formula

$$y_{\frac{1}{2}}' = \delta_{\frac{1}{2}}-\tfrac{1}{2}\delta_{\frac{1}{2}}^3+\left(\tfrac{3}{640}\delta_{\frac{1}{2}}^5- \cdots\right). \tag{5.53}$$

On the other hand, Stirling's formula is more convenient for $p = 0$, in which case

$$y_0' = \tfrac{1}{2}\left(\delta_{-\frac{1}{2}}+\delta_{\frac{1}{2}}\right)-\tfrac{1}{12}\left(\delta_{-\frac{1}{2}}^3+\delta_{\frac{1}{2}}^3\right)+\tfrac{1}{60}\left(\delta_{-\frac{1}{2}}^5+\delta_{\frac{1}{2}}^5\right)- \cdots. \tag{5.54}$$

Nevertheless, eqn. (5.53) converges more rapidly than eqn. (5.54).

Just as with interpolation formulae those involving forward differences are of more use at the top of a table, those with central differences at the centre, and those with backward differences at the bottom of a table.

As we have obtained them the above formulae for y_p' are given in terms of differences. However, these can be converted to give y_p' in terms of the tabulated values y_r, by the use of the relations

$$\Delta y_0 = \delta y_{\frac{1}{2}} = \nabla y_1 = f_1 - f_0,$$

$$\Delta^2 y_0 = \delta^2 y_1 = \nabla^2 y_2 = f_2 - 2f_1 + f_0, \quad \text{etc.}$$

When expressed in this form the formulae are used in the numerical solution of differential equations, and they have the advantage of avoiding the determination of the difference columns from a table [see Vol. 2, 2nd edn., Chaps. I and II].

Exercises 5 : 13

1. Define the operators E, D, Δ and show that $E = e^{h D} = 1 + \Delta$, where h is the interval of tabulation.

Hence obtain the formulae

$$hf_0' = (\Delta - \tfrac{1}{2}\Delta^2 + \tfrac{1}{3}\Delta^3 - \tfrac{1}{4}\Delta^4 + \ldots)f_0$$
$$= \tfrac{1}{2}(f_1 - f_{-1}) - \tfrac{1}{6}\Delta^3 f_{-1} + \ldots$$

Derive a formula for f_0'' and hence calculate $f'(2)$ and $f''(2)$ for the third-degree polynomial given by:

x	0	1	2	3	4
f	2	2	8	26	62

2. A cubic curve passes through the points (x_0, y_0), (x_1, y_1), (x_2, y_2) and (x_3, y_3). Show that the values of dy/dx and d^2y/dx^2 at the point (x_1, y_1) are given by

$$-\frac{1}{6h}(2y_0 + 3y_1 - 6y_2 + y_3) \quad \text{and} \quad \frac{1}{h^2}(y_0 - 2y_1 + y_2)$$

respectively, where $x_p = x_0 + ph$.

3. The following table gives the values of $y = \cosh x$ for values of x between $1\cdot0$ and $1\cdot7$:

x	1·0	1·1	1·2	1·3	1·4	1·5	1·6	1·7
y	1·54308	1·66852	1·81066	1·97091	2·15090	2·35241	2·57746	2·82832

Calculate the values of $\cosh 1\cdot06$ and $\cosh 1\cdot68$.

Calculate also the value of dy/dx when $x = 1\cdot2$.

4. The values of y corresponding to the values $x_0 - h$, x_0, $x_0 + h$ are y_{-1}, y_0, y_1 respectively. Show that the derivative has the approximate value y_0' at x_0, and that this value is exact whenever y is any polynomial of degree not exceeding two, where

$$y_0' = (-y_{-1} + y_1)/(2h).$$

5. If the operators E, δ, μ are defined by $Ef(x) = f(x+h)$; $\delta f(x) = f(x+\frac{1}{2}h)$ $-f(x-\frac{1}{2}h)$; $\mu f(x) = \frac{1}{2}[f(x+\frac{1}{2}h)+f(x-\frac{1}{2}h)]$ deduce that

$$\text{(i)} \quad \mu^2 = 1+\tfrac{1}{4}\delta^2, \qquad \text{(ii)} \quad E = 1+\mu\delta+\tfrac{1}{2}\delta^2.$$

By expanding $f_p = f(x+ph)$ in the form $E^p f_0$, and neglecting δ^4 and higher powers of δ, obtain the interpolation formula

$$f_p - f_0 = p\mu\,\delta f_0 + \frac{1}{2!}\,p^2\,\delta^2 f_0 + \frac{1}{3!}\,p(p^2-1)\mu\,\delta^3 f_0 + \;\cdots$$

and hence deduce that

$$hf_p' = \mu\delta f_0 + p\delta^2 f_0 + \tfrac{1}{6}(3p^2-1)\mu\delta^3 f_0 + \;\cdots.$$

If $y = f(x)$ is a cubic polynomial given by

x	1	1·2	1·4	1·6	1·8	2·0
y	0	−0·112	−0·016	0·336	0·992	2

find, correct to three places of decimals, the values of y and of dy/dx when $x = 1·45$.

6. Form a table of differences from the following values of $y = \log_{10} x$:

x	1·0	1·1	1·2	1·3	1·4	1·5
y	0·00000	·04139	·07918	·11394	·14613	·17609

Use the difference table to calculate dy/dx at $x = 1·0$, and compare the calculated value with that obtained by exact differentiation of the function.

Miscellaneous Exercises V

1. Prove that $\displaystyle\sum_{r=1}^{\infty} \frac{r+2}{r(r+1)3^r} = 1+\ln\frac{2}{3}$.

2. Show that $\displaystyle\lim_{x \to 0} \left(\frac{1+x}{1-x}\right)^{1/x} = e^2$.

3. Sketch the curve whose polar equation is $r^2 = a^2 \cos 2\theta$.

Show that, at the point P on the curve where $\theta = \pi/6$, the tangent to the curve is parallel to the initial line.

4. If $y = x^3 (\ln x)^n$ for $x > 0$, where n is a positive integer, find the number of changes of sign in dy/dx as x increases through positive values, considering separately the two cases (i) n odd, (ii) n even. Prove also that, if $n > 2$, d^2y/dx^2 is zero for three real values of x. Draw a *rough* sketch of the curve $y = x^3 (\ln x)^n$ in the two cases (i) n odd, (ii) n even.

5. Find the maximum and minimum values of the function $t^3 - 3m^2t + 2n$, where m and n are real constants. Hence prove that the equation $t^3 - 3m^2t + 2n = 0$ has three unequal real roots or only one real root according as m^6 is greater than or less than n^2.

Prove that the curve whose equation is

$$y(y^2-3) = x(x^2-12)$$

is such that there are two points on it at which the tangents are parallel to the x-axis, and six points at which the tangents are parallel to the y-axis.

6. If $f(x) = (2-x^2) \sin x - 2x \cos x$, show that
(i) the expansion of $f(x)$ in ascending powers of x is of the form

$$f(x) = kx^3 + \text{higher powers of } x,$$

where k is a constant, and find k;
(ii) the graph of $f(x)$ has a stationary point at $x = 0$ and another at $x = \frac{1}{2}\pi$, and determine in each case whether the point is a maximum or minimum point or a point of inflexion;
(iii) the equation $f(x) = 0$ has a root between $x = \frac{1}{2}\pi$ and $x = \pi$.

7. Find

(i) $\displaystyle\lim_{x \to \frac{\pi}{2}} \frac{\cos^2 x}{4x^2 - \pi^2}$,   (ii) $\displaystyle\lim_{x \to 1} \frac{\sin (\ln x)}{x^5 - 7x^3 + 6}$,   (iii) $\displaystyle\lim_{x \to 0} \frac{\tan x - x}{x - \sin x}$.

8. Write down the expansions of $(1+x)^{-3}$, $\ln(1+x)$ and $\sin x$ in ascending powers of x giving the first four terms in each series. State for what values of x the expressions are valid.

Find the values of p and q if the expansion of

$$f(x) = (1-px)^{-3} \ln(1+qx) - e^x \sin x$$

in ascending powers of x contains no terms in x and x^2.

With these values of p and q find the expansion of $f(x)$ as far as the term in x^4.

9. Express $[(1-t)^3 (1+t)]^{-1}$ in partial fractions. Hence by writing $t = x^2$, or otherwise, show that the coefficient of x^{4n} in the expansion of

$$[(1-x)(1-x^2)(1-x^4)]^{-1}$$

in ascending powers of x is $(n+1)^2$.

10. If $y = z \ln(x+z)$, where $z^2 = 1+x^2$, show that

$$(1+x^2)\left(\frac{\mathrm{d}y}{\mathrm{d}x} - 1\right) = xy,$$

and that

$$(1+x^2)y_{n+1} + (2n-1)xy_n + n(n-2)y_{n-1} = 0,$$

for $n > 2$, where $y_i \equiv \mathrm{d}^i y/\mathrm{d}x^i$.

Hence show that the Maclaurin expansion of y in ascending powers of x is

$$y = x + \tfrac{1}{3}x^3 - \tfrac{2}{15}x^5 + \tfrac{8}{105}x^7 \ldots$$

11. Sketch the curves $y = \sinh x$, $y = \operatorname{sech} x$ and show that they intersect at the point where $x = \frac{1}{2}\ln(2+\sqrt{5})$.

Obtain the expansion of $\operatorname{sech} x$ in ascending powers of x as far as the term in x^4.

12. Write down the expansions for $\ln[(1+x)/(1-x)]$ and $\tan^{-1} x$ in ascending powers of x, stating the values of x for which the expansions are valid.

If $0 < x < 1$ and $0 < y < 1$ and $\ln y + 2 \sum_{n=1}^{\infty} \dfrac{x^{2n-1}}{2n-1} = 0$, express y in terms of x and deduce that

$$\ln x + 2 \sum_{n=1}^{\infty} \frac{y^{2n-1}}{2n-1} = 0.$$

Prove also that

$$\sum_{n=1}^{\infty} (-1)^{n-1} \frac{x^{2n-1} + y^{2n-1}}{2n-1} = \frac{\pi}{4}.$$

13. A trapezium $ABCD$ is inscribed in a circle of radius r. The sides AB, CD are equal in length, and the side AD is a diameter of the circle. If each of the sides AB, CD subtends an angle θ at the centre of the circle, express the area S and the perimeter P of the trapezium in terms of θ.

Find the maximum value of the area and of the perimeter.

14. A solid consists of a right circular cylinder to which are fixed two right circular cones whose bases coincide with the circular ends of the cylinder. The semi-vertical angle of each cone is $\tan^{-1}\left(\frac{3}{4}\right)$. If y is the length of the cylinder and x its radius, show that the area of the surface of the solid is $\frac{2}{3}\pi x(3y + 5x)$. If the volume of the solid is fixed, find the ratio of y to x when the surface is a minimum.

15. In the manufacture of a certain article the number produced in one week is proportional to $x/(a+x)$, where a is constant and x is the amount paid in wages per article per week. The selling price of the article (less costs other than wages) is b, in the same units as x and a. Find the value of x for which the net profit on one week's production is a maximum. Show that, if b is small compared with a, this value of x is approximately $\frac{1}{2}b$.

16. A right circular cone is inscribed in a sphere of given radius. Prove that, if the volume of the cone is a maximum, the ratio of this maximum volume to that of the sphere is $\frac{8}{27}$.

17. The points P and Q are on a circle of variable radius, and are such that the minor arc PQ is of given length. Prove that the area of the segment bounded by the arc and the chord PQ is greatest when the arc PQ is a semicircle.

18. If x be the chord of a circular arc of length l and radius r, and y be the chord of half the same arc, prove that

$$x = 2r \sin \frac{l}{2r}, \qquad y = 2r \sin \frac{l}{4r}.$$

Prove that if fifth and higher powers of l/r are neglected, the length of the circular arc is given by $3l = 8y - x$.

19. Show that the expansion of $\lg \sec x$ in ascending powers of x is $(x^2/2 + x^4/12 + \ldots)\lg e$.

Hence evaluate approximately $\int_0^{\pi/4} \lg \sec x \, dx$.

20. Show graphically that the equation $\tan x = 1/x$ has an infinite number of real roots which, except for the two numerically smallest, are near to $n\pi$, where n is any integer.   (*Continued overleaf*)

Show that the root near $n\pi$ is $n\pi + \theta$ where θ is given by $\tan\theta = 1/(n\pi + \theta)$ and, by expanding both sides of this equation in powers of θ, or otherwise, show that a closer approximation to the root near $n\pi$ is

$$n\pi + \frac{1}{n\pi} - \frac{4}{3n^3\pi^3}.$$

21. Obtain, by Taylor expansion or otherwise, the first five terms of the series expansion of the solution of

$$(1+x)\frac{dy}{dx} = 1 + xy + y^2, \quad \text{with} \quad y = 0 \quad \text{when} \quad x = 0.$$

Hence calculate the values of y for which x equals $0\cdot 1$ to four significant figures.

22. $OABC$ is a square of side $4a$, and E is the mid-point of OA. A semicircle which lies inside the square is drawn on OE as diameter, and from a point P on EA, between E and A, a tangent is drawn to the semicircle to meet OC at a point Q lying between O and C.

If $EP = x$, show that the area of the triangle OPQ is $\dfrac{a}{2}\sqrt{\left\{\dfrac{(2a+x)^3}{x}\right\}}$, and that this is a minimum when P is at the mid-point of EA.

Find also the greatest value of the area of the triangle OPQ.

23. Show that the series $\displaystyle\sum_{n=1}^{\infty} \frac{n!}{n^n} x^n$ converges for $|x| < e$ and diverges for $|x| > e$.

24. (i) Decide whether or not each of the following series converges, and give reasons for your conclusions:

(a) $\displaystyle\sum_{n=2}^{\infty} \frac{\sqrt{n}}{n^2 - \sqrt{n}}$,   (b) $\displaystyle\sum_{n=1}^{\infty} \frac{n(n+1)}{(n+2)(n+3)}$,

(c) $\dfrac{1}{2} + \dfrac{1}{2+4} + \dfrac{1}{2+4+6} + \cdots$.

(ii) Find the real values of x for which the power series

$$\frac{x^2}{1.2} + \frac{x^3}{2.3} + \frac{x^4}{3.4} + \frac{x^5}{4.5} + \cdots$$

converges. Also find the sum function of this series for those real values of x for which the series converges.

25. Discuss the convergence and absolute convergence of the following series:

(i) $\displaystyle\sum \frac{\cos(n\pi/4)}{n(n+1)}$,   (ii) $\displaystyle\sum_{n=1}^{\infty} ne^{-n}$,

(iii) $\displaystyle\sum \frac{(-1)^n}{\sqrt[n]{n}}$,   (iv) $\displaystyle\sum_{n=1}^{\infty} \frac{1}{n^2} \sin\frac{n\pi}{3}$,

(v) $\displaystyle\sum (-1)^n \sin\frac{\pi}{n}$,   (vi) $\displaystyle\sum_{n=1}^{\infty} \frac{1}{n} \cos\frac{\pi}{n}$.

26. Find the maxima and minima of the function

$$f(x) = (x^2+2x-1)e^{-2x},$$

and show that the curve $y = f(x)$ has points of inflexion.
Sketch the curve.
Find

$$\lim_{x \to \infty} \int_1^x (t^2+2t-1)e^{-2t}\, dt.$$

27. The *sine integral* $Si(x)$ is defined by

$$Si(x) = \int_0^x \frac{\sin t}{t}\, dt.$$

Obtain a power series expansion for $Si(x)$ and determine its range of convergence.

28. The function $E(x)$ is defined by

$$E(x) = \int_0^x \frac{e^t-1}{t}\, dt, \qquad (x > 0).$$

Show that its series expansion is given by

$$E(x) = x+\frac{1}{2}\frac{x^2}{2!}+\frac{1}{3}\frac{x^3}{3!}+ \cdots +\frac{1}{n}\frac{x^n}{n!}+\cdots.$$

If the series is terminated at the term in x^n, show that the truncation error is less than the corresponding truncation error of the series for e^x, divided by $n+1$.

If $E(1)$ is to be computed from the series, show that five terms will suffice to give an answer correct to three decimal places, and evaluate $E(1)$.

29. Sketch in the same diagram the curves $y = x^2$ and $y = \sin x$. Hence or otherwise show that the inequality $x^2 \leqslant \sin x$ is only true in a certain range $0 \leqslant x \leqslant k$, and find the value of this number k correct to two places of decimals.

30. Show that, for large n and r,

$$\left(1-\frac{1}{n}\right)^{rn} \quad \text{and} \quad \left(1-\frac{r}{n}\right)^n$$

are both approximately equal to e^{-r}. Using this result together with the approximation $n! \approx \sqrt{(2\pi)} \cdot n^n e^{-n}$ show that

$$\frac{n!}{(n-r)!\, r!} \approx \frac{k^r}{\sqrt{(2\pi)}} \exp(r-r^2/n),$$

where both n and r are large, and $n/r = k$ is a finite constant.

31. Show that

$$\frac{d}{dx}(\sin^{-1} x) = 1/\sqrt{(1-x^2)}$$

and obtain the expansion

$$\sin^{-1} x = x + \tfrac{1}{6}x^3 + \tfrac{3}{40}x^5 + \dots.$$

State both the general term and the range of validity of this expansion.

32. Show that the function $e^{2\cos x}(1+\sin^2 x)$ oscillates with the period 2π between the extreme values e^2 and e^{-2}.

33. The functions $F(x)$ and $f(x)$ are related by the identity $F(x) = e^{-ax} f(x)$ where a is a constant. Show that

$$F'(x) = e^{-ax} \{f'(x) - a f(x)\}.$$

Prove that, if $f(x)f''(x) - \{f'(x)\}^2 > 0$ then $F''(x)$ has the same sign as $f''(x)$.

34. Sketch the graphs of e^{kx^2} in the cases $k > 0$, $k = 0$, $k < 0$; and hence show that the equation

$$e^{kx^2} = 2\cos x$$

has a finite even number of roots when $k > 0$ and an infinite number of roots otherwise.

Show that, if n is a positive integer, then there is just one positive value of k for which the equation has $4n$ solutions, but that there are infinitely many positive values of k for which the equation has $4n+2$ solutions.

35. Obtain a relation between I_{n-1} and I_{n+1} ($n > 0$), where

$$I_n = \int_0^x \frac{t^n}{1+t^2}\, dt.$$

Prove that, for any fixed x in the range $-1 \leqslant x \leqslant 1$, $I_n \to 0$ as $n \to \infty$. Deduce an expansion of (i) $\tan^{-1} x$, (ii) $\ln(1+x^2)$, in ascending powers of x, valid for $-1 \leqslant x \leqslant 1$.

36. (i) Find the function $f(x_0)$ required to make the following iterative formula for $a^{\frac{1}{2}}$ a second-order one:

$$x_1 = x_0 + f(x_0)(x_0^2 - a);$$

show that the formula then reduces to the Newton–Raphson formula.

(ii) Find to three significant figures the positive root of the equation

$$\tfrac{1}{2}x = x^5 - 1.$$

37. Show that if the iterative process

$$x_{r+1} = \frac{1}{n}\{(n-1)x_r + Nx_r^{1-n}\}$$

converges it does so to the nth root of N.

If $(a+\varepsilon)$ is the exact value of $N^{1/n}$, with ε small, expand $b = n^{-1}[(n-1)a + Na^{1-n}]$ in powers of ε, as far as the term in ε^2, and deduce that b is an over-estimate of $N^{1/n}$ if $n > 1$; also, that b has roughly twice as many significant figures correct as a.

Taking a two decimal value of $\pi^{\frac{2}{3}}$ from tables, improve it by use of the above *algorithm* so as to obtain a value correct to five figures.

38. Prove that $y = kex$ is the only tangent to the curve $y = e^{kx}$ which passes through the origin and deduce, or prove otherwise, that the equation

$$e^{kx} = x$$

has no real root when $k > e^{-1}$.

Show, further, that the equation cannot have more than two real roots whatever the (real) value of k and that, when k is small, one root is approximately equal to

$$1 + k + \tfrac{3}{2}k^2 .$$

39. The following iterative procedures can be applied to determine the solution $x = X$ of the equation $x = g(x)$:

(i) $a_{n+1} = g(a_n)$,   (ii) $b_{n+1} = G(b_n)$,   (iii) $c_{n+1} = G(a_n)$,

where a_n are the numbers computed in procedure (i), and where

$$G(x) = \{g(x)/x\}^p \, g(x)$$

with p a parameter.

Indicate geometrically how the sequence a_n ($n = 0, 1, 2 \ldots$) may lead to the value X. Also deduce an analytical result to show that the sequence b_n ($n = 0, 1, 2 \ldots$) will lead to the value X if $g'(X) \neq 1$ and p is suitably chosen.

Show how the value of X can be estimated using (iii), given a_0, a_1 and a_2, and obtain such an estimate if

$$a_0 = 1 \cdot 00, \qquad a_1 = 1 \cdot 22, \qquad a_2 = 1 \cdot 33.$$

40. The equation $x = f(x)$ is to be solved by the iteration process $x_{i+1} = f(x_i)$ where x_i is the ith iterate. If $x_i = X + \xi_i$ where $x = X$ is the exact solution and ξ_i is the error of the ith iterate, show that the iteration converges only if $|f'(X)| < 1$. Show also that if $f'(X) = 0$ the iteration is second order (i.e. the error in x_{i+1} is the square of that in x_i). Hence show that the Newton–Raphson iteration

$$x_{i+1} = x_i - \frac{\phi(x_i)}{\phi'(x_i)}$$

for the solution of $\phi(x) = 0$ is second order.

The following were three successive iterates in an iterative process where the true solution is X.

$$x_0 = 2 \cdot 3; \quad x_1 = 2 \cdot 3003; \quad x_2 = 2 \cdot 3002384329.$$

Write down the value of X to as many figures as this information will justify.

41. State Taylor's expansion of a function $f(x)$ in the neighbourhood of $x = a$.

If $f(x) = 0$ at $x = x_0$ near a, derive the approximate formula $x_0 = a - f(a)/f'(a)$, and show that a better approximation is

$$x_0 = a - f/f' - f^2 f''/2f'^3 .$$

Evaluate the root of $x^3 + 3x^2 + 2x - 5 = 0$ near $x = 1$, working to three decimal places.

42. Prove that, if λ is small, the equation $x = 1 + \lambda e^x$ has two solutions, and that one of these is approximately $1 + e\lambda + p\lambda^2 + q\lambda^3$. Find the coefficients p and q.

43. Show that in the Bessel formula

$$y_p = y_0 + p\,\delta y_{\frac{1}{2}} + \tfrac{1}{4}p(p-1)\,(\delta^2 y_0 + \delta^2 y_1) + \tfrac{1}{6}p(p-1)\left(p-\tfrac{1}{2}\right)\delta^3 y_{\frac{1}{2}}$$

$$+ \tfrac{1}{48}(p+1)\,p(p-1)\,(p-2)\,(\delta^4 y_0 + \delta^4 y_1) + \ldots,$$

where $y_r = y(x_r) = y\{x_0 + r(x_1 - x_0)\}$, the term in the fourth difference may be neglected if $|\delta^4| < 20$ units.

The following is an extract from a difference table for the function

$$f(x) = \frac{2}{\sqrt{\pi}} \int\limits_0^x e^{-t^2}\,dt:$$

x	$f(x)$	δ	δ^2	δ^3	δ^4
0·1	0·11246		−222		13
		11024		−209	
0·2	0·22270		−431		23

Evaluate $f(0\cdot12)$.

44. If $S_n(x) = a_0 + a_1 x + a_2 x^2 + \ldots + a_n x^n$ show that

$$S_n(x) = \frac{1 - (xE)^{n+1}}{1 - xE}\,a_0, \quad \text{where} \quad Ea_r = a_{r+1}.$$

If

$$S(x) = \lim_{n \to \infty} S_n(x)$$

exists show that

$$S(x) = \left(\frac{1}{1-x} + \frac{1}{(1-x)^2}\,x\Delta + \frac{1}{(1-x)^3}\,x^2\Delta^2 + \ldots\right)a_0,$$

where $E \equiv 1 + \Delta$ and $|x| < 1$.

Estimate the sum of the series

$$S(x) = 10030 + 10020x + 10010x^2 + \ldots \quad \text{for} \quad x = -0\cdot1.$$

45. In the table below, y is a polynomial function of x. Form the difference table and from it find the polynomial. Calculate the value of dy/dx at $x = 0\cdot5$ by differentiating the polynomial.

Confirm the result by using a finite difference formula for dy/dx.

x	0	0·1	0·2	0·3	0·4	0·5	0·6	0·7
y	0	−·099	−·193	−·273	−·336	−·375	−·384	−·357

46. Starting with Stirling's formula deduce that

$$hf_0' = \mu \, \delta f_0 - \tfrac{1}{6}\mu \, \delta^3 f_0 + \tfrac{1}{30}\mu \, \delta^5 f_0 - \cdots$$
$$h^2 f_0'' = \delta^2 f_0 - \tfrac{1}{12} \delta^4 f_0 + \tfrac{1}{90} \delta^6 f_0 - \cdots,$$

where

$$hf_p' = h \frac{d}{dx} f(x_0 + ph) = \frac{d}{dp} f_p .$$

The following table gives the coordinates (x, y) of points on a certain polynomial curve:

x	0	0·2	0·4	0·6	0·8	1·0	1·2
y	0·710	1·175	1·811	2·666	3·801	5·292	7·232

Calculate the radius of curvature at the point $x = 0.6$.

CHAPTER VI

APPLICATIONS OF INTEGRATION

6:1 Introduction—the area bounded by a plane curve

The use of definite integrals in problems of physics, chemistry and applied mathematics generally is based on the concept of a definite integral as the limit of a sum (see § 3:2), and in this chapter we show how this is used in various applications of integration.

First, we re-emphasise the features of § 3:2 which are basic to an understanding of the process. The illustration used there was the evaluation of the area under a curve. The area was divided into narrow strips of width δx and the area of each strip was obtained correct to the first order in δx; then the addition of the areas of these narrow strips led to the integral as the limit of the sum when $\delta x \to 0$. Leaving aside any interpretation in terms of areas, we recognise three essential features of this process:

(i) The integral is the sum of a large number of small quantities.

(ii) Each of these quantities is associated with a small (infinitesimal) interval of some variable.

(iii) The value of each of these quantities must be known correct to the first order in terms of these small intervals.

This last condition means that we are dealing with *differentials* which are the dominant terms in all relations of this nature between small increments.

As a first example of the use of a definite integral we derive a formula for the area of a sector bounded by a curve. Using eqn. (4.26) then the area of the triangle OPQ of Fig. 6.1 reckoned positive in the anticlockwise sense, is $\frac{1}{2}(x_1 y_2 - x_2 y_1)$. If we write the coordinates of P as (x, y) and those of Q as $(x + \delta x, y + \delta y)$, then the area of

$$\Delta OPQ = \tfrac{1}{2}x(y + \delta y) - \tfrac{1}{2}(x + \delta x)y = \tfrac{1}{2}(x\,\delta y - y\,\delta x).$$

Suppose now that $APQB$ is an arc of a curve given by the parametric equations

$$x = x(t) \quad y = y(t),$$

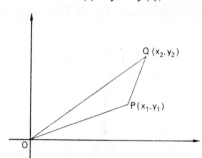

Fig. 6.1.

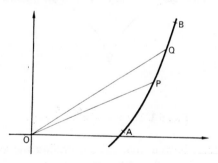

Fig. 6.2.

and that P, Q correspond to the values t, $t + \delta t$ respectively, and that the end points A, B (Fig. 6.2) correspond to t_1, t_2, $(t_2 > t_1)$ respectively. (The positive sense of rotation about O corresponds to increasing t.) The area δS of the elementary sector OPQ differs from the triangle OPQ by an amount less than $\delta x\,\delta y$.

$$\therefore\quad \delta S = \tfrac{1}{2}(x\,\delta y - y\,\delta x) + O\{(\delta t)^2\},$$

$$dS = \frac{1}{2}\left(x\frac{dy}{dt} - \frac{dx}{dt}\right)dt.$$

The area of the finite sector OAB is the sum of the elementary sectors and the three conditions above are satisfied so that the integral

$$S = \frac{1}{2} \int_{t_1}^{t_2} \left(x \frac{dy}{dt} - y \frac{dx}{dt} \right) dt \qquad (6.1)$$

is the area of the sector OAB. This is frequently written

$$S = \tfrac{1}{2} \int_{A}^{B} (x \, dy - y \, dx).$$

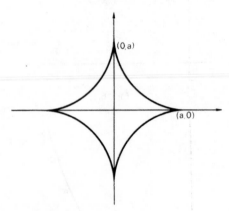

FIG. 6.3. The astroid $x^{\frac{2}{3}} + y^{\frac{2}{3}} = a^{\frac{2}{3}}$.

The form (6.1) is well adapted for finding the areas enclosed by curves which form closed loops.

Example 1. Calculate the area enclosed by the ellipse $x = a \cos t$, $y = b \sin t$, $0 \leqslant t \leqslant 2\pi$.

$$\text{Area} = \tfrac{1}{2} \int_{0}^{2\pi} (ab \cos^2 t + ab \sin^2 t) \, dt = \tfrac{1}{2} \int_{0}^{2\pi} ab \, dt = \pi ab.$$

Example 2. Find the area enclosed by the *astroid* $x = a \cos^3 t$, $y = a \sin^3 t$.

The curve is as shown in Fig. 6.3. The required area A is four times the area in the first quadrant,

i.e.
$$2A = 4 \int_0^{\pi/2} (3a^2 \cos^4 t \sin^2 t + 3a^2 \cos^2 t \sin^4 t) \, dt$$

$$= 12a^2 \int_0^{\pi/2} \cos^2 t \sin^2 t \, dt = \frac{3\pi a^2}{4},$$

by the extension of Wallis's formula.

---

6 : 2 Volumes and surfaces of revolution

If a plane curve $y = f(x)$ is revolved about one of the coordinate axes through α radians ($\alpha = 2\pi$ if the revolution is complete), the arc of the curve generates a portion of a surface of revolution.

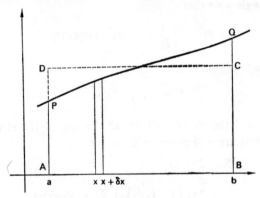

Fig. 6.4.

The area of this portion can be expressed as a definite integral. Similarly, if the plane area enclosed by a loop of a curve, or between the curve, two ordinates and an axis, is revolved about the axis this area sweeps out a volume which is a sector of a solid of revolution.

We consider the case of that portion of the curve $y = f(x)$ lying between $x = a$ and $x = b$ (assumed to be all above the x-axis) revolved through 4 right angles about the x-axis, cf. Fig. 6.4. We regard the volume as made up of a number of discs, a typical disc being generated by the revolution of a strip of height $y = f(x)$ and width δx. The volume of this disc is

$$\delta V = \pi y^2 \, \delta x + O\{(\delta x)^2\}.$$

In fact, for Fig. 6.4, $\pi y^2\,\delta x < \delta V < \pi(y+\delta y)^2\,\delta x$, so that $\pi y^2\,\delta x$ differs from the actual volume by an amount $O\{(\delta x)^2\}$. This is written in terms of differentials

$$dV = \pi y^2\,dx.$$

The three conditions in § 6 : 1 are satisfied, so that the complete volume of revolution is

$$V = \pi \int_a^b y^2\,dx. \tag{6.2}$$

If the revolution of the curve takes place through an angle α instead of four right angles, each of the elementary discs becomes a sector of angle α so that

$$\delta V = \left(\frac{\alpha}{2\pi}\right)\pi y^2\,\delta x + O\{(\delta x)^2\}$$

and the final volume is

$$V = \tfrac{1}{2}\alpha \int_a^b y^2\,dx. \tag{6.3}$$

If we regard the element of arc at the top of the strip as of length δs, this arc will generate a surface area

$$\delta S \approx 2\pi y\,\delta s$$

$$= 2\pi y\left[1+\left(\frac{dy}{dx}\right)^2\right]^{\frac{1}{2}}\delta x + O\{(\delta x)^2\},$$

where we have used the expression for δs from § 4 : 4. This leads to the integral

$$S = 2\pi \int_a^b y\left[1+\left(\frac{dy}{dx}\right)^2\right]^{\frac{1}{2}}dx, \tag{6.4}$$

for S the total surface area generated.

If the revolution is through an angle α instead of four right angles, δs generates the fraction $\alpha/2\pi$ of the curved surface of the frustum of a cone. The final formula in this case is

$$S = \alpha \int_a^b y\left[1+\left(\frac{dy}{dx}\right)^2\right]^{\frac{1}{2}}dx. \tag{6.5}$$

These results may also be written

$$S = 2\pi \int_{s_1}^{s_2} y \, ds \quad \text{or} \quad \alpha \int_{s_1}^{s_2} y \, ds, \qquad (6.6)$$

where the variable of integration is now the arc length s instead of the distance x along the x-axis. (s_1 and s_2 are the arc lengths corresponding to $x = a$ and $x = b$.) If y can conveniently be expressed in terms of arc length this may be a more useful formula than the first.

Example 1. Sketch the curve $y^2 = x^2(a-x)/(a+x)$, $a > 0$, and show that the tangents to the curve at the origin are perpendicular. Show also that the area enclosed by the loop of the curve is $(4-\pi)a^2/2$.

Show that the volume generated when the area enclosed by the loop is rotated through π about the x-axis is

$$\frac{\pi a^3(6 \ln 2 - 4)}{3}.$$

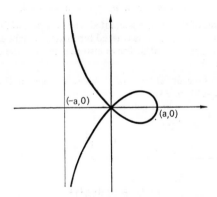

FIG. 6.5. The curve $y^2 = x^2(a-x)/(a+x)$.

The tangents to the curve at the origin have equation $y^2 = x^2$, i.e., the tangents are the perpendicular lines $y = \pm x$. The curve is sketched in Fig. 6.5.

The area A enclosed by the loop is twice the area in the first quadrant

$$\therefore A = 2 \int_0^a x \sqrt{\left(\frac{a-x}{a+x}\right)} \, dx.$$

The substitution $x = a \cos 2\theta$ gives

$$
\begin{aligned}
A &= 8a^2 \int\limits_0^{\pi/4} \cos 2\theta \sin^2 \theta \; d\theta \\
&= 4a^2 \int\limits_0^{\pi/4} \cos 2\theta (1 - \cos 2\theta) \; d\theta \\
&= 2a^2 \int\limits_0^{\pi/2} (\cos \varphi - \cos^2 \varphi) \; d\varphi
\end{aligned}
$$

on using the substitution $\varphi = 2\theta$.

Therefore, using Wallis's formula, $A = (4 - \pi)a^2/2$.

The volume of revolution $V = \pi \int\limits_0^a y^2 \; dx$.

$$
\begin{aligned}
\therefore \quad V &= \pi \int\limits_0^a \frac{x^2(a-x)}{(a+x)} \; dx = \pi \int\limits_0^a \left\{ -x^2 + 2ax - 2a^2 + \frac{2a^3}{a+x} \right\} dx \\
&= \pi \left[-\frac{1}{3} x^3 + ax^2 - 2a^2 x + 2a^3 \ln (a+x) \right]_0^a = \frac{\pi a^3 (6 \ln 2 - 4)}{3}.
\end{aligned}
$$

Example 2. The parametric equations of a *cycloid* are

$$x = a\theta - a \sin \theta, \quad y = a - a \cos \theta.$$

Prove that the area of the surface generated when the part of the cycloid which lies between two adjacent cusps is rotated through four right angles about the line joining the cusps is $64\pi a^2/3$. Prove also that the volume enclosed by the surface is $5\pi^2 a^3$.

Adjacent cusps occur at $\theta = 0$, $\theta = 2\pi$, and lie on Ox. The curve is sketched in Fig. 4.30, p. 238.

Therefore the surface area generated

$$
\begin{aligned}
S &= 2\pi \int\limits_{\theta=0}^{\theta=2\pi} y \left\{ 1 + \left(\frac{dy}{dx} \right)^2 \right\}^{\frac{1}{2}} dx \\
&= 2\pi \int\limits_0^{2\pi} y \left\{ \left(\frac{dx}{d\theta} \right)^2 + \left(\frac{dy}{d\theta} \right)^2 \right\}^{\frac{1}{2}} d\theta \\
&= 2\pi a^2 \int\limits_0^{2\pi} (1 - \cos \theta) \{ (1 - \cos \theta)^2 + \sin^2 \theta \}^{\frac{1}{2}} d\theta \\
&= 2\pi a^2 \int\limits_0^{2\pi} (1 - \cos \theta) \{ 2(1 - \cos \theta) \}^{\frac{1}{2}} d\theta \\
&= 8\pi a^2 \int\limits_0^{2\pi} \sin^3 \left(\frac{\theta}{2} \right) d\theta = 16\pi a^2 \int\limits_0^{\pi} \sin^3 \varphi \; d\varphi,
\end{aligned}
$$

where $\qquad \theta = 2\varphi.$

$$\therefore S = 32\pi a^2 \int_0^{\pi/2} \sin^3 \varphi \, d\varphi$$

$$= \frac{64\pi a^2}{3} \quad \text{by Wallis's formula.}$$

The volume generated

$$V = \pi \int_{\theta=0}^{\theta=2\pi} y^2 \, dx = \pi \int_0^{2\pi} y^2 \frac{dx}{d\theta} \, d\theta$$

$$= \pi a^3 \int_0^{2\pi} (1-\cos \theta)^3 \, d\theta = 8\pi a^3 \int_0^{2\pi} \sin^6 \left(\frac{\theta}{2}\right) \, d\theta = 16\pi a^3 \int_0^{\pi} \sin^6 \varphi \, d\varphi$$

$$= 32\pi a^3 \int_0^{\pi/2} \sin^6 \varphi \, d\varphi = 32\pi a^3 \, \frac{5 \times 3 \times 1 \times \pi}{6 \times 4 \times 2 \times 2} = 5\pi^2 a^3.$$

Example 3. The area between the parabola $y^2 = 4ax$ and the line $x = 3a$ is rotated through 360° about the directrix of the parabola. Find the volume generated.

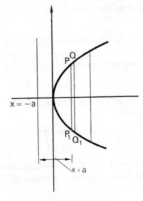

FIG. 6.6.

The volume δV generated by the strip PQQ_1P_1 (Fig. 6.6) forms a thin-walled cylinder of radius $a+x$, length $2y$, and thickness δx.

$$\therefore \quad \delta V = 4\pi(x+a)y\,\delta x + O\{(\delta x)^2\},$$

$$\therefore \quad V = 4\pi \int_0^{3a} (x+a)2a^{\frac{1}{2}}x^{\frac{1}{2}}\,dx = 8\pi a^{\frac{1}{2}}\left[\frac{2}{5}x^{\frac{5}{2}} + \frac{2}{3}ax^{\frac{3}{2}}\right]_0^{3a}$$

$$= \frac{144\sqrt{3}\pi a^3}{5} + 16\sqrt{3}\pi a^3 = \frac{224\sqrt{3}\pi a^3}{5}.$$

Exercises 6 : 2

1. Find by integration the volume of (i) a sphere of radius a, (ii) a right circular cone of height h and vertical angle 2α.

2. The area enclosed by the parabola $y^2 = 6ax + 16a^2$ and the ordinates $x = 0$, $x = 4a$ is rotated about the axis of x to form a solid of revolution. Show that the area of the curved surface of the solid is $436\pi a^2/9$.

The volume generated by rotating about the axis of x the area enclosed by the parabola $y^2 = 5ax + 6a^2$ and the ordinates $x = a$, $x = 4a$ is removed from the above solid to leave a hollow vessel. Find the volume of the material of the vessel.

3. A solid of revolution is formed by rotating the loop of the curve

$$ay^2 = x(x-a)^2$$

about the x-axis. Prove that the volume of the solid is nine-sixteenths of the volume of the cylinder of the same length whose generators touch the solid along the circumference of its greatest circular cross section.

4. The parabola $y^2 = 4x$ and the straight line $4x - 3y + 2 = 0$ are rotated about the y-axis. Show that the volume enclosed between the two surfaces thus generated is $\pi/20$.

5. The figure bounded by an ellipse and the lines through its foci perpendicular to the major axis is rotated through two right angles about the major axis. Prove that the volume of the solid of revolution so generated is

$$2\pi a^3 e(1 - \tfrac{4}{3}e^2 + \tfrac{1}{3}e^4),$$

where $2a$ is the major axis and e the eccentricity of the ellipse.

6. Sketch the curve

$$y = \frac{2x(x-4)}{2x+1}.$$

Find the volume of the solid formed by rotating completely about the y-axis the area bounded by the x-axis and that portion of the curve between $x = 0$ and $x = 4$.

7. Sketch the curve

$$y^2 = \frac{x(2-x)^2}{4-x}.$$

Find the volume generated when the area enclosed by the loop is rotated through 2π radians about the x-axis.

8. The region bounded by a quadrant of a circle of radius a, and the tangents at its extremities, revolves through $360°$ about one of these tangents. Prove that the volume of the solid thus generated is $(\frac{5}{3} - \frac{1}{2}\pi)\pi a^3$, and the area of its curved surface is $\pi(\pi - 2)a^2$.

9. A circular quadrant of radius $a/2$ and centre B is removed from a square $ABCD$ of side a. If the remaining portion is rotated through an angle of $360°$ about the side AD, prove that the volume generated is $\pi a^3 (13/12 - \pi/8)$.

10. Prove that the parabola $y^2 = x$ divides the circle $x^2 + y^2 = 2$ into two portions whose areas are in the ratio $9\pi - 2 : 3\pi + 2$.

11. Show that the curves
$$xy^2 = a^2(2a - x), \qquad yx^2 = a^2(2a - y)$$
have one, and only one, real common point and that the curves touch at this point.

Sketch the curves on the same diagram.

Show that the area enclosed by the common tangent and either curve is $\frac{1}{2}(\pi - 3)a^2$.

12. Prove that the area enclosed by the curve traced by the foot of the perpendicular from the centre to a variable tangent of the ellipse $b^2x^2 + a^2y^2 = a^2b^2$ is $\frac{1}{2}\pi(a^2 + b^2)$.

13. Show that the surface area generated by revolving the ellipse
$$x = a \cos\phi, \qquad y = b \sin\phi \qquad (a > b)$$
about its major axis is
$$2\pi b^2 + (2\pi ab/e) \sin^{-1} e$$
where $a^2e^2 = a^2 - b^2$.

14. Find the volume of revolution obtained by rotating the area bounded by the curve $y = x - 2 \ln x$, the ordinates $x = 1$ and $x = 2$, and the x-axis, through a complete revolution about the x-axis.

6 : 3 Polar coordinates

If the equation of a curve is given in the form $r = f(\theta)$, two neighbouring points P, Q with coordinates (r, θ), $(r + \delta r, \theta + \delta\theta)$ respectively define with the origin a triangle of area $\frac{1}{2}r(r + \delta r) \times \sin \delta\theta$, see Fig. 6.7. The narrow sector OPQ therefore has the area
$$\delta S = \frac{1}{2}r^2 \, \delta\theta + O\{(\delta\theta)^2\},$$
which, in terms of differentials, gives
$$dS = \frac{1}{2}r^2 \, d\theta.$$
The area of the sector OAB is the sum of these elementary

sectors and therefore

$$S = \tfrac{1}{2} \int_{\alpha}^{\beta} r^2 \, \mathrm{d}\theta. \tag{6.7}$$

If the arc AB is rotated about the initial line through γ radians, then the arc PQ generates a surface area

$$\delta S \approx \gamma y \, \delta s.$$

$$\therefore \ \delta S = \gamma r \sin \theta \left\{ r^2 + \left(\frac{\mathrm{d}r}{\mathrm{d}\theta} \right)^2 \right\}^{\frac{1}{2}} \delta \theta + O\{(\delta \theta)^2\}.$$

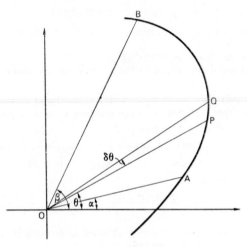

Fig. 6.7.

Therefore the total surface area generated is

$$S = \gamma \int_{\alpha}^{\beta} r \sin \theta \left\{ r^2 + \left(\frac{\mathrm{d}r}{\mathrm{d}\theta} \right)^2 \right\}^{\frac{1}{2}} \mathrm{d}\theta. \tag{6.8}$$

Example 1. Find the area enclosed by the curve $r = a \cos 3\theta$.

The curve is sketched in Fig. 4.15, on p. 209. It consists of three equal loops. Clearly the required area $= 6 \times \tfrac{1}{2} a^2 \int_{0}^{\pi/6} \cos^2 3\theta \, \mathrm{d}\theta = a^2 \int_{0}^{\pi/2} \cos^2 \varphi \, \mathrm{d}\varphi = \tfrac{1}{4} \pi a^2.$

Example 2. By conversion to polar coordinates, show that the area enclosed by the ellipse $Ax^2 + 2Hxy + By^2 = 1$, $A > 0$, $B > 0$, $AB > H^2$, is $\pi/\{AB - H^2\}^{\frac{1}{2}}$.

The polar equation of the ellipse is $r^2 = (A \cos^2 \theta + 2H \sin \theta \cos \theta + B \sin^2 \theta)^{-1}$. The required area S is twice the area between the ellipse and the radii $\theta = -\frac{1}{2}\pi$, $\theta = \frac{1}{2}\pi$.

$$\therefore \quad S = 2 \times \frac{1}{2} \int_{-\pi/2}^{\pi/2} r^2 \, d\theta = \int_{-\pi/2}^{\pi/2} \frac{d\theta}{(A \cos^2 \theta + 2H \sin \theta \cos \theta + B \cos^2 \theta)}.$$

Transforming to $\tan \theta = u$ as the independent variable,

$$S = \int_{-\infty}^{\infty} \frac{du}{(A + 2Hu + Bu^2)} = \int_{-\infty}^{\infty} \frac{du}{[\sqrt{B}u + (H/\sqrt{B})]^2 + (AB - H^2)/B}.$$

$$\therefore \quad S = \frac{1}{\sqrt{(AB - H^2)}} \left[\tan^{-1} \left\{ \frac{Bu + H}{\sqrt{(AB - H^2)}} \right\} \right]_{-\infty}^{\infty}$$

$$= \frac{1}{\sqrt{(AB - H^2)}} \left[\tan^{-1} \infty - \tan^{-1} (-\infty) \right] = \frac{\pi}{\sqrt{(AB - H^2)}}.$$

Example 3. The arc of the *cardioid* $r = a(1 + \cos \theta)$, $0 \leqslant \theta \leqslant \pi$, is rotated through 2π about the initial line. Find the area of the surface generated.

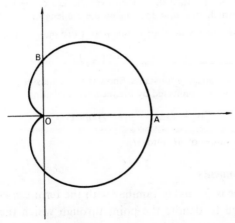

FIG. 6.8. The cardioid $r = a(1 + \cos \theta)$.

The cardioid is shown in Fig. 6.8. The area generated

$$S = 2\pi \int_0^\pi a(1+\cos\theta)\sin\theta \sqrt{\{a^2(1+\cos\theta)^2+a^2\sin^2\theta\}}\, d\theta$$

$$= 2\sqrt{2}\pi a^2 \int_0^\pi (1+\cos\theta)^{\frac{3}{2}}\sin\theta\, d\theta$$

$$= 2\sqrt{2}\pi a^2 \left[-\frac{2}{5}(1+\cos\theta)^{\frac{5}{2}}\right]_0^\pi = \frac{32\pi a^2}{5}.$$

Exercises 6 : 3

1. Find the total area enclosed by the following curves:

(i) $r^2 = a^2\cos 2\theta$,   (ii) $r = a(1+\cos\theta)$,

(iii) $r^2(a^2\sin^2\theta + b^2\cos^2\theta) = (a^2-b^2)b^2\cos^2\theta$ $(a > b > 0)$.

2. Find the area of the loop of the curve $r = a\theta\sin\theta$ between $\theta = 0$ and $\theta = \pi$.

3. By finding the area of the surface generated by rotating the circle $r = a$ through 2π about the initial line, show that the surface area of a sphere of radius a is $4\pi a^2$.

4. Show that

$$\int_0^\pi \frac{d\theta}{1+e\cos\theta} = \frac{\pi}{\sqrt{(1-e^2)}} \qquad (0 < e < 1).$$

If each focal radius vector of an ellipse is produced a constant length c, show that the area between the curve so formed and the ellipse is $\pi c(2b+c)$, b being the semi-minor axis of the ellipse.

5. Evaluate the integral $\int ds/r$ taken over the arc of the lemniscate $r^2 = a^2\cos 2\theta$ for which $0 < \theta < \frac{1}{6}\pi$, s being the arc length.

6. The density of a sphere of radius a at a distance r from the centre is

$$k\left(\frac{r}{a}\right)^n \cos\left(\frac{\pi r}{2a}\right),$$

where k and n are positive constants. Show that the masses M_n and M_{n-2} of two such spheres are connected by the recurrence relation

$$M_n = 8ka^3 - \frac{4}{\pi^2}(n+2)(n+1)M_{n-2}.$$

Determine the values of M_0 and M_4.

6 : 4 First moments

The reader is probably familiar with the term *centre of gravity* which is used to denote the point through which the weight of a body acts whatever the position of that body. Here we give an analytic definition of the centre of gravity (the c.g.) of a system of particles.

Suppose, see Fig. 6.9, that Ox, Oy and Oz are three mutually perpendicular straight lines, i.e. *three rectangular cartesian axes*, whose positive directions form a right-handed triad so that a rotation from Ox to Oy through 90° is in the clockwise sense to an observer looking along Oz. Then the coordinates of an arbitrary point P are (x, y, z) when x is the distance of P from the plane

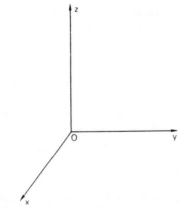

FIG. 6.9. Three-dimensional rectangular axes.

defined by Oy and Oz, y the distance of P from the plane of Oz and Ox, z the distance of P from the plane of Ox and Oy. Note that x is taken to be positive when P is on the same side of the plane defined by Oy, Oz (i.e. the plane $x = 0$) as the positive direction of the x-axis Ox. The three planes defined by the coordinate axes divide space into eight *octants*.

If n particles of masses m_i ($i = 1, 2, \ldots, n$) are situated at the respective points (x_i, y_i, z_i), the centre of gravity is defined as the point $(\bar{x}, \bar{y}, \bar{z})$, where

$$\bar{x} = \frac{\Sigma m_i x_i}{\Sigma m_i}, \quad \bar{y} = \frac{\Sigma m_i y_i}{\Sigma m_i}, \quad \bar{z} = \frac{\Sigma m_i z_i}{\Sigma m_i}. \qquad (6.9)$$

It can be shown that, if the particles are fixed, this definition gives a unique point in space independent of the particular system of axes chosen. The centre of gravity is usually denoted by G. If $M = \Sigma m_i$ is the total mass of the system, eqns. (6.9) can be written

$$M\bar{x} = \Sigma m_i x_i, \quad M\bar{y} = \Sigma m_i y_i, \quad M\bar{z} = \Sigma m_i z_i. \quad (6.10)$$

In these formulae there is no mention of gravity; the definition concerns solely positions referred to a frame of axes. The mechanical significance of the point $(\bar{x}, \bar{y}, \bar{z})$ is due to the fact that the forces of gravitation on every particle of a small scale system are all parallel. If the particles were so widely separated that these gravitational forces were not parallel then there would be no centre of gravity. But even if there were no gravitation or the set of particles was so extensive that it had no centre of gravity, the point $(\bar{x}, \bar{y}, \bar{z})$ defined above would be definite and possess important properties.

To express this significance independently of any special importance in other ways, the point $(\bar{x}, \bar{y}, \bar{z})$ defined by the formulae above is called the *centre of mass*, and the sums $\Sigma m_i x_i$, $\Sigma m_i y_i$, $\Sigma m_i z_i$, are called *first moments* with respect to the planes $x = 0$, $y = 0$, $z = 0$ respectively. The distinction between "turning-moments" and these first moments should be made clear. A turning moment is the product of a force and the perpendicular distance of its line of action from an axis. In the first moment formula, $\Sigma m_i x_i$, the quantity x_i is the perpendicular distance of m_i from a *plane*.

The centre of mass of a uniform rod is at its mid-point, but it is given by a formula similar to (6.10) except that we have a continuous distribution of mass instead of a number of point masses. The first moment sums, in such cases, are replaced by integrals. The centre of mass of a uniform thin disc is at its geometrical centre. This is also the *centroid of the area* of the disc; this result is also true for a disc whose *mass* is not uniformly distributed, because we refer to area only. In fact the centroid of any continuous body (arc, area, volume) is the centre of mass of the space, considered as of uniform density, occupied by that body.

The conception of a first moment, and the corresponding centre or mean, can be applied to any property which is distributed. The distribution may, moreover, be a distribution in space (e.g. the mass of a solid body, hydrostatic thrust), in time (e.g. radioactive disintegration), or over a population (e.g. the energies of gas molecules, the heights of a group of people). Any sum of the form, either discrete or continuous

$$\Sigma \mu_i x_i \quad \text{or} \quad \int_a^b \mu(x) x \, dx$$

is a first moment, and can be used to define a mean or centre, $\bar{x}$, by the formula

$$\bar{x} \Sigma \mu_i = \Sigma \mu_i x_i, \quad \text{or} \quad \bar{x} \int_a^b \mu(x) \, dx = \int_a^b x \mu(x) \, dx. \quad (6.11)$$

First we find a formula for the position of the centroid of a uniform wire bent into the form of a plane curve. We divide the wire into elementary arcs of length δs, a typical element passing through (x, y), see Fig. 6.13(a). Then the contribution to the first moments, M_x, M_y, are

$$\delta M_x = x \, \delta s + O\{(\delta s)^2\}, \quad \delta M_y = y \, \delta s + O\{(\delta s)^2\}.$$

The summations to give these moments are

$$M_x = \int_{s_1}^{s_2} x \, ds, \quad M_y = \int_{s_1}^{s_2} y \, ds,$$

where s_1 and s_2 are the arc lengths along the curve to A and B respectively. Here M_x is the first moment of the arc w.r. to the plane of Oy and Oz, but we loosely refer to M_x as the first moment *about* the line Oy. Hence

$$(s_2 - s_1)\bar{x} = \int_{s_1}^{s_2} x \, ds, \quad (s_2 - s_1)\bar{y} = \int_{s_1}^{s_2} y \, ds. \quad (6.12)$$

Example. In the special case of a circular arc AB which subtends an angle 2α at the centre we use θ as the variable of integration, Fig. 6.10, p. 368.

Since $s = a\theta$,

$$\bar{x} = \frac{1}{2a\alpha} \int_{-\alpha}^{\alpha} a \cos \theta \cdot a \, d\theta. \qquad \bar{y} = \frac{1}{2a\alpha} \int_{-\alpha}^{\alpha} a \sin \theta \cdot a \, d\theta.$$

$$\therefore \quad \bar{x} = \frac{a}{2\alpha} \left[\sin \theta \right]_{-\alpha}^{\alpha} = \frac{a \sin \alpha}{\alpha}, \qquad \bar{y} = 0.$$

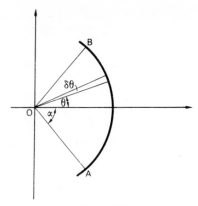

FIG. 6.10.

Next we find the centroid of a plane area $ABQP$ enclosed by a curve, Fig. 6.4. We know that the area is

$$S = \int_a^b f(x)\,\mathrm{d}x.$$

To find the first moment M_x we divide the area into strips parallel to Oy; a typical strip is of width δx. Then

$$\delta M_x = x f(x)\,\delta x + O\{(\delta x)^2\}.$$

The summation gives the first moment as an integral

$$M_x = \int_a^b x f(x)\,\mathrm{d}x.$$

$$\therefore \ \bar{x} = \frac{\int_a^b x f(x)\,\mathrm{d}x}{\int_a^b f(x)\,\mathrm{d}x}. \tag{6.13}$$

We find the value of $\bar{y}$ by noting that the first moment of a strip about Ox is

$$\delta M_y = \tfrac{1}{2} f(x) \cdot f(x)\,\delta x + O\{(\delta x)^2\}.$$

Here we are quoting the result that the centroid of a narrow strip (or straight rod) is at its mid point. Therefore its contribution to

M_y is the product of its area and half its length.

$$\therefore \quad M_y = \tfrac{1}{2} \int_a^b \{f(x)\}^2 \, dx = \bar{y} \int_a^b f(x) \, dx. \qquad (6.14)$$

The process of dividing a figure up into elementary figures whose centroids are known is a useful method of obtaining the centroids of complicated shapes.

Example 1. Find the centroid of the area enclosed by the curve $y = a^3/(a^2+x^2)$ and the lines $y = 0$, $x = a\sqrt{3}$, $x = -a\sqrt{3}$.

$$\bar{y} = \tfrac{1}{2} \int_{-a\sqrt{3}}^{a\sqrt{3}} y^2 \, dx \bigg/ \int_{-a\sqrt{3}}^{a\sqrt{3}} y \, dx.$$

$$\int_{-a\sqrt{3}}^{a\sqrt{3}} y \, dx = \int_{-a\sqrt{3}}^{a\sqrt{3}} \frac{a^3 \, dx}{(a^2+x^2)} = \left[a^2 \tan^{-1}\left(\frac{x}{a}\right) \right]_{-a\sqrt{3}}^{a\sqrt{3}}$$

$$= 2a^2 \tan^{-1} \sqrt{3} = \frac{2\pi a^2}{3}.$$

$$\int_{-a\sqrt{3}}^{a\sqrt{3}} y^2 \, dx = \int_{-a\sqrt{3}}^{a\sqrt{3}} \frac{a^6 \, dx}{(a^2+x^2)^2} = 2a^3 \int_0^{\pi/3} \cos^2 \theta \, d\theta = a^3(4\pi+3\sqrt{3})/12$$

(on using the substitution $x = a \tan \theta$).

$$\therefore \quad \bar{y} = \frac{a(4\pi+3\sqrt{3})}{16\pi}.$$

By symmetry $\bar{x} = 0$.

Example 2. Find expressions for the coordinates of the centroid of the sector bounded by the curve $r = f(\theta)$ and the radii $\theta = \alpha$, $\theta = \beta$.

The area of the elementary sector OPQ, Fig. 6.7, is $\delta S = \tfrac{1}{2}r^2 \, \delta\theta + O\{(\delta\theta)^2\}$ and referred to Ox, Oy the coordinates of its c.g. are (those of the triangle OPQ) $(\tfrac{2}{3}r \cos \theta, \tfrac{2}{3}r \sin \theta)$.

$$\therefore \quad \delta M_x = \tfrac{2}{3}r \cos \theta \, \tfrac{1}{2}r^2 \, \delta\theta + O\{(\delta\theta)^2\}, \quad \delta M_y = \tfrac{2}{3}r \sin \theta \, \tfrac{1}{2}r^2 \, \delta\theta + O\{(\delta\theta)^2\}.$$

$$\therefore \quad M_x = \tfrac{1}{3} \int_\alpha^\beta r^3 \cos \theta \, d\theta, \qquad\qquad M_y = \tfrac{1}{3} \int_\alpha^\beta r^3 \sin \theta \, d\theta,$$

and

$$\bar{x} = \frac{M_x}{S}, \quad \bar{y} = \frac{M_y}{S}, \quad \text{where} \quad S = \tfrac{1}{2} \int_\alpha^\beta r^2 \, d\theta.$$

Note that here we find the *cartesian* coordinates of G.

In particular, for the upper half of the *cardioid*, $r = a(1+\cos\theta)$,

$$S = \frac{1}{2}\int_0^\pi a^2(1+\cos\theta)^2\,d\theta = 2a^2\int_0^\pi \cos^4\left(\frac{1}{2}\theta\right)\,d\theta$$

$$= 4a^2\int_0^{\pi/2} \cos^4\varphi\,d\varphi = \frac{3\pi a^2}{4},$$

$$M_x = \frac{1}{3}\int_0^\pi a^3(1+\cos\theta)^3\cos\theta\,d\theta$$

$$= \frac{8a^3}{3}\int_0^\pi \cos^6\left(\frac{1}{2}\theta\right)\left[2\cos^2\left(\frac{1}{2}\theta\right)-1\right]\,d\theta$$

$$= \frac{16a^3}{3}\int_0^{\pi/2}(2\cos^8\varphi-\cos^6\varphi)\,d\varphi = \frac{5\pi a^3}{8},$$

$$M_y = \frac{1}{3}\int_0^\pi a^3(1+\cos\theta)^3\sin\theta\,d\theta = \frac{1}{3}a^3\left[-\frac{1}{4}(1+\cos\theta)^4\right]_0^\pi = \frac{4a^3}{3}.$$

$$\therefore\ \bar{x} = \frac{5a}{6},\qquad \bar{y} = \frac{16a}{9\pi}.$$

Example 3. Find the centroid of (i) the curved surface and (ii) the volume of a hemisphere of radius a.

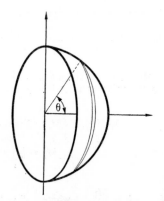

Fig. 6.11.

The symmetry of the figure shows that in each case the centroid lies on Ox.

(i) Divide the area into circular rings, a typical ring being of width δs and circumference $2\pi y$. Then

$$\delta M_x \approx x\, 2\pi y\, \delta s.$$

$$\therefore\ M_x = \int_{x=0}^{x=a} 2\pi\, xy\, \mathrm{d}s.$$

Changing the variable of integration to θ as shown in Fig. 6.1 we have

$$M_x = 2\pi a^3 \int_0^{\pi/2} \sin\theta\cos\theta\, \mathrm{d}\theta = \pi a^3.$$

But the surface area

$$2\pi \int_{x=0}^{x=a} y\, \mathrm{d}s = 2\pi a^2 \int_0^{\pi/2} \sin\theta\, \mathrm{d}\theta = 2\pi a^2.$$

$$\therefore\ \bar{x} = \tfrac{1}{2}a.$$

(ii) We divide the figure into circular discs; a typical disc is at a distance x from the origin and of thickness δx. The contributions δV and δM_x to the volume and first moment are

$$\delta V = \pi(a^2 - x^2)\,\delta x + O\{(\delta x)^2\}, \qquad \delta M_x = x\pi(a^2 - x^2)\,\delta x + O\{(\delta x)^2\}.$$

$$\therefore\ V = \pi \int_0^a (a^2 - x^2)\, \mathrm{d}x \qquad\qquad M_x = \pi \int_0^a x(a^2 - x^2)\, \mathrm{d}x$$

$$= \pi\left[a^2 x - \tfrac{1}{3}x^3\right]_0^a \qquad\qquad = \pi\left[\tfrac{1}{2}a^2 x^2 - \tfrac{1}{4}x^4\right]_0^a$$

$$= \tfrac{2}{3}\pi a^3. \qquad\qquad\qquad\qquad = \tfrac{1}{4}\pi a^4.$$

$$\therefore\ \bar{x} = \frac{3a}{8}.$$

Example 4. Find the centroid of the volume of a cone of arbitrary cross-section.

A cone can be generated by joining all the points of a plane curve to a point O, the vertex, not in the plane of the curve. These straight lines are the *generators* of the cone. We find the centroid of the volume by dividing the cone into sections by planes parallel to the base . A typical section is distant x below O and of thickness δx.

If B is the centroid of the base area, the centroid of each section lies at the intersection C of OB and the plane of the section, since the sections are all geometrically similar to the base area. Hence the centroid of the solid cone lies on OB (see Fig. 6.12).

The area of the section through C is $x^2 S/h^2$ where S is the base area and h is the height of the cone. Then the volume δV and moment δM w.r. to a plane

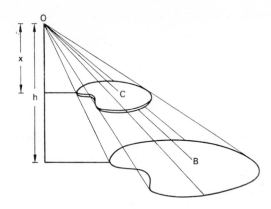

Fig. 6.12.

through the vertex parallel to the base are given by

$$\delta V \approx \frac{x^2 S \, \delta x}{h^2}, \qquad \delta M = x \cdot \delta V.$$

$$\therefore \quad V = \int_0^h \frac{x^2 S \, dx}{h^2} = \frac{1}{3} Sh, \qquad M = \int_0^h \frac{x^3 S \, dx}{h^2} = \frac{1}{4} Sh^2 .$$

Therefore $\bar{x} = \frac{3}{4}h$ and hence the centroid is $\frac{3}{4}$ of the way down OB.

Exercises 6 : 4

1. Find the centroid of (i) the curved surface, (ii) the volume of a right circular cone of height h and vertical angle 2α.

2. Find the centroid of the area bounded by the parabola $y^2 = 4ax$ and the line $y = 2x$. Find also the centroid of the volume obtained by rotating this area through 2π about (i) Ox, (ii) Oy.

3. Find the centroid of a sector of a circle of radius a which subtends an angle 2α at the centre O of the circle. Deduce that the centroid of the minor segment of the circle cut off by a chord of length $2a \sin \alpha$, $0 < \alpha < \frac{1}{2}\pi$, is at a distance $\frac{2}{3}a \sin^3 \alpha/(\alpha - \sin \alpha \cos \alpha)$ from O.

4. The equation of a curve is

$$y^2 = \frac{x-1}{x-2}.$$

Show that no part of the curve lies between $x = 1$ and $x = 2$; and sketch the curve for the remaining values of x.

The portion of the curve between $x = 0$ and $x = 1$ is rotated through 360° about the axis of x. Find the volume generated and the distance of its centroid from the origin.

5. An open thin-walled vessel of depth 2 metres is formed by the rotation about the x-axis of the parabola $y^2 = 8x$, x and y being measured in metres. Calculate the area of the outer surface of the vessel and the distance of the centre of gravity of the empty vessel from the vertex.

6. Sketch the curve $cy^2 = 4x^2(c - x)$, where $c > 0$, and find the area of its loop. Find also the x-coordinate of the centroid of this loop.

7. The area bounded by the arc of a quadrant of a circle and the tangents at its extremities is rotated about one of these tangents. If the volume so generated is filled with material of uniform density, find the position of the centre of gravity of the solid so formed.

8. Prove that the distance of the centre of gravity of a uniform semicircular lamina from the diameter of the semicircle is $4a/3\pi$, where a is the radius of the semicircle.

The middle point M of a straight line AB is taken and semicircles are described on AB as diameter and MB as diameter but on opposite sides of AB and in the same plane. Find the distances of the centroid of the area bounded by AM and the arcs of the semicircles from AB and its perpendicular bisector, when $AB = 2a$.

9. Find the area of the surface formed by revolving the arc of the parabola $y^2 = 4ax$ between the origin and the point $(4a, 4a)$ about the x-axis, and prove that the centre of mass of the surface is on the axis at a distance

$$\frac{a}{5} \cdot \frac{50\sqrt{5} + 2}{5\sqrt{5} - 1}$$

from the vertex.

10. Find the y-coordinate of the centroid of the area bounded by the curve $r = a\theta$ $(0 < \theta < \pi/2)$ and the line $\theta = \pi/2$.

11. A and B are points on the *catenary* $y = c \cosh (x/c)$ at which x has the values c and λc respectively with $\lambda > 1$. The region of the plane bounded by the arc AB of the curve, the ordinates at A and B, and the x-axis is rotated through 2π radians about the x-axis. If V is the volume and S is the curved surface area of the solid generated, prove that

$$V = \tfrac{1}{2}cS = \tfrac{1}{2}\pi c^3 \{\lambda - 1 + \cosh (\lambda + 1) \sinh (\lambda - 1)\}.$$

Show further that the centroids of the solid and of the curved surface coincide.

12. The cross-section A of a rod of length 100 cm varies from 2 cm^2 at one end to 1 cm^2 at the other, the value of A at distance x from the larger end being given by $A = 2e^{-ax}$. Calculate a.

If the density of the material of the rod is 7 g cm^{-3} show that the mass of the rod is slightly greater than 1 kg and find the distance of its centre of mass from the larger end.

6 : 5 The theorems of Pappus

The theorems of Pappus or Guldin can be stated as follows:

(i)　The area of the surface swept out by revolving an arc of a plane curve about an axis in its plane is equal to the length of the arc multiplied by the length of the path of the centroid of the arc.

(ii)　The volume of the solid swept out by revolving a plane area about an axis in its plane is equal to the area multiplied by the length of the path of the centroid of the area.

In each case the arc or area must not cross the axis of revolution.

(i) Let AB be the arc and Ox the axis of revolution about which the arc revolves through an angle α radians, Fig. 6.13(a). Then a typical element δs of the arc generates a strip of area $\alpha y\,\delta s + O\{(\delta s)^2\}$. Hence the total area generated is, correct to the first order, $\Sigma \alpha y\,\delta s = \alpha\,\Sigma y\,\delta s$. But by definition the distance of the centroid of the arc, $\bar{y}_{\text{arc}}$, from Ox is given by $l\bar{y}_{\text{arc}} = \Sigma y\,\delta s$, correct to the first order, where l is the arc length AB. Hence the area generated, $l\alpha\bar{y}_{\text{arc}}$, is the length of the arc multiplied by the length of the path of the centroid of the arc.

(ii) The area of Fig. 6.13(b) is divided into elements δS whose linear dimensions are of the order of ε, i.e. $\delta S = O(\varepsilon^2)$. In the revolution δS generates a volume $\alpha y\,\delta S + O(\varepsilon^3)$. Hence the total volume generated is $\Sigma \alpha y\,\delta S = \alpha\,\Sigma y\,\delta S$, correct to the second order in ε. But the distance of the centroid of the area $\bar{y}_{\text{area}}$ from Ox is given by $S\bar{y}_{\text{area}} = \Sigma y\,\delta S$, correct to the second order in ε where S is the total area. Hence the volume generated, $S\alpha\bar{y}_{\text{area}}$, is the plane area multiplied by the length of the path of the centroid of the area.

In both (i) and (ii) above the sums are, strictly speaking, the limiting values as δs or δS tend to zero. Then, as in integration, the approximate relations are strictly true in the limit.

Example 1. When a semicircular wire is rotated about its bounding diameter through 2π it generates a sphere. Using the first theorem

$$4\pi a^2 = 2\pi\bar{x}\cdot\pi a. \qquad \text{Therefore} \qquad \bar{x} = \frac{2a}{\pi},$$

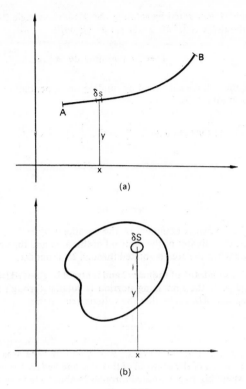

(a)

(b)

FIG. 6.13.

which is the distance of the centroid of the arc of a semicircle from its centre. The second theorem gives

$$\frac{4}{3}\pi a^3 = 2\pi\bar{x}\cdot\frac{1}{2}\pi a^2. \quad \text{Therefore} \quad \bar{x} = \frac{4a}{3\pi},$$

which is the distance of the centroid of a semicircular area from its centre.

Example 2. A circle of radius a is rotated through 2π about a line in its plane at a distance b from the centre of the circle, $b > a$. Find the volume and surface area of the anchor ring or torus thus generated.

The volume $= 2\pi b\cdot\pi a^2 = 2\pi^2 a^2 b$.
The surface area $= 2\pi b\cdot 2\pi a = 4\pi^2 ab$.

Example 3. Find the volume generated by rotating through 2π about the initial line the area bounded by the curve $r = f(\theta)$ and the lines $\theta = \alpha$, $\theta = \beta$.

The volume δV generated by rotating the sector or triangle OPQ, Fig. 6.7, through 2π about Ox is $\frac{1}{2}r^2\,\delta\theta\cdot 2\pi\cdot\frac{2}{3}r\sin\theta+O\{(\delta\theta)^2\}$.

$$\therefore\quad V = \tfrac{2}{3}\pi\int\limits_{\alpha}^{\beta} r^3\sin\theta\,\mathrm{d}\theta.$$

For example, the volume generated by rotating the upper half of the cardioid $r = a(1+\cos\theta)$ about Ox is

$$\frac{2}{3}\pi\int\limits_{0}^{\pi} a^3(1+\cos\theta)^3\sin\theta\,\mathrm{d}\theta = \frac{2}{3}\,\pi a^2\left[-\frac{1}{4}\,(1+\cos\theta)^4\right]_0^\pi = \frac{8\pi a^3}{3}.$$

Exercises 6 : 5

1. Prove that the area common to the parabolas $ay = 2x^2$, $y^2 = 4ax$ is $2a^2/3$. Find the coordinates of the centroid of this area and the volume of the solid generated when the area is rotated through 2π about Ox.

2. A circular quadrant of radius $a/2$ and centre B is removed from a square $ABCD$ of side a. If the remaining portion is rotated through an angle of $360°$ about the side AD, prove that the volume generated is

$$\pi a^3\left(\frac{13}{12}-\frac{\pi}{8}\right).$$

3. Sketch the curve $ay^2 = x^2(a-x)$, $a > 0$, and find the area of its loop. Find also the position of the centroid of this area and deduce the volume of the solid formed when this area is rotated through 2π about a tangent to the curve at the origin.

4. Apply the theorem of Pappus to find the centroid of (i) a wire in the form of one quarter of the circumference of a circle, and (ii) a lamina which is one quarter of an elliptic disc, whose major and minor semi-axes are a and b respectively.

5. A crescent-shaped area is bounded by the ellipse $(x^2/a^2)+(y^2/b^2) = 1$ and the parabola $y^2 = b(b-x)$, where $a > b$ and x is positive. Calculate the area, and also the volume of the solid of revolution formed when the area is rotated through four right angles about the y-axis.

Deduce the distance of the centroid of the area from the y-axis.

6. Sketch the cycloid $x = a(t-\sin t)$, $y = a(1-\cos t)$ from $t = 0$ to $t = 2\pi$. Find the area enclosed by the curve and the x-axis and the position of the centroid of this area. Deduce the volume of the solid obtained by rotating this area through 2π about the x-axis.

7. The area enclosed by the *lemniscate*

$$r^2 = a^2\cos 2\theta$$

is rotated through two right angles about the line $\theta = \frac{1}{2}\pi$. Prove that the volume of the solid so formed is

$$\frac{\sqrt{2}}{8}\,\pi^2 a^3 .$$

8. A plane curve is given by equations $x = f(t)$, $y = g(t)$. Show that the volume generated when the sectorial area OPQ is rotated through 2π about the x-axis, O being the origin and P, Q being the points of the curve where t has the values t_1, t_2 respectively, is

$$\frac{2\pi}{3} \int_{t_1}^{t_2} y\left(x\,\frac{dy}{dt} - y\,\frac{dx}{dt} \right)\, dt.$$

Prove that the volume generated when the area enclosed by the curve

$$x = a(1 - t^2), \quad y = 2a(1 + t)$$

and the y-axis is rotated through 2π about the x-axis is five times the volume generated when the same area is rotated about the y-axis.

9. Calculate the area of the region R enclosed between the x-axis and that part of the curve $y^2 = x^2(1 - x)$ which lies in the first quadrant.

Also calculate the volumes swept out when the region R is rotated through four right angles about (i) the x-axis, (ii) the y-axis.

Show further that the coordinates of the centroid of the region R are $(4/7, 5/32)$.

6 : 6 Second moments—moments of inertia

If n particles of masses m_i $(i = 1, 2, \ldots, n)$ are situated at the respective points (x_i, y_i, z_i) referred to a set of rectangular cartesian axes, then the *second moments* of the system with respect to the coordinate planes $x = 0$, $y = 0$, $z = 0$ are defined by $\Sigma m_i x_i^2$, $\Sigma m_i y_i^2$, $\Sigma m_i z_i^2$ respectively. Second moments are of importance in mechanics, hydrostatics and statistics.

The second moment arises in mechanics in the calculation of moments of inertia. The *moment of inertia*, I, of a system of particles, about any line, l, is $\Sigma m r^2$ where m and r are the mass and distance from the line of a typical particle of the system. If the total mass of the system is M, then the radius of gyration, k, of the system about l is defined by

$$I = Mk^2 = \Sigma m r^2. \tag{6.15}$$

In the case of a continuous body we replace the summation by an integral.

Example 1. The moment of inertia of a thin circular ring, of mass M and radius a, about its axis (the line through its centre and perpendicular to its plane) is $\Sigma ma^2 = a^2\, \Sigma m = Ma^2$ since all the mass is at distance a from the axis. (This result also holds for the moment of inertia of an open thin cylindrical shell of total mass M and radius a, about its axis.)

Example 2. For a uniform thin disc, of total mass M and radius a, we divide the disc into rings, a typical ring being of radius r and thickness δr, and replace the summation by integration. The mass of an elementary ring is

$$\delta M = \frac{M}{\pi a^2}\cdot 2\pi r\ \delta r + O\{(\delta r)^2\}.$$

The contribution of this ring to the moment of inertia I about the axis is

$$\delta I = \frac{M}{\pi a^2}\cdot 2\pi r\ \delta r\cdot r^2 + O\{(\delta r)^2\}.$$

$$\therefore\ I = \frac{2M}{a^2}\int_0^a r^3\ \mathrm{d}r = \frac{Ma^2}{2}.$$

In this case $k = a/\sqrt{2}$. (This result also holds for the moment of inertia of a uniform solid circular cylinder about its axis.)

Example 3. To calculate the moment of inertia of a uniform solid sphere, of mass M and radius a, about a diameter we divide the sphere into discs, with centres on the diameter. A typical disc is distant x from the centre of the sphere and of thickness δx (see Fig. 6.11). If ϱ is the density of the sphere, so that $M = \frac{4}{3}\pi\varrho a^3$, the moment of inertia of the typical disc is

$$\delta I = \pi\varrho(a^2 - x^2)\ \delta x\cdot\tfrac{1}{2}(a^2 - x^2) + O\{(\delta x)^2\}.$$

$$\therefore\ I = \frac{1}{2}\int_{-a}^a \pi\varrho(a^2 - x^2)^2\ \mathrm{d}x = \frac{8\pi\varrho a^5}{15} = \frac{2Ma^2}{5}.$$

This technique may be employed to find the moment of inertia of any solid of revolution about its axis; e.g. the reader should verify that, for a uniform solid right circular cone, of mass M and base radius r, $I_{\text{axis}} = 3Mr^2/10$.

Example 4. For a uniform rod, of mass M and length $2a$, about an axis through its mid-point O making an angle β with the rod we divide the rod into elements, a typical element being at a distance x from O and of length δx. Then

$$\delta I = \frac{M}{2a}\ \delta x\cdot(x\sin\beta)^2 + O\{(\delta x)^2\}.$$

$$\therefore\ I = \frac{M}{2a}\int_{-a}^a x^2\sin^2\beta\ \mathrm{d}x = \frac{1}{3}\ Ma^2\sin^2\beta.$$

The commonest application of this result occurs when $\beta = \frac{1}{2}\pi$, i.e. the moment of inertia of a rod about an axis through its mid-point and perpendicular to its length is $\frac{1}{3} Ma^2$.

If a distribution of matter lies wholly in the plane $z = 0$ and a typical particle P of the system is of mass m and has coordinates $(x, y, 0)$, then the total moments of inertia I_{Ox}, I_{Oy} about the axes Ox, Oy respectively are given by $I_{Ox} = \Sigma my^2$, $I_{Oy} = \Sigma mx^2$. But the distance of P from Oz is $\sqrt{(x^2+y^2)}$ and hence $I_{Oz} = \Sigma m(x^2+y^2)$.

$$\therefore \quad I_{Oz} = I_{Ox}+I_{Oy}. \qquad (6.16)$$

This constitutes the *theorem of perpendicular axes*. *It is only valid when the material lies wholly in a plane* (i.e., for a *lamina*).

Example 1. *ABCD* is a rectangle of mass M; $AB = 2a$, $BC = 2b$. To find I_{AB} we divide the rectangle into strips parallel to AB. Then for a typical strip

$$\delta I_{AB} = \frac{M}{4ab} \cdot 2a \; \delta x \cdot x^2$$

$$\therefore \quad I_{AB} = \frac{M}{2b} \int_0^{2b} x^2 \; \mathrm{d}x = \frac{4Mb^2}{3}.$$

Similarly $\qquad I_{AD} = \dfrac{4Ma^2}{3}.$

Therefore by the perpendicular axes theorem, the moment of inertia about an axis through A perpendicular to the plane of the rectangle is

$$I_{AB}+I_{AD} = \frac{4M(a^2+b^2)}{3}.$$

Example 2. The moment of inertia of a uniform disc, of radius a and mass M, about its axis is $\frac{1}{2}Ma^2$. By the perpendicular axes theorem this is the sum of the moments of inertia about any two perpendicular diameters. Hence, since the moment of inertia, I_d, is the same for every diameter, $2I_d = \frac{1}{2}Ma^2$, i.e. $I_d = \frac{1}{4}Ma^2$.

We now establish the *theorem of parallel axes* which may be stated as follows: *The moment of inertia of a system of total mass M about any given axis is equal to the moment of inertia of the system about the parallel axis through the centre of mass G plus the moment of inertia about the given axis of a particle of mass M placed at G.*

Choose the coordinate system $Oxyz$ so that Oz is the given axis and G lies on Ox and $OG = h$, Fig. 6.14. Through G take coordinate axes GX, GY, GZ so that GX is along Gx and GY, GZ are parallel to Oy, Oz respectively. Then a typical particle of mass m has coordinates (x, y, z), (X, Y, Z) referred to the two coordinate frames where

$$x = X + h, \quad y = Y, \quad z = Z.$$
$$\therefore \ I_{Oz} = \Sigma m(x^2 + y^2) = \Sigma m\{(X+h)^2 + Y^2\}$$
$$= \Sigma m(X^2 + Y^2) + \Sigma m h^2 + 2\Sigma m X h.$$

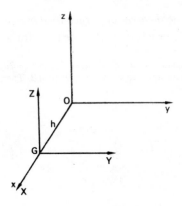

Fig. 6.14.

But since G is the centre of mass $\bar{X} = \Sigma m X / \Sigma m = 0$. Hence $\Sigma m X h = h \Sigma m X = 0$ and

$$I_{Oz} = \Sigma m(X^2 + Y^2) + h^2 \Sigma m,$$

i.e.

$$I_{Oz} = I_{GZ} + Mh^2 \tag{6.17}$$

which proves the theorem.

Note that if f and g are two parallel lines distant p_f and p_g from G and I_f is known, then I_g can be calculated by two successive applications of the theorem. For, if l is the parallel line through G, $I_f = I_l + Mp_f^2$ and $I_g = I_l + Mp_g^2$.

Example 1. The moment of inertia of a uniform solid circular cylinder of mass M and radius a about a generator is $\frac{1}{2}Ma^2 + Ma^2 = 3Ma^2/2$.

Example 2. The moment of inertia of a uniform thin rod, of mass M and length $2a$, about a perpendicular axis through one end is

$$\tfrac{1}{3}Ma^2 + Ma^2 = (4Ma^2)/3.$$

Example 3. For the moment of inertia of a cone about a line l through its vertex O perpendicular to its axis, we divide the cone into elementary circular discs, a typical disc being at distance x from O and of thickness δx. (See Fig. 6.12.) The mass of the disc is

$$\delta M = \varrho\pi(x \tan \alpha)^2 \, \delta x + O\{(\delta x)^2\},$$

where 2α is the vertical angle and ϱ the density of the cone. By the parallel axes theorem the moment of inertia of the disc about Ol is

$$\delta I_{Ol} = \delta M \{\tfrac{1}{4}(x \tan \alpha)^2 + x^2\}.$$
$$\therefore \ \ \delta I_{Ol} = \pi\varrho x^4 \tan^2 \alpha(\tfrac{1}{4} \tan^2 \alpha + 1) \ \delta x + O\{(\delta x)^2\}.$$
$$\therefore \ \ I_{Ol} = \int_0^h \pi\varrho x^4 \tan^2 \alpha \left(\frac{1}{4} \tan^2 \alpha + 1 \right) \, \mathrm{d}x$$
$$= \frac{\pi\varrho h^5 \tan^2 \alpha(\tan^2 \alpha + 4)}{20} .$$

Since $M = \tfrac{1}{3}\pi\varrho h^3 \tan^2 \alpha$ we have

$$I_{Ol} = \frac{3Mh^2(\tan^2 \alpha + 4)}{20} = \frac{3M(a^2 + 4h^2)}{20} ,$$

where a is the radius of the base. To calculate I_d, the moment of inertia about a diameter of the base, we must use a parallel axis through G. In fact $I_G = I_{Ol} - M(\tfrac{3}{4}h)^2$, $I_d = I_G + M(\tfrac{1}{4}h)^2$ and hence

$$I_d = I_{Ol} - \frac{1}{2} Mh^2 = \frac{[M(3a^2 + 2h^2)]}{20} .$$

Example 4. A solid of uniform density ϱ is in the form of a ring and is generated by rotating a plane area possessing an axis of symmetry about an axis in its plane parallel to the axis of symmetry and not cutting the boundary of the area.

Show that the radius of gyration k of the ring about the axis of rotation is given by $k^2 = c^2 + 3\lambda^2$, where c is the distance of the centroid of the area from the axis of rotation, and λ is the radius of gyration of the area about its axis of symmetry.

Let l_1 be the axis of symmetry of the figure and l the line about which the area is rotated (Fig. 6.15). Then the centroid G of the area must be on l_1 (the axis of symmetry of the figure), which is distant c from l. Consider now the element of the solid generated by rotating an element of area δS distant r from l about l. This element generates, to the first order in δS, a ring of mass δM and moment of inertia δI, where

$$\delta M = 2\pi r\varrho \ \delta S, \quad \delta I = 2\pi r^3\varrho \ \delta S.$$

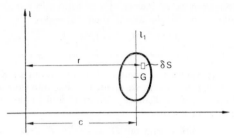

FIG. 6.15.

Therefore

$$M = 2\pi \int r\varrho \, \mathrm{d}S, \quad I = 2\pi \int r^3 \varrho \, \mathrm{d}S,$$

where the integrations are taken over the area A.

Writing $r = c+x$, so that x is the distance of δS from l_1, we find

$$M = 2\pi\varrho \int (c+x) \, \mathrm{d}S = 2\pi\varrho \int c \, \mathrm{d}S + 2\pi\varrho \int x \, \mathrm{d}S.$$

The second integral vanishes by definition of the centroid and we find that

$$M = 2\pi\varrho cA.$$

This follows also from the first theorem of Pappus.

Similarly,

$$I = 2\pi\varrho \int (c+x)^3 \, \mathrm{d}S$$
$$= 2\pi\varrho \left\{ \int c^3 \, \mathrm{d}S + 3 \int c^2 x \, \mathrm{d}S + 3c \int x^2 \, \mathrm{d}S + \int x^3 \, \mathrm{d}S \right\}.$$

Of these integrals the second and fourth vanish by virtue of the symmetry of the area about l_1 and

$$\int c^3 \, \mathrm{d}S = Ac^3, \quad \int x^2 \, \mathrm{d}S = A\lambda^2,$$

where λ is the radius of gyration of the area about l_1. Therefore

$$I = 2\pi\varrho(c^3 A + 3cA\lambda^2) = M(c^2 + 3\lambda^2).$$

To calculate the second moments or moments of inertia of an area $ABQP$ bounded by a plane curve and given ordinates, as shown in Fig. 6.4, we divide the area into strips parallel to Oy. Then the second moment of a typical strip about Oy is $x^2 y \, \delta x + O\{(\delta x)^2\}$ whereas the second moment about Ox (treating the strip as a rod of length y) is $\frac{1}{3}y^3 \, \delta x + O\{(\delta x)^2\}$. Hence the required second moments are $\int_a^b x^2 y \, \mathrm{d}x$ and $\frac{1}{3}\int_a^b y^3 \, \mathrm{d}x$ about Oy and Ox respectively. The squares of the respective radii of gyration are obtained on dividing by the area $\int_a^b y \, \mathrm{d}x$.

Example. Find the radii of gyration of one loop of the curve $a^2y^2 = x^2(a^2 - x^2)$ about Ox and Oy.

This curve is sketched in Fig. 4.12 (curve 2). By symmetry the second moments about Oy and Ox of the loop for which $x > 0$ are

$$\frac{2}{a} \int_0^a x^3 \sqrt{(a^2 - x^2)} \, dx, \qquad \frac{2}{3a^3} \int_0^a x^3(a^2 - x^2)^{\frac{3}{2}} \, dx$$

and the area of the loop is

$$\frac{2}{a} \int_0^a x \sqrt{(a^2 - x^2)} \, dx.$$

The substitution $x = a \sin \theta$ enables the values of these integrals to be written down as $4a^4/15$, $4a^4/105$ and $2a^2/3$ respectively and hence

$$k_{Oy} = a \sqrt{(\tfrac{2}{5})}, \qquad k_{Ox} = a \sqrt{(\tfrac{2}{35})}.$$

Exercises 6 : 6

1. Prove that the moment of inertia of a uniform triangular plate of mass M and height h about the base is $\frac{1}{6}Mh^2$.

A uniform lamina is in the form of an isosceles triangle with base angles θ, equal sides a and area density s. Find the moments of inertia about (i) the axis of symmetry and (ii) a line through the vertex parallel to the base.

Find, also, their greatest values if θ is the only variable.

2. A uniform solid of mass M is generated by rotating the whole area bounded by the curve

$$a^2y^2 = x^2(a^2 - x^2)$$

through two right angles about Ox.

Prove that the density of the solid is $15M/(4\pi a^3)$, and that its moment of inertia about Ox is $(2Ma^2)/21$.

3. Sketch the curve $y^2 = a^2(x - a)/x$.

Calculate the radius of gyration about the line $x = a$ of the solid of revolution obtained by rotating about the x-axis that part of the curve lying between $x = a$ and $x = 2a$.

4. The area enclosed between the curve $y = \sin x$, the x-axis, and the ordinate $x = \pi/2$, is rotated through 2π radians about the x-axis. Find the radius of gyration about the y-axis of the volume generated.

5. Prove that the moment of inertia of a thin hollow spherical shell of mass M and radius a about a diameter is $2Ma^2/3$ and deduce that, if the shell is divided into two parts by a plane through the centre O, the radius of gyration of one part about any line through O is $a \sqrt{(\tfrac{2}{3})}$. Find the radius of gyration of this part about a tangent line through its vertex.

6. The area bounded by the curve $y = c \cosh (x/c)$, the coordinate axes and the line $x = a$ is occupied by a lamina of uniform thickness and mass M. Show that the moment of inertia of the lamina about the y-axis is

$$M \left(a^2 - 2ca \coth \frac{a}{c} + 2c^2 \right).$$

7. A uniform piece of wire, of mass m and length $9a$, is bent to form a right angle ABC in which $AB = 6a$ and $BC = 3a$. It is free to rotate in its own plane, which is vertical, about a smooth horizontal axis through A. Show that the moment of inertia of the wire about the axis is $21ma^2$.

8. A uniform sphere of radius a and mass M has a cylindrical hole of radius $a \sin \alpha$ bored through it, whose axis passes through the centre.

Prove (i) that the mass of the remainder is $M \cos^3 \alpha$, (ii) that the radius of gyration, k, of the remainder about the axis of the hole is given by

$$k^2 = \frac{a^2(5 - 3 \cos^2 \alpha)}{5}.$$

Hence deduce the radius of gyration of the portion removed.

9. The area bounded by the curve $y^2 = x^3$, the lines $y = 0, y = 1, x+1 = 0$, rotates about the line $x+1 = 0$. Find, correct to one-tenth of a unit, the radius of gyration of the volume developed about the axis of rotation.

10. Prove that the volume of the solid of revolution formed by rotating the loop of the curve $y^2 = x^2(1-x)/(1+x)$ about the x-axis is $\pi(2 \ln 2 - 4/3)$ and find the radius of gyration of this solid about axis of revolution.

11. A uniform lamina is the segment of the parabola $y^2 = 4ax$ cut off by the line $x = h$. Show that the radius of gyration about the tangent at the vertex is $h \sqrt{(3/7)}$.

12. An area in the first quadrant of the x, y plane is bounded by the axes Ox, Oy, the lines $x = 2a, y = 2a$ and the arc of the curve $xy = 2a^2$ cut off by these lines. A uniform solid is generated by revolution of this area through $360°$ about the y-axis. Show that the centre of mass of the solid is at distance $a(1 + \ln 4)/3$ from the origin. Show also that the radius of gyration of the solid about the y-axis is $(a \sqrt{62})/6$.

13. Find the radius of gyration:

    (i) of a uniform square of side $2a$ about an axis through the centre parallel to a side;

    (ii) of the same square about an axis through the centre perpendicular to its plane;

    (iii) of a uniform pyramid with a square base of side $2a$, about the line joining the apex to the centre of the base (this line being perpendicular to the base);

    (iv) of the same pyramid about the line through a corner of the base and perpendicular to the base.

6 : 7 Applications to hydrostatics

The total fluid thrust on one side of a plane area immersed in a liquid is the resultant of the fluid thrusts on each element of the area. Consider a plane area inclined at an angle α to the horizontal and immersed in a uniform liquid of density ϱ, Fig. 6.16. Let l be the line in which the plane of the lamina meets the (horizontal) free

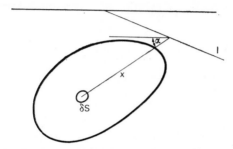

FIG. 6.16. A plane area immersed in a liquid.

surface and consider the fluid thrust on an element δS at distance x from l, i.e. at a slant depth x, the linear dimensions of δS being of the order of δx. Since the pressure at depth z below the free surface (where the pressure is zero) is ϱgz, the thrust, δT, on the element δS is $\varrho gx \sin \alpha\, \delta S + O\{(\delta x)^3\}$ and is perpendicular to that element. Hence the total thrust on one side of the lamina is

$$T = \Sigma \varrho gx \sin \alpha\, \delta S + O(\delta x) = \varrho g \sin \alpha\, \Sigma x\, \delta S + O(\delta x).$$

But $\Sigma x\, \delta S = \bar{x} S$ correct to first order of δx where S is the area of the lamina and hence we have in the limit as $\delta S \to 0$ the fundamental result

$$T = \varrho g\bar{x} \sin \alpha S, \tag{6.18}$$

i.e. the total thrust is equal to the pressure at G, the centroid of the area, multiplied by the area.

The *centre of pressure* P is the point of the lamina through which the resultant thrust on one side acts. Taking moments about l gives for the slant depth x_p of the centre of pressure

$$Tx_p = \Sigma \varrho g \sin \alpha x^2\, \delta S + O(\delta x) = \varrho g \sin \alpha\, \Sigma x^2\, \delta S + O(\delta x).$$

But $\Sigma x^2 \delta S$ is the second moment of the area about l correct to the first order in δx and may be written Sk_l^2 where k_l is the radius of gyration about l. Hence we find, in the limit,

$$x_p = \frac{k_l^2}{\bar{x}}. \tag{6.19}$$

The slant depth h of P below the level of G is given by $h = x_p - \bar{x}$. But, if k_G is the radius of gyration of the area about the horizontal through G in its plane, $k_l^2 = k_G^2 + \bar{x}^2$.

$$\therefore \quad h = \frac{k_G^2}{\bar{x}}. \tag{6.20}$$

Exercises 6 : 7

1. A circular disc of radius a is immersed in a homogeneous liquid. Show by integration that its centre of pressure is at distance $a^2/4b$ from the centre, where b is the distance of the centre from the line in which the plane of the disc cuts the surface.

2. An equilateral triangle of height h is immersed vertically in liquid so that one vertex is in the surface and the opposite side is horizontal. Show that the depth of the centre of pressure is $3h/4$. The triangle is then rotated about the horizontal base until it is again vertical. Find the consequent change in the depth of the centre of pressure.

3. A lamina has the shape of a plane annulus of inner and outer radii a and b respectively. It is completely immersed in a liquid subject to gravity so that its plane is vertical and its centre is at depth c below the surface. Prove that the depth of the centre of pressure is

$$\frac{a^2 + b^2 + 4c^2}{4c}.$$

4. A plane lamina is immersed in homogeneous liquid with its plane vertical, its centroid at a depth h and the centre of pressure of a face at a depth p. If the lamina is lowered, without rotation, through a distance k, prove that the depth of the centre of pressure of a face is now $k + h(p+k)/(h+k)$.

Find the centre of pressure of an elliptic lamina, with axes $2a$, $2b$, which is just immersed, with its major axis vertical, in homogeneous liquid. If the lamina is now lowered without rotation until the thrust on it is doubled, find the distance of the centre of pressure from the centroid of the lamina.

5. A sector of angle 2α is cut from a circle, centre C and radius c. The sector is completely immersed in uniform fluid with C in the surface and its plane vertical. If the central radius of the sector makes an angle β with the surface, prove that the horizontal distance of the centre of pressure from the vertical line through C is

$$\tfrac{3}{4}c \cos \alpha \cos \beta.$$

6 : 8 Inequalities involving integrals

Although many indefinite integrals cannot be evaluated in closed form, numerical values of definite integrals involving the same integrands may be obtained by means of the techniques of § 6 : 9.

However, some additional confidence in such results and rough approximations to other definite integrals can be obtained by considering inequalities. Also questions of convergence of integrals may sometimes be resolved by the use of inequalities.

$$\text{If } f(x) \geq 0 \quad \text{for} \quad a \leq x \leq b, \quad a < b, \quad \text{then} \int_a^b f(x)\,dx \geq 0.$$

This result follows at once by considering the definite integral as the limit of a sum (see § 3 : 2). Note that if $f(x) > 0$ in the interval $[a, b]$, then $\int_a^b f(x)\,dx > 0.$

Corollaries

(i) Since $f(x) \leq |f(x)|$, it follows that

$$\int_a^b \{|f(x)| - f(x)\}\,dx \geq 0,$$

i.e.
$$\int_a^b |f(x)|\,dx \geq \int_a^b f(x)\,dx. \tag{6.21}$$

Note than eqn. (6.21) implies the inequality

$$\int_a^b |f(x)|\,dx \geq \left| \int_a^b f(x)\,dx \right|. \tag{6.22}$$

(ii) If $\phi(x) \geq \psi(x)$ for $a \leq x \leq b$, then by considering $f(x) = \phi(x) - \psi(x)$ we have

$$\int_a^b \phi(x)\,dx \geq \int_a^b \psi(x)\,dx.$$

Also, if $\phi(x) > \psi(x)$ for $a \leq x \leq b$, $a < b$, then

$$\int_a^b \phi(x)\,dx > \int_a^b \psi(x)\,dx.$$

These results are illustrated by considering the graphs of the various functions concerned.

Example 1. By considering

$$\int_a^b \{f(x) + \lambda g(x)\}^2 \, dx$$

show that

$$\left\{ \int_a^b fg \, dx \right\}^2 \le \int_a^b f^2 \, dx \times \int_a^b g^2 \, dx.$$

Since $\{f(x) + \lambda g(x)\}^2 \ge 0$ for real functions and real λ, it follows that

$$\int_a^b \{f(x) + \lambda g(x)\}^2 \, dx \ge 0,$$

i.e. $\qquad \int_a^b \{f(x)\}^2 \, dx + 2\lambda \int_a^b f(x) \, g(x) \, dx + \lambda^2 \int_a^b \{g(x)\}^2 \, dx \ge 0. \qquad (1)$

Regarding the left-hand side of inequality (1) as a quadratic form in λ we see that it cannot have real distinct factors (see § 1 : 6). Hence

$$\left\{ \int_a^b fg \, dx \right\}^2 \le \int_a^b f^2 \, dx \times \int_a^b g^2 \, dx. \qquad (2)$$

This result is the analogue of Cauchy's inequality (see p. 38) and is known as *Schwarz's inequality*.

Example 2. We consider the convergence of $I = \int_\pi^\infty \frac{\sin x}{x} \, dx$,

i.e. $\qquad \qquad \lim_{N \to \infty} \int_\pi^N \frac{\sin x}{x} \, dx.$

Integrating by parts

$$I = \lim_{N \to \infty} \left\{ \left[-\frac{\cos x}{x} \right]_\pi^N - \int_\pi^N \frac{\cos x}{x^2} \, dx \right\}.$$

But $\qquad \left| \int_\pi^N \frac{\cos x}{x^2} \, dx \right| \le \int_\pi^N \left| \frac{\cos x}{x^2} \right| \, dx < \int_\pi^N \left| \frac{1}{x^2} \right| \, dx$

$$= \int_\pi^N \frac{1}{x^2} \, dx = \left[-\frac{1}{x} \right]_\pi^N = \frac{1}{\pi} - \frac{1}{N} \to \frac{1}{\pi} \quad \text{as} \quad N \to \infty.$$

It follows that $\int_0^\pi \frac{\cos x}{x^2} \, dx$ is absolutely convergent and therefore is convergent. Hence I converges to a finite limit.

Note that since $\sin x < x$ for $x > 0$ (see Example 2, p. 255),

$$J = \int\limits_0^\pi \frac{\sin x}{x}\ dx < \int\limits_0^\pi 1\ dx = \pi,$$

and hence $\int\limits_0^\infty \dfrac{\sin x}{x} dx = J+I$ converges at the lower limit also.

$$\left[\text{In fact } \int\limits_0^\infty \frac{\sin x}{x} dx = \frac{\pi}{2}\ ,\ \ (\text{see Vol. 5, § 3 : 6).}\right]$$

Example 3. Show that, if $p > q > 0$ and $x > 0$,

$$\frac{x^p-1}{p} \geqslant \frac{x^q-1}{q}\ . \tag{1}$$

Prove also that, for n a positive integer and for $s > 0$,

$$\frac{1}{p}\left\{\frac{x^p}{(p+s)^n}-\frac{1}{s^n}\right\} \geqslant \frac{1}{q}\left\{\frac{x^q}{(q+s)^n}-\frac{1}{s^n}\right\}.$$

Consider $f(x) = x^{p-1}-x^{q-1} = x^{q-1}(x^{p-q}-1)$.

Since $p > q > 0$ and $x > 0$,

$$f(x) > 0 \quad \text{if} \quad x > 1, \tag{2}$$
$$f(x) < 0 \quad \text{if} \quad 0 < x < 1. \tag{3}$$

Integrating inequality (2) w.r. to x from 1 to x we have, if $x > 1$,

$$\int\limits_1^x (x^{p-1}-x^{q-1})\ dx = \frac{x^p-1}{p}-\frac{x^q-1}{q} > 0.$$

Similarly integrating inequality (3) w.r. to x from x to 1 we have, if $0 < x < 1$,

$$\int\limits_x^1 (x^{p-1}-x^{q-1})\ dx = \frac{1-x^p}{p}-\frac{1-x^q}{q} < 0.$$

Therefore inequality (1) is true for $x > 0$, equality holding only when $x = 1$.

Now multiplying inequality (1) by x^{s-1} and integrating w.r. to x from 1 to x we find, for $x > 0$ and $s > 0$,

$$\frac{1}{p}\left\{\frac{x^{q+s}}{p+s}-\frac{x^s}{s}\right\} \geqslant \frac{1}{q}\left\{\frac{x^{q+s}}{(q+s)}-\frac{x^s}{s}\right\}$$

or

$$\frac{1}{p}\left\{\frac{x^p}{p+s}-\frac{1}{s}\right\} \geqslant \frac{1}{q}\left\{\frac{x^q}{q+s}-\frac{1}{s}\right\}.$$

Repeating this operation [multiplication by x^{s-1} and integration w.r. to x from 1 to x], $n-1$ further times, the required result follows.

Exercises 6 : 8

1. Show that, for $0 < x < \pi/2$,

$$x > \sin x > 2x/\pi.$$

Deduce that

$$1 - e^{-\frac{1}{2}\pi} < \int_0^{\frac{1}{2}\pi} e^{-\sin x}\, dx < (e-1)\pi/2e.$$

2. Prove that, if $0 \leqslant x < 1$,

$$\left(1 + \frac{x^2}{2}\right)^2 \leqslant \frac{1}{1-x^2}$$

and deduce that

$$x + \frac{x^3}{6} \leqslant \sin^{-1} x,$$

if $0 \leqslant x < 1$.

3. The continuous functions $\phi(x)$, $\psi(x)$ and $g(x)$ satisfy the inequalities

(i)　$\phi(x) \geqslant 0$,

(ii)　$\psi(x) \geqslant g(x)$,

when $a \leqslant x \leqslant b$. Prove that

$$\int_a^b \phi(x)\, \psi(x)\, dx \geqslant \int_a^b \phi(x)\, g(x)\, dx.$$

Use this result to prove that

$$0{\cdot}78 \leqslant \int_0^1 \frac{x\, dx}{\sqrt{(1-x^3)}} \leqslant 1{\cdot}00.$$

4. Prove that

$$\int_0^1 \frac{x^4(1-x)^4\, dx}{1+x^2} = \frac{22}{7} - \pi.$$

Show that $\dfrac{1}{2} \displaystyle\int_0^1 x^4(1-x)^4\, dx < \int_0^1 \frac{x^4(1-x)^4\, dx}{1+x^2} < \int_0^1 x^4(1-x)^4\, dx$,

and hence deduce that $\dfrac{22}{7} - \dfrac{1}{1260} > \pi > \dfrac{22}{7} - \dfrac{1}{630}$.

5. The functions $f(x)$ and $g(x)$ are both positive and $f(x) = \phi(x)\, g(x)$, where $\phi(x) > 0$. Prove that, if

$$F(x) = \int_0^x f(t)\, dt \quad \text{and} \quad G(x) = \int_0^x g(t)\, dt,$$

then

$$F(x) \leqslant \phi(x)\, G(x);$$

Deduce that $F(x)/G(x)$ is also an increasing function of x.

Prove that

$$\frac{1}{x^{4n+2}} \left\{ x - \frac{1}{3!} x^3 + \frac{1}{5!} x^5 - \cdots + \frac{1}{(4n+1)!} x^{4n+1} - \sin x \right\}$$

is a positive increasing function of x for $0 < x < \pi/2$.

6. $I_n = \int\limits_0^{\frac{1}{2}\pi} \sin^n \theta \, d\theta$, where n is a positive integer or zero, prove

$$\text{(i)} \quad I_{2n} I_{2n+1} = \frac{\pi}{4n+2},$$

$$\text{(ii)} \quad \frac{\pi}{4n} > (I_{2n})^2 > \frac{\pi}{4n+2}.$$

7. If $\quad f(x) = \int\limits_0^x \sin^n t \, dt \quad (n > -1), \quad \phi(\alpha) = \int\limits_0^\alpha f(u) \, du$,

prove that $\qquad \phi(\alpha) = \int\limits_0^\alpha (\alpha - x) \sin^n x \, dx.$

Deduce that, if $0 < \alpha \leqslant \frac{1}{2}\pi$, then

$$0 < \phi(\alpha) < \frac{1}{n+1} \alpha \sin^{n+1} \alpha.$$

8. Show that

$$g(x) = \int\limits_x^{2x} \frac{\sin u}{u} \, du$$

is bounded for $x > 0$, and find the points x at which it attains its greatest and least values in this range.

6 : 9 Numerical integration

1. Introduction. There are many circumstances when a function which is known only through its tabulated values must be integrated over a specified interval. For example, this arises if we wish to know erf x for a specific value of x; it is also the case if the function to be integrated is given in terms of experimentally determined figures and not as a result of certain analytical operations. We discuss here methods of estimating numerically the value of a definite integral whose range of integration coincides, more or less, with the range of values of x covered by the table. (The numerical integration of differential equations involves estimating the value of a function just outside the range of a table. This "prediction" of values is rather a different problem and will not be discussed here. See, however, Vol. II, 2nd edn., Chaps. I and II.)

In § 5 : 11 we used polynomials to give approximate values of a function for purposes of interpolation. These polynomials were usually given in terms of p, where $x_p = x_0 + ph$, and were such that, when p had integral values $p = r$, the corresponding tabulated values y_r were given by the polynomial. For interpolation we used non-integral values of p. The basis of the formulae we obtain here is integration of these polynomials w.r. to p.

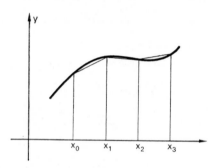

FIG. 6.17. Illustrating the trapezoidal rule for numerical integration.

An approximate method of evaluating the area under a curve is to divide this area into strips of equal width and close the top of each strip by a straight line. Then the area enclosed, see Fig. 6.17, between $x = x_0$ and $x = x_3$, is approximately

$$\tfrac{1}{2}h(y_0+y_1)+\tfrac{1}{2}h(y_1+y_2)+\tfrac{1}{2}h(y_2+y_3) = \tfrac{1}{2}h(y_0+2y_1+2y_2+y_3).$$
$$(6.23)$$

If there were n strips, then the area would be, to the same approximation,

$$\int_{x_0}^{x_n} f(x)\,\mathrm{d}x \approx \tfrac{1}{2}h(y_0+2y_1+2y_2+ \ \ldots \ +2y_{n-1}+y_n). \quad (6.24)$$

This formula (6.24) is called the *trapezoidal* rule, for the area has been made up as a sum of n trapeziums.

In effect this method replaces the actual curve by a polynomial of degree one for the purposes of integration; a different poly-

nomial is used for each strip. Thus, for a typical strip,
$$y_p = y_0 + p\,\Delta y_0 = y_0(1-p) + py_1,$$
which is integrated w.r. to p by means of the substitution $x = x_0 + ph$, $\mathrm{d}x = h\,\mathrm{d}p$ to give
$$\int_{x_0}^{x_1} y\,\mathrm{d}x = h\int_0^1 \{y_0(1-p) + py_1\}\,\mathrm{d}p = \tfrac{1}{2}h(y_0 + y_1).$$

More accurate estimates can be obtained if we use polynomials of higher degree. In § 5 : 11 we obtained three such polynomials, viz., two Newton formulae, forward and backward, and Stirling's formula with central differences. If we use three values of x, i.e. two strips of Fig. 6.17, we can replace the actual curve by a parabola through the end points of the three consecutive ordinates. In general, we can use $n+1$ consecutive ordinates, enclosing n strips, replace the actual curve by a polynomial of degree n, and integrate this polynomial to estimate the area under the curve corresponding to the n strips. There are three well-known formulae, in addition to the trapezoidal rule. They are

  (i) *Simpson's rule*, which uses three ordinates, or two strips,

  (ii) *Newton's "three-eighths" rule*, which uses four ordinates,

  (iii) *Weddle's formula*, which uses seven ordinates.

Example 1. We use the figures of Table 9 to evaluate the integral $\int_0^{1\cdot2} e^{-x}\,\mathrm{d}x$, by means of the trapezoidal rule.

Using six strips,

$$\int_0^{1\cdot2} e^{-x}\,\mathrm{d}x = \tfrac{1}{2}h(y_0 + 2y_1 + 2y_2 + 2y_3 + 2y_4 + 2y_5 + y_6)$$

$$\begin{aligned}
&= 0\cdot1\times\{1\cdot000\,000 + 2\times0\cdot818\,731 \qquad\qquad = 0\cdot701\,134.\\
&\quad + \ 0\cdot301\,194 + 2\times0\cdot670\,320\\
&\qquad\qquad\qquad + 2\times0\cdot548\,812\\
&\qquad\qquad\qquad + 2\times0\cdot449\,329\\
&\qquad\qquad\qquad + 2\times0\cdot367\,879\}
\end{aligned}$$

The correct value is $e^0 - e^{-1\cdot2} = 1 - 0\cdot301\,194 = 0\cdot698\,806$.

Since the curve $y = e^{-x}$ is concave upwards, we expect our result to be an overestimate.

2. Simpson's rule. When we use three ordinates, or any odd number of ordinates, it is best to choose y_0 to be the central value in the table and take the other two as y_{-1}, y_{+1}. Further, the best formula (polynomial approximation) to use in these circumstances is Stirling's central difference formula. Since we are assuming a second degree polynomial, the third differences $\delta^3 y$ are taken to be zero. Stirling's formula is, in this case,

$$y_p = y_0 + S_1 \mu \, \delta_0 + S_2 \, \delta_0^2.$$

$$\therefore \int_{x_{-1}}^{x_{+1}} f(x) \, dx = h \int_{-1}^{1} f(x_0 + ph) \, dp$$

$$= 2hy_0 + h\mu \, \delta_0 \int_{-1}^{1} S_1 \, dp + h \, \delta_0^2 \int_{-1}^{1} S_2 \, dp.$$

Now S_1 is an odd function of p and so $\int_{-1}^{1} S_1 \, dp$ vanishes. Further, since $S_2 = \frac{1}{2} p^2$,

$$\int_{-1}^{1} S_2 \, dp = [\tfrac{1}{3} p^3]_0^1 = \tfrac{1}{3}.$$

$$\therefore \int_{x_{-1}}^{x_{+1}} f(x) \, dx = h(2y_0 + \tfrac{1}{3}\delta_0^2) = \tfrac{1}{3}h(6y_0 + y_{-1} - 2y_0 + y_1)$$

$$= \tfrac{1}{3}h(y_{-1} + 4y_0 + y_1).$$

If we had used the ordinates y_0, y_1 and y_2 instead of y_{-1}, y_0 and y_1 the area of the corresponding strips would have been

$$\int_{x_0}^{x_2} f(x) \, dx \approx \tfrac{1}{3}h(y_0 + 4y_1 + y_2). \tag{6.25}$$

We apply this formula to a table with $2m + 1$ entries $y_0, y_1, \ldots, y_{2m}$. The area of the $2m$ strips is made up of m expressions such as in (6.25) and we find

$$\int_{x_0}^{x_{2m}} y \, dx \approx \tfrac{1}{3}h(y_0 + 4y_1 + y_2) + \tfrac{1}{3}h(y_2 + 4y_3 + y_4)$$

$$+ \ldots + \tfrac{1}{3}h(y_{2m-2} + 4y_{2m-1} + y_{2m})$$

$$= \tfrac{1}{3}h\{y_0 + y_{2m} + 4(y_1 + y_3 + \ldots + y_{2m-1})$$

$$+ 2(y_2 + y_4 + \ldots + y_{2m-2})\}. \tag{6.26}$$

This formula, *Simpson's rule*, is probably familiar to many readers, and can, of course, be obtained without specifically referring to an interpolation formula. [Note that it is essential that there should be an even number of strips when Simpson's rule is used.]

Example 2. We use Simpson's rule to evaluate the integral $\int\limits_{0}^{1\cdot 2} e^{-x}\,dx$.

Using six strips,

$$\int\limits_{0}^{1\cdot 2} e^{-x}\,dx \approx \frac{0\cdot 2}{3}\{y_0+4(y_1+y_3+y_5)+2(y_2+y_4)+y_6\}$$

$$= \frac{0\cdot 2}{3}\{1\cdot 000\,000+4\times 0\cdot 818\,731+2\times 0\cdot 670\,320$$
$$+0\cdot 301\,194+4\times 0\cdot 548\,812+2\times 0\cdot 449\,329$$
$$+4\times 0\cdot 367\,879\}$$

$$= 0\cdot 698\,812.$$

(Correct value $0\cdot 698\,806$.)

---

3. Newton's "three-eighths" rule. We obtain Newton's three-eighths rule thus. Assuming that we are given four values y_0, y_1, y_2 and y_3, the polynomial, of degree 3, going through the ends of these ordinates is obtained from the forward interpolation formula thus:

$$y_p = y_0+\binom{p}{1}\Delta_0+\binom{p}{2}\Delta_0^2+\binom{p}{3}\Delta_0^3.$$

The integral, or area under the curve, is given by

$$\int\limits_{x_0}^{x_3} f(x)\,dx = h\int\limits_{0}^{3} y_p\,dp$$
$$= h\{3y_0+\tfrac{9}{2}(y_1-y_0)+\tfrac{9}{4}(y_2-2y_1+y_0)$$
$$+\tfrac{3}{8}(y_3-3y_2+3y_1-y_0)\},$$

where we have inserted the explicit expressions for the differences. This reduces to

$$\int\limits_{x_0}^{x_3} f(x)\,dx = \tfrac{3}{8}h(y_0+3y_1+3y_2+y_3), \qquad (6.27)$$

which is *Newton's three-eighths rule.* To use this formula we must employ $3m+1$ ordinates.

Example 3. We evaluate the same integral $\int_0^{1\cdot2} e^{-x}\, dx$ by two applications of Newton's three-eighths rule.

$$\int_0^{1\cdot2} e^{-x}\, dx = \frac{3}{8}\, h(y_0+3y_1+3y_2+y_3)+\frac{3}{8}\, h(y_3+3y_4+3y_5+y_6)$$

$$= \frac{3\times0\cdot2}{8}\, \{1\cdot000\,000+3\times0\cdot818\,731+2\times0\cdot548\,812\}$$
$$+0\cdot301\,194+3\times0\cdot670\,320$$
$$+3\times0\cdot449\,329$$
$$+3\times0\cdot367\,879$$

$$= 0\cdot698\,820.$$

(Correct value $0\cdot698\,806$.)

Example 4. *Weddle's formula* is obtained as above with one additional adjustment. This formula uses seven ordinates and so we start from Stirling's formula and write

$$y_p = y_0+S_1\mu\delta_0+S_2\delta_0^2+S_3\mu\delta_0^3+S_4\delta_0^4+S_5\mu\delta_0^5+S_6\delta_0^6\,,$$

which is a sixth degree polynomial. We integrate w.r. to p from $p = -3$ to $+3$, and find

$$\int_{x_{-3}}^{x_{+3}} f(x)\, dx = h \int_{-3}^{3} y_p\, dp.$$

Because S_{2r+1} is an odd function of p, only the even order terms survive. Using the formulae for Stirling's coefficients we find

$$\int_{-3}^{3} S_2\, dp = \int_{-3}^{3} \frac{1}{2}\, p^2\, dp = 9, \qquad \int_{-3}^{3} S_4\, dp = \frac{1}{4!} \int_{-3}^{3} p^2(p^2-1)\, dp = \frac{33}{10}\,,$$

$$\int_{-3}^{3} S_6\, dp = \frac{1}{6!} \int_{-3}^{3} p^2(p^2-1)(p^2-4)\, dp = \frac{41}{140}\,.$$

$$\therefore \int_{x_{-3}}^{x_{+3}} f(x)\, dx = h\,\{6y_0+9\delta_0^2+\tfrac{33}{10}\delta_0^4+\tfrac{41}{140}\delta_0^6\}. \tag{1}$$

Since the sixth differences are usually small the error introduced by writing $\frac{42}{140}$ in place of $\frac{41}{140}$ in eqn. (1) is very slight. But this change simplifies the values of the coefficients so that we can write

$$\int_{x_{-3}}^{x_3} f(x)\,dx \approx \tfrac{3}{10}h\,\{20y_0+30(y_{-1}-2y_0+y_1)$$

$$+11(y_{-2}-4y_{-1}+6y_0-4y_1+y_2)$$
$$+(y_{-3}-6y_{-2}+15y_{-1}-20y_0+15y_1-6y_2+y_3)\}$$
$$=\tfrac{3}{10}h(y_{-3}+5y_{-2}+y_{-1}+6y_0+y_1+5y_2+y_3).$$

This is *Weddle's formula.*

The advantage of simple values for the coefficients in this formula lies in the fact that the calculations can be performed on a desk calculator very much more swiftly than with the "correct" values from Stirling's formula. The loss of accuracy is usually unimportant.

Formulae for numerical integration of definite integrals are always given in terms of y_r rather than in terms of differences. This avoids the necessity of evaluating the differences and computations can be made directly from the tables.

Example 5. We can apply Weddle's formula also to the evaluation of $\int_0^{1\cdot2} e^{-x}\,dx$. The application is

$$\int_0^{1\cdot2} e^{-x}\,dx = \tfrac{3}{10}h\,\{y_0+5y_1+y_2+6y_3+y_4+5y_5+y_6\}$$

$$= 0\cdot06\,\{1\cdot000\,000+5\times0\cdot818\,731+6\times0\cdot548\,812$$
$$+0\cdot670\,320+5\times0\cdot367\,879$$
$$+0\cdot449\,329$$
$$+0\cdot301\,194\}$$
$$= 0\cdot698\,806.$$

(Correct value 0·698 806.)

---

4. Estimates of error. As with interpolation, so in numerical integration we must know the likely limits of error arising from the use of rules such as Simpson's rule. We obtain estimates of errors by using, say, Stirling's formula without truncation. The formula is

$$y_p = y_0+S_1\mu\,\delta_0+S_2\,\delta_0^2+S_3\mu\,\delta_0^3+S_4\,\delta_0^4+\,\ldots$$

If we integrate this equation w.r. to p from -1 to 1 we are performing the integration for Simpson's rule. Using the formulae for the coefficients S_{2r+1}, S_{2r+2} we obtain

$$h \int_{-1}^{1} y_p \, dp = 2h \left(y_0 + \frac{1}{6} \delta_0^2 - \frac{1}{180} \delta_0^4 + \frac{1}{1512} \delta_0^6 - \dots \right)$$

$$= \frac{h}{3} (y_{-1} + 4y_0 + y_1) + 2h \left(-\frac{\delta_0^4}{180} + \dots \right).$$

The last term here is the correction to be made to Simpson's rule. By several applications to an even number of strips we obtain

$$\int_{x_0}^{x_{2m}} f(x) \, dx \approx \frac{1}{3} h\{ y_0 + y_{2m} + 4(y_1 + y_3 + \dots + y_{2m-1})$$

$$+ 2(y_2 + y_4 + \dots + y_{2m-2}) \} - \frac{h}{90} (\delta_1^4 + \delta_3^4 + \dots + \delta_{2m-1}^4).$$

For a function which is well behaved we can take the error to have the same order as the first of the rejected terms of the polynomial (as we did in estimating errors in interpolation).

Example. The sum of the fourth differences in the table for e^{-x} related to the range $x = 0$ to $1 \cdot 2$ is

$$\Sigma \delta^4 = 1321 + 886 + 591 = 2798.$$

Hence the error is approximately

$$-\frac{h}{90} \Sigma \delta^4 = -6$$

in units of the last decimal place of the table. The difference between the value obtained by Simpson's rule and the correct value is in fact $0 \cdot 698\,806 - 0 \cdot 698\,812$ which is -6 units of the last place.

If the integrand has not been evaluated (perhaps it is given by an explicit function or formula) the fewer evaluations of the integrand involved the better. In the use of Simpson's rule it is convenient to start with only two intervals each of length $h = \frac{1}{2}(b - a)$ spanning the range (a, b). This requires three evaluations of the integrand, and a first estimate I_1 of the integral is obtained. Now the interval is halved, two more evaluations of the integrand are required, to give a second estimate I_2. The interval is halved again, requiring four more evaluations. This process is continued until two consecutive estimates differ by less than the required accuracy.

Example. We evaluate the $\int_0^{1·6} e^{-x}\, dx$ correct to three decimal places using the minimum number of intervals. (Instead of evaluating e^{-x} we read its values, correct to four places, from Table 9.)

Two intervals:

x	0	0·8	1·6	$I_1 = \dfrac{0·8}{3}\{1·201\ 9 + 4\times 0·449\ 3\}$
y	1·000 0	0·449 3	0·201 9	$= 0·799\ 8.$

Four intervals:

x	0	0·4	0·8	1·2	1·6
y	1·000 0	0·670 3	0·449 3	0·301 2	0·201 9

$$I_2 = \frac{0·4}{3}\{1·201\ 9 + 4\times 0·971\ 5 + 2\times 0·449\ 3\} = 0·798\ 2.$$

Eight intervals:

x	0	0·2	0·4	0·6	0·8	1·0	1·2	1·4	1·6
y	1·000 0	0·818 7	0·670 3	0·548 8	0·449 3	0·367 9	0·301 2	0·246 6	0·201 9

$$I_3 = \frac{0·2}{3}\{1·201\ 9 + 4\times 1·982\ 0 + 2\times 1·420\ 8\} = 0·798\ 1.$$

I_2 and I_3 differ only in the fourth place, so that Simpson's rule gives the integral as 0·798 correct to three places of decimals. The correct value is $1 - e^{-1·6} \approx 0·798\ 1$.

Another method of obtaining an approximate value for some integrals which have no closed expression for the indefinite integral is to expand the integrand as a power series (e.g. by the binomial theorem) and to integrate this series term by term. Provided that the series converges sufficiently rapidly, only a limited number of terms are needed to obtain a good approximation to the integral. The method is most successful where there is a parameter in the integrand which is small enough to enable a rapidly convergent series to be found.

Example. Show that the length of the arc of the ellipse $x = a\cos\theta$, $y = b\sin\theta$ from $\theta = \beta$ to $\theta = \gamma$ is

$$\int_\beta^\gamma (a^2 \sin^2\theta + b^2 \cos^2\theta)^{\frac{1}{2}}\, d\theta,$$

and hence show that the length of the arc from $\theta = \frac{1}{4}\pi - \alpha$ to $\theta = \frac{1}{4}\pi + \alpha$ is

$$l \int_{-\alpha}^{\alpha} (1 + k^2 \sin 2\varphi)^{\frac{1}{2}} \, d\varphi,$$

where $2l^2 = a^2 + b^2$ and $k^2(a^2 + b^2) = a^2 - b^2$.

Deduce that, neglecting terms in k^4, the circumference of the ellipse is $2\pi l$.

Since $(ds/d\theta)^2 = a^2 \sin^2 \theta + b^2 \cos^2 \theta$ the arc length, s, is given by

$$s = \int_{\beta}^{\gamma} (a^2 \sin^2 \theta + b^2 \cos^2 \theta)^{\frac{1}{2}} \, d\theta$$

$$= \int_{\beta}^{\gamma} [\tfrac{1}{2}(a^2 + b^2) + \tfrac{1}{2}(b^2 - a^2) \cos 2\theta]^{\frac{1}{2}} \, d\theta.$$

In this we substitute $2\theta = \frac{1}{2}\pi + 2\varphi$, so that $\cos 2\theta = -\sin 2\varphi$, $d\theta = d\varphi$; when $\theta = \frac{1}{4}\pi \pm \alpha$, $\varphi = \pm \alpha$. Therefore

$$s = \int_{-\alpha}^{\alpha} [\tfrac{1}{2}(a^2 + b^2) + \tfrac{1}{2}(a^2 - b^2) \sin 2\varphi]^{\frac{1}{2}} \, d\varphi = l \int_{-\alpha}^{\alpha} (1 + k^2 \sin 2\varphi)^{\frac{1}{2}} \, d\varphi.$$

Provided k^2 is small enough the integrand here may be expanded by the binomial series to give a rapidly convergent series in powers of $(k^2 \sin 2\varphi)$.

Therefore

$$s = l \int_{-\alpha}^{\alpha} (1 + \tfrac{1}{2}k^2 \sin 2\varphi - \tfrac{1}{8}k^4 \sin^2 2\varphi + \dots) \, d\varphi.$$

We now ignore k^4 and higher powers, and put $\alpha = \pi$, to give the complete circumference. Therefore

$$s \approx l \int_{-\pi}^{\pi} (1 + \tfrac{1}{2}k^2 \sin 2\varphi) \, d\varphi = l \cdot 2\pi + 0.$$

The integral $\int_{-\alpha}^{\alpha} (1 + k^2 \sin 2\varphi)^{\frac{1}{2}} \, d\varphi$ is called an *elliptic* integral and cannot be evaluated in a closed form by means of elementary functions.

Exercises 6:9

1. (i) Evaluate $\int_{0}^{0\cdot8} \dfrac{dx}{(1-x^2)^{\frac{1}{3}}}$ by means of Simpson's rule, using eight strips, giving the result to three decimal places.

(ii) Evaluate $\int_{0\cdot8}^{1} \dfrac{dx}{(1-x^2)^{\frac{1}{3}}}$ to three decimal places, by making the substitution $x = 1-t$, and then expanding the integrand by means of the binomial theorem.

2. The coordinates of a point on a curve are given by the following table:

x	0	0·5	1·0	1·5	2·0	2·5	3·0
y	2	2·03	2·24	2·72	3·46	4·43	5·57

Calculate

(i) the area under the curve between the ordinates $x = 0$ and $x = 3$,

(ii) the first moment of this area about the x-axis.

Deduce the volume of the solid formed by rotating the area through 2π about the x-axis.

3. Obtain an approximate value of $\int_0^{\pi/4} \lg \sec x \, dx$. Use Simpson's rule with five ordinates.

4. The speed in m/s of an aircraft accelerating from rest is recorded at 5-s intervals as follows:

t s	0	5	10	15	20	25	30	35	40
v m/s	0	3·9	10·4	18·1	26·4	35·4	44·7	54·5	64·5

Estimate the distance in metres covered in the 40 s.

5. A river 40 m wide has soundings, taken at 5 m intervals across its width, which are given in the table below:

Distance from bank	0	5	10	15	20	25	30	35	40
Depth of water		0	3	6	8	7	6	4	3	0

Use Simpson's rule to estimate the area of cross section of the river.
The maximum speed of the current is 1 m/s in the middle of the river. Assuming that the speed at a given horizontal distance from the bank is the same at all depths, and that it decreases uniformly to zero at either edge, estimate the flow of the river in m³/s.

6. (i) By expanding the integrand in powers of x, evaluate

$$\int_0^{\frac{1}{2}} \frac{1}{x} \ln (1+x) \, dx$$

correct to three decimal places.

(ii) Using Simpson's rule with four intervals, evaluate

$$\int_0^1 \sin \left(\frac{\pi}{2} x^2 \right) dx,$$

giving the result to three decimal places.

7. Using a suitable expansion of the integrand and integrating term by term, find the value of

$$\int_0^{\frac{1}{2}} \frac{dx}{(1+x^3)^{\frac{1}{2}}}$$

correct to three decimal places.

Evaluate the integral also by using Simpson's rule, taking five ordinates.

8. The following table gives the coordinates (x, y) of points on a certain curve.

x	0	0·1	0·2	0·3	0·4	
y	1	0·990 1	0·961 5	0·917 4	0·862 1	

x	0·5	0·6	0·7	0·8	0·9	1·0
y	0·800 0	0·735 3	0·671 1	0·609 8	0·552 5	0·500 0.

Use Simpson's rule to calculate the area bounded by this curve, the coordinate axes and the line $x = 1$. Find also, correct to two significant figures, the x-co-ordinate of the centroid of this area.

9. The co-ordinates of points on a curve are given in the following table:

x	0	0·2	0·4	0·6	0·8	1·0	1·2
y	1	1·1	1·3	1·5	1·6	1·4	1·3

Find, using Simpson's rule, the volume of revolution obtained when the area under this curve bounded by the lines $x = 0$, $x = 1·2$ and the x-axis is rotated through 2π radians about the x-axis.

Obtain the coordinates of the centroid of this volume of revolution.

10. The velocity at time t of a particle moving along the x-axis is given by $\sqrt{(27-t^3)}$ for $0 \leqslant t \leqslant 3$. Use Simpson's rule with 6 strips to calculate the distance travelled by the particle during the interval $t = 0$ to $t = 3$.

11. Values of a function $f(x)$ for given values of x are shown in the following table:

x	0	1	2	3	4
$f(x)$	2·073 6	2·856 1	3·841 6	5·062 5	6·062 5

x	5	6	7	8
$f(x)$	8·352 1	10·497 6	13·032 1	16·000 0

Assuming that $f(x)$ is a fourth degree polynomial and that there is an error in one of the given values, trace the error and correct the table.

Find, using Simpson's rule, the value of

$$\int_2^6 f(x)\, dx.$$

12. Apply the substitution $x = (a-t)/(1+at)$ to

$$I = \int\limits_{(a-1)/(a+1)}^{a} \frac{(a-x)^{\frac{1}{2}}\, dx}{(ax+1)^2}$$

and, by expanding the resulting integrand in series for small values of the constant a, show that

$$I = \frac{2}{3} - \frac{1}{5}\, a - \frac{19}{18}\, a^2$$

approximately.

13. The function $f(x)$ has a continuous fourth derivative $f^{(4)}(x)$ satisfying $|f^{(4)}(x)| \leqslant M$ on the interval $c-h \leqslant x \leqslant c+h$. By using Taylor's formula with a remainder term, show that:

(i) $\frac{1}{3}h[f(c-h)+4f(c)+f(c+h)] = 2hf(c)+\frac{1}{3}h^3 f''(c)+K,$

where $|K| \leqslant Mh^5/36;$

(ii) $\int\limits_{c-h}^{c+h} f(x)\, dx = 2hf(c)+\frac{1}{3}h^3 f''(c)+L,$

where $|L| \leqslant Mh^5/60.$

If $|f^{(4)}(x)| \leqslant M$ on the interval $a \leqslant x \leqslant b$, obtain an upper bound for the error in approximating

$$\int\limits_a^b f(x)\, dx$$

by Simpson's rule with $n = 2m$ intervals.

If the value of $\ln(3/2)$ is to be calculated by Simpson's rule applied to

$$\int\limits_2^3 x^{-1}\, dx,$$

what is the least number of intervals that will ensure an error not exceeding 10^{-5}?

Miscellaneous Exercises VI

1. A uniform solid of mass M has the form generated by rotating the area under the curve $y^2 = x^2+a^2$ and between the ordinates $x = \pm a$, through 2π radians about Ox.

Prove that

(i)   the density of the solid is $3M/(8\pi a^3)$,

(ii) its moment of inertia about its axis is $7Ma^2/10$,

(iii) its moment of inertia about a line perpendicular to its axis through its centre of mass is $3Ma^2/4$.

2. Sketch the curve whose equation is

$$a^2 y^2 = x^2(a^2 - x^2)$$

and find, for either loop, the greatest width measured parallel to the axis of y and the area.

If the area enclosed by the curve is rotated through $180°$ about the axis of y, show that the volume generated is $\frac{1}{4}\pi^2 a^3$.

3. A solid of revolution is generated by rotation about the axis of x of the area bounded by the curve $y = \sec x$ and the lines $x = 0$, $x = \pi/4$ and $y = 0$. Find the volume of the solid, the position of its centroid and its radius of gyration about its axis.

4. Show that if the tangent at the point (x_0, y_0) on the curve $x = a\cos^2 t \sin t$, $y = a\cos t \sin^2 t$ meets the x-axis at the point $(x_1, 0)$, then x_1 does not lie between 0 and $\frac{1}{2}x_0$.

Show also that the loop of the curve corresponding to the range

$$0 \leqslant t \leqslant \frac{\pi}{2} \quad \text{has an area} \quad \frac{\pi a^2}{32} .$$

5. Prove that the length of the whole perimeter of the ellipse given by the parametric equations

$$x = 3\cos\theta, \quad y = 2\sin\theta$$

is equal to

$$2\sqrt{2} \int_0^{\pi/2} \sqrt{(13 - 5\cos 2\theta)}\, d\theta$$

and evaluate this integral by Simpson's rule, dividing the range $(0, \pi/2)$ into six equal intervals.

6. Show that $\sin x \geqslant 2x/\pi$ for $0 \leqslant x \leqslant \pi/2$. Deduce that

$$\lim_{y \to \infty} y \int_0^{\pi/2} e^{-y \sin x}\, dx \leqslant \frac{\pi}{2} .$$

7. The area bounded by the curve $y^2 = 4a(b - x)$ and the y-axis is rotated through two right angles about the x-axis. Show that the volume of the solid of revolution is $2\pi ab^2$, and find the radius of gyration of this solid about the y-axis.

8. Find the position of the centroid of that part of the area of the cardioid, $r = a(1 + \cos\theta)$, lying in the first quadrant. If this area is rotated about the x-axis, find the volume of revolution.

9. Show that the limit, as x tends to zero, of $x/\sinh x$ is 1. Use Simpson's rule with five ordinates to evaluate, to three significant figures, the integral

$$\int_0^4 \frac{x\, dx}{\sinh x} .$$

10. Sketch the curve $r = a\sin^2\theta$ and show that the initial line is the tangent at the pole. Find the area enclosed by either loop of the curve. Find also the position of the centroid of the upper loop. Hence show that if the upper loop is rotated through an angle of 2π radians about the tangent at the point $r = a$, $\theta = \pi/2$, the volume of the solid so formed is

$$2\pi a^3 \left(\frac{3\pi}{16} - \frac{23}{105} \right).$$

Find the distance between the line $\theta = \pi/2$ and the tangent to the curve parallel to the line $\theta = \pi/2$. Hence show that the volume obtained by rotating the area enclosed by one of the loops through 2π radians about this tangent is $\pi^2 a^3 / 4\sqrt{3}$.

Find also the length of one loop of the curve.

11. Find the area of the loop of the curve $r = a \cos 3\theta$, where $-\pi/6 \leqslant \theta \leqslant \pi/6$ and the distance of its centre of mass from the origin. Show also that its radius of gyration about an axis through the origin perpendicular to the lamina is $a\sqrt{(\frac{3}{8})}$.

12. A lamina in the shape of a quadrant of a circle of radius a rotates about an axis AB in the plane of the lamina and parallel to one of the straight edges, and distant a from it, thus generating a uniform solid of revolution. Show that the moment of inertia of this solid about AB is

$$\frac{Ma^2}{20} \left(\frac{105\pi + 272}{3\pi + 4} \right),$$

where M is the mass of the solid.

13. Prove that the moment of inertia of a uniform solid right circular cone of mass M, height h and vertical angle 2α about a diameter of its base is

$$\frac{Mh^2(3 \tan^2 \alpha + 2)}{20}.$$

Find, also, the moment of inertia about a parallel axis through the vertex.

14. A surface is obtained by revolving through 4 right angles about the axis of x that part of the curve

$$x = a \cos^3 t, \quad y = a \sin^3 t,$$

which corresponds to the range $0 \leqslant t \leqslant \pi$. Show that the area of this surface is $12\pi a^2 / 5$ and find the volume enclosed by it. Show also that the length of this part of the curve is $3a$.

15. Sketch the curve whose equation is $r^2 = a^2 \cos 2\theta$.

For the area enclosed by one loop find the radius of gyration about the line $\theta = 0$.

Show that the centroid of this area is distant $\pi a/(4\sqrt{2})$ from the origin.

16. The base ABC of a uniform tetrahedron of mass M is an equilateral triangle of side a. The vertex O is at a height h above the base, and the edges OA, OB, OC are equal. Show that the moment of inertia about an axis through O perpendicular to the base is $Ma^2/20$.

17. Prove that

$$\int_0^1 \frac{\mathrm{d}x}{x^2+4} > \int_0^1 \frac{\mathrm{d}x}{\sqrt{(x^3+8x^2+16)}} > \int_0^1 \frac{\mathrm{d}x}{\sqrt{(9x^2+16)}} \, .$$

Evaluate the first and third of these integrals, and show that they determine the second integral within limits of error ± 0.0005.

$$[\tan^{-1} \tfrac{1}{2} = 0.4636, \quad \ln 2 = 0.6931.]$$

18. Through a solid sphere of radius a is bored a cylindrical hole of radius b with the axis of the cylinder lying along a diameter of the sphere. Prove that the volume of the solid remaining is equal to that of a sphere whose diameter is equal to the length of the hole. Show also that the area of the outer surface of the remaining part of the sphere is the same as that of the outside of a hollow cylinder of the same length as that of the hole, but of radius equal to that of the sphere.

If M is the mass of the remaining part of the sphere show that the moment of inertia of this part about the axis of the hole is

$$\frac{M}{5} (2a^2 + 3b^2).$$

19. A thin rod of length a is so constructed that its mass per unit length at distance x from one end A is $c \sin (\tfrac{1}{2}\pi x/a)$. Prove that the total mass M of the rod is $2ac/\pi$.

The rod is rotated in a horizontal plane about the end A, which is fixed, with constant angular velocity ω. Prove that its kinetic energy is

$$\frac{2(\pi-2)Ma^2\omega^2}{\pi^2} \, .$$

20. If $0 < a < b$ and if for $a \leqslant x \leqslant b$

$$f(x) \geqslant 0, \qquad xf'(x)+f(x) \geqslant 0,$$

prove that

$$\left| \int_a^b f(x) \cos (\ln x) \, \mathrm{d}x \right| \leqslant 2bf(b).$$

21. The function $f(x)$ is continuous in the range $a \leqslant x \leqslant b$. Show that a value of θ can be found with $0 < \theta < 1$ such that

$$\int_a^b f(x) \, \mathrm{d}x = (b-a)f\{a+\theta(b-a)\}.$$

[This is a form of the *mean value theorem for integrals*. It can be generalised to

$$\int_a^b f(x)g(x) \, \mathrm{d}x = f(\xi) \int_a^b g(x) \, \mathrm{d}x,$$

where $a \leqslant \xi \leqslant b$ and $g(x) \geqslant 0$ for $a \leqslant x \leqslant b$.]

22. For $y_p = y(x_p) = y(x_0 + ph)$, determine the constants a_1, a_2 and a_3 so that the integration formula

$$\int_{x_0}^{x_4} y \, dx = a_1 y_1 + a_2 y_2 + a_3 y_3,$$

is correct for each of the functions

$$y = \left(\frac{x - x_0}{h}\right)^i \qquad (i = 0, 1, 2).$$

Show that the formula is then correct when y is any cubic polynomial.
   Use the formula with the constants determined to evaluate

$$\int_0^{0 \cdot 8} y \, dx$$

when y is given by

x	0	0·1	0·2	0·3	0·4	0·5	0·6	0·7	0·8
y	901	1616	2181	2656	3125	3696	4501	5696	7461

23. Determine the coefficients in the quadrature formula

$$\int_{-\pi/2}^{\pi/2} f(x) \cos x \, dx \approx w_{-2} f\left(-\frac{\pi}{2}\right) + w_{-1} f\left(-\frac{\pi}{4}\right) + w_1 f\left(\frac{\pi}{4}\right) + w_2 f\left(\frac{\pi}{2}\right)$$

by making the formula *exact* for the functions $f(x) = 1$, x, x^2 and x^3.
   Use the formula to estimate

$$\int_0^{\pi} u^{\frac{1}{2}} \sin u \, du$$

to two significant figures.

CHAPTER VII

COMPLEX NUMBERS

7 : 1 Introduction—the Argand diagram

The central feature of the theory of complex numbers is the introduction of i (or j), the "square root of minus one". The equation $i^2 = -1$ is the *definition* of i. A *complex number* is made up of two real numbers and i in the combination

$$z = x + iy$$

where the single symbol z denotes the complex number and must not be confused with the z-coordinate of three-dimensional coordinate geometry. The *real part* of z is the real number x; the *imaginary part* of z is the real number y (NOT iy). If two complex numbers are equal, then their real and imaginary parts are equal, i.e. if

$$x_1 + iy_1 = z_1 = z_2 = x_2 + iy_2,$$

then $$x_1 = x_2 \quad \text{and} \quad y_1 = y_2.$$

This is an important feature: a single relation between complex numbers is equivalent to two relations between real numbers. We must equate the real parts of the two sides of an equation and we must also equate the imaginary parts of each side. Further, in any equation involving complex numbers the equation remains true if i is replaced by $-i$.

The algebraic operations of addition, subtraction and multiplication are performed with complex numbers in exactly the same way as with real numbers provided that the symbol i is treated as a number and i^2 is replaced by -1 wherever it occurs. Therefore, if $z_1 = x_1 + iy_1$, and $z_2 = x_2 + iy_2$, then

(i) $\qquad z_1 \pm z_2 = (x_1 \pm x_2) + i(y_1 \pm y_2),$

(ii) $\qquad z_1 z_2 = (x_1 x_2 - y_1 y_2) + i(x_1 y_2 + x_2 y_1).$

We defer any further manipulations until we have introduced a geometrical representation for complex numbers. A real number x may be represented by a point P on an infinite straight line when an origin O on the line has been chosen. The length OP is numerically equal to x and the sign of x decides whether P lies to the right, $x > 0$, or left, $x < 0$, of O. Two real numbers x, y are needed to define the complex number $z = x + iy$. The *Argand diagram*, or z-plane, represents z by a point P in a plane whose rectangular coordinates (x, y) are the real and imaginary parts respectively of z, Fig. 7.1.

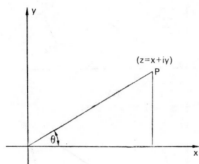

FIG. 7.1. The Argand diagram (z-plane).

The axis Ox is often called the *real axis* because the points on it represent numbers whose imaginary part is zero; they are of the form $x + i0$. Similarly the axis Oy is the *imaginary axis* because the points on it correspond to numbers $0 + iy$, i.e. *pure imaginary* numbers.

We can now define the other terms we need by reference to the Argand diagram. In Fig. 7.1 where P represents z $(= x + iy)$:

(i) the *modulus*, $|z|$, is a positive number equal to the length OP

$$|z| = \sqrt{(x^2 + y^2)} = r$$

(the modulus of a negative real number is a special case of this definition);

(ii) the *argument* (or amplitude) of z is the angle θ between OP and Ox, taken to be positive when the rotation from Ox towards OP is in the anticlockwise sense and we write

$$\arg z = \theta;$$

(iii) the *complex conjugate*, z^*, is the number represented by the optical image of P in the real axis. [In earlier editions the symbol $\bar{z}$ was used for z^*.]

$$\therefore \quad z^* = x - \mathrm{i}y, \qquad \arg z^* = -\arg z,$$
$$|z^*| = |z| \quad \text{and} \quad zz^* = (x+\mathrm{i}y)(x-\mathrm{i}y) = x^2+y^2 = |z|^2.$$

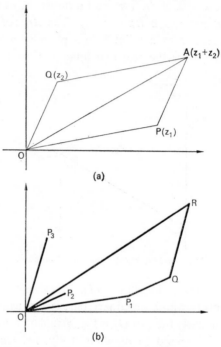

FIG. 7.2. Illustrating the addition of complex numbers.

The quotient of two complex numbers can be expresssed as a complex number by multiplying numerator and denominator by the conjugate of the denominator. Thus

$$\frac{z_2}{z_1} = \frac{x_2+\mathrm{i}y_2}{x_1+\mathrm{i}y_1} = \frac{(x_2+\mathrm{i}y_2)(x_1-\mathrm{i}y_1)}{(x_1+\mathrm{i}y_1)(x_1-\mathrm{i}y_1)}$$
$$= \frac{(x_1x_2+y_1y_2)+\mathrm{i}(x_1y_2-x_2y_1)}{x_1^2+y_1^2}.$$

The representation of addition on the Argand diagram leads to a "parallelogram law" for the addition of two complex numbers,

Fig. 7.2(a). For, if $z_1 = x_1 + iy_1$ and $z_2 = x_2 + iy_2$ are represented by P, Q respectively, the point A representing $z_1 + z_2$ has coordinates $x_1 + x_2$, $y_1 + y_2$ and hence lies at the fourth vertex of the parallelogram which has OPQ as three vertices. This implies that we can to some extent treat complex numbers as vectors and denote z_1 by $\overrightarrow{OP}$, etc. Note that

$$\overrightarrow{PQ} = z_2 - z_1 \quad \text{and}$$
$$PQ^2 = (z_2 - z_1)(z_2 - z_1)^* = (z_2 - z_1)(z_2^* - z_1^*).$$

Repeated application of this leads to a "polygon rule" for the addition of several complex numbers, Fig. 7.2(b). If P_1, P_2 and P_3 represent z_1, z_2, z_3 respectively, the sum $z_1 + z_2 + z_3$ is represented by R, where $P_1 Q$ is equal and parallel to OP_2 and QR is equal and parallel to OP_3. If a sum $z_1 + z_2 + z_3 + \ldots = 0$, then the corresponding polygon $OP_1 QR \ldots$ is a closed one finishing at the origin. From the parallelogram law it is immediately obvious that

$$|z_1 + z_2| \leqslant |z_1| + |z_2|. \tag{7.1}$$

Equality only occurs if z_1 and z_2 have the same argument. Note that writing $z_1 - z_2$ in place of z_1 in inequality (7.1) we obtain the inequality

$$|z_1 - z_2| \geqslant |z_1| - |z_2|.$$

The *modulus inequality* (7.1), which is an extension to the field of complex numbers of the result of Example 2, p. 38, can be proved analytically as follows:

$$\{|z_1| + |z_2|\}^2 - |z_1 + z_2|^2 = 2[\sqrt{\{(x_1^2 + y_1^2)(x_2^2 + y_2^2)\}} - (x_1 x_2 + y_1 y_2)]. \tag{7.2}$$

But, by Cauchy's inequality, Example 3, p. 38,

$$(x_1^2 + y_1^2)(x_2^2 + y_2^2) \geqslant (x_1 x_2 + y_1 y_2)^2$$

unless $y_1/x_1 = y_2/x_2$. It follows, on taking positive square roots, that the right-hand side of eqn. (7.2) is positive unless z_1, z_2 have the same argument. Therefore

$$\{|z_1| + |z_2|\}^2 \geqslant |z_1 + z_2|^2$$

and, taking positive square roots, inequality (7.1) follows.

This result can be generalised by mathematical induction to

$$|z_1+z_2+ \ldots +z_n| \leqslant |z_1|+|z_2|+ \ldots +|z_n|. \qquad (7.3)$$

Use of the modulus and argument gives an important alternative form for a complex number. It corresponds to using polar coordinates, instead of cartesian, in the Argand diagram. If

$$r = |z| = +(x^2+y^2)^{\frac{1}{2}} \quad \text{and} \quad \theta = \arg z,$$

then

$$x = r \cos \theta, \quad y = r \sin \theta, \quad z = r(\cos \theta + i \sin \theta).$$

It should be noted here that values of θ differing from one another by a multiple of 2π correspond to the same direction in the Argand diagram and therefore

$$\arg z = \theta \quad \text{or} \quad \text{Arg } z = \theta \pm 2n\pi \qquad (n = 1, 2, 3 \ldots).$$

If we choose the value of θ such that $-\pi < \theta \leqslant \pi$ we call this the *principal* value of arg z. (It is denoted by a small "a".)

Sometimes, in place of equating real and imaginary parts, it is more useful to use the result that two complex numbers z_1, z_2 are equal if

$$\arg z_1 = \arg z_2, \quad |z_1| = |z_2|.$$

Example 1. (i) $\qquad i^3 = -i, \quad i^{4n} = 1, \quad \dfrac{1}{i} = -i.$

(ii) $\qquad (2+3i)(4-2i) = 8+12i-4i-6i^2 = 14+8i.$

(iii) $\qquad \dfrac{2+3i}{4+2i} = \dfrac{(2+3i)(4-2i)}{(4+2i)(4-2i)} = \dfrac{14+8i}{4^2+2^2} = \dfrac{14+8i}{20} = \dfrac{7+4i}{10}.$

Example 2. Find the modulus and principal argument of

(a) $\quad 1+\sqrt{3}i,$ (b) $\quad -1+i,$ (c) $\quad -\sqrt{3}-\dfrac{i}{\sqrt{3}}.$

(a) $\quad |1+\sqrt{3}i| = +(1+3)^{\frac{1}{2}} = 2; \quad \arg(1+\sqrt{3}i) = \tan^{-1}(\sqrt{3}) = \frac{1}{3}\pi.$

(b) $\quad |-1+i| = +(1+1)^{\frac{1}{2}} = \sqrt{2}; \quad \arg(-1+i) = \tan^{-1}(-1) = \frac{3}{4}\pi.$

(c) $\quad \left|-\sqrt{3}-\dfrac{i}{\sqrt{3}}\right| = \sqrt{\left(\dfrac{10}{3}\right)}; \quad \arg\left(-\sqrt{3}-\dfrac{i}{\sqrt{3}}\right) = -\pi+\tan^{-1}\left(\dfrac{1}{3}\right).$

Example 3. Find α^2 if

$$\alpha+i\beta = \sqrt{[(R+i\omega L)(S+i\omega M)]}. \qquad (1)$$

Squaring and equating real parts gives

$$\alpha^2 - \beta^2 = RS - \omega^2 LM. \tag{2}$$

Replacing i by $-$i in (1) gives

$$\alpha - i\beta = \sqrt{[(R - i\omega L)(S - i\omega M)]}. \tag{3}$$

Multiplying eqns. (1) and (3) gives

$$\alpha^2 + \beta^2 = \sqrt{[(R^2 + \omega^2 L^2)(S^2 + \omega^2 M^2)]}. \tag{4}$$

Addition of (2) and (4) gives

$$\alpha^2 = \tfrac{1}{2}\{RS - \omega^2 LM + \sqrt{[(R^2 + \omega^2 L^2)(S^2 + \omega^2 M^2)]}\}.$$

Example 4. Find a complex number z whose argument is $\pi/6$ such that

$$|z - \sqrt{3} + i| = |z - 2\sqrt{3} - 2i|.$$

The number is of the form $r(\cos \pi/6 + i \sin \pi/6)$ and hence can be expressed as $p(\sqrt{3} + i)$.

$$\therefore \quad |(p-1)\sqrt{3} + i(p+1)| = |(p-2)\sqrt{3} + i(p-2)|.$$
$$\therefore \quad 3(p-1)^2 + (p+1)^2 = 3(p-2)^2 + (p-2)^2.$$

Therefore $p = 1$ and the number $z = \sqrt{3} + i$.

Example 5. In the complex polynomial equation

$$z^n + a_{n-1}z^{n-1} + a_{n-2}z^{n-2} + \cdots + a_2 z^2 + a_1 z + 1 = 0, \tag{1}$$

it is given that the complex numbers $a_{n-1}, a_{n-2}, \ldots, a_2, a_1$ satisfy

$$|a_{n-1}| \leqslant 1, \quad |a_{n-2}| \leqslant 1, \ldots, \quad |a_2| \leqslant 1, \quad |a_1| \leqslant 1.$$

Show that any root of the equation must lie in the (annular) region of the Argand diagram for which $\tfrac{1}{2} < |z| < 2$.

The proof given below depends upon the fact that a complex number is zero if and only if its modulus is zero. A complex number cannot vanish if its modulus is always positive.

First we show that eqn. (1) has no root for $|z| \leqslant \tfrac{1}{2}$ by showing that the modulus of the left-hand side of eqn. (1) is positive when $|z| \leqslant \tfrac{1}{2}$. In fact, for $|z| \leqslant \tfrac{1}{2}$,

$$|z^n| + |a_{n-1}z^{n-1}| + \cdots + |a_2 z^2| + |a_1 z|$$
$$\leqslant (\tfrac{1}{2})^n + |a_{n-1}|(\tfrac{1}{2})^{n-1} \cdots + |a_2|(\tfrac{1}{2})^2 + |a_1|\tfrac{1}{2}$$
$$\leqslant (\tfrac{1}{2})^n + (\tfrac{1}{2})^{n-1} + \cdots + (\tfrac{1}{2})^2 + (\tfrac{1}{2}) < 1$$

after using the given inequalities on $|a_{n-1}|$, $|a_{n-2}|$, etc. Hence

$$|z^n + a_{n-1}z^{n-1} + \cdots + a_1 z + 1| \geqslant 1 - |z^n + \cdots + a_1 z| > 0.$$

It follows that eqn. (1) cannot have a root for $|z| \leqslant \tfrac{1}{2}$.

Second, dividing eqn. (1) by z^n and writing $Z = z^{-1}$, we find that Z satisfies the equation

$$Z^n + a_1 Z^{n-1} + a_2 Z^{n-2} + \cdots + a_{n-1}Z + 1 = 0.$$

But, by an argument similar to the above this equation cannot have a root for $|Z| \leqslant \frac{1}{2}$. It follows that eqn. (1) cannot have a root for $|z| \geqslant 2$ and therefore all roots of eqn. (1) must lie in the range $\frac{1}{2} < |z| < 2$.

Since $|z| = \frac{1}{2}$ implies that the point z is distant $\frac{1}{2}$ from the origin O, it follows that the points for which $|z| = \frac{1}{2}$ lie on a circle centre O and radius $\frac{1}{2}$. Similarly, the points for which $|z| = 2$ lie on a concentric circle of radius 2. The roots of eqn. (1) therefore lie in the annular region shown in Fig. 7.3.

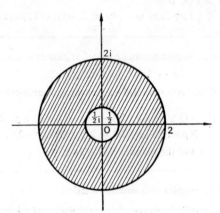

FIG. 7.3. The domain $\frac{1}{2} < |z| < 2$.

Exercises 7 : 1

1. Find the modulus and the principal value of the argument of the complex number $(2+i)(3+2i)$.

2. If p is real and the complex number $\dfrac{1+i}{2+pi} + \dfrac{2+3i}{3+i}$ is represented in the Argand diagram by a point on the line $x = y$, show that $p = -5 \pm \sqrt{21}$.

3. If w is the complex number $u+iv$, and w^* is the conjugate of w, express u, v and u^2+v^2 in terms of w and w^*.

4. If $z = x+iy$, find x and y when
$$\frac{2z}{1+i} - \frac{2z}{i} = \frac{5}{2+i} \, .$$

5. If R, L, C and ω are real, and
$$\frac{1}{z} = \frac{1}{R+i\omega L} + i\omega C,$$
show that
$$|z|^2 = \frac{R^2+\omega^2 L^2}{(1-C\omega^2 L)^2 + \omega^2 C^2 R^2} \, .$$
If $L = CR^2$ show that $\arg z = \tan^{-1}(-\omega CR)^3$.

6. (i) If points P_1 and P_2 on the Argand diagram represent the complex numbers z_1 and z_2 respectively, prove that the length of $P_1 P_2$ equals $|z_2 - z_1|$.

(ii) Find the complex number z such that

$$|z + i2 - 3| = |z + i3|$$

and arg $z = \pi/4$.

7. If z and w are any two complex numbers, prove that $|z + w| \leqslant |z| + |w|$, and deduce that $|z + w| \geqslant |z| - |w|$. Show that the equation $z^4 + z + 2 = 0$ cannot have a root with modulus less than 1.

8. Find the greatest value of the modulus of

$$1 + \cos \theta + i \sin \theta \text{ when } \theta \text{ is real.}$$

7 : 2 De Moivre's theorem

The modulus-argument form of a complex number introduces an important special type of number, namely $\cos \theta + i \sin \theta$ which has modulus 1 and argument θ. Complex numbers of this type satisfy the relation

$$(\cos \theta_1 + i \sin \theta_1)(\cos \theta_2 + i \sin \theta_2)$$
$$= (\cos \theta_1 \cos \theta_2 - \sin \theta_1 \sin \theta_2) + i(\sin \theta_1 \cos \theta_2 + \cos \theta_1 \sin \theta_2)$$
$$= \cos(\theta_1 + \theta_2) + i \sin(\theta_1 + \theta_2).$$

This relation is easily generalised, by induction (see § 1 : 7), to the case with n factors on the left-hand side, giving

$$\prod_{r=1}^{n} (\cos \theta_r + i \sin \theta_r) = \cos \left(\sum_{r=1}^{n} \theta_r \right) + i \sin \left(\sum_{r=1}^{n} \theta_r \right). \quad (7.4)$$

(The relation above between θ_1 and θ_2 provides both the starting point for the induction and the proof of the step from k to $k+1$.)

A particular case of equation (7.4) ocurs when $\theta_1 = \theta_2 = \ldots = \theta_n = \theta$ giving *De Moivre's theorem* for a *positive* integer n in the form

$$(\cos \theta + i \sin \theta)^n = \cos n\theta + i \sin n\theta. \quad (7.5)$$

Since

$$1 = \cos^2 n\theta + \sin^2 n\theta = (\cos n\theta + i \sin n\theta)(\cos n\theta - i \sin n\theta),$$
$$\therefore \quad \cos n\theta - i \sin n\theta = (\cos n\theta + i \sin n\theta)^{-1} = (\cos \theta + i \sin \theta)^{-n}.$$
$$\therefore \quad (\cos \theta + i \sin \theta)^{-n} = \cos(-n\theta) + i \sin(-n\theta)$$

which proves De Moivre's theorem for a negative integer.

If p/q is a positive rational fraction in its lowest terms, then by eqn. (7.5)

$$\left(\cos\frac{p\theta}{q}+\mathrm{i}\sin\frac{p\theta}{q}\right)^q = \cos p\theta+\mathrm{i}\sin p\theta = (\cos\theta+\mathrm{i}\sin\theta)^p.$$

Taking the qth root of this equation we find that $\cos\dfrac{p\theta}{q}+\mathrm{i}\sin\dfrac{p\theta}{q}$ is *one of the values* of $(\cos\theta+\mathrm{i}\sin\theta)^{p/q}$, thus proving De Moivre's theorem for a positive rational fractional index. (We say "one of the values" since the equation $z^q = a$, being of degree q, has q roots and hence the qth root of any number has q possible values). Similarly, De Moivre's theorem holds for a negative rational fraction and hence, eqn. (7.5) holds for all rational positive or negative values of n.

If we substitute $z = \mathrm{i}\theta$ in the exponential series (assuming that it is justifiable to substitute complex values into an infinite series

$$\mathrm{e}^z = 1+z+\frac{z^2}{2!}+\frac{z^3}{3!}+ \dots,$$

we obtain

$$\mathrm{e}^{\mathrm{i}\theta} = \left(1-\frac{\theta^2}{2!}+\frac{\theta^4}{4!}- \dots\right)+\mathrm{i}\left(\theta-\frac{\theta^3}{3!}+\frac{\theta^5}{5!}- \dots\right),$$

i.e.

$$\mathrm{e}^{\mathrm{i}\theta} = \cos\theta+\mathrm{i}\sin\theta, \tag{7.6}$$

which is known as *Euler's relation*. De Moivre's theorem can be written in the form

$$(\mathrm{e}^{\mathrm{i}\theta})^n = \mathrm{e}^{n\mathrm{i}\theta}. \tag{7.7}$$

Also, since

$$(\cos\theta+\mathrm{i}\sin\theta)(\cos\varphi+\mathrm{i}\sin\varphi) = \cos(\theta+\varphi)+\mathrm{i}\sin(\theta+\varphi)$$

Euler's relation gives

$$\mathrm{e}^{\mathrm{i}\theta}\cdot\mathrm{e}^{\mathrm{i}\varphi} = \mathrm{e}^{\mathrm{i}(\theta+\varphi)},$$

where θ, φ may be irrational numbers. All this suggests that the laws of algebra for real indices hold for complex indices also and in fact the generalisation of De Moivre's theorem to cover irrational and complex numbers given in books on analysis implies that eqn. (7.7) holds for all n and θ.

Euler's relation leads at once to the expressions

$$\cos \theta = \frac{(e^{i\theta}+e^{-i\theta})}{2}, \quad \sin \theta = \frac{(e^{i\theta}-e^{-i\theta})}{2i} \qquad (7.8)$$

for the trigonometric functions. A comparison between these relations and the definitions of the hyperbolic functions shows that

$$\cos ix = \cosh x, \qquad \sin ix = i \sinh x,$$
$$\cosh ix = \cos x, \qquad \sinh ix = i \sin x. \qquad (7.9)$$

These results can be used to obtain the hyperbolic analogue of any trigonometric formula as suggested in § 2 : 4.

Example. $\tan (x+y) = \dfrac{\sin (x+y)}{\cos (x+y)} = \dfrac{\tan x+\tan y}{1-\tan x \tan y}$.

$\therefore \quad \tan i(x+y) = \dfrac{\sin i(x+y)}{\cos i(x+y)} = \dfrac{i \sinh (x+y)}{\cosh (x+y)} = i \tanh (x+y)$.

But
$$\frac{\sin (ix+iy)}{\cos (ix+iy)} = \frac{\sin ix \cos iy+\cos ix \sin iy}{\cos ix \cos iy-\sin ix \sin iy}$$
$$= \frac{i \sinh x \cosh y+i \cosh x \sinh y}{\cosh x \cosh y+\sinh x \sinh y}$$
$$= \frac{i \tanh x+i \tanh y}{1+\tanh x \tanh y} \cdot$$

This gives the formula

$$\tanh (x+y) = \frac{\tanh x+\tanh y}{1+\tanh x \tanh y} \cdot$$

Any complex number $x+iy$ can be expressed in the form $re^{i\theta}$ since we can always find a positive r and a θ for which $-\pi < \theta \leqslant \pi$ so that $x = r \cos \theta, y = r \sin \theta$ and hence $x+iy = r(\cos \theta+i \sin \theta) = re^{i\theta}$. In fact r and θ are the polar coordinates of the point x, y on the Argand diagram.

Example. (i) $1+i = \sqrt{2}e^{i\pi/4}$.

(ii) $\qquad (1-i)^3 = (\sqrt{2}e^{i\pi/4})^3 = 2\sqrt{2}e^{-(3i\pi/4)}$.

---

7 : 3 Multiplication and division on the Argand diagram

If $z_1 = r_1e^{i\theta_1}$ and $z_2 = r_2e^{i\theta_2}$, then

$$z_1z_2 = r_1r_2 \, e^{i(\theta_1+\theta_2)}.$$
$$\therefore \quad |z_1z_2| = r_1r_2 = |z_1|\cdot|z_2|$$

and

$$\arg(z_1 z_2) = \theta_1 + \theta_2 = \arg z_1 + \arg z_2.$$

Thus the multiplication of two complex numbers can be carried out by multiplying their moduli and adding their arguments. Since

$$\frac{1}{z_2} = \frac{1}{(r_2 e^{i\theta_2})} = \frac{e^{-i\theta_2}}{r_2}, \qquad \frac{z_1}{z_2} = \left(\frac{r_1}{r_2}\right) e^{i(\theta_1 - \theta_2)}.$$

$$\therefore \quad \left|\frac{z_1}{z_2}\right| = \frac{r_1}{r_2} = \frac{|z_1|}{|z_2|}$$

and

$$\arg\left(\frac{z_1}{z_2}\right) = \theta_1 - \theta_2 = \arg z_1 - \arg z_2.$$

Thus division of one complex number by another can be carried out by dividing the modulus of the numerator by the modulus of the denominator and subtraction of the argument of the denominator from the argument of the numerator. These formulae may be generalised as follows:

$$\left|\frac{z_1 z_2 \dots}{z_1' z_2' \dots}\right| = \frac{|z_1| \cdot |z_2| \dots}{|z_1'| \cdot |z_2'| \dots}, \tag{7.10}$$

$$\arg\left(\frac{z_1 z_2 \dots}{z_1' z_2' \dots}\right) = (\arg z_1 + \arg z_2 + \dots) - (\arg z_1' + \arg z_2' + \dots).$$

The above results may be used to obtain geometrical constructions on the Argand diagram for the product and quotient of two complex numbers. Suppose, Fig. 7.4(a), P and Q represent the points z_1, z_2 respectively and A represents the number 1. If R represents the point z and is the vertex of the triangle OQR which is similar to OAP, then by similar triangles $OR/OQ = OP/OA$,

i.e. $|z| = OP \cdot OQ = |z_1| \cdot |z_2| = |z_1 z_2|$. Also $\arg z = \theta_1 + \theta_2$,

i.e. $\arg z = \arg z_1 + \arg z_2 = \arg(z_1 z_2)$. Hence z has the same modulus and the same argument as $z_1 z_2$ and therefore must be equal to $z_1 z_2$. Therefore the point R represents the number $z_1 z_2$. Similarly, Fig. 7.4(b), the point S representing the number z_2/z_1 can be constructed as the vertex S of the triangle OQS similar to the triangle OPA.

An important special case of multiplication occurs when one of the factors is of unit modulus: suppose $z_1 = e^{i\theta_1}$ $(OP = 1)$. The two triangles are isosceles and the product point R is obtained from $Q(z_2)$ by rotating OQ through an angle θ_1. If $\theta_1 = \frac{1}{2}\pi$, the factor $z_1 = e^{i\pi/2} = i$, so that multiplication by i corresponds to a rotation, in the positive sense, through 90°. If $z_1 = e^{i\pi} = -1$, the rotation is through 180°.

There is an important application of this representation to simple harmonic oscillations. For example, in alternating cur-

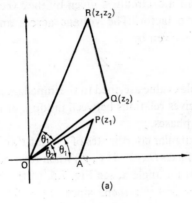

(a)

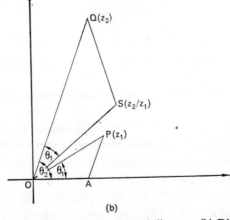

(b)

FIG. 7.4. (a) Multiplication on the Argand diagram. (b) Division on the Argand diagram.

rents the voltage and current are given by expressions such as $V = V_0 \cos (pt+\alpha)$, $I = I_0 \cos (pt+\beta)$. These are represented in an Argand diagram by "vectors" or complex numbers V and I where

$$|V| = V_0, \quad |I| = I_0, \quad \arg V = \alpha, \quad \arg I = \beta.$$

These vectors are multiplied by the time factor e^{ipt} which makes them rotate with angular velocity p. The real parts of the complex numbers Ve^{ipt} and Ie^{ipt} are the instantaneous values given above. The behaviour of an a.c. circuit is given by the "vectors" V and I, omitting the time factor. The voltage across an impedance carrying a current is given by

$$V = ZI,$$

where Z is the complex value ascribed to the impedance. This single complex equation gives relations between moduli, or peak values, and arguments, or phases.

Suppose the rectangular coordinates of a point P are (x, y) when referred to one set of axes Oxy and (x', y') when referred to another set $Ox'y'$ inclined at an angle α, see Fig. 7.5, to the first set. Let $z = x+iy$ and $z' = x'+iy'$; then, since $|z| = OP = |z'|$ and $\arg z = \theta = \varphi+\alpha = \arg z'+\alpha$,

$$z = z'e^{i\alpha}$$

or

$$z' = ze^{-i\alpha}. \tag{7.11}$$

$$\therefore \quad x' = x \cos \alpha+y \sin \alpha, \quad y' = -x \sin \alpha+y \cos \alpha.$$

This provides an alternative proof of the formulae given by eqns. (4.25).

If we imagine the point P to move in the plane, the motion of P is determined by the "complex velocity" dz/dt, where z corresponds to P in the Argand diagram. A velocity v in the direction Oy corresponds to $\dot{z} = iv$. A velocity V inclined at the angle θ to Ox is given by $\dot{z} = Ve^{i\theta}$. Let us represent P by its modulus-argument form $z = re^{i\theta}$. Then its "complex velocity" is

$$\dot{z} = \dot{r}e^{i\theta}+r\dot{\theta}ie^{i\theta}. \tag{7.12}$$

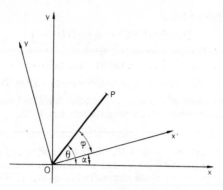

FIG. 7.5. Rotation of axes.

Now $e^{i\theta}$ is a complex number of modulus 1 whose argument gives the direction of r, and $ie^{i\theta} = e^{i(\theta+\pi/2)}$ is another of unit modulus at right angles to $e^{i\theta}$. Equation (7.12) shows that the velocity of P has

$$\text{a radial component} \qquad \dot{r} = \frac{dr}{dt},$$

$$\text{a transverse component} \qquad r\dot{\theta} = \frac{r\,d\theta}{dt}.$$

Similarly the acceleration is given by

$$\ddot{z} = \ddot{r}e^{i\theta} + 2\dot{r}\dot{\theta}ie^{i\theta} - r\dot{\theta}^2 e^{i\theta} + r\ddot{\theta}ie^{i\theta},$$

i.e.

$$\ddot{z} = (\ddot{r} - r\dot{\theta}^2)e^{i\theta} + (r\ddot{\theta} + 2\dot{r}\dot{\theta})ie^{i\theta}. \tag{7.13}$$

Hence the acceleration of P has

$$\text{a radial component} \qquad \ddot{r} - r\dot{\theta}^2,$$

$$\text{a transverse component} \qquad r\ddot{\theta} + 2\dot{r}\dot{\theta} = \frac{1}{r}\frac{d}{dt}(r^2\dot{\theta}).$$

Example 1. A represents the number 6i, B the number 3, and P some complex number z. If P moves so that $PA = 2PB$ show that

$$zz^* = (4+2i)z + (4-2i)z^*.$$

Show that this is a circle and find its radius and the complex number corresponding to its centre.

$$\overrightarrow{AP} = z - 6i, \quad \therefore \ PA^2 = (z - 6i)(z - 6i)^* = (z - 6i)(z^* + 6i).$$
$$\overrightarrow{BP} = z - 3, \quad \therefore \ PB^2 = (z - 3)(z - 3)^* = (z - 3)(z^* - 3).$$

Since $PA^2 = 4PB^2$ we have

$$(z-6i)(z^*+6i) = 4(z-3)(z^*-3)$$

which gives on reduction the required relation.

Writing $z = x+iy$, $z^* = x-iy$, this relation becomes

$$x^2+y^2 = 8x-4y \quad \text{or} \quad (x-4)^2+(y+2)^2 = 20.$$

Therefore the locus of P is a circle of radius $2\sqrt{5}$ and centre $(4, -2)$ so that the complex number representing its centre is $4-2i$.

Example 2. The eqn. $|z-a-ib| = k$, where a, b and k are real, represents a circle centre the point C, $a+ib$, and of radius k. The complex number representing the point P on the circumference of this circle is $a+ib+ke^{i\varphi}$ where φ is the angle CP makes with Ox.

Example 3. Interpret geometrically the following loci on the Argand diagram:

> (i) $\qquad\qquad |z-2|+|z+2| = 6,$
>
> (ii) $\qquad\qquad |z+2| = 3|z-2|,$
>
> (iii) $\qquad\qquad \arg\left(\dfrac{z-2}{z+2}\right) = \dfrac{\pi}{3}.$

(i) The required locus is that of a point which moves so that the sum of its distances from the points A, B representing $2+0i$ and $-2+0i$ respectively is constant and equal to 6. The locus is an ellipse with foci at A, B and whose major axis is of length 6.

(ii) If P is the point z, then $PA = 3PB$. By pure geometry the locus of P is the circle (of Apollonius) which has as a diameter the line joining the points Q and R which divide AB internally and externally in the ratio $3:1$. An alternative analytical solution is as follows:

$$|z+2|^2 = (z+2)(z^*+2); \quad |z-2|^2 = (z-2)(z^*-2).$$

Therefore the equation of the required locus is

$$(z+2)(z^*+2) = 9(z-2)(z^*-2)$$

or $\qquad\qquad 8zz^*-20(z+z^*)+32 = 0,$

i.e. $\quad 8(z-\tfrac{5}{2})(z^*-\tfrac{5}{2}) = 50-32 = 18,$

i.e. $\quad (z-\tfrac{5}{2})(z^*-\tfrac{5}{2}) = \tfrac{9}{4} \quad \text{or} \quad |z-\tfrac{5}{2}| = \tfrac{3}{2},$

which is a circle with centre $\tfrac{5}{2}+i0$ and radius $\tfrac{3}{2}$. This circle cuts AB in the points Q, R as stated above.

(iii) Since $\arg\left(\dfrac{z-2}{z+2}\right) = \arg(z-2)-\arg(z+2) = \alpha-\beta$ (Fig. 7.6), we require the locus of P for which $A\widehat{P}B = \tfrac{1}{3}\pi$. This locus is an arc of a circle on AB as chord. It is easy to show that the centre of this circle is the point representing $2i/\sqrt{3}$ and the radius of the circle is $4/\sqrt{3}$.

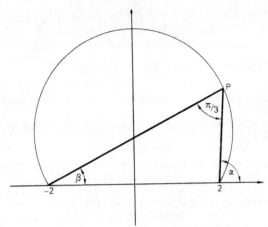

Fig. 7.6. The locus $\arg\left(\dfrac{z-2}{z+2}\right) = \dfrac{\pi}{3}$.

Example 4. The complex numbers $z_1 = x_1 + iy_1$ and $z_2 = x_2 + iy_2$ are connected by the relation $z_1 = z_2 + 1/z_2$. If the point representing z_2 in the Argand diagram describes a circle of radius a and centre at the origin, show that the point representing z_1 describes the ellipse

$$\frac{x^2}{(1+a^2)^2} + \frac{y^2}{(1-a^2)^2} = \frac{1}{a^2}.$$

Since $z_2 = ae^{i\theta}$, where $-\pi < \theta \leqslant \pi$,

$$\therefore \quad z_1 = ae^{i\theta} + \frac{e^{-i\theta}}{a} = \left(a + \frac{1}{a}\right)\cos\theta + i\left(a - \frac{1}{a}\right)\sin\theta.$$

$$\therefore \quad x_1 = \left(a + \frac{1}{a}\right)\cos\theta, \quad y_1 = \left(a - \frac{1}{a}\right)\sin\theta.$$

These are the parametric equations of the ellipse

$$\frac{x_1^2}{(a+1/a)^2} + \frac{y_1^2}{(a-1/a)^2} = 1$$

(using x_1, y_1 as current coordinates) which is described once as θ increases from $-\pi$ to π. This gives the required result.

Example 5. Using the Argand diagram, or otherwise, find the least value of $|z|$ if

$$|z-1| = |z+3-4i|.$$

The given equation implies that the point z is equidistant from the points 1, $-3+4i$. Hence z lies on the perpendicular bisector of the line joining these points, i.e. on the line $x - y + 3 = 0$. The least value of $|z|$ is the length of the perpendicular from the origin onto this line, i.e. $3/\sqrt{2}$.

Example 6. Find the loci in the complex plane given by

$$|z + ia| = |z - ia| + na,$$

where n is any integer, positive, negative, or zero and a is real and positive.

Let S, S', P be the points ia, $-ia$, z respectively. Then the given equation can be written

$$S'P - SP = na$$

so that the locus of P is one branch of a hyperbola with foci at S, S' and major axis $2na$ (see § 4 : 14). However, the distance $SS' (= 2a)$ must exceed the major axis and so there is no locus for $|n| > 2$. [This follows also from the modulus inequality which requires that $|SP - S'P| \leqslant SS'$.]

When $n = 2$, the locus consists of that part of the imaginary axis for which $y < -a$, i.e. below S'.

When $n = -2$, the locus consists of that part of the imaginary axis for which $y > a$, i.e. above S.

When $n = 1$, the locus consists of that branch, of the hyperbola, with foci S, S', major axis of length a and eccentricity 2, which surrounds S.

When $n = -1$, the locus consists of the branch of this hyperbola which surrounds S'.

When $n = 0$, $SP = S'P$ and the locus consists of the real axis.

Example 7. The complex number $z(= r \cos \theta + ir \sin \theta)$ is related to the complex number $w(= u + iv)$ by the equation $w = z + 1/z$. Show that the curves traced out by the point w corresponding to curves of constant r are ellipses, and those corresponding to constant θ are hyperbolae; find the foci of these ellipses and hyperbolae.

Show on a sketch the curves traced out by the point w corresponding to the following lines and curves.

(a) $r = 1$, $(0 < \theta < 2\pi)$;

(b) $r = 2$, $(0 < \theta < \pi)$;

(c) $r = \frac{1}{2}$, $(0 < \theta < \pi)$;

(d) $r > 1$, $(\theta = \frac{1}{4}\pi)$;

(e) $r > 0$, $(\theta = 0)$;

(f) $0 < r < 1$, $(\theta = \frac{1}{2}\pi)$.

$$u + iv = re^{i\theta} + (1/r)e^{-i\theta}.$$

$$\therefore \quad u = (r + 1/r) \cos \theta, \quad v = (r - 1/r) \sin \theta. \tag{1}$$

When r is constant eqns. (1) are the parametric equations of an ellipse (cf. $x = a \cos \theta$, $y = b \sin \theta$) with major axis $2(r + 1/r)$ and minor axis $2|(r - 1/r)|$. Since $(r + 1/r)^2 - (r - 1/r)^2 = 4$ for all values of r, every such ellipse has foci at ± 2.

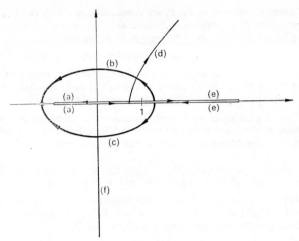

FIG. 7.7.

When $\theta = \alpha$ (constant), $(u/\cos \alpha)^2 - (v/\sin \alpha)^2 = 4$. This is the equation of a hyperbola with major axis $4 \cos \alpha$ and minor axis $4 \sin \alpha$. Since $(2 \cos \alpha)^2 + (2 \sin \alpha)^2 = 4$ for all values of α, every such hyperbola has foci at ± 2 also.

The various curves are shown in Fig. 7.7.

Exercises 7 : 3

1. If
$$|z+a|^2 + |z-a|^2 = 4a^2,$$
where a is a real positive constant, find the locus of the point z in the Argand diagram.

2. Prove that the locus of a point z in the Argand diagram such that $\left| \dfrac{z-1}{z+1} \right| = k$, where k is a constant, is a circle if $k \neq 1$.

3. On an Argand diagram z is a representative point and $w = \dfrac{z-2}{z-i}$. Show that, when the point represented by w moves along the real axis, z traces the line through 2 and i. Find the locus of z when w moves along the imaginary axis.

4. (i) Find the coordinates of the point in the Argand diagram which represents the complex number
$$\frac{(3-4i)}{(2+i)}.$$

Find also the complex number represented by the reflection of this point in the line $x = -y$.

(*Continued overleaf*)

(ii) Complex numbers z_1, z_2, z_3 are represented in the Argand diagram by the points A, B, C respectively, which are the vertices of an isosceles right-angled triangle with the right angle at C. Prove that

$$(z_1 - z_2)^2 = 2(z_1 - z_3)(z_3 - z_2).$$

5. In the Argand diagram a square $OABC$ (lettered anti-clockwise) has a vertex at the origin O. If the centre of the square represents the complex number z, find the complex numbers represented by A, B and C.

6. If $z = 1 + i$, mark in an Argand diagram the four points A, B, C and D representing z, z^2, z^3 and z^4 respectively. Find, by calculation or from your diagram, the moduli and arguments of the complex numbers $(z^3 - 1)$ and $(z + z^4)$.

Show that $\arg\{(z^3 - z^4)/(z^2 - z^4)\}$ is given by the angle BDC and hence, or otherwise, show that the angles BDC and ACB are equal.

7. $ABCD$ is a rhombus whose vertices in this order are in the anti-clockwise sense, and the angles A and C are each $60°$. If A, B represent $2 + i$, $2 + 2\sqrt{3} - i$, find the numbers represented by C and D.

8. If $z_1 = 2 + i$, $z_2 = -2 + 4i$, and

$$\frac{1}{z_3} = \frac{1}{z_1} + \frac{1}{z_2}$$

find z_3.

If z_1, z_2, z_3 are represented on an Argand diagram by the points P_1, P_2, P_3, show that

$$\overrightarrow{OP_2} = 2i\overrightarrow{OP_1} \quad \text{and} \quad \overrightarrow{OP_3} = \tfrac{2}{5}i\overrightarrow{P_2P_1}.$$

Hence, or otherwise, prove that P_3 is the foot of the perpendicular from O on the line P_1P_2.

9. Interpret geometrically the following loci on the Argand diagram

(i) $$|z - c|^2 + |z + c|^2 = 6c^2 \qquad (c > 0),$$

(ii) $$\arg\left(\frac{z + c}{z - c}\right) = \frac{\pi}{2},$$

(iii) $$|z - ic| + |z + ic| = 4c.$$

10. Three distinct complex numbers z_1, z_2, z_3 are represented in the complex plane by points A_1, A_2, A_3. Prove that a necessary and sufficient condition for the triangle $A_1A_2A_3$ to be equilateral is

$$z_1^2 + z_2^2 + z_3^2 = z_2z_3 + z_3z_1 + z_1z_2.$$

If $z_1 = 1$, $z_2 = i$, find the coordinates of the (two) possible positions of A_3.

11. Show on an Argand diagram the locus of the point P, representing the complex number z, if

(i) $\dfrac{z - i}{z - 1}$ is purely imaginary, (ii) $\dfrac{z - i}{z - 1}$ is real.

12. A and B are points in the Argand diagram representing constant complex numbers a and b respectively and P represents a variable complex number z. Prove that

(i) if P lies on the perpendicular bisector of AB,
$$(a^*-b^*)z+(a-b)z^* = aa^*-bb^*, \quad \text{and}$$

(ii) if P lies on the circle having AB as diameter,
$$2zz^*-(a^*+b^*)z-(a+b)z^*+ab^*+a^*b = 0.$$

13. If $w = z-(1/z)$, where z and w are complex numbers such that $z = 2e^{i\theta}$, show that as θ varies the point representing $w(= u+iv)$ in an Argand diagram traces the ellipse whose equation is
$$\frac{u^2}{9}+\frac{v^2}{25} = \frac{1}{4}.$$

14. If the point z describes the circle $|z-1| = 1$, show that the point z^2 describes the curve $r = 2+2\cos\theta$.

15. By considering the modulus of the left-hand side of the following equation in z, or otherwise, prove that all roots of
$$z^n\cos n\alpha+z^{n-1}\cos(n-1)\alpha+ \dots +z\cos\alpha = 1,$$
where α is real, lie outside the circle $|z| = \frac{1}{2}$.

16. The complex numbers z_1, $z_2(z_1 \neq z_2)$ are represented in an Argand diagram by points P_1, P_2 respectively, where the line P_1P_2 does not pass through the origin. Show that, if $z = az_1+bz_2$, where a, b are real, then the point representing z lies on P_1P_2 if and only if $a+b = 1$.

17. If the point z describes the circle $|z-1| = 1$, show that the point $1/z$ describes a straight line.

18. Prove that, if the complex number
$$\frac{z_2+z_1}{z_2-z_1}$$
has real part zero, then $|z_1| = |z_2|$.

19. Draw a diagram to indicate clearly the part of the Argand diagram representing the complex numbers z which satisfy the inequalities
$$|z+1| \leqslant 2 \leqslant 2|z|.$$

20. In the equation $z^2+2\lambda z+1 = 0$, λ is a parameter which can take any *real* value. Show that if $-1 < \lambda < 1$ the roots of this equation lie on a certain circle in the Argand diagram, but that if $\lambda > 1$, one root lies inside the circle and one outside.

Prove that for very large values of λ the roots are approximately -2λ and $-1/2\lambda$.

21. If z is a complex number prove that $|z|^2 = zz^*$. In the Argand diagram the point z_1 is the reflexion of the point z in the line $\theta = \alpha$ through the origin. Prove that $|z_1| = |z|$ and $\arg z_1+\arg z = 2\alpha$. Hence prove that
$$z_1z = |z|^2(\cos 2\alpha+i\sin 2\alpha)$$
and
$$z_1 = z^*(\cos 2\alpha+i\sin 2\alpha).$$
If z_2 is the reflexion of z_1 in the line $\theta = \beta$, prove that
$$z_2 = z\{\cos(2\beta-2\alpha)+i\sin(2\beta-2\alpha)\}.$$

22. (i) If $|z-\mathrm{i}| = 1$, prove that the real part of $1/(z+1-\mathrm{i})$ is constant.

(ii) Indicate by shaded areas in an Argand diagram the regions represented by the inequalities

$\quad$ (a) $\quad |z-1| < 1,$ $\qquad$ (b) $\quad 3 < \operatorname{Re} z < 4,$ $\qquad$ (c) $\quad |z+1| > |z+2|,$

where $\operatorname{Re} z$ denotes the real part of z.

23. Show that, if

$$w = \frac{z-\mathrm{i}}{z+\mathrm{i}},$$

then the region $|w| < 1$ corresponds to the upper z half-plane.

24. Show that there are two points in the Argand diagram which satisfy the two equations

$$\arg \frac{z-1}{z+1} = \frac{3\pi}{4}, \quad |z| = \frac{1}{\sqrt{5}},$$

and find them.

25. The complex numbers $z = x+\mathrm{i}y$, $Z = X+\mathrm{i}Y$ are related by

$$Z = z^2.$$

The point z describes the line $y = b(> 0)$ from $x = 0$ to infinity. Show that the point Z describes part of a parabola, identify that part and illustrate by diagrams of the z-plane and the Z-plane.

26. If ζ is a non-zero complex constant and z is a complex variable given by $z = \zeta + \mathrm{i}t\zeta$ where t is a *real* variable, prove that

$$\left| \frac{1}{z} - \frac{1}{2\zeta} \right|$$

is independent of t. Interpret geometrically.

Sketch, and describe the main features of, the locus of the point $1/z$ in the Argand diagram when z traverses the sides of the triangle with vertices at -1, $1+2\mathrm{i}$, $1-2\mathrm{i}$.

27. If $|z+c| + |z-c| < 2d$, where c is complex and $d > |c|$, and also

$$\pi < \arg z < 2\pi,$$

describe geometrically the region of the complex plane in which z must lie.

7 : 4 The roots of complex numbers

Using De Moivre's theorem we can find n different nth roots of a complex number $a+\mathrm{i}b$ by solving the equation

$$z^n = a+\mathrm{i}b. \tag{7.14}$$

First, we find the nth roots of unity as the roots of the equation

$$z^n = 1. \tag{7.15}$$

The most general way of writing the number 1 as a complex number is

$$1 = \cos(2p\pi) + i\sin(2p\pi) = e^{2ip\pi}, \qquad (p = 0, \pm 1, \pm 2, \ldots).$$
$$(7.16)$$

Hence we must solve the equation

$$z^n = e^{2ip\pi}. \qquad (7.17)$$

Taking the nth root of eqn. (7.17) gives

$$z = e^{2ip\pi/n} = \cos\left(\frac{2p\pi}{n}\right) + i\sin\left(\frac{2p\pi}{n}\right) \qquad (7.18)$$

for $p = 0, \pm 1, \pm 2, \ldots$ However, substitution of the values $p = 0, 1, 2, \ldots, n-1$ into eqn. (7.18) gives the nth roots of unity in the form $\omega_0, \omega_1, \omega_2, \ldots, \omega_{n-1}$ where

$$\omega_0 = 1, \quad \omega_p = \cos\left(\frac{2p\pi}{n}\right) + i\sin\left(\frac{2p\pi}{n}\right) = e^{2ip\pi/n},$$
$$(p = 1, 2, \ldots n-1). \qquad (7.19)$$

Substitution of other, positive or negative, integral values for p merely repeats one or other of the ω_p already obtained. In fact any n consecutive integral values of p will give the n roots. If n is an even number, one of the ω_p, namely $\omega_{n/2}$, is real since then $\omega_{n/2} = \cos\pi + i\sin\pi = -1$.

It is helpful to see the representation of the nth roots of unity on the Argand diagram. The circumference of the unit circle, $|z| = 1$, is divided into n equal arcs, Fig. 7.8, by the points A_0 (representing the number 1), $A_1, A_2, \ldots, A_{n-1}$. These points represent the various nth roots. If the geometrical representation of multiplication is used with any one of these points to obtain $(\omega_p)^n$ it gives A_0 as the final point. Since the complex roots given by eqn. (7.19) corresponding to $p = s$ and $p = n-s$, where $s > 0$, $s \neq \frac{1}{2}n$, are $\cos(2s\pi/n) + i\sin(2s\pi/n)$, and $\cos(2\pi - 2s\pi/n) + i\sin(2\pi - 2s\pi/n) = \cos(2s\pi/n) - i\sin(2s\pi/n)$, the complex roots of unity can be arranged in conjugate pairs. This illustrates the general result that, where all the coefficients in an equation $f(z) = 0$ are real, the complex roots must occur in complex conjugate pairs. For if $\alpha + i\beta$ is a root of the equation so that $f(\alpha + i\beta) = 0$ then changing i into $-i$ gives $f(\alpha - i\beta) = 0$

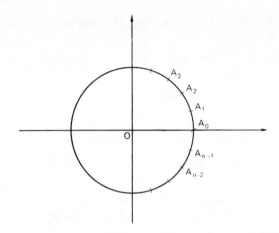

FIG. 7.8. The nth roots of unity on the Argand diagram.

so that $\alpha - i\beta$ is a root also. This result is applicable to both polynomial and transcendental equations with real coefficients. It follows from this that any polynomial with real coefficients is the product of either linear or quadratic factors or a number of each (with real coefficients).

If the cubic equation

$$x^3 + px^2 + qx + r = 0$$

has one real root $x = c$ and two (conjugate) complex roots $\alpha \pm i\beta$, then eqns. (1.7) give

$$c + 2\alpha = -p, \quad (\alpha^2 + \beta^2)c = -r.$$

If c is known, these equations suffice to determine α and β. In particular, if c has been approximately determined by an iterative process or otherwise, the real and imaginary parts α, β of the complex roots may be determined to the same degree of approximation. (As a check we may use the relation $\alpha^2 + \beta^2 + 2\alpha c = q$.) A similar method can be employed for an equation of any degree with only two complex roots.

The use of De Moivre's theorem to solve eqn. (7.14) is straightforward. Writing $a + ib$ in modulus-argument form $re^{i\theta}$, eqn. (7.14) can be written

$$z^n = r\,e^{i(\theta + 2p\pi)} \qquad (p = 0, 1, 2, \ldots, n-1). \qquad (7.20)$$

Then taking the nth root of eqn. (7.20) we obtain all the values
of $(a+ib)^{1/n}$ in the form

$$(a+ib)^{1/n} = r^{1/n}\,e^{i(\theta+2p\pi)/n}$$

$$= r^{1/n}\left[\cos\left(\frac{\theta+2p\pi}{n}\right)+i\sin\left(\frac{\theta+2p\pi}{n}\right)\right], \quad (7.21)$$

where $p = 0, 1, 2, \ldots, n-1$ and $r^{1/n}$ means the real positive nth
root of r. Here, however, unless $b = 0$, roots do not occur in
conjugate pairs since the coefficients in eqn. (7.14) are not real.

Example 1. If $z^2 = 1-i$ find $|z|$ and arg z.

$$1-i = \sqrt{2}\,e^{-\frac{i\pi}{4}} = \sqrt{2}\,e^{i(2p-1/4)\pi}$$

Therefore the solutions of the eqn. $z^2 = 1-i$ are

$$z = 2^{\frac{1}{4}}e^{i(8p-1)\pi/8},$$

where $p = 0, 1$.

$$\therefore \; |z| = 2^{\frac{1}{4}} \quad \text{and} \quad \arg z = -\frac{\pi}{8}, \quad \text{or} \quad \frac{7\pi}{8}.$$

Example 2. Resolve $x^{2n} - 2x^n a^n \cos n\theta + a^{2n}$, where a is real, into n real
quadratic factors.

Deduce that

(a) $\qquad \cos n\varphi - \cos n\theta = 2^{n-1} \displaystyle\prod_{p=0}^{n-1}\left[\cos\varphi - \cos\left(\theta+\frac{2p\pi}{n}\right)\right],$

(b) $\qquad 2^{\frac{1}{2}-n} = \displaystyle\prod_{p=0}^{n-1} \sin\left\{\frac{(4p+1)\pi}{4n}\right\}.$

The eqn. $f(x) = x^{2n} - 2x^n a^n \cos n\theta + a^{2n} = 0$ can be written

$$x^{2n} - 2x^n a^n \cos n\theta + a^{2n}(\cos^2 n\theta + \sin^2 n\theta) = 0,$$

i.e. $\qquad (x^n - a^n \cos n\theta)^2 = -a^{2n}\sin^2 n\theta = a^{2n}i^2 \sin^2 n\theta.$

$$\therefore \; x^n - a^n \cos n\theta = \pm a^n i \sin n\theta,$$

i.e. $\qquad x^n = a^n(\cos n\theta \pm i \sin n\theta) = a^n e^{\pm in\theta},$

or $\qquad x^n = a^n e^{\pm i(n\theta+2p\pi)}, \quad p = 0, 1, 2, \ldots.$

Therefore the $2n$ roots of the eqn. $f(x) = 0$ are

$$x = ae^{\pm i\left(\theta+\frac{2p\pi}{n}\right)}, \quad (p = 0, 1, 2, \ldots, n-1).$$

$$\therefore \; f(x) = A \prod_{p=0}^{n-1}\left\{x-ae^{i\left(\theta+\frac{2p\pi}{n}\right)}\right\}\left\{x-ae^{-i\left(\theta+\frac{2p\pi}{n}\right)}\right\},$$

where A is a numerical constant. Comparison of the coefficients of x^{2n} gives $A = 1$.

$$\therefore \quad x^{2n} - 2a^n x^n \cos n\theta + a^{2n} = \prod_{p=0}^{n-1} \left\{ x^2 - 2ax \cos \left(\theta + \frac{2p\pi}{n} \right) + a^2 \right\}$$

which is the required expression.

Writing $x = e^{i\varphi/2}$, $a = e^{-i\varphi/2}$ gives identity (a) at once. In (a) writing $\theta = \pi/2n$, $\varphi = 0$ gives

$$1 - \cos \frac{1}{2}\pi = 2^{n-1} \prod_{p=0}^{n-1} \left(1 - \cos \frac{(4p+1)\pi}{2n} \right) = 2^{2n-1} \prod_{p=0}^{n-1} \sin^2 \left(\frac{4p+1}{4n} \right) \pi.$$

Taking the positive square root, since all the factors are positive, gives identity (b).

Example 3. Find correct to two places of decimals the real and imaginary parts of the complex roots of the equation

$$f(x) \equiv x^3 + x^2 + 5 = 0.$$

By Descartes' rule there is only one real root and by means of a graph this root $x_0 \approx -2 \cdot 12$. Newton's method gives $x_1 = -2 \times 12 + \dfrac{0 \cdot 337}{9 \cdot 24} = -2 \cdot 116$. Since $f(-2 \cdot 116) = 0 \cdot 00316$ the next correction term is $-0 \cdot 0003$ approx. Hence the real root $\approx -2 \cdot 116$. Correct to two places of decimals this root is $-2 \cdot 12$.

If $\alpha \pm i\beta$ are the complex roots, then

$$2\alpha + (-2 \cdot 116) = -1. \quad \therefore \quad \alpha = 0 \cdot 558.$$

Also

$$(\alpha^2 + \beta^2)(-2 \cdot 116) = -5. \quad \therefore \quad \beta^2 = 2 \cdot 052, \quad \beta \approx 1 \cdot 43.$$

Therefore the required complex roots are $0 \cdot 56 \pm 1 \cdot 43i$.

Exercises 7:4

1. Simplify

$$\frac{(3 + i4)^2}{(24 + i7)}$$

and find its fourth roots in the form $(a + ib)$, giving the values of a and b correct to two decimal places.

2. Use De Moivre's theorem to find the roots of the equation $(1 - x)^5 = x^5$ in the form $a + ib$. (Numerical evaluation is not required.)

3. Show that the roots of the equation

$$(1 + z)^{2n+1} = (1 - z)^{2n+1}$$

are

$$z = \pm i \tan \left\{ \frac{r\pi}{2n+1} \right\}, \quad (r = 0, 1, 2, \ldots, n).$$

4. Solve the equation $z^3 = 1 - i\sqrt{3}$ giving your answers in the form $re^{i\theta}$.

5. Solve the equation $z^2 + 2(1+i)z + 2 = 0$, giving the result correct to three decimal places.

6. Express $\sqrt{(-33 + i56)}$ in the form $x + iy$ where x and y are both positive. (*Hint:* solve the equations $x^2 - y^2 = -33$, $2xy = 56$.)

7. Show that the roots of the equation

$$(z+1)^6 = 64(z-1)^6$$

are represented in the Argand diagram by points lying on a circle of radius $\frac{4}{3}$ and that the values of z are

$$\frac{3 - 4i \sin \left(\frac{1}{3}k\pi\right)}{5 - 4 \cos \left(\frac{1}{3}k\pi\right)} \quad \text{for} \quad k = 0, 1, 2, \ldots 5.$$

8. Show that $z^2 - 2z \cos (2\pi/7) + 1$ is a factor of $(z^7 - 1)$ and write down the two other real quadratic factors of $(z^7 - 1)$.

9. If n is a positive integer, prove that

$$x^{2n} - 1 = (x^2 - 1) \prod_{k=1}^{n-1} \left\{ x^2 - 2x \cos \left(\frac{k\pi}{n}\right) + 1 \right\}.$$

Deduce that

(i) $$\frac{\sin n\theta}{\sin \theta} = 2^{n-1} \prod_{k=1}^{n-1} \left\{ \cos \theta - \cos \left(\frac{k\pi}{n}\right) \right\},$$

(ii) $$\sqrt{n} = 2^{n-1} \prod_{r=1}^{n-1} \sin \left(\frac{k\pi}{2n}\right).$$

10. Show that

$$(1+x)^{2n} - (1-x)^{2n} = 4nx \prod_{p=1}^{n-1} \left(x^2 + \tan^2 \frac{r\pi}{2n} \right).$$

Deduce that

$$\prod_{r=1}^{n-1} \cos \frac{r\pi}{2n} = 2^{1-n} \sqrt{n}.$$

11. Find the two complex roots of $x^3 + 2x^2 + 5 = 0$.

12. Prove that the conditions for the roots of the equation

$$z^2 + az + b = 0$$

to be of the form $e^{i\theta_1}$, $e^{i\theta_2}$ are

$$|b| = 1 \quad \text{and} \quad 2 \arg a = \arg b + 2\pi.$$

13. Solve the equation

$$z^6 + z^4 + z^2 + 1 = 0$$

giving the six roots in the form $r e^{i\theta}$.

14. If α and β are two distinct solutions of the equation $z^5 = 1$, prove that the greatest possible value of $|\alpha + \beta|$ is $2 \cos (\pi/5)$, and find its smallest possible value.

15. The complex number z satisfies the equation

$$(z-a)^4 = b^4,$$

where a and b are complex numbers. Show that the points that represent the roots in the Argand plane are the vertices of a square and find the length of the side of this square in the case $b = 1+i$.

7:5 Trigonometric expansions

Two important applications of De Moivre's theorem for integral n are:

(i) the expansion of $\cos n\theta$, $\sin n\theta$ in terms of $\cos \theta$ or $\sin \theta$, and

(ii) the expression of $\cos^n \theta$, $\sin^n \theta$, in terms of cosines or sines of multiple angles.

Expanding $(\cos \theta + i \sin \theta)^n$ by the binomial theorem and using De Moivre's theorem, we find

$$(\cos n\theta + i \sin n\theta) = (\cos \theta + i \sin \theta)^n$$

$$= \cos^n \theta - \binom{n}{2} \cos^{n-2} \theta \sin^2 \theta$$

$$+ \binom{n}{4} \cos^{n-4} \theta \sin^4 \theta - \ldots$$

$$+ i \left\{ \binom{n}{1} \cos^{n-1} \theta \sin \theta \right.$$

$$\left. - \binom{n}{3} \cos^{n-3} \theta \sin^3 \theta + \ldots \right\}.$$

Equating real and imaginary parts gives $\cos n\theta$ and $\sin n\theta$ separately, viz.

$$\cos n\theta = \cos^n \theta - \binom{n}{2} \cos^{n-2} \theta \sin^2 \theta + \binom{n}{4} \cos^{n-4} \theta \sin^4 \theta - \ldots,$$

$$\sin n\theta = \binom{n}{1} \cos^{n-1} \theta \sin \theta - \binom{n}{3} \cos^{n-3} \theta \sin^3 \theta + \ldots. \quad (7.22)$$

It is not advisable to remember the formula for all the special cases which occur but to use the method indicated here in any particular problem. Use of the formula $\sin^2 \theta = 1 - \cos^2 \theta$ enables $\cos n\theta$ to be expanded in powers of $\cos \theta$ for all n and in powers of $\sin \theta$ (actually $\sin^2 \theta$) when n is even. Similarly, when n is odd $\sin n\theta$ can be expressed in powers of $\sin \theta$ but, when n is even, $\sin n\theta / \sin \theta$ can be expressed in powers of $\cos \theta$ only.

Division of the second of eqns. (7.22) by the first gives

$$\tan n\theta = \frac{\binom{n}{1} \tan \theta - \binom{n}{3} \tan^3 \theta + \ldots}{1 - \binom{n}{2} \tan^2 \theta + \binom{n}{4} \tan^4 \theta - \ldots}. \qquad (7.23)$$

The formulae of eqns. (7.22) and (7.23) can be generalised by multiplying out the left-hand side of eqn. (7.4) and equating real and imaginary parts. Division then gives

$$\tan (\theta_1 + \theta_2 + \ldots + \theta_n) = \frac{\Sigma t_1 - \Sigma t_1 t_2 t_3 + \Sigma t_1 t_2 t_3 t_4 t_5 - \ldots}{1 - \Sigma t_1 t_2 + \Sigma t_1 t_2 t_3 t_4 - \ldots} \qquad (7.24)$$

where $t_1 = \tan \theta_1$, etc.

Example.

(i) $\qquad \cos 3\theta = \cos^3 \theta - 3 \cos \theta \sin^2 \theta = 4 \cos^3 \theta - 3 \cos \theta.$

(ii) $\qquad \sin 3\theta = 3 \cos^2 \theta \sin \theta - \sin^3 \theta = 3 \sin \theta - 4 \sin^3 \theta.$

(iii) $\qquad \cos 4\theta = \cos^4 \theta - 6 \cos^2 \theta \sin^2 \theta + \sin^4 \theta$
$$= 8 \cos^4 \theta - 8 \cos^2 \theta + 1 = 8 \sin^4 \theta - 8 \sin^2 \theta + 1.$$

(iv) $\qquad \sin 4\theta = 4 \cos^3 \theta \sin \theta - 4 \cos \theta \sin^3 \theta$
$$= 4 \sin \theta (2 \cos^3 \theta - \cos \theta).$$

(v) $\quad \cos (\theta_1 + \theta_2 + \theta_3) = \cos \theta_1 \cos \theta_2 \cos \theta_3 - \cos \theta_1 \sin \theta_2 \sin \theta_3$
$$- \cos \theta_2 \sin \theta_3 \sin \theta_1 - \cos \theta_3 \sin \theta_1 \sin \theta_2.$$

(vi) $\quad \tan (\theta_1 + \theta_2 + \theta_3) = \dfrac{t_1 + t_2 + t_3 - t_1 t_2 t_3}{1 - t_1 t_2 - t_2 t_3 - t_3 t_1}.$

The exponential forms (7.8) for $\sin \theta$ and $\cos \theta$ can be used to express $\cos^n \theta$ and $\sin^n \theta$ as cosines and sines of multiples of θ when n is an integer. For if $z = e^{i\theta}$, then

$$z + z^{-1} = 2 \cos \theta, \qquad z - z^{-1} = 2i \sin \theta,$$
$$z^p + z^{-p} = 2 \cos p\theta, \qquad z^p - z^{-p} = 2i \sin p\theta \qquad (7.25)$$

and expanding $(z+z^{-1})^n$ by the binomial theorem gives

$$(z+z^{-1})^n = z^n + \binom{n}{1}z^{n-2} + \binom{n}{2}z^{n-4} + \ldots + \binom{n}{n-2}z^{-(n-4)}$$

$$+ \binom{n}{n-1}z^{-(n-2)} + z^{-n}$$

$$= (z^n + z^{-n}) + \binom{n}{1}(z^{n-2} + z^{-(n-2)})$$

$$+ \binom{n}{2}(z^{n-4} + z^{-(n-4)}) + \ldots$$

on rearrangement. Hence using eqns. (7.25) we have

$$2^n \cos^n \theta = 2 \cos n\theta + \binom{n}{1}2 \cos (n-2)\theta$$

$$+ \binom{n}{2}2 \cos (n-4)\theta + \ldots \quad . \quad (7.26)$$

The last term on the right-hand side of eqn. (7.26) is $2\binom{n}{\frac{1}{2}(n-1)} \cos \theta$ if n is odd, $\binom{n}{\frac{1}{2}n}$ if n is even.

Similarly, the expansion of $(z-z^{-1})^n$ will provide expressions for $\sin^n \theta$ in cosines or sines of multiple angles according as n is even or odd. This is to be expected since $\sin^n\theta$ is an even or odd function according as n is even or odd and must be expressible in terms of even or odd functions accordingly. Again it is inadvisable to state or remember the general formulae but to work out each case as required.

Example 1. Find $\sin^7 \theta$ in terms of multiple angles.

$$2\mathrm{i} \sin \theta = z - z^{-1}, \quad 2\mathrm{i} \sin p\theta = z^p - z^{-p}.$$

$$\therefore \quad 2^7 \mathrm{i}^7 \sin^7 \theta = -\mathrm{i}2^7 \sin^7 \theta = (z - z^{-1})^7$$

$$= z^7 - 7z^5 + 21z^3 - 35z + 35z^{-1} - 21z^{-3} + 7z^{-5} - z^{-7}$$

$$= (z^7 - z^{-7}) - 7(z^5 - z^{-5}) + 21(z^3 - z^{-3}) - 35(z - z^{-1})$$

$$= 2\mathrm{i} (\sin 7\theta - 7 \sin 5\theta + 21 \sin 3\theta - 35 \sin \theta)$$

Hence

$$\sin^7 \theta = -\frac{(\sin 7\theta - 7 \sin 5\theta + 21 \sin 3\theta - 35 \sin \theta)}{2^6}$$

Example 2. Find $\sin^4 \theta$ in terms of multiple angles.

$$(2i \sin \theta)^4 = 16 \sin^4 \theta = (z - z^{-1})^4$$
$$= z^4 - 4z^2 + 6 - 4z^{-2} + z^{-4}$$
$$= (z^4 + z^{-4}) - 4(z^2 + z^{-2}) + 6$$
$$= 2\{\cos 4\theta - 4\cos 2\theta + 3\}$$
$$\therefore \quad \sin^4 \theta = \tfrac{1}{8}\{\cos 4\theta - 4\cos 2\theta + 3\}.$$

This result can also be obtained by two applications of the double-angle formulae of elementary trigonometry.

Example 3. Sum the series $\cos \theta + \cos 2\theta + \ldots + \cos n\theta$. Hence find the sum of the series $\sin \theta + 2 \sin 2\theta + \ldots + n \sin n\theta$.

If
$$C = \cos \theta + \cos 2\theta + \ldots + \cos n\theta$$

and
$$S = \sin \theta + \sin 2\theta + \ldots + \sin n\theta,$$

then
$$C + iS = e^{i\theta} + e^{2i\theta} + \ldots + e^{in\theta} = e^{i\theta}\frac{(1 - e^{in\theta})}{(1 - e^{i\theta})},$$

i.e.
$$C + iS = \frac{e^{i\theta} \cdot e^{\frac{1}{2}in\theta}\left(e^{-\frac{1}{2}in\theta} - e^{\frac{1}{2}in\theta}\right)}{e^{\frac{1}{2}i\theta}\left(e^{-\frac{1}{2}i\theta} - e^{\frac{1}{2}i\theta}\right)} = \frac{e^{\frac{1}{2}(n+1)i\theta}(-2i)\sin \frac{1}{2}n\theta}{(-2i)\sin \frac{1}{2}\theta}.$$

$$\therefore \quad C = \frac{\sin \frac{1}{2}n\theta \cos \frac{1}{2}(n+1)\theta}{\sin \frac{1}{2}\theta} \quad \text{and} \quad S = \frac{\sin \frac{1}{2}n\theta \sin \frac{1}{2}(n+1)\theta}{\sin \frac{1}{2}\theta}.$$

This example shows that it is often helpful to do the manipulations with complex numbers before separating out the real and imaginary parts. The second sum required is $-dC/d\theta$.

Exercises 7 : 5

1. Prove that:

(i) $\quad 1 + (\cos \theta + i \sin \theta)^6 = 2 \cos 3\theta(\cos 3\theta + i \sin 3\theta),$

(ii) $\quad \dfrac{1 + (\cos \theta + i \sin \theta)^6}{1 + (\cos \theta - i \sin \theta)^6} = \cos 6\theta + i \sin 6\theta.$

2. Prove that
$$32 \cos^4 \theta \sin^2 \theta = 2 + \cos 2\theta - 2 \cos 4\theta - \cos 6\theta.$$

Deduce the coefficient of θ^{2n} in the expansion of $32 \cos^4 \theta \sin^2 \theta$ in ascending powers of θ.

3. Establish the formulae

$$16 \sin^5 \theta = \sin 5\theta - 5 \sin 3\theta + 10 \sin \theta,$$
$$32 \cos^6 \theta = \cos 6\theta + 6 \cos 4\theta + 15 \cos 2\theta + 10.$$

Solve completely the equation

$$\cos 5\theta + 5 \cos 3\theta + 10 \cos \theta = \tfrac{1}{2},$$

where θ is real.

4. (i) By using the exponential form for $\cos \theta$ and $\sin \theta$, express $\sin^6 \theta \cos^4 \theta$ as the sum of cosines of multiples of θ and evaluate

$$\int_0^{\pi/4} \sin^6 \theta \cos^4 \theta \, d\theta.$$

(ii) Expand $\sin^5 \theta$ in a series of sines of multiples of θ and hence evaluate

$$\int_{\pi/3}^{\pi/2} \sin^5 \theta \, d\theta.$$

5. If $(1+z)^n = c_0 + c_1 z + c_2 z^2 + \ldots + c_n z^n$ prove that

$$c_0 - c_2 + c_4 - \ldots = 2^{n/2} \cos (n\pi/4).$$

6. If $y = e^x \cos^2 x$, where x is real, expand y in a series of ascending powers of x, and prove that the coefficient of x^n is

$$\frac{1}{2} \frac{(1 + 5^{n/2} \cos n\theta)}{n!},$$

where $\theta = \tan^{-1} 2$.

7. Find the sum of n terms of

$$S_n = \sin (x+2a) + \sin (x+4a) + \sin (x+6a) + \ldots$$

8. Find (i) $\sum_{n=1}^{\infty} \frac{\cos n\theta}{2^n}$, (ii) $\sum_{n=1}^{\infty} \frac{\sin n\theta}{n!}$.

9. If $|x| < 1$, show that $\sum_{n=0}^{\infty} x^n \cos (2n+1)\theta = \frac{(1-x) \cos \theta}{1 - 2x \cos 2\theta + x^2}$.

10. If $z = e^{i\theta}$, use De Moivre's theorem to show that

$$z^n + z^{-n} = 2 \cos n\theta.$$

Use this result to express $\cos^5 \theta$ in terms of cosines of multiples of θ. Show that

$$\int_0^{\pi/6} \cos^5 \theta \, d\theta = \frac{203}{480}.$$

11. Prove that

$$(1 + \cos 2\theta + i \sin 2\theta)^n = (2 \cos \theta)^n (\cos n\theta + i \sin n\theta).$$

Hence, or otherwise, show that

$$16 \cos^4 \theta \cos 4\theta = 1 + 4 \cos 2\theta + 6 \cos 4\theta + 4 \cos 6\theta + \cos 8\theta.$$

12. Using de Moivre's theorem, or otherwise, show that, if θ is real,

$$\sin\theta + \frac{\sin 2\theta}{2} + \frac{\sin 3\theta}{4} + \frac{\sin 4\theta}{8} + \ldots = \frac{4\sin\theta}{5 - 4\cos\theta}.$$

13. Prove that $\displaystyle\sum_{n=1}^{\infty} \frac{\cos n\theta \sin^n \alpha}{n} = -\frac{1}{2}\ln(1 - 2\cos\theta\sin\alpha + \sin^2\alpha)$.

7 : 6 Functions of $x + iy$

When applied to complex numbers the operations of algebra, such as addition, subtraction, multiplication, division, taking square roots, etc., result in complex numbers. Therefore any function $f(z)$ of the complex number $z = x + iy$ is another complex number which we denote by $w = u + iv$ so that u and v are the real and imaginary parts of $w = f(z)$. We use the notation Re and Im to denote real and imaginary parts so that

$$u = \mathrm{Re}\, f(z), \quad v = \mathrm{Im}\, f(z). \tag{7.27}$$

Since

$$u + iv = f(z), \tag{7.28}$$

$$\therefore \quad u - iv = \{f(z)\}^*. \tag{7.29}$$

Here $\{f(z)\}^*$ is the complex conjugate of $f(z)$ and is *not* equal to $f(z^*)$ unless the coefficients in $f(z)$ are all real. For example, if $f(z) = (a + ib)z^2$, then $f(z^*) = (a + ib)(x - iy)^2$ whereas $\{f(z)\}^* = (a - ib) \times (x - iy)^2$. The essential point to notice is that to derive $\{f(z)\}^*$ from $f(z)$ the complex conjugates of the coefficients in $f(z)$ must be used as well as z^* in place of z. From eqns. (7.28) and (7.29) we find by addition and subtraction

$$2u = f(z) + \{f(z)\}^*, \quad 2iv = f(z) - \{f(z)\}^*. \tag{7.30}$$

In the following examples we illustrate some of the techniques useful in finding the real and imaginary parts of some standard functions. The results illustrate the general fact that one relation between complex numbers is equivalent to two relations between real numbers.

Example 1. $\quad w = \dfrac{1}{z} = \dfrac{1}{x + iy} = \dfrac{x - iy}{(x + iy)(x - iy)} = \dfrac{x - iy}{x^2 + y^2}.$

$$\therefore \quad u = \frac{x}{x^2 + y^2}, \qquad v = \frac{-y}{x^2 + y^2}.$$

Here we make the denominator real by multiplication above and below by the complex conjugate of the denominator.

Example 2. $w = \mathrm{e}^z = \mathrm{e}^{x+\mathrm{i}y} = \mathrm{e}^x\mathrm{e}^{\mathrm{i}y} = \mathrm{e}^x(\cos y + \mathrm{i}\sin y)$.

$\therefore\ \ u = \mathrm{e}^x\cos y, \quad v = \mathrm{e}^x\sin y.$

If we write w in its modulus-argument form $R\,\mathrm{e}^{\mathrm{i}\varphi}$, then

$$R = |w| = \mathrm{e}^x, \quad \varphi = \arg w = y+2p\pi.$$

Example 3. $w = \sin z = \sin(x+\mathrm{i}y) = \sin x\cos \mathrm{i}y + \cos x\sin \mathrm{i}y.$

$\therefore\ \ u+\mathrm{i}v = \sin x\cosh y + \mathrm{i}\cos x\sinh y.$

$\therefore\ \ u = \sin x\cosh y, \quad v = \cos x\sinh y.$

Here we have used eqns. (7.9).

Example 4. $w = \tan z.$

From the first of eqns. (7.30),

$$2u = \tan z + \tan z^* = \frac{\sin z}{\cos z} + \frac{\sin z^*}{\cos z^*} = \frac{\sin z\cos z^* + \cos z\sin z^*}{\cos z\cos z^*}$$

$$= \frac{\sin(z+z^*)}{\frac{1}{2}\{\cos(z+z^*)+\cos(z-z^*)\}} = \frac{2\sin 2x}{\cos 2x + \cos 2\mathrm{i}y} = \frac{2\sin 2x}{\cos 2x + \cosh 2y}.$$

$$\therefore\ \ u = \frac{\sin 2x}{\cos 2x + \cosh 2y}.$$

Similarly $2\mathrm{i}v = \tan z - \tan z^*$ leads to

$$v = \frac{\sinh 2y}{\cos 2x + \cosh 2y}.$$

Example 5. Find $|w|$ when $w = \tanh z$.

To find $|w|$ it is usually advisable to use the relation $|w|^2 = ww^*$ rather than $|w|^2 = u^2+v^2$. In our case

$$|w|^2 = ww^* = \tanh z\tanh z^* = \frac{\sinh z\sinh z^*}{\cosh z\cosh z^*} = \frac{\frac{1}{2}[\cosh(z+z^*)-\cosh(z-z^*)]}{\frac{1}{2}[\cosh(z+z^*)+\cosh(z-z^*)]}$$

$$= \frac{\cosh 2x - \cosh 2\mathrm{i}y}{\cosh 2x + \cosh 2\mathrm{i}y} = \frac{\cosh 2x - \cos 2y}{\cosh 2x + \cos 2y}.$$

The operation of finding a logarithm is not possible by means of the elementary algebraic processes of addition, multiplication, etc. We defined the logarithm $y = \ln x$ of a real number x as the inverse of the relation $x = \mathrm{e}^y$. We use this definition for complex numbers also. If

$$z = e^w, \tag{7.31}$$

then w is a *logarithm* of z. (We use the phrase *a logarithm* since, as we shall see, the logarithm function is many-valued.) Using the modulus argument form $z = r\,e^{i\theta}$, eqn. (7.31) may be written

$$re^{i\theta} = e^u e^{iv}.$$
$$\therefore \ r = e^u, \quad e^{i\theta} = e^{iv}.$$

The first of these relations, since it involves only real numbers, gives $u = \ln r$ which is the unique logarithm of the real number r. The relation $e^{i\theta} = e^{iv}$ shows that v and θ must differ by a multiple of 2π.

$$v = \theta \pm 2p\pi \quad (p = 0, 1, 2 \ldots).$$
$$\therefore \ w = \text{Log } z = u + iv = \ln|z| + i\{\arg z \pm 2p\pi\}.$$

We conclude that, in this definition, a complex number z has infinitely many logarithms. The notation $w = \text{Log } z$, with a capital L, denotes the most general complex value of the logarithm. If we choose a value p such that $-\pi < v \leqslant \pi$ we obtain the *principal value* of the logarithm written $\log z$ (with a small l). We keep the notation $\ln x$ to refer exclusively to real numbers.

Consider the product of two numbers

$$re^{i\theta} = z = z_1 z_2 = r_1 r_2 e^{i(\theta_1 + \theta_2)}.$$

Then

$$\text{Log } z = \ln r + i(\theta + 2p\pi)$$
$$= \ln r_1 r_2 + i(\theta_1 + \theta_2 + 2p\pi)$$
$$= \ln r_1 + i(\theta_1 + 2p_1\pi) + \ln r_2 + i(\theta_2 + 2p_2\pi).$$
$$\therefore \ \text{Log } z = \text{Log } z_1 + \text{Log } z_2, \tag{7.32}$$

where $p = p_1 + p_2$. This shows that a familiar property of logarithms is still true of the complex values. However, the relation (7.32) means that *one* of the values of $\text{Log } z$ is the sum of *one* of the values of $\text{Log } z_1$ and *one* of the values of $\text{Log } z_2$; which of the possible values satisfy this relation is not stated.

Example. If $z_1 = -1$, $z_2 = i$, then

$$\log z_1 = \ln(1) + i\pi, \quad \log z_2 = \ln(1) + \tfrac{1}{2}i\pi.$$
$$\therefore \ \log z_1 + \log z_2 = \frac{3i\pi}{2}.$$

But $z_1 z_2 = -i$ and

$$\text{Log}(-i) = \ln 1 + i(-\tfrac{1}{2}\pi + 2p\pi). \tag{1}$$

But $v = \text{Im} \log(-i)$, the principal value is such that $-\pi < v \leqslant \pi$.

$$\therefore \quad \log(-i) = \log(z_1 z_2) = -\tfrac{1}{2} i\pi$$

which is not equal to $\log z_1 + \log z_2$. Nevertheless if we choose $p = 1$ in eqn. (1) we obtain one of the values of $\text{Log}(-i)$ as

$$\ln 1 + i\left(-\frac{1}{2}\pi + 2\pi\right) = \frac{3i\pi}{2}.$$

This means that if we add the principal values of the logarithms of two numbers we do not necessarily obtain the *principal value* of the logarithm of their product.

The logarithm of a real number, as we have been accustomed to use it, with zero as its imaginary part, is the principal value, and as long as we are concerned only with real numbers, manipulations with logarithms use only principal values, which is in accordance with the use of a small "l" in the notation.

Earlier in this chapter we showed that $a^{p/q}$ has q different values, which are complex if a is complex; we also defined e^z by means of an infinite series. So far, however, we cannot ascribe a value to a^z where both a and z may be complex.

The definition of a logarithm is used to give a value to a^z. Since

$$a = e^{\text{Log}\, a}$$

is true whichever value of the general $\text{Log}\, a$ is used, we *define*

$$a^z = e^{z\,\text{Log}\, a}.$$

Since $\text{Log}\, a$ has infinitely many values this equation implies that a^z also may have infinitely many values.

If we choose $a = 1$ and $z = 1/n$ this definition leads to the n values for the nth roots of unity given by eqn. (7.19). For in this case

$$\text{Log}\, a = \text{Log}\, 1 = p\, 2\pi i, \quad \text{where} \quad p = 0, \pm 1, \pm 2, \ldots$$

$$\therefore \quad a^{1/n} = e^{p 2\pi i/n} = \cos\left(\frac{2p\pi}{n}\right) + i \sin\left(\frac{2p\pi}{n}\right).$$

Example 1. If x, y, u, v are real and $\cosh(x+iy) = \tan(u+iv)$, prove that

$$\cosh 2x + \cos 2y = 2\left\{\frac{\cosh 2v - \cos 2u}{\cosh 2v + \cos 2u}\right\}.$$

Since
$$\cosh (x+iy) = \tan (u+iv),$$
$$\cosh (x-iy) = \tan (u-iv).$$
$$\therefore \ \ \cosh (x+iy) \cosh (x-iy) = \tan (u+iv) \tan (u-iv)$$
$$= \frac{\sin (u+iv) \sin (u-iv)}{\cos (u+iv) \cos (u-iv)}.$$
$$\therefore \ \ \frac{1}{2} (\cosh 2x + \cosh 2iy) = \frac{\frac{1}{2} (\cos 2iv - \cos 2u)}{\frac{1}{2} (\cos 2iv + \cos 2u)}.$$

Use of eqns. (7.9) gives the required result.

Example 2. Find the most general values of the expressions

$$\text{(a)} \ \ \text{Log} \left(\frac{3+i}{3-i}\right), \quad \text{(b)} \ \ \cos^{-1} (3i).$$

(a)
$$\text{Log} \left(\frac{3+i}{3-i}\right) = \text{Log} (3+i) - \text{Log} (3-i).$$

But $3+i = \sqrt{10} e^{i(\theta+2p\pi)}$ where $\theta = \tan^{-1} (\frac{1}{3})$.

$$\therefore \ \ \text{Log} (3+i) = \ln \sqrt{10} + i(\theta+2p\pi).$$

Similarly $\text{Log} (3-i) = \ln \sqrt{10} + i(-\theta+2q\pi).$

$$\therefore \ \ \text{Log} \left(\frac{3+i}{3-i}\right) = 2i \{\theta+(p-q)\pi\} = 2i \{\theta+n\pi)\}$$

where
$$n = 0, \pm 1, \pm 2, \ldots$$

(b) If $z = x+iy = \cos^{-1}(3i)$, we must solve the equation

$$\cos (x+iy) = 3i \tag{1}$$

where x and y are real,
i.e.

$$\cos x \cos iy - \sin x \sin iy = \cos x \cosh y - i \sin x \sinh y = 3i.$$

Equating real and imaginary parts gives

$$\cos x \cosh y = 0, \tag{2}$$
$$\sin x \sinh y = -3. \tag{3}$$

From eqn. (2) either $\cos x = 0$ or $\cosh y = 0$. But $\cosh y \geqslant 1$ for real y and hence $\cos x = 0$, i.e. $x = \frac{1}{2}\pi + n\pi$. Then eqn. (3) gives

$$(-1)^n \sinh y = -3$$

or

$$y = \sinh^{-1} \{3(-1)^{n-1}\} = (-1)^{n-1} \sinh^{-1} 3 = (-1)^{n-1} \ln (3+\sqrt{10}).$$
$$\therefore \ \ z = x+iy = (n+\tfrac{1}{2})\pi + (-1)^{n-1} i \ln (3+\sqrt{10})$$

for
$$n = 0, \pm 1, \pm 2, \ldots . \tag{4}$$

Aliter. Write eqn. (1) in the form

$$\tfrac{1}{2} (e^{iz} + e^{-iz}) = 3i.$$

Then $e^{2iz} - 6ie^{iz} + 1 = 0$,

i.e. $\qquad\qquad\qquad (e^{iz})^2 - 6ie^{iz} + 1 = 0$.

Solution of this quadratic in e^{iz} gives

$$e^{iz} = i(3 \pm \sqrt{10})$$
$$\therefore \quad iz = \text{Log}\,\{i(3 \pm \sqrt{10})\}.$$

Taking the positive sign gives

$$iz = \text{Log}\,\{i(3 + \sqrt{10})\} = \ln(3 + \sqrt{10}) + i(\tfrac{1}{2}\pi + 2p\pi),$$

i.e.

$$z = (2p\pi + \tfrac{1}{2}\pi) - i\ln(3 + \sqrt{10}). \tag{5}$$

Taking the negative sign gives

$$iz = \text{Log}\,\{i(3 - \sqrt{10})\} = \text{Log}\left\{\frac{-i}{3 + \sqrt{10}}\right\} = i\left(2q\pi - \frac{1}{2}\pi\right) - \ln(3 + \sqrt{10}),$$

i.e.

$$z = (2q\pi - \tfrac{1}{2}\pi) + i\ln(3 + \sqrt{10}). \tag{6}$$

Equations (5) and (6) give the solution and together are equivalent to eqn. (4).

Example 3. Prove that the equation $e^x = x + a$ has two real roots if a is real and greater than 1 and no real roots if a is less than 1.

Prove that the equation has no root of the form iv, where v is real and not zero, and that, if $u + iv$ is a complex root, $u > 0$.

We consider the function $f(x) = e^x - x$. Since $f'(x) = e^x - 1$, it follows that $f(x)$ has one stationary value occurring when $x = 0$ and that this gives a minimum for $f(x)$. Hence $f(x) \geqslant 1$ and so, if $a < 1$, the equation $f(x) = a$ has no real roots whereas, when $a > 1$, it has one positive and one negative real root. [The two cases are illustrated in Fig. 7.9(a), (b).]

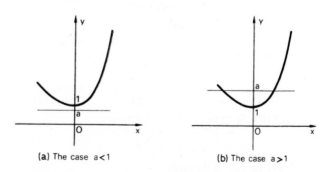

(a) The case $a < 1$ (b) The case $a > 1$

FIG. 7.9. The real roots of $e^x - x = a$.

Suppose that the equation has a root of the form iv, where v is real and non-zero. Then

$$e^{iv} = \cos v + i \sin v = iv + a,$$

i.e.

$$\cos v = a, \quad \sin v = v.$$

Since $\sin v < v$ for $v > 0$, (see p. 255), and $(\sin v)/v$ is an even function, the second of these equations has only one real root $v = 0$ contradicting our assumption that $v \neq 0$. Hence there is no purely imaginary root.

If $u + iv$ is a complex root, then

$$e^{u+iv} = e^u(\cos v + i \sin v) = u + iv + a,$$

i.e.

$$e^u \cos v = u + a, \quad e^u \sin v = v. \tag{1}$$

If $u < 0$, the second of these equations implies that $(\sin v)/v > 1$ which cannot be so. Hence $u \geqslant 0$. If now $u = 0$, then $\cos v = a$, $\sin v = v$. The second of these equations has only one real root $v = 0$, (and for this to be so $a = 1$), i.e. the complex root is, in fact, real. Hence for a complex root (with non-zero imaginary part), $u > 0$.

Example 4. Show that, if $z = x + iy$,

$$|\sinh z| = (\sinh^2 x + \sin^2 y)^{\frac{1}{2}}.$$

The complex potential $w = U + iV$ of an electrostatic field in the plane of $z = x + iy$ is

$$w = i \log \left\{ \sinh \left(\frac{\pi z}{a} \right) \right\},$$

where a is a real positive constant, V being the electrostatic potential. Show that

$$\sinh^2 \left(\frac{\pi x}{a} \right) + \sin^2 \left(\frac{\pi y}{a} \right) = \exp (2V).$$

Deduce that, for large positive values of V the equipotentials are approximately the lines $x = $ constant. Deduce also that, for a large negative value of V, the equipotential $V = $ constant consists approximately of a row of circles with centres $(0, 0)$, $(0, \pm a)$, $(0, \pm 2a)$, ... and common radius $(a/\pi) \exp (V)$.

$$|\sinh z| = \sqrt{(\sinh z \sinh z^*)}$$
$$= \sqrt{\{\sinh (x+iy) \sinh (x-iy)\}}$$
$$= \sqrt{\{\tfrac{1}{2}(\cosh 2x - \cosh 2iy)\}}$$
$$= \sqrt{\{\tfrac{1}{2}(\cosh 2x - \cos 2y)\}},$$

i.e.

$$|\sinh z| = \sqrt{(\sinh^2 x + \sin^2 y)}. \tag{1}$$

When

$$w = U + iV = i \log \sinh \left(\frac{\pi z}{a} \right),$$

eqn. (1) implies that

$$|e^{w/i}| = e^V = \left| \sinh\left(\frac{\pi z}{a}\right) \right|$$

$$= \sqrt{\left\{\sinh^2\left(\frac{\pi x}{a}\right) + \sin^2\left(\frac{\pi y}{a}\right)\right\}}.$$

$$\therefore \quad \sinh^2\left(\frac{\pi x}{a}\right) + \sin^2\left(\frac{\pi y}{a}\right) = e^{2V}. \tag{2}$$

Since $|\sin(\pi y/a)| \leqslant 1$, when V is large and positive $\sinh^2(\pi x/a)$ must be large. In fact, $\sinh(\pi x/a) \approx e^V$,

i.e. $$e^{\pi x/a} - e^{-\pi x/a} \approx 2e^V,$$

i.e. $$x \approx \frac{a}{\pi}(V + \ln 2) \approx \frac{aV}{\pi}$$

when V is large. It follows that the equipotentials approximate to the lines $V = $ constant for large V.

When V is large and negative the right-hand side of eqn. (2) is very small and so $\sinh(\pi x/a)$, $\sin(\pi y/a)$ must each be very small. In fact, we can take

$$\sinh\left(\frac{\pi x}{a}\right) \approx \frac{\pi x}{a}, \quad \frac{\pi y}{a} \approx r\pi + \frac{\pi Y}{a},$$

where $r = 0, \pm 1, \pm 2, \ldots$ and Y is small. Then

$$\left(\frac{\pi x}{a}\right)^2 + \left(\frac{\pi Y}{a}\right)^2 = e^{2V}$$

or $$x^2 + Y^2 = \left(\frac{ae^V}{\pi}\right)^2,$$

i.e. $$x^2 + (y - ra)^2 = \left(\frac{ae^V}{\pi}\right)^2.$$

It follows that, in this case, the equipotential $V = $ constant is as stated.

Exercises 7:6

1. (i) Find the general values of x and y which satisfy the equation $\cos(x + iy) = -3$, where x and y are real.

(ii) If $u + iv = \coth(x + iy)$, where u, v, x and y are real, show that

$$u = \frac{\sinh 2x}{\cosh 2x - \cos 2y}.$$

2. If $u + iv = \log \sin(x + iy)$ show that

$$2e^{2u} = \cosh 2y - \cos 2x.$$

3. Prove that, if x and y are real,

$$|\cosh(x + iy)|^2 = \tfrac{1}{2}(\cosh 2x + \cos 2y).$$

4. If w is a complex number and $\bar{w}$ is its conjugate, show that

$$|w|^2 = ww^* \quad \text{and} \quad \arg w = \tan^{-1}\left\{\frac{w-w^*}{i(w+w^*)}\right\}.$$

If $w = \tan(z/2)$, where $w = u+iv$ and $z = x+iy$, prove that

$$\frac{1+u^2+v^2}{1-u^2-v^2} = \frac{\cosh y}{\cos x} \quad \text{and} \quad \frac{v}{u} = \frac{\sinh y}{\sin x}.$$

5. If

$$\frac{x+iy-a}{x+iy+a} = e^{u+iv},$$

where x, y, u, v, a are all real, show that

$$x = \frac{-a\sinh u}{\cosh u - \cos v}, \quad y = \frac{a\sin v}{\cosh u - \cos v}.$$

6. If $\operatorname{cosec}[(\pi/4)+iy] = u+iv$, where y, u, v, are all real, show that

$$(u^2+v^2)^2 = 2(u^2-v^2).$$

7. (i) If $\tan(x+iy) = \sin(u+iv)$ prove that

$$\frac{\tan u}{\tanh v} = \frac{\sin 2x}{\sinh 2y}.$$

(ii) Find all the values of z that satisfy the equation $\tan z = \frac{1}{2}(1-i)$.

8. If $\cos(\pi/4+ia)\cosh(x+i\pi/4) = 1$, a and x being real quantities, show that $2x = \pm\ln(2+\sqrt{3})$.

What is the value of the real part of $\sinh(x+i\pi/4)$ if the above condition holds true?

9. Show that all solutions of the equation

$$\sin z = 2i\cos z$$

are given by $z = (\frac{1}{2}\pm n)\pi+\frac{1}{2}i\ln 3$ where n is zero or any positive integer.

10. Show that $\cosh^{-1}i$ has the values $\ln[(-1)^{n-1}+\sqrt{2}]+i(2n-1)\pi/2$, n being a positive integer.

11. If $x+iy = \tanh(u+i\pi/4)$, where x, y and u are real, prove that, for all values of u, $x^2+y^2 = 1$.

12. (i) Show that the general value of $\cos^{-1}2$ is

$$2n\pi \pm i\ln(2+\sqrt{3}),$$

where n is any integer.

(ii) Prove that, if $\tan z = \cos\alpha+i\sin\alpha$ where α is real and acute, then

$$z = \left(n+\frac{1}{4}\right)\pi+\frac{1}{2}i\ln\tan\left(\frac{\pi}{4}+\frac{\alpha}{2}\right),$$

where n is any integer.

13. If

$$w = \log\frac{z+a}{z-a},$$

where $z = x+iy$, $w = u+iv$, and x, y, u, v, a are all real, prove that

$$\tanh u = \frac{2ax}{x^2+y^2+a^2} \quad \text{and} \quad \tan v = -\frac{2ay}{x^2+y^2-a^2}.$$

14. If $u+iv = \log \dfrac{x+iy+a}{x+iy-a}$, prove that

(a)
$$x^2+y^2-2ax \coth u+a^2 = 0,$$

(b)
$$x = \frac{a \sinh u}{\cosh u-\cos v},$$

(c)
$$|x+iy|^2 = \frac{a^2(\cosh u+\cos v)}{\cosh u-\cos v}.$$

15. The complex number $f(x) = z+a^2/z$ where $z = x+iy$ is used to describe the flow of a fluid past a cylinder of radius a, which occupies the region $|z| \leqslant a$ in the Argand diagram. Prove that $f(z)$ is real only on the x-axis and at points on the surface of the cylinder $|z| = a$.

The velocity of the fluid is the modulus of $df/dz = 1-(a^2/z^2)$. Find the velocity in terms of r and θ at any point with coordinates $x = r\cos\theta$, $y = r\sin\theta$.

16. The partial differential equations satisfied by the potential V and the current I in a transmission line are

$$L\frac{\partial I}{\partial t}+RI = -\frac{\partial V}{\partial x}, \quad C\frac{\partial V}{\partial t}+GV = -\frac{\partial I}{\partial x},$$

where L, C, R, G are constants. Show that they are satisfied by

$$V = V_0 \exp\{-(\lambda+i\mu)x+i\omega t\},$$
$$I = I_0 \exp\{-(\lambda+i\mu)x+i\omega t\},$$

where V_0, I_0, λ, μ, ω are constants and λ, μ, ω are real, provided that
$$\lambda^2-\mu^2 = RG-\omega^2LC, \quad 2\lambda\mu = \omega(RC+LG).$$

17. If x, y, u, v are real and $\sinh(x+iy) = \cot(u+iv)$, show that

$$\sinh x \cos y = \frac{\sin 2u}{\cosh 2v-\cos 2u}.$$

18. If $w = u+iv = \log(x+iy)$ where u, v, x, y are all real, find u, v in terms of x and y. *Verify* that

$$\frac{\partial u}{\partial x} = \frac{\partial v}{\partial y}, \quad \frac{\partial u}{\partial y} = -\frac{\partial v}{\partial x}.$$

19. Determine all the values of the complex number $z = x+iy$ which satisfy the equation $e^z = 3$.

Obtain a particular value of $w = u+iv$ which satisfies $e^{1/w} = 3$ and $|w| < 10^{-6}$.

20. Find all the solutions, real and complex, of the following equations:

(i)
$$z^3 +8 = 0,$$

(ii)
$$\cosh z+4 = 0.$$

21. Find the real and imaginary parts of the complex numbers

(i) $e^{2+\frac{1}{3}i\pi}$, (ii) $\sin\left(\dfrac{\pi}{3}+i\right)$, (iii) $\text{Log}\,(1+i\sqrt{3})$.

Miscellaneous Exercises VII

1. Express in the form $a+ib$, where a and b are real and in their simplest form:

(i) $\dfrac{3+4i}{2-5i}$;   (ii) $(1+i\sqrt{3})^8$;   (iii) $\cos\left(\dfrac{\pi}{3}+i\ln 2\right)$.

Prove that

$$\sum_{n=1}^{\infty}\frac{\sin nx}{n!} = e^{\cos x}\sin(\sin x).$$

2. (i) Prove that $|\sin(\alpha+i\beta)|^2+|\cos(\alpha+i\beta)|^2 = \cosh 2\beta$.

(ii) If P represents the number $z = x+iy$ in an Argand diagram and if Q represents $w = 1/(1+z)$, trace the locus of Q as P describes a circle of unit radius with its centre at the origin.

3. (i) If $(x+iy)(u+iv) = ik$, where x, y, u, v are real variables and k is a real constant, show that the curves in the x, y plane given by $u = $ constant and $v = $ constant are circles.

(ii) If $(w-1)/(w+1) = \sin(x+iy)$, show that the argument (amplitude) of w is $\alpha+\beta$ where $\tan\alpha = \dfrac{\cos x\sinh y}{1+\sin x\cosh y}$, $\tan\beta = \dfrac{\cos x\sinh y}{1-\sin x\cosh y}$, and find the modulus of w.

4. (i) If the real part of $(z+1)/(z+i)$ is equal to 1, prove that the point z lies on a certain straight line in the Argand plane.

(ii) Find the roots of the equation

$$z^2-(3+5i)z+8i-4 = 0.$$

5. Indicate on the Argand diagram the positions of the points $z = 1+\sin\theta$ $\pm i\cos\theta$ for a given value of the angle θ. Prove that one of the values of $\left(\dfrac{1+\sin\theta+i\cos\theta}{1+\sin\theta-i\cos\theta}\right)^n$ is equal to $\cos\left\{n\left(\dfrac{\pi}{2}-\theta\right)\right\}+i\sin\left\{n\left(\dfrac{\pi}{2}-\theta\right)\right\}$. Obtain all the values of $\left(\dfrac{\sqrt{2}+1+i}{\sqrt{2}+1-i}\right)^{\frac{1}{4}}$ in the form $a+ib$, where a and b are real.

6. (i) The points representing the complex numbers z_1 and z_2 on an Argand diagram and the origin are the vertices of an equilateral triangle. Show that $z_1^2-z_1z_2+z_2^2 = 0$.

(ii) Express $\cos\{\frac{1}{4}\pi(1-i)\}$ in the form $a+ib$, where a and b are real and show that its modulus is $\{\frac{1}{2}\cosh(\pi/2)\}^{\frac{1}{2}}$.

7. (i) Find the general solution of the equation $\sinh z = 2\cosh z$, where z is complex.

(ii) If $u+iv = \cot(x+iy)$ show that

$$u = \frac{\sin 2x}{\cosh 2y-\cos 2x}.$$

Hence show that

$$iu = \frac{1}{1-e^{2(ix-y)}} - \frac{1}{1-e^{-2(ix+y)}},$$

and deduce that, if $y > 0$, u can be expressed as the infinite series

$$2 \sum_{r=1}^{\infty} e^{-2ry} \sin 2rx.$$

8. Find the general solution of the equation $\sin z = 3i \cos z$.

9. (i) If $z = x+iy$ and $0 \le \tan^{-1}(y/x) < 2\pi$ find the real and imaginary parts of (a) $\log z$, (b) $(z+1)/(z-1)$.

(ii) Find the three complex roots of the equation $z^3 = 1+i$ in the form $re^{i\theta}$ giving r correct to three decimals and the three values of θ in degrees. Indicate their positions in the Argand diagram.

10. (i) If $z = \dfrac{1+e^{i\theta}}{1-e^{i\theta}}$ express z in the form

$$r(\cos \varphi + i \sin \varphi).$$

(ii) Obtain the general value of $\text{Log} \left(\dfrac{1+e^{i\theta}}{1-e^{i\theta}} \right)$ when $\theta = \dfrac{\pi}{3}$.

11. If

$$I_n = \int x^n e^{az} \, dx,$$

prove that

$$aI_n = x^n e^{az} - nI_{n-1}.$$

Assuming this result to be true for real and complex values of a, prove that

(i) $\quad \int x^n \sin bx \, dx = \dfrac{n}{b} \int x^{n-1} \cos bx \, dx - \dfrac{1}{b} x^n \cos bx,$

(ii) $\quad \int_0^{\pi} x^4 \sin \tfrac{1}{2}x \, dx = 16(\pi^3 - 24\pi + 48).$

12. Express $\dfrac{[2(\cos \theta + i \sin \theta)]^3}{[3(\cos \theta - i \sin \theta)]^2}$ in the form $x+iy$, when $\theta = \dfrac{\pi}{15}$.

13. Express $\cos^6(2\theta)$ in terms of cosines of multiples of θ and hence evaluate

$$\int_0^{\pi/2} \cos^6(2\theta) \, d\theta.$$

14. Assuming the existence of the expansion, show that

$$2 \cos x \cosh x = \sum_0^{\infty} 2^{\frac{1}{2}n} \{1+(-1)^n\} \frac{x^n}{n!} \cdot \cos \frac{n\pi}{4}.$$

15. (i) If $z = x+iy$ and $\sin z = 1+i$, prove that $\cos 2x = \sqrt{5}-2$ and $\cosh 2y = \sqrt{5}+2$.

(ii) If $z = re^{i\theta}$ and ze^{-z} is real, prove that

$$\theta - r \sin \theta = n\pi \qquad (n = 0, \pm 1, \pm 2, \ldots).$$

16. If x, y, u, v are real numbers such that

$$u+iv = e^{x+iy},$$

prove that $u^2+v^2 = e^{2x}$ and $v/u = \tan y$.

Indicate in an Argand diagram the path of the point (u, v) when the point (x, y) moves in the positive sense round the boundary of the rectangle formed by the coordinate axes and the lines $x = 1$, $y = \pi/4$.

17. (i) Show that for any complex numbers z_1, z_2.

$$|az_1-z_2|^2+|z_1+az_2|^2 = (1+a^2)(|z_1|^2+|z_2|^2)$$

where a is real.

(ii) If $x^2+y^2 = 1$, $z = x+iy$ and $u+iv = z^2+z+1$
show that

$$(u^2-2u+v^2)^2 = u^2+v^2.$$

18. (i) Express $\cos^{-1} 2$ and $\cosh^{-1}\frac{1}{2}$ in the form $a+ib$ where a and b are real.

(ii) Prove that

$$256 \sin^9 \theta = \sin 9\theta - 9 \sin 7\theta + 36 \sin 5\theta - 84 \sin 3\theta + 126 \sin \theta.$$

19. (i) Solve the equation

$$z^4+z^2+1 = 0,$$

giving each of the four roots in the form $r(\cos \theta + i \sin \theta)$, where $0 \leqslant \theta < 2\pi$.

(ii) In an Argand diagram the points A and B represent the complex numbers $1+i$ and $5+4i$ respectively. Find the complex number represented by C if ABC is an equilateral triangle in the first quadrant.

20. (i) Apply De Moivre's theorem to obtain the expansion of $\cos 7\theta$ as a polynomial in $\cos \theta$.

(ii) If $y = \cos 7\theta$, $x = \cos \theta$ and $f^{(n)}(x) = \dfrac{d^n y}{dx^n}$, prove that

(a) $$(1-x^2)\left(\frac{dy}{dx}\right)^2 = 49(1-y^2),$$

(b) $$(1-x^2)\frac{d^2y}{dx^2} - x\frac{dy}{dx} + 49y = 0,$$

(c) $$f^{(n+2)}(0) = (n^2-49)f^{(n)}(0).$$

Hence, apply Maclaurin's theorem to obtain the expansion of y in ascending powers of x.

21. Specify the loci in the complex plane given by

(i) $|z-2|+|z+2| = 4$,

(ii) $|z|+|z-1-i| = 2$,

(iii) $|z| = |z-x+2ia|$, a real and positive,

(iv) $|z+1+i|-|z-1-i| = 2$,

where $z = x+iy$.

22. (i) Express the real and imaginary parts of the complex numbers

$$\text{(a)} \quad z^2, \qquad \text{(b)} \quad \tan z,$$

in terms of the real part x and imaginary part y of the complex number z.

(ii) Solve for z the simultaneous equations

$$|z| = 1, \qquad |z+1| = \sqrt{3}\,|z-1|.$$

23. The point P_n represents the number z^n, where $z \neq 0$. Show that the points P_n, for $n = 0, \pm 1, \pm 2, \ldots$ must either be collinear or concyclic, or lie on a certain equiangular spiral, that is, a curve such that the tangent at the general point P makes a constant angle with OP; and in the latter case, find the constant angle in terms of z.

24. If $I_n = \int\limits_0^\infty x^n e^{-ax} \cos bx \, dx$, $J_n = \int\limits_0^\infty x^n e^{-ax} \sin bx \, dx$, where n is a positive integer and a and b are positive, prove that:

$$I_n(a^2+b^2) = n(aI_{n-1}-bJ_{n-1}),$$
$$J_n(a^2+b^2) = n(bI_{n-1}+aJ_{n-1}).$$

Show that

$$(a^2+b^2)^{\frac{n+1}{2}} I_n = n!\, \cos\,(n+1)\phi,$$

$$(a^2+b^2)^{\frac{n+1}{2}} J_n = n!\, \sin\,(n+1)\phi,$$

where $\tan\phi = b/a$ and $0 < \phi < \pi/2$.

25. In two electrical networks, the complex impedance Z and the frequency ω are connected by the relations.

$$\text{(i)} \quad Z = \frac{i\omega+1+2i}{-\omega^2+i\omega+1}, \qquad \text{(ii)} \quad Z = \frac{e^{2+i\omega}}{i-\omega}.$$

Find $|Z|$ and $\arg Z$ as a function of ω in both cases [ω is real].

26. Complex numbers z_r ($z_r = x_r+iy_r$) are represented in the Argand diagram by points P_r with coordinates (x_r, y_r). Prove that a necessary and sufficient condition for the points P_1, P_2, P_3, P_4 to be concyclic is that

$$\frac{(z_1-z_2)\,(z_3-z_4)}{(z_1-z_4)\,(z_3-z_2)}$$

should be real. Use this result to show that if these points are concyclic so are the points $1/z_1, 1/z_2, 1/z_3, 1/z_4$.

27. If $u+iv = \cosh(x+iy)$, where u, v, x, y are real, express each of u and v as a function of x and y. Show that

$$\left(\frac{\partial u}{\partial x}\right)_y = \left(\frac{\partial v}{\partial y}\right)_x, \qquad \left(\frac{\partial u}{\partial y}\right)_x = -\left(\frac{\partial v}{\partial x}\right)_y.$$

If x is held constant while y varies, show that the locus of the point with rectangular cartesian coordinates (u, v) is an ellipse. If y is held constant while x varies, show that the point (u, v) describes a hyperbola, which intersects the ellipse at right angles.

28. If real numbers a and b satisfy the relation

$$a + be^{2\pi i/n} = e^{4\pi i/n},$$

prove that they must have the values $a = -1$, $b = 2\cos(2\pi/n)$. For what values of n is b a (non-zero) integer?

29. Obtain an expression for $|\cos(x+iy)|^2$ in terms of trigonometric and hyperbolic functions of the real variables x, y.

Show that $|\cos(x+ix)|$ increases with x for all positive values of x.

30. Define the functions $\sinh z$, $\cosh z$, $\sin z$ and $\cos z$ in terms of the exponential function, and show that

$$\sin z = \sin x \cosh y + i \cos x \sinh y,$$

where $z = x + iy$.

In the transformation

$$Z = \sin z,$$

where $Z = X + iY$, show that the segment $y = \beta(>0)$, $-\pi/2 \leqslant x \leqslant \pi/2$ is mapped on to the upper half of the ellipse

$$X^2 \operatorname{sech}^2 \beta + Y^2 \operatorname{cosech}^2 \beta = 1.$$

Show also that the semi-infinite line $x = \alpha(\pi/2 > \alpha > 0)$, $0 \leqslant y < \infty$ is mapped on to part of the hyperbola

$$X^2 \operatorname{cosec}^2 \alpha - Y^2 \sec^2 \alpha = 1,$$

and identify that part. Illustrate by sketches the area in the Z-plane corresponding to the square in the z-plane with sides $x = \alpha$, $x = \alpha + \varepsilon$, $y = \beta$, $y = \beta + \varepsilon$, where $0 < \varepsilon < \pi/2 - \alpha$.

31. If x and y are real and

$$|\cos(x+iy)| = \exp\{\operatorname{Re}(\log - 3)\}$$

prove that

(i) $17 \leqslant \cosh 2y \leqslant 19$,

(ii) $2\sqrt{2} \leqslant |\sinh y| \leqslant 3$.

CHAPTER VIII

STATISTICS AND PROBABILITY

8 : 1 Introduction

All quantitative experimental investigations in the physical, biological and social sciences involve measurements or counts of one kind or another. Numerical information so expressed concerns many topics such as:

   (i) the number of daily attendances at an exhibition;
  (ii) the different results of a measurement obtained by different experimenters or in different circumstances;
 (iii) the number of defective lamps produced in a batch of 1000 by a machine manufacturing them; or
 (iv) the heights of children in a school.

The quantity under consideration is called the variable (or variate) and may take discrete, usually integral, values as in (i), (iii) above, or it may take a value from a continuous range as in (ii), (iv) above. The behaviour of the variable in any given case is described by the *frequency* or the *frequency distribution*. The frequency is the number of times the variable takes a stated value, or the number of times the value of the variable falls within a stated range. Usually the frequency is given as a number, which takes integral values, but it may also be stated as a fraction of some total—for example, in (iii) the number of defective lamps may be expressed as a fraction of the 1000, or perhaps as a percentage. There are three different, but related, methods of representing information of this kind graphically.

(a) **The frequency polygon.** When both the variate and the frequency are discrete, the diagram consists of a number of ordinates of appropriate height, one drawn for each value of the variate.

The polygon is completed by joining the tops of the ordinates by straight lines, and closing it by joining the extreme ordinates to the axis one unit beyond the ends of the range, as shown in Fig. 8.1. By this means the area of the polygon is made equal to the total frequency, e.g. the total attendance at the exhibition.

(b) **The histogram.** This is illustrated by considering the heights of children in a school. These heights, although they may have a value from a continuous range, are measured correct to (say) the

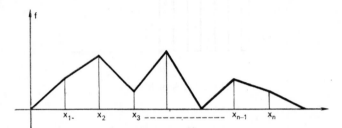

FIG. 8.1. A frequency polygon.

nearest centimetre. The distribution of the heights is then given by stating the number with heights between 90·5 and 91·5 cm, 91·5 and 92·5 cm, etc. The range of the variate (the height) is divided into "class intervals" centred on the values ..., 90, 91, 92, ... cm. The histogram representing these consists of blocks with the mid-points of their bases at points representing ..., 90, 91, 92, ... cm, of width corresponding to 1 cm and height representing the *frequency* of this class, i.e. the number of children with heights in the corresponding range (see Fig. 8.2). The area of this figure then gives the total frequency or number of children measured.

(c) **The frequency curve.** If the class interval of the histogram is made very narrow (presuming a sufficient accuracy of measurement), or if the ordinates of a frequency polygon are closely spaced, each diagram approximates closely to a continuous curve (see Fig. 8.3). In such a diagram the area of the strip below the curve and with width δx represents the frequency with which values of the variate x lie in the range $(x - \frac{1}{2} \delta x, x + \frac{1}{2} \delta x)$. Such

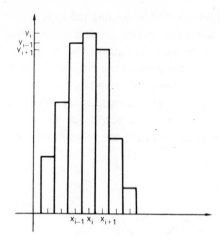

FIG. 8.2. A histogram.

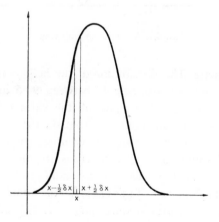

FIG. 8.3. A frequency distribution curve.

a continuous curve cannot arise from measurements performed on a finite group; hence such curves can only apply (approximately) to groups with very large numbers, e.g. the population of a city or a country, or measurements connected with the vast number of molecules in a specimen of gas.

A frequency distribution, in abstract, is a set of numbers f_i—the frequency—associated with values x_i of a variate; the variate may in practice take only discrete values x_i or, if continuous, its range may have been subdivided into class intervals with mid-points x_i. Or the distribution is a function $f(x)$ associated with a range (a, b) of a continuous variate x; in this case the total frequency is $\int_a^b f(x)\, dx$.

8 : 2 The properties of a frequency distribution

There are a number of important quantities of a frequency distribution, which express properties displayed by all distributions. The most important of these is the *mean* or average. If a number of attempts at measuring a length lead to values 10·1, 9·8, 10·2, 9·9, 9·8, 10·0, 10·1 cm, we interpret the arithmetic mean, viz.,

$$\frac{1}{7}(10{\cdot}1+9{\cdot}8+10{\cdot}2+9{\cdot}9+9{\cdot}8+10{\cdot}0+10{\cdot}1) = \frac{69{\cdot}9}{7} \approx 10{\cdot}0 \text{ cm,}$$

as the actual length. Similarly, the average height of the children in a class, or the average attendance at an exhibition, or the average production of defective parts by a machine, are all figures which may be required and are calculated in the same way. For a discrete distribution, represented by a frequency polygon or histogram, the mean is given by

$$\bar{x} = \frac{\Sigma f_i x_i}{\Sigma f_i}. \tag{8.1}$$

It is the sum of all the values of the variate divided by the total number of values. This is the x-coordinate of the centroid of the area enclosed by the histogram or polygon. In the case of the continuous distribution the summations are replaced by integrations, so that

$$\bar{x} = \int_a^b x f(x)\, dx \bigg/ \int_a^b f(x)\, dx. \tag{8.2}$$

The bar above the symbol is one of the commonest notations for the mean or average.

It sometimes happens that, in a set of readings for, say, the length of an object, certain readings are more reliable, or are given *greater weight* than others. This is expressed numerically by attaching a weight w_i to the reading x_i, and this reading x_i is then regarded as occurring w_i times instead of just once. (The weight w_i need not be an integer.) The mean is then given by

$$\bar{x} = \frac{\Sigma w_i f_i x_i}{\Sigma w_i f_i}. \tag{8.3}$$

There is another type of average which can occur but is not quite the same as the mean described above. This is illustrated by the mean cross-section of a non-uniform tube. This is the cross-section of a uniform tube of the same length and which has the same internal volume. If we measure x along the tube and the cross section is $f(x)$, then the mean cross-section $\bar{f}$ between $x = a$ and $x = b$ is the height of the rectangle $ABCD$, Fig. 6.4, which stands on the base AB and has the same area as is enclosed by the arc PQ of the curve $y = f(x)$, Ox and the lines $x = a$, $x = b$.

In fact

$$\bar{f} = \frac{1}{b-a} \int_a^b f(x)\,\mathrm{d}x; \tag{8.4}$$

this equation gives the average value of $f(x)$ for $a \leqslant x \leqslant b$.

The important difference between these two averages is that the mean $\bar{x}$ is a value of the variate x, whereas the mean cross-section calculated here is a value of the ordinate in Fig. 6.4. Unless the context makes it clear that the latter type of mean is intended, the mean of a frequency distribution is always that defined in eqns. (8.1)–(8.3). In the following examples the means calculated are *not* means of frequency distributions; they are average values in the sense just described. In cases such as alternating currents where the average value is zero, the average value of the square of the current is important.

The root mean square or R.M.S. of a function over a given range is the square root of the mean value of the square of the function over that range;

i.e. R.M.S. of $f(x)$ for $a \leqslant x \leqslant b$ is $\left(\overline{f^2}\right)^{\frac{1}{2}}$, where

$$\bar{f^2} = \frac{1}{b-a} \int_a^b \{f(x)\}^2 \, dx. \tag{8.5}$$

A quantity of particular importance is the R.M.S. value of an alternating current. Although it is seldom stated explicitly, the mean of an expression which varies harmonically with the time is always taken over one or more complete periods.

Example 1. Find the mean value of each of the following functions over the given interval:

(i) $\quad g(t) = \dfrac{a^2}{a^2+t^2} \quad$ for $\quad 0 \leqslant t \leqslant a, \quad a > 0,$

(ii) $\quad k(t) = (b^2-t^2)/b^2 \quad$ for $\quad -b \leqslant t \leqslant b, \quad b > 0.$

(i) $\qquad \bar{g} = \dfrac{1}{a} \int_0^a \dfrac{a^2}{a^2+t^2} \, dt = \left[\tan^{-1}\left(\dfrac{t}{a}\right) \right]_0^a = \dfrac{\pi}{4}.$

(ii) $\qquad \bar{k} = \dfrac{1}{2b} \int_{-b}^b \dfrac{(b^2-t^2)}{b^2} \, dt = \dfrac{2}{3}.$

Example 2. A point P is situated at a distance f from the centre of a thin spherical shell of radius a, and R is the distance of P from any point of the shell. Show that the mean value of R, averaged with respect to elements of area of the shell, is $f+(a^2/3f)$ or $a+(f^2/3a)$ according as f is greater or less than a.

In both cases, Fig. 8.4(a), (b),

$$R^2 = a^2 + f^2 - 2af \cos\theta. \tag{1}$$

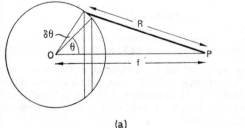 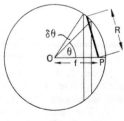

(a)   (b)

FIG. 8.4.

For the strip which subtends an angle $\delta\theta$, at O, as shown in Fig. 8.4(a), (b) the value of R is fixed; for a neighbouring strip R has a different, but also fixed, value. To find the "average" required we must proceed thus: multiply the value R by the area of the zone on the sphere for which it has this value and sum all these products for all the different possible values of R; this sum is then divided by the total area of the sphere. The area of the strip in Fig. 8.4 (a), (b) is $2\pi a^2 \sin\theta\, \delta\theta$ and so the average $\bar{R}$ is given by the formula

$$\bar{R} = \frac{1}{4\pi a^2} \int_0^\pi R2\pi a^2 \sin\theta\, \mathrm{d}\theta = \frac{1}{2} \int_0^\pi R\sin\theta\, \mathrm{d}\theta,$$

where R is given by (1). We change the variable of integration from θ to R using eqn. (1) which gives

$$2R\,\mathrm{d}R = 2af\sin\theta\, \mathrm{d}\theta.$$

However, the limits of integration depend upon whether P is outside or inside the sphere.

In case (i), $f > a$ the limits for R are $f-a$ and $f+a$ so that

$$\bar{R} = \frac{1}{2af} \int_{f-a}^{f+a} R^2\, \mathrm{d}R = f+\frac{a^2}{(3f)} \quad \text{for} \quad f > a.$$

Similarly, in case (ii), $a > f$, the limits for R are $a-f$ and $a+f$ so that

$$\bar{R} = \frac{1}{2af} \int_{a-f}^{a+f} R^2\, \mathrm{d}R = a+\frac{f^2}{(3a)} \quad \text{for} \quad a > f.$$

Example 3. If $j = I\sin(\omega t + \varepsilon)$ where I, ω and ε are constant, then

$$\bar{j} = \frac{1}{2\pi/\omega} \int_0^{2\pi/\omega} I\sin(\omega t + \varepsilon)\, \mathrm{d}t = 0,$$

whereas

$$\overline{j^2} = \frac{1}{2\pi/\omega} \int_0^{2\pi} I^2 \sin^2(\omega t + \varepsilon)\, \mathrm{d}t = \frac{1}{2} I^2.$$

Hence the mean value of j is zero but the R.M.S. of j is $I/\sqrt{2}$.

Notes. 1. A similar result holds for the mean value of $\sin(m\omega t + \varepsilon)$ over the range $0 \leqslant t \leqslant 2n\pi/(m\omega)$, where m, n are integers, i.e. the mean value of the sine (or cosine) function over an integral number of periods is zero.

2. The result concerning the R.M.S. of $I\sin(\omega t + \varepsilon)$ is generalised in question 5 of Exercises 8 : 2(a) overleaf.

Exercises 8 : 2(a)

Find the mean values and root mean squares of the following functions over the stated intervals:

1. $e^{-kt} \sin \omega t$, $0 \leqslant t \leqslant \pi/\omega$.   **2.** $t \sin \omega t$, $0 \leqslant t \leqslant \dfrac{2\pi}{\omega}$.

3. $\dfrac{x^2(a-x)^2}{a^3}$, $0 \leqslant x \leqslant a$.   **4.** $\ln x$, $2 \leqslant x \leqslant 4$.

5. If $j = I_0 + I_1 \sin(\omega t + \varepsilon_1) + I_2 \sin(2\omega t + \varepsilon_2) + \ldots + I_n \sin(n\omega t + \varepsilon_n)$ show that the R.M.S. of j is

$$\sqrt{[I_0^2 + \tfrac{1}{2}(I_1^2 + I_2^2 + \ldots + I_n^2)]}.$$

6. Find the mean distance of a variable point on a circle of radius a from a fixed point on the circle.

7. The density at distance r from the centre of a sphere of radius a is

$$\frac{a\varrho_0 \sin(\pi r/a)}{\pi r}.$$

Find (i) the mass, (ii) the mean density of the sphere.

The mode. There is another feature of a frequency distribution which can be used in some circumstances to denote the central, or most important, or "most popular" entry. The *mode* is the entry which has the highest frequency; if two consecutive entries have the same (highest) frequency in a discrete distribution, the mode is taken halfway between them. If the distribution (either discrete or continuous) has two maxima it is "bimodal". For example, the following twenty numbers

3, 4, 2, 0, 6, 8, 5, 2, 3, 1, 0, 6, 2, 3, 7, 6, 7, 3, 3, 2

have a mean $73/20 = 3\cdot65$. If we group the numbers in ascending order (i.e. effectively form a histogram), we obtain

0, 0, 1, 2, 2, 2, 2, 3, 3, 3, 3, 3, 4, 5, 6, 6, 6, 7, 7, 8,

and it is clear that the mode is 3.

The median. This is another central value of a frequency distribution. The median is that value of the variate which divides the distribution in half, i.e. the sum of the frequencies of all values above the median is equal to the sum of the frequencies of all values below the median. In the above set of numbers, the 10th and 11th entries in the "histogram" are both 3 so that the median is 3. Further, that part of the distribution above the median is divided in a similar manner into two by the *upper quartile*, and that part below by the *lower quartile*. These are respectively 6 and 2. In general, $n-1$ *quantiles* divide the distribution into n groups containing equal frequencies; similarly, *percentiles* divide the distribution into groups containing certain percentages of the total frequency.

The quantiles of a distribution can be most easily read from a *cumulative frequency curve*. In such a curve the percentage $p\%$ of the distribution less than the variable x is plotted against x. Such a graph is illustrated in Fig. 8.5(b) of the example below. The kth percentile is that value of x which is such that $k\%$ of the distribution is less than x.

Example. The crushing loads in tons on 50 wooden cubes are given in the following table:

5·70	6·04	6·21	6·29	6·35	6·45	6·59	6·70
6·72	6·75	6·84	6·88	6·94	6·99	6·99	7·04
7·10	7·12	7·15	7·17	7·20	7·21	7·24	7·24
7·26	7·28	7·31	7·37	7·38	7·42	7·49	7·51
7·55	7·56	7·58	7·59	7·60	7·66	7·66	7·69
7·70	7·74	7·81	7·84	7·86	7·90	8·00	8·15
8·55	8·80						

Taking intervals of 0·5 tons, of which the first is centred at 5·5 tons approximately, group the results as a frequency distribution. Draw a histogram to illustrate the results.

On a separate diagram plot the frequencies up to the end of each interval and sketch a cumulative frequency curve. From this curve read off the median and the 80th percentile of the distribution.

The results are grouped in the table below. Note for example that the frequency f centred on 6·5 includes all measurements x tons within the range $6·25 \leqslant x < 6·75$.

Load x	5·5	6·0	6·5	7·0	7·5	8·0	8·5	9·0
f	1	2	6	15	18	6	1	1

The histogram is shown in Fig. 8.5(a) and cumulative frequency curve is shown in Fig. 8.5(b).

The results read from this curve are:

Median	7·28 tons,
80th percentile	7·68 tons.

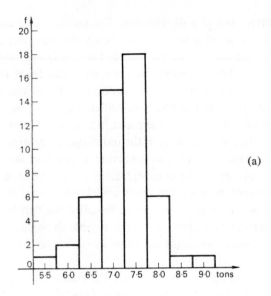

(a)

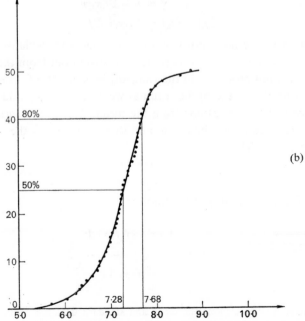

(b)

FIG. 8.5. (a) A histogram. (b) A cumulative frequency curve.

The dispersion of a distribution. The mean, mode and median denote the central value of a frequency distribution; this value —usually the mean—can be regarded as the typical value of the distribution. The quantiles, by their distances from the central value, indicate whether the distribution is spread out or is concentrated. In a distribution the difference $x_i - c$ is called the *deviation* of x_i from the value c and in a group of measurements, for example, the deviations of the individual determinations from the mean value—accepted as the actual value—give an impression of the reliability of the determinations (or of the experimenter). The difference between the upper and lower quartiles gives one measure of this spread and used to be called the "probable error" of a determination. However, this is now dropping out of use and a quantity called the *standard deviation*, or its square, the *variance*, is used instead.

From the definition of the mean, the sum of the deviations of a distribution from the mean is zero. Thus, with $n = \Sigma f_i$,

$$x_i - \bar{x} = x_i - \Sigma f_i x_i / n.$$
$$\therefore \ \Sigma f_i(x_i - \bar{x}) = \Sigma f_i x_i - \Sigma f_i x_i = 0.$$

If there are large positive and large negative deviations from the mean, i.e. if the readings are spread well out from the mean, this will not be shown in the value of the mean itself. In order to measure the spread of the readings we find the mean value of the square of the deviations from the mean. This is the *variance* of the readings about the mean, and its square root is the *standard deviation* σ. Thus

$$\sigma^2 = \frac{\Sigma f_i(x_i - \bar{x})^2}{\Sigma f_i}, \tag{8.6}$$

or, for a continuous distribution,

$$\sigma^2 = \frac{\int_a^b (x - \bar{x})^2 f(x)\,\mathrm{d}x}{\int_a^b f(x)\,\mathrm{d}x}. \tag{8.7}$$

Example 1. We calculate the mean and standard deviation of the grouped distribution of the example of p. 462.

Load x	Frequency f	fx	$x - \bar{x}$	$(x - \bar{x})^2$	$f(x - \bar{x})^2$
5·5	1	5·5	−1·74	3·028	3·028
6·0	2	12·0	−1·24	1·538	3·076
6·5	6	39·0	−0·74	0·548	3·288
7·0	15	105·0	−0·24	0·058	0·870
7·5	18	135·0	+0·26	0·068	1·224
8·0	6	48·0	+0·76	0·578	3·468
8·5	1	8·5	+1·26	1·588	1·588
9·0	1	9·0	+1·76	3·098	3·098
Sum	50	362·0			19·640

$$\bar{x} = \frac{\Sigma fx}{\Sigma f} = \frac{362}{50} = 7 \cdot 24.$$

$$\sigma^2 = \frac{\Sigma f(x - \bar{x})^2}{\Sigma f} = \frac{19 \cdot 640}{50} = 0 \cdot 3928.$$

$$\sigma = 0 \cdot 63.$$

Example 2. Calculate (i) $\bar{x}$, (ii) σ when $f(x) = x(c - x)$ for $0 \leqslant x \leqslant c$.

(i)
$$\bar{x} = \int_0^c x f(x) \, dx \bigg/ \int_0^c f(x) \, dx$$

$$= \int_0^c x^2(c - x) \, dx \bigg/ \int_0^c x(c - x) \, dx$$

$$= \left[\tfrac{1}{3}cx^3 - \tfrac{1}{4}x^4 \right]_0^c \bigg/ \left[\tfrac{1}{2}cx^2 - \tfrac{1}{3}x^3 \right]_0^c = \tfrac{1}{2}c.$$

This result was to be expected since the distribution is symmetrical about $x = \tfrac{1}{2}c$.

(ii)
$$\sigma^2 = \int_0^c (x - \tfrac{1}{2}c)^2 f(x) \, dx \bigg/ \int_0^c f(x) \, dx$$

$$= \int_0^c (x - \tfrac{1}{2}c)^2 x(c - x) \, dx \bigg/ \int_0^c x(c - x) \, dx$$

$$= \int_{-c/2}^{c/2} u^2(\tfrac{1}{4}c^2 - u^2) \, du \bigg/ (c^3/6) = 1/20.$$

Hence
$$\sigma = 1/(2 \sqrt{5}).$$

The moments of a distribution. The two quantities *mean* and *variance* are special cases of a set of quantities which are defined in relation to any distribution; these quantities are the *moments of the distribution* about a given value. These moments about a value c are defined as

$$r\text{th moment} \quad \frac{\Sigma(x_i-c)^r f_i}{\Sigma f_i} \quad \text{or} \quad \frac{\int_a^b (x-c)^r f(x)\,\mathrm{d}x}{\int_a^b f(x)\,\mathrm{d}x}. \quad (8.8)$$

That is to say, the rth moment about c is the mean value of the rth power of the deviation from c. There are two particularly important moments, viz.

$$m_r' = \frac{\Sigma x_i^r f_i}{\Sigma f_i} \quad \text{or} \quad \frac{\int_a^b x^r f(x)\,\mathrm{d}x}{\int_a^b f(x)\,\mathrm{d}x} \quad (8.9)$$

which are *moments about the origin* (denoted by a prime); the second special set is

$$m_r = \frac{\Sigma(x_i-\bar{x})^r f_i}{\Sigma f_i} \quad \text{or} \quad \frac{\int_a^b (x_i-\bar{x})^r f(x)\,\mathrm{d}x}{\int_a^b f(x)\,\mathrm{d}x} \quad (8.10)$$

which are *moments about the mean*.

The mean value is therefore the first moment about the origin, i.e. $\bar{x} = m_1'$. The variance is the second moment about the mean, viz. $\sigma^2 = m_2$. (These relations are calculated here for a discrete distribution; the modifications for a continuous distribution are straightforward.)

We can obtain a relation between m_r and m_r' by the use of the binomial theorem. Thus

$$nm_2 = \Sigma(x_i-\bar{x})^2 f_i = \Sigma(x_i^2-2\bar{x}x_i+\bar{x}^2) f_i = nm_2'-2\bar{x}nm_1'+\bar{x}^2 n.$$
$$\therefore \quad m_2 = \sigma^2 = m_2'-2\bar{x}^2+\bar{x}^2.$$
$$\therefore \quad \sigma^2 = m_2'-\bar{x}^2. \quad (8.11)$$

Hence the *variance* is less than the second moment about any other point. In general, if we write ξ_i for the deviation of x_i from the mean, i.e. $x_i = \bar{x} + \xi_i$,

$$m'_r = \frac{1}{n}\Sigma x_i^r f_i = \frac{1}{n}\Sigma(\bar{x}+\xi_i)^r f_i$$

$$= \frac{1}{n}\Sigma\left\{\bar{x}^r + \binom{r}{1}\bar{x}^{r-1}\xi_i + \binom{r}{2}\bar{x}^{r-2}\xi_i^2 + \ldots\right.$$

$$\left. + \binom{r}{s}\bar{x}^{r-s}\xi_i^s + \ldots + \xi_i^r\right\}f_i$$

$$= \bar{x}^r + \binom{r}{1}\bar{x}^{r-1}m_1 + \binom{r}{2}\bar{x}^{r-2}m_2 + \ldots$$

$$+ \binom{r}{s}\bar{x}^{r-s}m_s + \ldots + m_r f_i. \tag{8.12}$$

(From the definition of ξ_i, $m_1 = 0$.)

It is often useful, as illustrated in some of the following examples, to use deviations from an approximate mean to assist the calculation of various quantities. The most important of these relations is that relating to second moments. If we denote the *standard deviation from* c by s, then, using a continuous distribution for illustration,

$$s^2\int_a^b f(x)\,dx = \int_a^b (x-c)^2 f(x)\,dx = \int_a^b \{(x-\bar{x})-(c-\bar{x})\}^2 f(x)\,dx$$

$$= \int_a^b (x-\bar{x})^2 f(x)\,dx - 2(c-\bar{x})\int_a^b (x-\bar{x})f(x)$$

$$+ (c-\bar{x})^2\int_a^b f(x)\,dx.$$

$$\therefore \quad s^2 = \sigma^2 - 2(c-\bar{x})m_1 + (c-\bar{x})^2.$$

But, as usual, $m_1 = 0$. Therefore

$$s^2 = \sigma^2 + (c-\bar{x})^2. \tag{8.13}$$

(Because this is effectively the theorem of parallel axes for moments of inertia this result is sometimes called the theorem of parallel axes.)

In later volumes we shall introduce the idea of *moment and probability generating functions*.

Example 1. Eight independent measurements of an angle are:

$$54°25'56'' \qquad 54°25'59'' \qquad 54°26'02'' \qquad 54°25'51''$$
$$54°25'54'' \qquad 54°26'05'' \qquad 54°25'50'' \qquad 54°26'11''$$

Find the mean of the measurements and their standard deviation.

In this case we take our 'fictitious mean' x_0 to be $54°26'0''$ and the deviations, ξ, from this mean are

$$-4'', \quad -1'', \quad +2'', \quad -9'', \quad -6'', \quad +5'', \quad -10'', \quad +11'' \, .$$

Then $$\bar{\xi} = \tfrac{1}{8}\Sigma\xi = \tfrac{1}{8}(-12'') = -1{\cdot}5'' \, .$$

Hence $$\bar{x} = x_0 + \bar{\xi} = 54°25'58{\cdot}5'' \, .$$

The standard deviation s, in seconds of arc, from x_0 is given by

$$s^2 = \tfrac{1}{8}\Sigma\xi^2 = \tfrac{384}{8} = 45{\cdot}5.$$

Therefore $$\sigma^2 = 45{\cdot}5 - (1{\cdot}5)^2 = 42{\cdot}25,$$

i.e. $$\sigma = 6{\cdot}8'' \, .$$

Example 2. A variate x can assume values only between 0 and 5 and the equation of its frequency curve is

$$y = A \sin \tfrac{1}{5}\pi x, \qquad (0 \leqslant x \leqslant 5),$$

where A is a constant such that the area under the curve is unity. Determine the value of A and obtain the median and quartiles of the distribution. Show also that the variance of the distribution is

$$50 \left\{ \frac{1}{8} - \frac{1}{\pi^2} \right\} \, .$$

The area under the frequency curve is

$$\int\limits_0^5 A \sin (\pi x/5) \, \mathrm{d}x = \left[-(5A/\pi) \cos (\pi x/5) \right]_0^5 = 10A/\pi.$$

Therefore $A = \pi/10$.

Since $\sin (\pi x/5)$ is symmetric about $x = 5/2$ for $0 \leqslant x \leqslant 5$, the median is $x = 5/2$.

The lower quartile is $x = a$ where

$$\int\limits_0^a A \sin (\pi x/5) \, \mathrm{d}x = \tfrac{1}{4},$$

i.e. $$(5A/\pi) \{1 - \cos (\pi a/5)\} = \sin^2 (\pi a/10) = \tfrac{1}{4} \, .$$

Therefore $\pi a/10 = \pi/6$ or $a = 5/3$. By symmetry the upper quartile lies at $x = 5 - 5/3 = 10/3$.

The standard deviation from the origin is given by

$$s^2 = \int_0^5 A x^2 \sin(\pi x/5) \, \mathrm{d}x$$

$$= A \left[-\frac{5x^2}{\pi} \cos\left(\frac{\pi x}{5}\right) + \frac{50x}{\pi^2} \sin\left(\frac{\pi x}{5}\right) + \frac{250}{\pi^3} \cos\left(\frac{\pi x}{5}\right) \right]_0^5$$

$$= A \left(\frac{125}{\pi} - \frac{500}{\pi^3} \right) = \frac{25}{2} - \frac{50}{\pi^2}.$$

By the parallel axes theorem

$$\sigma^2 = \left(\frac{25}{2} - \frac{50}{\pi^2} \right) - \left(\frac{5}{2} \right)^2 = 50 \left(\frac{1}{8} - \frac{1}{\pi^2} \right).$$

Example 3. Two samples, consisting of n_1 and n_2 observations, have means m_1 and m_2 and standard deviations σ_1 and σ_2 respectively. Show that the standard deviation σ of the combined sample of (n_1+n_2) observations is given by

$$\sigma^2 = \frac{n_1\sigma_1^2 + n_2\sigma_2^2}{n_1+n_2} + \frac{n_1 n_2 (m_1-m_2)^2}{(n_1+n_2)^2}.$$

Let the samples consist of x_i ($i = 1, 2, \ldots, n_1$) and y_j ($j = 1, 2, \ldots, n_2$). Then

$$m_1 = (\Sigma x_i)/n_1, \qquad m_2 = (\Sigma y_j)/n_2,$$
$$\sigma_1^2 = \Sigma(x_i - m_1)^2/n, \qquad \sigma_2^2 = \Sigma(y_j - m_2)^2/n_2.$$

The mean m of the combined sample is

$$m = \{\Sigma(x_i + \Sigma y_j)\}/(n_1+n_2) = (n_1 m_1 + n_2 m_2)/(n_1+n_2). \tag{1}$$

The standard deviation of the combined sample is

$$\sigma^2 = \frac{\Sigma(x_i - m)^2 + \Sigma(y_j - m)^2}{n_1 + n_2}.$$

But $\quad \Sigma x_i^2 = n_1(\sigma_1^2 + m_1^2), \quad \Sigma y_j^2 = n_2(\sigma_2^2 + m_2^2).$

$$\therefore \; \sigma^2(n_1+n_2) = n_1(\sigma_1^2 + m_1^2) + n_2(\sigma_2^2 + m_2^2) - 2m(n_1 m_1 + n_2 m_2) + m^2(n_1+n_2),$$

$$= n_1\sigma_1^2 + n_2\sigma_2^2 + n_1 m_1^2 + n_2 m_2^2 - \frac{2(n_1 m_1 + n_2 m_2)^2}{n_1 + n_2} + \frac{(n_1 m_1 + n_2 m_2)^2}{n_1 + n_2},$$

where we have substituted from (1) for m. Therefore

$$\sigma^2(n_1+n_2) = n_1\sigma_1^2 + n_2\sigma_2^2 + \frac{m_1^2 n_1 n_2 - 2m_1 m_2 n_1 n_2 + m_2^2 n_1 n_2}{n_1 + n_2}.$$

i.e. $\qquad \sigma^2 = \dfrac{n_1\sigma_1^2 + n_2\sigma_2^2}{n_1+n_2} + \dfrac{n_1 n_2 (m_1 - m_2)^2}{(n_1+n_2)^2}.$

Exercises 8 : 2(b)

1. (i) From the accompanying list of raw data set up a frequency distribution in the following way:

Take the first class from 17·5–22·5 (midpoint = 20), take the second class from 22·5–27·5 (midpoint = 25), and so on until the last class from 37·5–42·5 (midpoint = 40). Check off the frequency for each class.

(ii) Calculate in the simplest way

(a) the (average) mean $\bar{x}$,
(b) the standard deviation σ.

List of raw data

28	26	35	32	27
24	31	28	25	31
33	22	34	30	23
31	30	29	26	32
36	25	34	37	24
38	32	41	30	27
32	34	28	19	28
23	39	20	40	29
18	28	36	23	36
25	42	31	38	31

2. Given the frequency distribution

Class	Midpoint x_i	Frequency f_i	Cumulative frequency
20–24	22	3	3
25–29	27	7	10
30–34		14	
35–39		20	
40–44		12	
45–49		9	
50–54		5	

(i) Calculate in the simplest way:

(a) the mean $\bar{x}$,
(b) the standard deviation σ.

(ii) Sketch a cumulative frequency curve and estimate the median, the lower quartile and the upper quartile.

3. Find the standard deviation from the mean for the following 40 measurements of x, taking a 'fictitious mean' of 20.

x	16	17	18	19	20	21	22
frequency f	2	5	8	10	9	5	1

4. The standard deviation of two sets of readings X, Y respectively, each n in number, are σ_1 and σ_2 measured from their means M_1, M_2. The two sets are now grouped as a set of $2n$ readings. Show that the standard deviation σ of this set from its mean is given by

$$\sigma^2 = \tfrac{1}{2}(\sigma_1^2 + \sigma_2^2) + \tfrac{1}{4}(M_1 - M_2)^2.$$

Two sets of 6 readings have the same mean. The first set has the values 185, 189, 190, 194, 199, 201, and the second has a standard deviation 6. Find the standard deviation of the 12 values grouped as a set.

5. The numbers of members, the means and the standard deviations of three distributions are as follows:

Number of members	250	350	400
Mean	45	55	50
Standard deviation	8	10	9

Calculate the mean and the standard deviation of the distribution formed by the three distributions taken together.

6. If n is a positive integer show that $\int\limits_0^\infty x^n e^{-x}\,dx = n!$

A variate has for its frequency distribution curve the graph of $y = xe^{-x/a}$ for $x > 0$, where $a > 0$. Find (i) the total frequency, (ii) the mean and (iii) the standard deviation of the variate.

7. A variate x has for its frequency curve the graph of $y = Ax \cos x$ (where A is a constant) between $x = 0$ and $x = \tfrac{1}{2}\pi$. Find, in terms of π, the total frequency, the mean and the standard deviation of x.

8. A variate x can assume values only between 0 and a, and the equation of its frequency curve is

$$y = A(a-x)^2, \quad (0 \leqslant x \leqslant a),$$

where A and a are constants such that the area under the curve and the mean of the distribution are both unity. Determine the numerical values of A and a and find the 10th and 90th percentiles of the distribution.

8 : 3 Introduction to the theory of probability

We are all familiar with phrases such as "it will probably rain tomorrow" or "the odds that ... will win the Derby are 100 to 1 against". There are two elements in such statements: there is uncertainty about the outcome of some trial or event; sometimes this uncertainty can be given a numerical estimate.

The theory of probability is concerned with the allocation of a value to p the probability of a success, or favourable outcome of some event. We take $p = 1$ to mean that the outcome is certain to be favourable (a success); $p = 0$ means that the outcome is certain to be unfavourable (a failure). Other values $0 < p < 1$ represent intermediate degrees of certainty.

In abstract discussions we shall make use of such trials or events as the tossing of a coin, throwing a die, selecting a card from a pack, or drawing coloured balls at random from a bag. A basic proviso of all such trials is that the coin or die shall be "unbiased"; the selection of the card or ball shall be made "at random".

A pack of (playing) cards contains equal numbers of red and black cards, so the (random) selection of a single card is "equally likely" to give a red as a black card. Without going into a discussion of the exact meaning of probability we define the value of p to be a ratio of frequencies. We consider all the possible outcomes of an event, e.g. the selection of a card from a pack; some of these outcomes are favourable, e.g. the selection of an ace, and others are unfavourable, e.g. the selection of any other card. We define the probability p of a success to be the ratio of the frequency of favourable outcomes to the total frequency; the probability q of a failure is the ratio of unfavourable outcomes to the total frequency.

In the case of a pack of cards the total frequency is 52, the frequency of favourable outcomes (the occurrence of an ace) is 4. Hence $p = \frac{4}{52} = \frac{1}{13}$, and $q = \frac{48}{52} = \frac{12}{13}$. From our definition it is clear that $p+q = 1$.

Example. A coin is tossed three times; calculate the probabilities of 3 heads, 2 heads, 1 head, 0 heads appearing, in any order.

The tossing must result in one of the following eight cases, which give the order of the results,

$$\text{HHH, HHT, HTH, THH, TTH, THT, HTT, TTT.}$$

We see that

$$\Pr\{3H\} = \tfrac{1}{8}, \quad \Pr\{2H, 1T\} = \tfrac{3}{8}, \quad \Pr\{1H, 2T\} = \tfrac{3}{8}, \quad \Pr\{3T\} = \tfrac{1}{8}.$$

[The notation $\Pr\{3H\}$, $\Pr\{2H, 1T\}$ gives the value of p for the outcome indicated in the braces.]

The probability that at least one head turns up is

$$\Pr\{3H\} + \Pr\{2H, 1T\} + \Pr\{1H, 2T\} = \tfrac{7}{8}.$$

This can also be calculated as $1 - \Pr\{3T\}$.

There are two important theorems which are essential to the development of the theory of probability. They are:

(1) The theorem of addition of probabilities of mutually exclusive events; and

(2) the theorem of multiplication of probabilities of independent events.

In order to develop the theory it is essential that we must be able to determine whether events are exclusive or not, and whether they are independent or not.

In the example of tossing a coin three times, the occurrence of one head and two tails can take place in one of three mutually exclusive ways, TTH, THT, HTT, in the list of total possibilities. The probability of each one of these is $\frac{1}{8}$, so that $\Pr\{1H, 2T\} = \frac{3}{8}$. These different permutations are mutually exclusive for neither of the others can occur if one of them has already occurred. The theorem is expressed in general terms, thus: Suppose that the probabilities that the *mutually exclusive* events $E_1, E_2, \ldots, E_n$ occur are $p_1, p_2, \ldots, p_n$ respectively. Then the probability that one of $E_1, E_2, \ldots, E_n$ takes place is

$$\Pr\{E_1 \text{ or } E_2 \text{ or } \ldots \text{ or } E_n\} = p_1 + p_2 + \ldots + p_n. \quad (8.14)$$

Example. We find the probability of drawing one white and one black ball, without replacement, from a bag containing five white balls and five black balls.

The sequence of events is given by the table below:

E_A	$\Pr\{E_A\}$	E_B	$\Pr\{E_B\}$	Result	Probability
W	$\frac{1}{2}$	W	$\frac{4}{9}$	2W	$\frac{2}{9}$
W	$\frac{1}{2}$	B	$\frac{5}{9}$	WB	$\frac{5}{18}$
B	$\frac{1}{2}$	W	$\frac{5}{9}$	BW	$\frac{5}{18}$
B	$\frac{1}{2}$	B	$\frac{4}{9}$	2B	$\frac{2}{9}$

Since there are two, mutually exclusive, methods of obtaining the result one white and one black, the probability for this final result is $\frac{5}{18} + \frac{5}{18} = \frac{5}{9}$.

The second theorem concerns *independent* events. Two events are independent if the outcome of one cannot affect the outcome of the other in any way. If events E_A, E_B represent respectively the tossing of coins A, B, then E_A, E_B are independent.

Suppose a bag contains five white and five black balls; E_A stands for drawing one ball at random and E_B stands for drawing a second ball at random. We investigate the probabilities of drawing a white ball in each event E_A and E_B. For E_A, Pr {white} = $\frac{1}{2}$. However, the outcome of E_B will be affected if the ball drawn in E_A is not replaced. (If the ball is replaced the probability of a white in E_B is also $\frac{1}{2}$.) If, in fact, a black ball is drawn in E_A, and not replaced, the probability of drawing a white in E_B is $\frac{5}{9}$; if a white ball is drawn in E_A and not replaced, the probability of drawing a white in E_B is $\frac{4}{9}$. Thus the outcome of E_A affects E_B. The two events are independent only if the ball is replaced after the drawing E_A. (They *are* independent when drawing take place without replacement if the bag contains an infinite number of each colour ball.) The statement of the theorem can be expressed thus:

Suppose that the probability that event E_1 takes place in trial T_1 is p_1, and that the probability that the *independent* event E_2 takes place in trial T_2 is p_2. Then the probability that events E_1 and E_2 *both* take place is

$$\text{Pr}\{E_1 \text{ and } E_2\} = p_1 p_2. \tag{8.15}$$

This is the law of *compound probabilities*.

By *independent* events we mean that E_1 and E_2 cannot influence each other in any way, in contrast to the mutually exclusive events considered above where the occurrence of one precludes the other taking place.

Result (8.15) is generalised for the n independent events $E_1, E_2, \ldots, E_n$ in the form

$$\text{Pr}\{E_1 \text{ and } E_2 \text{ and } \ldots \text{ and } E_n\} = p_1 p_2 \ldots p_n. \tag{8.16}$$

Example 1. An unbiased penny is tossed and an unbiased six-sided die is then thrown. Calculate the probability of a head and a six turning up.

The probability of a head turning up is $\frac{1}{2}$.
The probability of a six turning up is $\frac{1}{6}$.

These events are independent of each other. Therefore the probability of a head and a six turning up is

$$\tfrac{1}{2} \times \tfrac{1}{6} = \tfrac{1}{12}.$$

Note: When the probability of an event E taking place is p, we say that the *odds* against E taking place are $(1-p) : p$. In the above case the odds against a head and a six both turning up are $11 : 1$.

Example 2. When three marksmen A, B and C take part in a shooting contest their chances of hitting the target are $\tfrac{1}{2}$, $\tfrac{1}{3}$ and $\tfrac{1}{4}$ respectively. Calculate the chance that one, and only one, bullet will hit the target if all three men fire at it simultaneously.

Making the (reasonable) assumption that the chances of A, B, C hitting the target are independent we have as the required result

$$\text{Pr } \{A \text{ hits, } B \text{ and } C \text{ miss}\} + \text{Pr } \{B \text{ hits, } C \text{ and } A \text{ miss}\}$$

$$+ \text{Pr } \{C \text{ hits, } A \text{ and } B \text{ miss}\}$$

$$= \tfrac{1}{2}(1-\tfrac{1}{3})(1-\tfrac{1}{4}) + \tfrac{1}{3}(1-\tfrac{1}{4})(1-\tfrac{1}{2}) + \tfrac{1}{4}(1-\tfrac{1}{2})(1-\tfrac{1}{3}) = \tfrac{1}{4} + \tfrac{1}{8} + \tfrac{1}{12} = \tfrac{11}{24}.$$

Permutations and combinations. We give here some results concerning permutations and combinations which are often required to calculate the frequencies being considered.

Permutations are arrangements, combinations are selections. Thus the possible combinations of the letters A, B, C taken two at a time are AB, BC, CA (irrespective of the order within each group) but the possible permutations of the three letters taken two at a time are AB, BA, AC, CA, BC, CB.

The combined operation principle. Suppose that one operation can be performed in m different ways and that a second (independent) operation can be performed in n different ways. Then for *each* of the ways in which the first operation can be performed the two operations combined can be performed in n different ways. The total number of ways in which the *combined* operation can be performed is therefore $m \times n$. This is a most important principle in the theory of permutations and combinations and in the theory of probability. The principle may be extended to cover combined operations involving any number of *independent* operations, and may be stated thus: "The number of ways in which the combined operation can be performed is equal to the product of the numbers of ways in which the independent separate operations can be performed."

Example. A coded message is of the form $A8B$ in which the first item must be a vowel, the second a digit chosen from the digits 1 to 9, and the third a consonant. Calculate the number of different messages which can be sent in this code.

The vowel can be chosen in 5 ways, the digit in 9 ways, and the consonant in 21 ways.

Therefore the total number of ways in which all three can be chosen is

$$5\times9\times21 = 945.$$

The number of permutations of n things all at a time, i.e. the number of different ways in which the n things may be *ordered*, is denoted by $_nP_n$. The arrangement of the n things in the n different places which are available involves an operation combining the separate operations of filling the several places.

The first place can be filled in n different ways.

For each way in which the first place is filled there are $(n-1)$ ways of filling the second place.

For each way in which the first two places are filled there are $(n-2)$ ways of filling the third place.

For each way in which the first $(n-2)$ places are filled there are two ways of filling the last place but one.

Finally for each way in which the first $(n-1)$ places are filled there is only 1 way of filling the last place.

Therefore the total number of ways in which *all* places can be filled is $n(n-1)(n-2)\ldots 2.1 = n!$

We therefore have the result

$$_nP_n = n! \tag{8.17}$$

The number of permutations of n things r at a time, $_nP_r$. In this case, only r places have to be filled. Therefore

$$_nP_r = n(n-1)(n-2)\ldots(n-r+1)$$
$$= \frac{n(n-1)(n-2)\ldots(n-r+1)(n-r)(n-r-1)\ldots 3.2.1}{(n-r)(n-r-1)(n-r-2)\ldots 3.2.1};$$

$$\therefore \;\; _nP_r = \frac{n!}{(n-r)!}. \tag{8.18}$$

The number of combinations of n things, r at a time, $_nC_r$. If the r things in each of the combinations were arranged in the $r!$ possible ways among themselves, the total number of arrangements would be equal to the total number of arrangements of the n things r at a time.

$$\therefore \quad _nC_r \times r! = {_nP_r}.$$

$$\therefore \quad _nC_r = \frac{n!}{r!(n-r)!}. \tag{8.19}$$

Notation. $_nC_r$ may also by written in either of the ways ^nC_r and $\binom{n}{r}$.

Example 1. A box contains ten radio valves all apparently sound, although four of them are actually substandard. Find the chance that, if two of the valves are taken from the box together, they are both substandard.

Since any pair of valves are equally likely to be chosen, the required probability p is equal to the number of ways n_1 of choosing two valves from the four sub-standard ones divided by the number of ways n_2 of choosing two valves from all ten,

i.e. $$p = \frac{n_1}{n_2} = \binom{4}{2} \Big/ \binom{10}{2} = \frac{2}{15}.$$

Example 2. A rare event occurs, on average, once in n trials ($n \gg 1$), but is equally likely to occur in every trial. Find the possibility that it will not occur in m successive trials where $m/n = O(1)$.

The chance that the event takes place in any one trial is $1/n$. Therefore the probability that it does not take place in that trial is $(1-1/n)$. The probability that it does not take place in m trials is

$$\left(1-\frac{1}{n}\right)^m = \left\{\left(1-\frac{1}{n}\right)^n\right\}^{m/n} \approx e^{-m/n}$$

on using the result of Example 4, p. 272.

Note that this result only holds when $n \gg 1$.

Example 3. A motorist has an accident on average every k years. Find the probability that he goes a years without an accident.

We divide each year into n intervals where $n \gg 1$. Then the probability that the motorist has an accident in the first interval is $1/(nk)$. Therefore the probability that he does not have an accident in this interval is $1-1/(nk)$. The probability p that he goes na intervals (a years) without an accident is $\{1-1/(nk)\}^{na}$. Using the result of Example 4, p. 272, we find, letting $n \to \infty$,

$$p = \lim_{n \to \infty} \left(1-\frac{1}{nk}\right)^{na} = e^{-a/k}.$$

In this problem we subdivide the period of 1 year into smaller periods because the "trial" event, when the accident may occur, is any journey undertaken by the motorist, at any time, unlike the 'trial' of Example 2.

Probability distributions. Earlier, p. 456, we represented on a histogram the heights of children in a school and took this as an example of a frequency distribution; the number of children with heights in the interval x_i was f_i; the total number of children measured was n, which was given by the area of the histogram. The same information is given by saying that f_i/n is the probability that a child selected at random from the school has height in the interval x_i. We could therefore say that $\phi_i = f_i/n$, gives the probability distribution of the heights of the children in the school. The set of numbers ϕ_i, with $\Sigma\phi_i = 1$ constitute the distribution and can be obtained by dividing each term of the frequency distribution by the total frequency.

We also defined the quantities mean, standard deviation and moments, to measure certain properties of the frequency distribution. The same quantities can be defined for a probability distribution ϕ_i as follows:

$$
\begin{aligned}
\text{mean} \qquad & \mu' = \Sigma x_i \phi_i \quad (= \mu_1'), \\
\text{variance} \qquad & \sigma^2 = \Sigma(x_i - \mu')^2 \phi_i, \\
\text{standard deviation} \qquad & \sigma, \\
r\text{th moment about origin} \qquad & \mu_r' = \Sigma x_i^r \phi_i, \\
r\text{th moment about mean} \qquad & \mu_r = \Sigma(x_i - \mu')^r \phi_i.
\end{aligned}
\tag{8.20}
$$

These definitions are simpler in that they do not require division by the total frequency. There is a convention, adopted by some authors and which we follow, to use m_r' and m_r to refer to a frequency distribution and the corresponding Greek letters μ_r' and μ_r for the moments of a probability distribution.

A continuous probability distribution $\phi(x)$ can be defined in a similar manner. For a variate x which must lie in a range $a \leqslant x \leqslant b$ the probability that x lies in the range $(x - \frac{1}{2}\delta x,$

$x + \frac{1}{2}\delta x$) is $\phi(x)\,\delta x$. Since x must have some value in (a, b),

$$1 = \int_a^b \phi(x)\,dx. \qquad (8.21)$$

In short, probability distributions can be regarded as frequency distributions which have been divided by the total frequency.

Example 1. The probability that a machine becomes defective between time t and time $t + \delta t$ after commencing operation is $At\,e^{-t/T}\,\delta t$, where A is constant. Find the probability that the machine does not become defective before time $2T$.

The machine must break down in the interval $0 \leqslant t < \infty$. Therefore the sum of all the probabilities in intervals δt for $0 \leqslant t < \infty$ must be unity, i.e.

$$\sum_{t=0}^{\infty} At e^{-t/T}\,\delta t = A \int_0^{\infty} t e^{-t/T}\,dt = 1.$$

After integration by parts [or use of the substitution $t = Tu$ and eqn. (3.22)] we find $AT^2 = 1$, i.e. $A = T^{-2}$.

The probability p that the machine does not become defective before time $t = 2T$ is equal to the probability that it does become defective in one of the intervals δt for $t > 2T$,

i.e. $$p = \sum_{t=2T}^{\infty} At e^{-t/T}\,\delta t = \int_{2T}^{\infty} At e^{-t/T}\,dt = 3e^{-2}.$$

Note that we could equally well calculate p from the fact that p plus the probability that the machine breaks down in the interval $0 \leqslant t \leqslant 2T$ must equal unity,

i.e. $$p + \int_0^{2T} At e^{-t/T}\,dt = 1.$$

Example 2. The two equal sides of an isosceles triangle are each of unit length and the angle θ included between them is rectangularly distributed between 0 and $\pi/6$, i.e. θ is equally likely to lie anywhere in the range $0 \leqslant \theta \leqslant \pi/6$. Show that the area y of the triangle is distributed between 0 and $\frac{1}{4}$ with a probability distribution

$$p(y)\,\delta y = \frac{12}{\pi}(1 - 4y^2)^{-\frac{1}{2}}\,\delta y. \qquad (1)$$

Sketch the probability curve and calculate the mean and variance of the area of the triangle.

By definition the probability distribution for θ is

$$p(\theta)\,\delta\theta = \delta\theta/(\pi/6) = 6\,\delta\theta/\pi. \qquad (2)$$

But

$$y = \tfrac{1}{2}\sin\theta \qquad (3)$$

and therefore

$$\delta y = \tfrac{1}{2} \cos \theta \, \delta \theta = \tfrac{1}{2}(1 - 4y^2)^{\frac{1}{2}} \, \delta \theta.$$

Therefore

$$\delta \theta = 2(1 - 4y^2)^{-\frac{1}{2}} \, \delta y \qquad (4)$$

so that

$$p(\theta) \, \delta \theta = \frac{12}{\pi} (1 - 4y^2)^{-\frac{1}{2}} \, \delta y.$$

When the angle θ lies in the range $\theta - \tfrac{1}{2} \delta \theta$ to $\theta + \tfrac{1}{2} \delta \theta$, the area y lies in the range $y - \tfrac{1}{2} \delta y$ to $y + \tfrac{1}{2} \delta y$ where y and θ are related by (3) and (4). Since $p(\theta) \, \delta \theta$ is the probability that θ occurs in the above range, then y has the same probability of lying in the corresponding range.

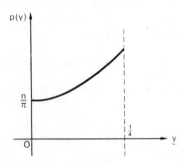

Fig. 8.6.

It follows that the probability distribution for the area is as given by eqn. (1). Clearly from eqn. (3) the least and greatest values of the area are 0 and $\tfrac{1}{4}$. The probability curve is sketched in Fig. 8.6. (The calculation here, in fact, is simply a change of variable from angle θ to area y, describing the same distribution.)

The mean value of y is

$$\bar{y} = \int\limits_0^{\frac{1}{4}} yp(y) \, \mathrm{d}y = \frac{12}{\pi} \int\limits_0^{\frac{1}{4}} y(1 - 4y^2)^{-\frac{1}{2}} \, \mathrm{d}y$$

$$= \left[-\frac{3}{\pi} (1 - 4y^2)^{\frac{1}{2}} \right]_0^{\frac{1}{4}} = \frac{3}{\pi} \left(1 - \frac{\sqrt{3}}{2} \right).$$

The second moment about the origin is

$$s^2 = \int\limits_0^{\frac{1}{4}} y^2 p(y) \, \mathrm{d}y = \frac{12}{\pi} \int\limits_0^{\frac{1}{4}} y^2 (1 - 4y^2)^{-\frac{1}{2}} \, \mathrm{d}y.$$

Making the substitution $y = \frac{1}{2} \sin x$ we find

$$s^2 = \frac{3}{2\pi} \int\limits_0^{\pi/6} \sin^2 x \, \mathrm{d}x = \frac{4\pi - 6\sqrt{3}}{16} .$$

Therefore, by eqn. (8.13), the variance is

$$s^2 - \bar{y}^2 = \frac{4\pi - 6\sqrt{3}}{16\pi} - \frac{9}{4\pi^2}(7 - 4\sqrt{3}) = (4\pi^2 - 6\pi\sqrt{3} + 144\sqrt{3} - 252)/16\pi^2.$$

Example 3. A variable chord of the ellipse

$$\frac{x^2}{a^2} + \frac{y^2}{b^2} = 1$$

is drawn parallel to the minor axis, all distances from the minor axis being equally likely. Show that the mean length of the chord is $\frac{1}{2}\pi b$ and that its variance is $(32 - 3\pi^2)\,b^2/12$.

Show that, for the ellipse $x^2/3 + y^2 = 1$, the probability that the length of the chord exceeds that of a side of the square inscribed in the ellipse is $\frac{1}{2}$.

By symmetry we need consider only the chords for $0 \leqslant x \leqslant a$. Then since all distances from the minor axis are equally likely we can take the number of chords lying between $x - \frac{1}{2}\delta x$ and $x + \frac{1}{2}\delta x$ as $k\delta x$, where k is constant, i.e. the probability is proportional to the length of the interval of x. The length of each of these chords is $l = 2b\sqrt{(1 - x^2/a^2)}$ and so the mean length is

$$\bar{l} = \frac{\int\limits_0^a lk \, \mathrm{d}x}{\int\limits_0^a k \, \mathrm{d}x} = \frac{2b}{a} \int\limits_0^a \sqrt{(1 - x^2/a^2)} \, \mathrm{d}x$$

$$= 2b \int\limits_0^{\pi/2} \cos^2 \theta \, \mathrm{d}\theta = \frac{1}{2}\pi b.$$

The standard deviation of l about $l = 0$ is

$$s^2 = \int\limits_0^a l^2 k \, \mathrm{d}x \bigg/ \int\limits_0^a k \, \mathrm{d}x$$

$$= \frac{1}{a} \int\limits_0^a 4b^2(1 - x^2/a^2) \, \mathrm{d}x = 8b^2/3.$$

Therefore the variance about the mean $\bar{l}$ is

$$s^2 - \bar{l}^2 = 8b^2/3 - \pi^2 b^2/4 = (32 - 3\pi^2)b^2/12.$$

The side of the square inscribed in the ellipse $x^2/3 + y^2 = 1$ is $2c$ where $c = \sqrt{(1 - c^2/3)}$, i.e. $c = \frac{1}{2}\sqrt{3}$.

Since the length of the chord exceeds c when $x < c$, and the length is less than c when $c < x < \sqrt{3}$, and all values of x between 0 and $\sqrt{3}$ are equally likely the required probability is given by the ratio of the ranges, thus

$$p = \frac{\text{range of } x \text{ for } l > c}{\text{whole range of } x} = \frac{c}{\sqrt{3}} = \frac{\sqrt{3}}{2} \frac{1}{\sqrt{3}} = \frac{1}{2}.$$

Example 4. A boy cycles 3 km to school every morning at a uniform speed of 12 km/hour if he has no punctures. If he has a puncture he can either repair it, which takes him 10 min, and cycle on, or else he can walk for the rest of the way at 3 km/hour. Ignoring the possibility of two or more punctures, show that it is worthwhile to repair a puncture if he is less than $2\frac{1}{3}$ km from the start.

If the boy always does what is worthwhile and if the probability of a puncture on any one journey is 1/30, a puncture being equally likely on any part of the journey, find (i) the mean time for the journey, (ii) the probability that any particular journey will take more than 20 min.

Suppose the cycle has a puncture when the boy is distant l km from school. To walk this distance he takes $20\,l$ min, whereas repairing the puncture and cycling on to complete the journey takes $10 + 5\,l$ min. Therefore it is worth while to repair a puncture provided that

$$20l > 10 + 5l,$$

i.e.
$$l > \tfrac{2}{3}.$$

This is the case if the boy is less than $2\frac{1}{3}$ km from the start.

(i) The probability that the boy does not have a puncture is $\frac{29}{30}$, in which case the travel time is 15 min. The probability that the boy does have a puncture is $\frac{1}{30}$, and if this puncture occurs between $x - \frac{1}{2}\delta x$ and $x + \frac{1}{2}\delta x$ km from home the journey time is

$$10 + 15 = 25 \text{ min} \qquad \text{if } x < 7/3,$$
$$5x + 20(3 - x) = 60 - 15x \text{ min} \qquad \text{if } 7/3 < x < 3.$$

The probability that the puncture, when it occurs, takes place between $x - \frac{1}{2}\delta x$ and $x + \frac{1}{2}\delta x$ km from home is proportional to δx, i.e. is equal to $\delta x/3$. The probability of the occurrence of a puncture is then the combined probability $(1/30) \times (\delta x/3)$. Hence we can set out the information:

Journey	Time	Probability
No puncture	15 min	$\dfrac{29}{30}$
Puncture for $x < 7/3$	25 min	$\dfrac{1}{30} \times \dfrac{7/3}{3}$
Puncture between $x - \frac{1}{2}\delta x$ and $x + \frac{1}{2}\delta x$ for $7/3 < x < 3$	$60 - 15x$ min	$\dfrac{\delta x}{90}$

The mean time for the journey is therefore

$$15 \times \frac{29}{30} + 25 \times \frac{7}{270} + \int_{7/3}^{3} \frac{(60-15x)\,dx}{90} = \frac{215}{9} \text{ min} = 23\frac{8}{9} \text{ min}.$$

(ii) The probability that any one journey takes more than 20 min is $p_1 p_2$ where $p_1 = \frac{1}{30}$ is the probability that the boy has a puncture and p_2 is the probability that he takes more than 20 min when he does have a puncture. But in this latter case he takes more than 20 min if $60 - 15x > 20$, i.e. if $x < 8/3$ and so $p_2 = (8/3)/3 = 8/9$. Therefore the probability that the time for a particular journey exceeds 20 min, is $\frac{1}{30} \times \frac{8}{9} = \frac{4}{105}$.

Exercises 8 : 3

1. A machine is powered by three similar batteries and will function provided that two of the batteries are in working order. The probability of any one battery failing during the first 8 hours of operation of the machine is $\frac{1}{5}$; the probability of failure during the next 8 hours is $\frac{2}{5}$. Find the chance that the machine will continue to function (i) for 8 hours, (ii) for 16 hours.

2. In an examination the respective probabilities of three candidates solving a certain problem are $\frac{4}{5}$, $\frac{3}{4}$ and $\frac{2}{3}$. Calculate the probability that the examiner will receive from these candidates

 (i)   one, and only one, correct solution,

 (ii) not more than one correct solution,

 (iii) at least one correct solution.

3. A variate x can take the values $1, 2, 3, \ldots, n$, with probabilities proportional to $1, 2, 3, \ldots, n$ respectively. Calculate the mean value of x.

4. A machine is powered by three similar storage batteries; it will function satisfactorily only if at least two of these batteries are serviceable. The probability of any one battery becoming unserviceable in less than 50 hours is $0\cdot2$, and of becoming unserviceable in less than 100 hours is $0\cdot6$.
Find the probability that the machine will function satisfactorily for (i) at least 50 hours, (ii) between 50 and 100 hours.

5. In a uniform gas the molecular speeds are distributed so that the probability of a molecule having a speed between v and $v + \delta v$ is

$$Av^2 e^{-mhv^2} \, \delta v \quad (0 \leqslant v < \infty),$$

where A, m, h are constants.
Prove that $A = 4\pi \, (mh/\pi)^{3/2}$, and find the mean speed of the molecules. You may use the result

$$\int_0^{\infty} e^{-x^2} \, dx = \tfrac{1}{2} \sqrt{\pi}.$$

6. A variate is distributed between 0 and ∞ so that the probability that it lies between x and $x+\delta x$ is $Ax\mathrm{e}^{-x}\,\delta x$. Calculate A and find the mean and standard deviation of the distribution.

7. The radius x of a circle is rectangularly distributed between 1 and 2. Show that the area y of the circle is distributed between π and 4π with probability distribution

$$p(y)\,\mathrm{d}y = \tfrac{1}{2}\pi^{-\frac{1}{2}}y^{-\frac{1}{2}}\,\mathrm{d}y.$$

Sketch the probability curve and calculate the mean and the variance of the area of the circle.

8. The probability that an electronic component will fail in the time interval $(t, t+\delta t)$ after commencing operation at $t = 0$ is $k(t/T^2)\mathrm{e}^{-t/T}\,\delta t$, where k is a constant of proportionality. Calculate the coefficient k and show that the probability that the component has life of at least t is

$$(1+t/T)\mathrm{e}^{-t/T}.$$

Find also the mean life and the variance about this mean.

9. A bag contains b black balls and w white balls where b is greater than w. If they are drawn one by one from the bag, find the probability of drawing first a black, then a white and so on alternately until only black balls remain.

10. When a large number n of unit vibrations of varying phase are compounded at random the probability of the resultant amplitude lying between r and $r+\mathrm{d}r$ is given to be $2n^{-1}\mathrm{e}^{-r^2/n}r\,\mathrm{d}r$. Show that the probability of the resultant amplitude exceeding a number a is $\mathrm{e}^{-a^2/n}$.

Show also that the mean value of the resultant amplitude is $\tfrac{1}{2}(\pi n)^{1/2}$. $\left[\text{It may}\right.$

be assumed that $\displaystyle\int_{0}^{\infty}\mathrm{e}^{-x^2}\,\mathrm{d}x = \tfrac{1}{2}\sqrt{\pi}.\Big]$

8:4 Some special probability distributions

The binomial distribution. Suppose that the probability of a success at a trial is p. Then the probability of a failure is $q = 1-p$. The binomial distribution enables us to calculate the probability that in n similar (independent) trials (with constant p), exactly r of the trials are successful.

First we consider the case in which r particular (specified) trials are successes and the remaining $n-r$ trials are failures. The (compound) probability of this occurring is $p^r q^{n-r}$. But we can choose the r successes (each with probability $p^r q^{n-r}$) from the n trials in ${}_nC_r$ ways and so the law of addition gives the probability that there are exactly r successes occurring in any order in n

trials as

$$p_r = \Pr \{r \text{ successes in } n \text{ trials}\} = {}_nC_r p^r q^{n-r} \qquad (r = 0, 1, 2, \ldots, n),$$
$$(8.22)$$

i.e. p_r is the coefficient of t^r in the expansion of $(pt+q)^n$. (8.22a)

The discrete probability distribution function given by (8.22a) is called the *binomial distribution*.

The mean μ of the distribution is given by

$$\mu = \sum_{r=0}^{n} r p_r = \sum_{r=0}^{n} r {}_nC_r p^r q^{n-r}.$$

To evaluate this sum we differentiate both sides of the equation

$$(pt+q)^n = p^n t^n + {}_nC_1 p^{n-1} q t^{n-1} + \ldots + {}_nC_r p^r q^{n-r} t^r + \ldots$$

w.r. to t and then put $t = 1$ and use the relation $p+q = 1$ to find

$$\mu = np. \qquad (8.23)$$

The second moment about $r = 0$ is

$$\sum_{r=0}^{n} r^2 p_r = \left\{ \frac{d}{dt} \left[t \frac{d}{dt} (pt+q)^n \right] \right\}_{t=1} = np + n(n-1) p^2.$$

Therefore by eqn. (8.13) the variance is

$$\sigma^2 = np + n(n-1) p^2 - \mu^2$$
$$= np + n(n-1) p^2 - n^2 p^2$$
$$= np(1-p),$$

i.e. $\qquad\qquad\qquad \sigma^2 = npq. \qquad (8.24)$

Example 1. Assuming that the probability that any one of four telephone lines is engaged at an instant is $\frac{1}{3}$, calculate the probability:

 (i)   that two lines are engaged and the other two are free,
 (ii) that all four lines are engaged,
 (iii) that at least one of the lines is engaged.

It follows from the binomial theorem that the probabilities of various numbers of lines being engaged are given by the successive terms of the binomial expansion of $(\frac{2}{3}+\frac{1}{3})^4$, as given in the table below.

Number of engaged lines	0	1	2	3	4
Probability	$(\tfrac{2}{3})^4$	$_4C_1(\tfrac{2}{3})^3(\tfrac{1}{3})$	$_4C_2(\tfrac{2}{3})^2(\tfrac{1}{3})^2$	$_4C_3(\tfrac{2}{3})(\tfrac{1}{3})^3$	$(\tfrac{1}{3})^4$
	$=\tfrac{16}{81}$	$=\tfrac{32}{81}$	$=\tfrac{24}{81}$	$=\tfrac{8}{81}$	$=\tfrac{1}{81}$

(i) The probability that just two *(any two)* lines are engaged is 24/81 = 8/27.

(ii) The probability that all four lines are engaged is 1/81.

(iii) The two cases in which none and at least one of the lines are engaged are mutually exclusive and cover all the possibilities. Hence the required probability in this case is unity minus the probability that none of the lines is engaged,

i.e. $$1-\tfrac{16}{81} = \tfrac{65}{81}.$$

Of course this result can also be obtained in this case by adding the mutually exclusive probabilities that just 1, 2, 3, 4 lines are engaged. In more complicated cases [see Example 2 below] the method adopted at first here is preferable.

Example 2. Six dice, each numbered in the usual way from 1 to 6, were thrown together 216 times. At each throw the number of 1's turned up was noted, and when all the throws were completed the following table was constructed:

Number of 1's turned up	0	1	2	3	4	5	6
Frequency	79	82	33	20	2	0	0

Exhibit graphically the data given in the table.

Calculate the theoretical frequencies and display them in a similar table.

The results of the experiment are shown in the histogram of Fig. 8.7.

The probability that a one turns up in any one throw with one die is $\tfrac{1}{6}$. Hence the probabilities of

$$0, \quad 1, \quad 2, \quad 3, \quad 4, \quad 5, \quad 6$$

ones turning up in any one throw with the six dice are respectively the coefficients of the powers t^0, t^1, t^2, ..., t^6 in the expansion of

$$(\tfrac{5}{6}+\tfrac{1}{6}t)^6.$$

The expected numbers after 216 trials are therefore the corresponding terms in the expansion of $216(\tfrac{5}{6}+\tfrac{1}{6}t)^6$ and are tabulated in the table below. (Since the frequency must be an integral number the theoretical results have beem rounded off to the nearest whole number and, in this case, do not add up to the number of trials.)

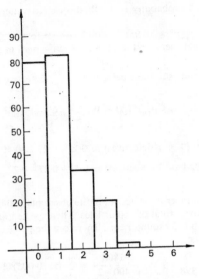

Fig. 8.7.

Number of 1's expected	0	1	2	3	4	5	6
Frequency	72	87	43	9	2	0	0

Example 3. Samples of forty articles are selected at random from a large bulk of articles produced by a machine. The following list shows the number of defective articles in each of twenty such samples:

$$1, 0, 4, 0, 0, 4, 4, 1, 4, 2, 3, 3, 2, 3, 0, 2, 4, 2, 0, 1.$$

Calculate the mean number of defective articles per sample and estimate the percentage of defective articles in the total output of the machine.

Assuming that the binomial law applies,

(i) calculate the probability of there being *one or more* defective articles in a sample of forty,

(ii) find the least integer N such that the probability of there being N or more defective articles in a sample of forty is less than $\frac{1}{2}$.

Supposing that 10% of the whole bulk is sampled in the above way and that the defective articles found in each sample are rejected, estimate the percentage of defective articles finally remaining in the bulk.

The mean number of defective items per sample is $40/20 = 2$. The percentage of defective items is, therefore, $2/40 \times 100\% = 5\%$. In fact the probability that any one item is defective is $\frac{1}{20}$.

(i) The required probability is $1 - \text{Pr}$ {no defective items in a sample of forty}, i.e. $1 - (\frac{19}{20})^{40}$.

By logarithms $(\frac{19}{20})^{40} = (0.95)^{40} = 0.13$ correct to two significant figures. The probability that there is at least one defective item in a sample is therefore 0.87.

(ii) The probabilities of there being 0, 1, 2, ... defective articles in a batch of forty are

$$(\tfrac{19}{20})^{40} \approx 0.13, \quad _{40}C_1(\tfrac{19}{20})^{39}(\tfrac{1}{20}) \approx 0.27, \quad _{40}C_2(\tfrac{19}{20})^{38}(\tfrac{1}{20})^2 \approx 0.27, \ldots.$$

Hence

$$\text{Pr} \{0 \text{ or } 1 \text{ defectives}\} \approx 0.13 + 0.27 = 0.40,$$

$$\text{Pr} \{0, 1 \text{ or } 2 \text{ defectives}\} \approx 0.13 + 0.27 + 0.27 = 0.67.$$

Therefore $N = 3$.

The expected number of defectives in the unsampled 90% is 2 per sample, i.e. 18 defectives for a total of 360 articles. The expected number remaining in a sampled batch is 38 sound items. Therefore the percentage of defectives finally remaining is

$$\frac{18}{398} \times 100 = \frac{1800}{400-2} = \frac{9}{2}(1-0.005)^{-1}$$

$$\approx 4.525\%.$$

Example 4. Five per cent of a large consignment of eggs are bad. Find the probability of getting at least one bad egg in a random sample of a dozen.

The probability of any one being bad is $\frac{1}{20}$, the probability of any one being good is $\frac{19}{20}$.

$$\text{Pr} \{\text{at least one bad}\} = 1 - \text{Pr} \{\text{all good}\}$$

$$= 1 - \left(\frac{19}{20}\right)^{12}$$

$$\approx 1 - 0.54 = 0.46.$$

The Poisson distribution. The binomial distribution arises from considering a sample of definite size n for which the number of times an event with probability p did and did not occur can be calculated. The Poisson distribution is the limiting case of the binomial distribution when n becomes very large and p becomes very small, e.g. when we consider isolated events in time. Such events have a small probability of happening in any one trial but a large number of trials takes place. In illustration consider the (radioactive) disintegration of uranium 238. The probability that any one atom disintegrates, and so activates a Geiger counter, within a small interval of time is extremely small. However, in say 10^{-3} g of uranium there are about $2{\cdot}5 \times 10^{18}$ atoms and the result is that approximately 12 atoms disintegrate per second.

We consider the binomial distribution with mean m so that $np = m$ and consider the probability of a (usually small) finite number k of successes when $n \to \infty$, $p \to 0$ but m is a non-zero finite constant. Then

$$
\begin{aligned}
\Pr\{k \text{ successes}\} &= \lim_{\substack{n \to \infty \\ p \to 0}} \frac{n!}{k!(n-k)!} p^k (1-p)^{n-k} \\
&= \lim_{n \to \infty} \frac{n!}{k!(n-k)!} \left(\frac{m}{n}\right)^k \left(1-\frac{m}{n}\right)^{n-k} \\
&= \lim_{n \to \infty} \frac{m^k}{k!} \left(1-\frac{m}{n}\right)^n \\
&\quad \times \frac{1[1-(1/n)][1-(2/n)]\ldots[1-(k-1)/n]}{[1-(m/n)]^k} \\
&= \frac{m^k e^{-m}}{k!}
\end{aligned}
$$

on using the results

$$
\lim_{n \to \infty} \left(1-\frac{m}{n}\right)^n = e^{-m},
$$

$$
\lim_{\substack{n \to \infty \\ k \text{ finite}}} \left(1-\frac{1}{n}\right)\left(1-\frac{2}{n}\right)\ldots\left(1-\frac{k-1}{n}\right) = 1,
$$

$$
\lim_{\substack{n \to \infty \\ k \text{ finite}}} \left(1-\frac{m}{n}\right)^k = 1.
$$

In fact we have derived the *Poisson distribution* which can be described thus: If the average number of occurrences of a rare event in a large number of trials is m, then

$$
\Pr\{k \text{ successes}\} = \frac{m^k e^{-m}}{k!}. \tag{8.25}
$$

The mean of the Poisson distribution is

$$\mu = \sum_{k=1}^{\infty} k \, \frac{m^k e^{-m}}{k!}$$

$$= m e^{-m} \sum_{k=1}^{\infty} \frac{m^{k-1}}{(k-1)!} = m e^{-m} e^m = m. \qquad (8.26)$$

The variance is, by eqn. (8.13),

$$\sigma^2 = \sum_{k=0}^{\infty} \frac{k^2 m^k e^{-m}}{k!} - m^2$$

$$= m e^{-m} \sum_{k=1}^{\infty} \frac{k m^{k-1}}{(k-1)!} - m^2$$

$$= m e^{-m} \frac{\mathrm{d}}{\mathrm{d}m}(m e^m) - m^2 = m.$$

Therefore $\qquad\qquad\qquad \sigma = \sqrt{m}. \qquad\qquad (8.27)$

Example 1. A car takes one minute to cross a bridge, and 270 cars cross it each hour. Find, approximately, the probability that there are at least two cars on the bridge at any given time.

The mean number of cars on the bridge at any moment is $270/60 = 9/2$. We assume that the distribution is a Poisson one with $m = 9/2$. Then

Pr {at least two cars} $= 1 - \text{Pr \{no car\}} - \text{Pr \{1 car\}}$

$$= 1 - e^{-\frac{9}{2}} - \tfrac{9}{2} e^{-\frac{9}{2}}$$

$$\approx 0 \cdot 94.$$

Example 2. The number of emergency calls received at a telephone exchange during the interval from 10 p.m. to midnight was recorded over one hundred consecutive days recently, as follows:

Number of calls	0	1	2	3	4	5
Frequency	21	34	26	13	5	1

Show that the mean number of calls was $1 \cdot 5$ and calculate the theoretical Poisson frequency corresponding to each number of calls.

Estimate the probability that during the same interval of two hours (i) no calls will be received tonight, (ii) only one call will be received in a period of three such consecutive nights.

The mean number of calls is

$$(0 \times 21 + 1 \times 34 + 2 \times 26 + 3 \times 13 + 4 \times 5 + 5 \times 1)/100$$

$$= 150/100 = 1 \cdot 5.$$

The theoretical Poisson frequency distribution is calculated from the terms

$$100e^{-1.5}, \quad 100 \times 1.5e^{-1.5}, \quad 100 \times \frac{(1.5)^2 e^{-1.5}}{2!}, \ldots$$

to be rounded off to the nearest integer.

Number of calls	0	1	2	3	4	5
Frequency	22	33	25	13	5	2

(i) The probability that no calls are received (in one 2-hour period) tonight is $e^{-1.5} \approx 0.223$.

(ii) The probability that one call will be received in one specified night is $1.5e^{-1.5} \approx 0.334$. Therefore the probability that only one call is received in three such successive nights is

$$_3C_1(0.223)^2 (0.334) \approx 0.050.$$

Example 3. The number of alpha particles emitted per unit time by a radio-active substance was counted over a period of time and the number of occasions f on which n particles were emitted is recorded in the following table:

n	0	1	2	3	4	5	6	7	8	9	10
f	80	206	254	212	136	68	30	10	3	1	0

Assuming that the distribution is of Poisson type, calculate correct to two significant figures the probability that the substance will emit (i) exactly five particles, (ii) more than two particles in any unit of time.

The mean number of particles emitted in one period is $2517/1000 = 2.517$.

(i) The theoretical Poisson distribution implies that the probability of exactly five particles being emitted is

$$\frac{(2.517)^5 e^{-2.517}}{5!} \approx 0.068.$$

(ii) The probabilities of 0, 1, 2, particles being emitted are

$$e^{-2.517}, \quad (2.517)e^{-2.517}, \quad \tfrac{1}{2}(2.517)^2 e^{-2.517}.$$

These cases are mutually exclusive and so the probability required is

Pr {more than 2 particles emitted}
$$= 1 - e^{-2.517} - (2.517)e^{-2.517} - \tfrac{1}{2}(2.517)^2 e^{-2.517} \approx 0.461.$$

Exercises 8 : 4

1. If 4 dice are tossed together, what is the probability that

(i) they will all fall in the same way,

(ii) exactly 2 sixes come uppermost,

(iii) at most 2 sixes come uppermost,

(iv) at least 2 sixes come uppermost.

2. If at any instant the independent probability of any one of eight telephone lines being engaged is $\frac{1}{4}$, show that the probability of at least one of the lines being engaged is approximately $\frac{9}{10}$, but that the probability of all eight being engaged is less than $\frac{1}{60\,000}$.

Calculate, further, the most probable number of engaged lines at any instant.

3. In the manufacture of a certain article, it is found that on the average, 1 article in 10 has to be rejected. What is the probability that 3 samples of 10 articles contain between them not more than 2 rejects?

4. In a large lot of electric light bulbs 5 % of the bulbs are defective. Calculate the probability that a random sample of 20 will contain at most 1 defective bulb.

One-third of the lots presented for inspection have 5% defective, the rest 10% defective. If a lot is rejected when a random sample of 20 taken from it contains more than 1 defective bulb, find the proportion of lots which are rejected.

5. A box contains 36 batteries of which 4 are defective. If a random sample of 5 batteries is drawn from the box, calculate, correct to two places of decimals, the probability of the number of defective batteries in the sample being (i) 0, (ii) 1, (iii) more than 1.

6. A competition consists of filling in a form which contains N spaces and each space has to be filled up in one of n ways. There is a unique correct solution. If the spaces are filled up in a random manner, prove that the probability of there being r mistakes is the coefficient of x^r in the expansion of

$$n^{-N}\{1+x(n-1)\}^N.$$

If $N = 12$ and $n = 3$ prove that the probability of there being *not more* than 2 mistakes is 289×3^{-12}.

7. Razor blades of a certain kind are sold in packets of five. The following table shows the frequency distribution of 100 packets according to the number of faulty blades contained in them:

Number of faulty blades	0	1	2	3	4	5
Number of packets	84	10	3	2	1	0

Calculate the mean number of faulty blades per packet and, assuming that the binomial law applies, estimate the probability that a blade taken at random from any packet will be faulty.

8. The number of road accidents notified to a certain police station in a day is shown in the following frequency table relating to 300 successive days:

Accidents	0	1	2	3	4	5	6	7	Total
Frequency	90	113	64	21	7	3	1	1	300

Calculate the mean number of accidents notified daily.

Use the Poisson distribution with this mean to calculate the chance of four or more accidents being notified on a particular day.

9. Prove that the mean and the variance of a Poisson distribution are equal. The frequency of accidents per shift in a factory is shown in the following table:

Accidents per shift	0	1	2	3	4	5
Frequency	300	96	34	9	1	0

Prove that the distribution is approximately Poissonian and find the probability of the occurrence of more than two accidents in a shift.

10. A large batch of manufactured articles is accepted if either

(i) a random sample of six articles contains not more than one defective article, or

(ii) a random sample of six contains two defective articles and a second random sample of six is then drawn and found to contain no defective articles.

If, in fact, 20 % of the articles in the batch are defective, what is the chance of the batch being accepted?

8 : 5　The normal distribution and the error function

When a quantity is measured several times, the values obtained are distributed about a mean value. Even when all possible precautions have been taken to eliminate systematic errors, there is still a deviation between this mean value and the result of a single trial measurement. These remaining deviations are usually taken to be due to "random" errors arising from factors either unknown or beyond the control of the experimenter. These random deviations can occur either in integral values, e.g. the deviations about the mean in the number of passengers on a given train every weekday, or they can arise from different values of a continuous variable, e.g. the reading on an instrument dial.

By considering a limiting case of the binomial distribution we can obtain, by a plausible argument, the probability distribution for the errors in the value of a continuous variable.

Consider a variable whose measurement has zero for the mean value. Suppose that there are $2n$ factors each of which can cause a deviation $\pm\eta$ in the reading, and that $n+r$ cause a positive deviation. Then, for this case, the resultant deviation is

$$v = (n+r)\eta - (n-r)\eta = 2r\eta.$$

If we assume, plausibly, that positive or negative deviations are equally likely, the probability of this deviation occurring is

$$\Pr\{y\} = \frac{(2n)!}{(n+r)!\,(n-r)!} \cdot \frac{1}{2^{n+r}2^{n-r}} \tag{8.28}$$

and the standard deviation σ is given (from the properties of the binomial distribution) by

$$\sigma^2 = 2n \cdot \tfrac{1}{2} \cdot \tfrac{1}{2}(2\eta)^2 = 2n\eta^2.$$

In order to make the transition to continuous variables we suppose that n and r tend to infinity and η tends to zero, i.e. the number of factors at work is very large and the size of each of the individual deviations is infinitesimally small. For the error to be small we must have r small when compared with n.

Since

$$y = 2r\eta, \quad \sigma^2 = 2n\eta^2$$

we can eliminate η by writing

$$\frac{y^2}{2\sigma^2} = \frac{r^2}{n}.$$

Hence, we consider the limiting case in which r^2/n is finite, i.e. $n = O(r^2)$, and η tends to zero in such a manner that y, σ are comparable to the error found in practice.

To obtain the limiting value of the left-hand side of eqn. (8.28) we use *Stirling's approximation* for factorials of large numbers

$$N! \approx (2\pi N)^{\frac{1}{2}} N^N e^{-N}.$$

This leads to

$$\Pr(y) = \frac{(2n)!}{(n+r)!\,(n-r)!} \frac{1}{2^{2n}}$$

$$\approx \frac{1}{\sqrt{(\pi n)}} \left(1-\frac{r^2}{n^2}\right)^{-n} \left(1+\frac{r}{n}\right)^{-r-\frac{1}{2}} \left(1-\frac{r}{n}\right)^{r-\frac{1}{2}}.$$

Because of the relative orders of magnitude we can replace these terms as follows:

$$\left(1\pm\frac{r}{n}\right)^{\pm r-\frac{1}{2}} \approx 1,$$

$$\left(1-\frac{r^2}{n^2}\right)^{-n} = \left(1-\frac{r^2}{n^2}\right)^{-(n^2/r^2)\cdot(r^2/n)} = e^{-r^2/n}.$$

Then

$$\Pr(y) \approx \frac{1}{\sqrt{(\pi n)}} e^{-r^2/n}. \qquad (8.29)$$

Now the value of y can alter either way only by a step of η. Hence eqn. (8.29) gives the probability that y falls inside a range $dy = 2\eta = \sigma\sqrt{(2/n)}$, and we replace r^2/n by $y^2/(2\sigma^2)$. Hence the probability of y falling within the range dy enclosing the value $y = 2r\eta$ is

$$p(y)\,dy = \Pr\{y\} = \frac{dy}{\sigma\sqrt{(2\pi)}} e^{-y^2/(2\sigma^2)}. \qquad (8.30)$$

This probability density $p(y)$ is called the *normal distribution*. It is usually taken to give the distribution of the errors around the mean zero with standard deviation σ when these errors arise at random. If the errors are distributed about a mean μ with standard deviation σ, the probability density is

$$p(y) = \frac{1}{\sigma\sqrt{(2\pi)}} \exp\left\{-\frac{(y-\mu)^2}{2\sigma^2}\right\}. \qquad (8.31)$$

The above discussion, following the lines used by Gauss originally, is in no sense a "proof" of the normal distribution. It gives a reason for thinking that errors which arise from unknown causes are distributed according to the normal probability density.

If a population of N measurements is distributed about a mean μ with standard deviation σ, then the number of measurements lying between $x - \frac{1}{2}\,\delta x$ and $x + \frac{1}{2}\,\delta x$ is

$$\frac{N}{\sigma\sqrt{(2\pi)}} \exp\{-(x-\mu)^2/(2\sigma^2)\}\,\delta x. \qquad (8.32)$$

It can be shown by numerical integration that for the above normal distribution the probability of a random measurement lying within a certain distance (*measured in terms of the standard deviation*) from the mean (in either the positive or the negative direction) is given approximately by the following table.

Deviation from the mean (either side) d/σ	Probability of value x in range $\mu - d < x < \mu + d$
0·1	0·08
0·25	0·20
0·5	0·38
0·67	0·50
0·8	0·58
1·0	0·68
1·25	0·79
1·50	0·88
2·0	0·954
3·0	0·997
4·0	0·999

Notes. (1) Almost all the distribution lies within three standard deviations of the mean.

(2) The probability that a measurement differs by more than $1 \cdot 96\sigma$ from the mean is $\frac{1}{20}$ or 5%.

(3) The probability that a measurement differs by more than $2 \cdot 58\sigma$ from the mean is $\frac{1}{100}$ or 1%.

(4) Table 7 (at end of book) gives the values of the normal probability integral $\dfrac{1}{\sqrt{(2\pi)}} \displaystyle\int_{-\infty}^{x} e^{-t^2/2} \, dt$. However, eqn. (8.32) implies that the probability of a single measurement lying in the range $x - \frac{1}{2} \, \delta x$ to $x + \frac{1}{2} \, \delta x$ is

$$\frac{1}{\sigma\sqrt{(2\pi)}} \exp\{-(x-\mu)^2/(2\sigma^2)\} \, \delta x,$$

and so the probability that it lies in the range $\mu + a\sigma < x < \mu + b\sigma$ is

$$\Pr\{\mu + a\sigma < x < \mu + b\sigma\} = \frac{1}{\sigma\sqrt{(2\pi)}} \cdot \int_{\mu+a\sigma}^{\mu+b\sigma} \exp\{-(x-\mu)^2/(2\sigma^2)\} \, dx.$$

The substitution $x = \mu + t\sigma$ gives

$$\Pr\{\mu + a\sigma < x < \mu + b\sigma\} = \frac{1}{\sqrt{(2\pi)}} \int_{a}^{b} e^{-t^2/2} \, dt. \quad (8.33)$$

The use of this table is illustrated in Examples 1 and 2 following.

From formula (8.30) we see that the probability that an error lies in the range $-k\sigma$ to $k\sigma$ is

$$\frac{1}{\sigma\sqrt{(2\pi)}} \int_{-k\sigma}^{k\sigma} e^{-x^2/(2\sigma^2)}\,dx = \frac{2}{\sqrt{\pi}} \int_{0}^{k/\sqrt{2}} e^{-t^2}\,dt = \mathrm{erf}\,(k/\sqrt{2}) \quad (8.34)$$

on using the substitution $t = x/(\sigma\sqrt{2})$. See the definition of the error function, $\mathrm{erf}\,(x)$, on p. 166.

Example 1. The following are the weights in ounces of a random sample of fifteen 32 g packets delivered by an automatic packing machine:

32·11	31·97	32·18	32·03	32·25
32·07	32·05	32·14	32·19	31·98
32·07	31·99	32·16	32·03	32·18

Calculate the mean and the standard deviation. Assuming the distribution to be normal, estimate the percentage of underweight packets which the machine is delivering.

The Board of Trade stipulates that such a machine must not deliver more than 5% underweight packets. If the machine is to comply with this regulation and if its variability cannot be better controlled, calculate the value to which the mean must be raised.

Using a fictitious mean of 32 g the mean is obtained as follows:

x	$x-32$ +	$x-32$ −	$(x-32)^2$
32·11	0·11		0·0121
31·97		0·03	0·0009
32·18	0·18		0·0324
32·03	0·03		0·0009
32·25	0·25		0·0625
32·07	0·07		0·0049
32·05	0·05		0·0025
32·14	0·14		0·0196
32·19	0·19		0·0361
31·98		0·02	0·0004
32·07	0·07		0·0049
31·99		0·01	0·0001
32·16	0·16		0·0256
32·03	0·03		0·0009
32·18	0·18		0·0324
	1·46	0·06	0·2262

The mean is $\qquad \mu = 32 + \dfrac{1.46 - 0.06}{15} = 32.09.$

The variance is $\qquad \dfrac{0.2262}{15} - (0.09)^2 = 0.0070.$

Therefore $\qquad\qquad\qquad\qquad\qquad \sigma = 0.084.$

The mean is $\left(\dfrac{9}{8.4}\right)\sigma = 1.07\sigma$ above the critical value of 32·00. Table 7 indicates that 85·77% of the population lies below $\mu + 1.07\sigma$ and so 14·23% lies above $\mu + 1.07\sigma$. Since the normal distribution is symmetrical about the mean it follows that 14·23% of the population lies below $\mu - 1.07\sigma$, i.e. below 32 g.

In order that only 5% of the packets shall be underweight the mean must be approximately 1·65σ above 32 g, i.e. the mean must be increased to 0·139 g above 32 g, i.e. to 32·14 g approximately.

Example 2. (i) Jackets for young men are made in the following sizes, according to chest measurement:

Size	1	2	3	4	5	6
Chest measurement	30–	32–	34–	36–	38–	40–42

The chest measurements of young men in a certain age range are known to be normally distributed with mean 35·63 and standard deviation 2·00. Estimate to the nearest unit the percentages of young men in this age range likely to require each of the six sizes and also the percentages likely to fall above or below the size range.

In this case $\mu = 35.63$, $\sigma = 2.00$ and so we tabulate the range of sizes below, interpreting them in terms of μ and σ and then reading off the percentages from Table 7 (printed at end of book) as follows:

Jacket size	x	$x - \mu$ in terms of σ	% in range
<1	<30	$< -2.82\sigma$	0·24
1	30–32	-2.82σ to -1.82σ	3·20
2	32–34	-1.82σ to -0.82σ	17·17
3	34–36	-0.82σ to 0.18σ	36·53
4	36–38	0.18σ to 1.18σ	30·96
5	38–40	1.18σ to 2.18σ	10·44
6	40–42	2.18σ to 3.18σ	1·37
>6	>42	$> 3.18\sigma$	0·07
			99·99

Note the effect of rounding off errors on the cumulative percentage.

Exercises 8 : 5

1. The following table gives a frequency distribution of the I.Q.'s of 480 children in a primary school, X being the mid-point of a group. Find the mean and S.D. of the distribution, correct to 1 decimal place, and fit a normal distribution to the data.

X	70	74	78	82	86	90	94	98	102	106	110	114	118	122	126
f	4	9	16	28	45	66	85	72	54	38	27	18	11	5	2

2. An investigation into the weekly spending money of the 400 boys in a certain school showed that the mean was 82p and the standard deviation 11p. Assuming that the distribution was normal, calculate the theoretical frequencies for the intervals 48p to 60p, 60p to 72 p, ..., 108p to 120p. Draw the histogram.

3. In the manufacture of a certain piece of scientific equipment great importance is attached to the life of a particular component. After the lives of 1000 of these components had been recorded the following frequency table was obtained:

Life (hours)	No. of components
980–1000	5
1000–1020	31
1020–1040	123
1040–1060	261
1060–1080	305
1080–1100	194
1100–1120	67
1120–1140	14

Draw a cumulative frequency graph and use it to estimate the range in life of the central 50% of the components.

Calculate the mean and the standard deviation and obtain the range of the central 50% of the normal distribution with this mean and standard deviation. State, with reasons, any conclusion that might be drawn from your results.

4. Steel bolts of circular cross-section are being manufactured to a specification which requires that their lengths be between 8·45 and 8·65 cm and their diameters between 1·55 and 1·60 cm. A machine produces these bolts so that their lengths are normally distributed about a mean of 8·54 cm with standard deviation 0·05 cm and their diameters are independently normally distributed about a mean of 1·57 cm with standard deviation 0·01 cm.

Find (i) the percentage of bolts produced that will not be within the specified limits for lengths,

(ii) the percentage of bolts produced that will not be within the specified limits for diameters,

(iii) the percentage of bolts that will not meet the specifications,

(iv) the chance that in a sample of five bolts taken at random four should meet the specifications and one should fail.

5. An automatic machine produces bolts whose diameters are required to lie within the tolerance limits 0·496 cm to 0·504 cm. A random sample of bolts produced by the machine is found to have a mean diameter of 0·498 cm and a standard deviation of 0·002 cm. Assuming that the diameters are normally distributed, estimate the probability that any bolt produced by the machine will have a diameter outside the tolerance limits.

If the machine is adjusted to produce bolts of mean diameter 0·500 cm, the standard deviation being unaltered, estimate the percentage of bolts likely to be rejected on full inspection.

6. The following observations are heights in cm of a random sample of twenty compression springs taken from current production in a works:

$$\begin{array}{ccccc}
1·010 & 1·002 & 1·009 & 1·005 & 1·006 \\
1·002 & 1·007 & 1·007 & 1·011 & 1·002 \\
1·007 & 1·008 & 1·003 & 1·002 & 1·001 \\
1·007 & 1·005 & 1·000 & 1·008 & 1·008
\end{array}$$

Calculate the mean and the standard deviation of these observations, and estimate limits which, if the distribution is normal, will contain approximately the central 50% of production.

If the mean remains unchanged, find the value to which the standard deviation must be reduced in order that these limits should contain 90% of production.

8:6 Further probability problems

We conclude this chapter with some more difficult examples on probability.

Example 1. A match between two players A and B is won by whoever first wins 2 games. A's chances of winning, drawing or losing any particular game are p, q and r respectively. Prove that his chance of winning the match is $p^2(p+3r)/(p+r)^3$.

Since each game must be won, drawn or lost by A it follows that

$$p+q+r = 1. \tag{1}$$

In order to win the match in exactly n ($\geqslant 2$) games, A must win the last (nth) game *and* one and only one of the preceding $n-1$ games whilst B wins only 1 or none of these $n-1$ games. Using the binomial distribution we find that the relevant probabilities are as follows:

A wins one and the remaining $n-2$ are drawn,

$$P_1 = (n-1)pq^{n-2}.$$

A wins one, B wins one and the remaining $n-3$ are drawn,

$$P_2 = (n-1)(n-2)prq^{n-3}.$$

Hence the probability that A wins in exactly n games is

$$P(n) = P_1 + P_2 = p\{(n-1)pq^{n-2}+(n-1)(n-2)prq^{n-3}\}$$
$$= (n-1)p^2q^{n-2}+(n-1)(n-2)p^2rq^{n-3}.$$

The chance that A wins the match is

$$\sum_{r=2}^{\infty} P(r) = p^2 \sum_{2}^{\infty}(n-1)q^{n-2}+p^2r\sum_{2}^{\infty}(n-1)(n-2)q^{n-3}$$

$$= p^2 \frac{d}{dq}\left(\sum_{2}^{\infty} q^{n-1}\right)+p^2r\frac{d^2}{dq^2}\left(\sum_{2}^{\infty} q^{n-1}\right)$$

$$= p^2 \frac{d}{dq}\left(\frac{q}{1-q}\right)+p^2r\frac{d^2}{dq^2}\left(\frac{q}{1-q}\right)$$

$$= p^2\left\{\frac{1}{1-q}+\frac{q}{(1-q)^2}\right\}+p^2r\left\{\frac{2}{(1-q)^2}+\frac{2q}{(1-q)^3}\right\}$$

$$= \frac{p^2}{(1-q)^2}+\frac{2p^2r}{(1-q)^3}.$$

Using eqn. (1) this gives the required result.

Example 2. Two numbers x and y are chosen at random between 0 and 2. Find the chance that $x^m y^n \leqslant 1$ in the three cases

(i) $m = n = 1$,   (ii) $m = 2$, $n = 1$,   (iii) $m = 2$, $n = -1$.

Since each of x, y is chosen at random in the range $(0, 2)$ the point (x, y) in the plane of the cartesian axes Oxy is equally likely to lie anywhere within the square with the sides $x = 0$, $x = 2$, $y = 0$, $y = 2$. Using the ideas of § 1 : 6, it follows that the probabilities that $x^m y^n \leqslant 1$ for the stated cases are obtained by dividing the shaded areas of Fig. 8.8 by the area of the square.
The results are

(i) $\dfrac{1}{4}\left\{\dfrac{1}{2}\times2+\displaystyle\int_{\frac{1}{2}}^{2}\dfrac{1}{x}\,dx\right\} = \dfrac{1}{4}(1+\ln 4),$

(ii) $\dfrac{1}{4}\left\{2\times\dfrac{1}{\sqrt{2}}+\displaystyle\int_{1/\sqrt{2}}^{2}\dfrac{1}{x^2}\,dx\right\} = \dfrac{1}{4}\left(2\sqrt{2}-\dfrac{1}{2}\right),$

(iii) $\dfrac{1}{4}\displaystyle\int_{0}^{2} y^{\frac{1}{2}}\,dy = \dfrac{\sqrt{2}}{3}.$

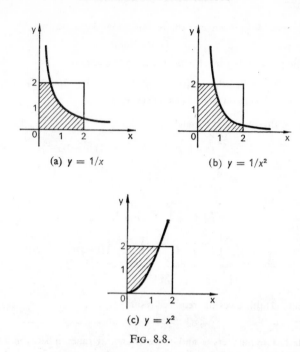

(a) $y = 1/x$

(b) $y = 1/x^2$

(c) $y = x^2$

FIG. 8.8.

Example 3. In a set of biased coins each coin has chance p of showing the head after any throw. In the first trial of a series all n coins are thrown; in the second trial only those coins are thrown which did not show a head at the first trial. The series continues in this way until a head has been obtained with every coin; let the probability that this process requires r trials be $P(r, n)$. Determine $P(r, 1)$ and show that the mean of r is $1/p$.

$P(r, 1)$ is the probability that a head does not show when tossing a single coin until the rth throw, i.e. a tail shows for each of the first $r-1$ throws and then a head shows on the rth throw. Using the results of p. 485 this implies that

$$P(r, 1) = q^{r-1}p,$$

where $q = 1-p$ is the probability of a tail at each throw. In this case the mean value of r is

$$\sum_{r=1}^{\infty} rP(r, 1) = p \sum_{r=1}^{\infty} rq^{r-1}$$

$$= p \frac{\mathrm{d}}{\mathrm{d}q} \left(\sum_{0}^{\infty} q^r \right) = p \frac{\mathrm{d}}{\mathrm{d}q} \left(\frac{1}{1-q} \right) = \frac{p}{(1-q)^2} = \frac{1}{p}.$$

Example 4. (i) A circular disc of radius r is thrown at random onto a large board divided into squares of side a (where $a \geqslant 2r$). Show that the probability that the disc comes to rest entirely within one square is $[1 - (2r/a)]^2$.

(ii) If, instead of a disc, a thin pencil of length l (where $l \leqslant a$) is thrown on to the board, show that the probability that the pencil does *not* come to rest entirely within one square is $[(4a - l)l]/\pi a^2$.

(i) If the disc comes to rest entirely within a square C, the centre O of the disc must lie within a square C_1, concentric with C and of side $a - 2r$. Since O is equally likely to come to rest anywhere on the board, the required probability is

$$\frac{\text{area of } C_1}{\text{area of } C} = \frac{(a-2r)^2}{a^2} = \left(1 - \frac{2r}{a}\right)^2.$$

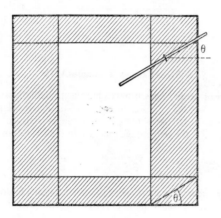

Fig. 8.9.

(ii) Consider the situation when the rod falls in a position making the angle θ with one side of the square. If the rod is to protrude over the boundary of the square its centre must fall in the shaded area shown in Fig. 8.9. The probability of this occurring is the ratio of this area to that of the square. Therefore

$$\Pr\{\text{overlap in direction } \theta\} = \frac{al(\cos\theta + \sin\theta) - l^2 \sin\theta \cos\theta}{a^2}. \quad (1)$$

All directions of θ are equally likely and so the probability required is the mean value of expression (1).

For obtuse values of θ, $\sin\theta$ and $\cos\theta$ take negative values, but the areas in question must be taken positively so we average only over the range

$0 \leqslant \theta \leqslant \pi/2$, instead of the whole range $0 \leqslant \theta \leqslant 2\pi$, for which all the functions in (1) are positive.

$$\overline{\cos \theta} = \overline{\sin \theta} = \frac{2}{\pi} \int_0^{\pi/2} \cos \theta \, d\theta = \frac{2}{\pi},$$

$$\overline{\cos \theta \sin \theta} = \frac{2}{\pi} \int_0^{\pi/2} \sin \theta \cos \theta \, d\theta = \frac{2}{\pi} \times \frac{1}{2} = \frac{1}{\pi}.$$

Hence the result is

$$\text{Pr \{overlap in any direction\}} = \frac{al \, (\overline{\cos \theta + \sin \theta}) - l^2 \, \overline{\sin \theta \, \cos \theta}}{a^2}$$

$$= \frac{al(2/\pi + 2/\pi) - l^2/\pi}{a^2} = \frac{(4a - l)l}{\pi a^2}.$$

Miscellaneous Examples VIII

1. An index of retail prices is a weighted arithmetic mean calculated by assigning weights $w_1, w_2, \ldots, w_n$, to each constituent retail price index x_1, $x_2, \ldots, x_n$, respectively. Show that, if p_r is the percentage increase in x_r, where $r = 1, 2, \ldots, n$, the percentage increase in the overall index is given by

$$\frac{\Sigma w_r x_r p_r}{\Sigma w_r x_r}.$$

Calculate the percentage increase of the overall index figure for 1950 over that for 1949, given the following data for citrus fruit prices:

Fruit	Retail price index		Weight
	1949	1950	
Grapefruit	121·2	161·2	17·8
Lemons	115·1	112·9	14·3
Oranges	128·4	146·6	32·7

2. A man aged 35 and his wife aged 30 buy a joint endowment insurance policy, the sum assured to be paid immediately if one or other or both die within a period of 10 years, or at the end of the period if both survive.

Using the information in the table below, find the probability that

(i) the man dies within the period,

(ii) the sum assured is paid before the end of the period.

Probability of death within 5 years

Age	Male	Female
30	0·0181	0·0166
35	0·0235	0·0195
40	0·0319	0·0243

3. (i) The probability of the success of an event is p. Show that in n independent trials the most probable number of successes is given by the integral part of $(n+1)p$. If p may vary, show that the probability of m successes is greatest when $p = m/n$.

(ii) The frequency of an event in a large number of independent trials takes the value r with probability proportional to $a^r/r!$, ($r = 0, 1, 2, 3, \ldots$). Calculate the mean frequency of the event and show that the most probable frequency is zero unless the mean exceeds 1.

(iii) The digits $1, 2 \ldots n$, where $n > 5$, appear in random order in a row. Find the probability that 4 and 5 will be adjacent.

4. (i) It is claimed that 90 % of women use Froth soap powder. In a random survey of 400 homes, 60 women said that they did not use Froth. Investigate whether the claim is justified.

(ii) Twenty pennies are tossed together a large number of times. State the theoretical mean and the standard deviation of the distribution of the number of heads. Assuming that the distribution closely approximates to the normal curve, use tables to find the probability that 14 or more 'heads' will appear together in a single toss.

5. A department in a works has ten machines which may need adjustment from time to time during the day. Three of these machines are old, each having a probability of $\frac{1}{11}$ of needing adjustment during the day, and seven are new, having corresponding probabilities of $1/21$.

Assuming that no machine needs adjustment twice on the same day, determine the probabilities that on a particular day

(i) just two old and no new machines need adjustment,

(ii) if just two machines need adjustment, they are of the same type.

6. The length x of the edge of a cube is rectangularly distributed between 5 and 10. Show that the volume y of the cube is distributed between 125 and 1000 with a probability distribution $p(y) \, dy = \frac{1}{15} y^{-\frac{2}{3}} \, dy$.

Sketch the frequency curve, and calculate the mean and variance of the volume of the cube.

7. A sector of a circle, of unit radius and angle θ, is cut from a sheet of thin metal and bent to form the curved surface of a right circular cone of height x. If, for a large number of such sectors, the angle θ is rectangularly distributed between 0 and 2π, show that x is distributed between 0 and 1 with a probability distribution

$$p(x)\,\mathrm{d}x = \frac{x}{\sqrt{(1-x^2)}}\,\mathrm{d}x.$$

Sketch the probability curve and calculate the median and the quartiles

8. A variate has for its frequency distribution curve the graph of $y = x\,\mathrm{e}^{-x/a}$ for $x > 0$, where $a > 0$. Find the total frequency and the mean of the variate

9. Given the continuous frequency function $f(x) = 2/x^2$, where $1 \leqslant x \leqslant 2$ determine the mean and variance of x and find the probability that x exceed 1·5. Calculate also the median and quartile values for x and state the inter quartile range.

10. A point P is taken at random inside an ellipse of eccentricity e. Calcu late (in terms of e) the probability that the sum of the focal distances of P should be not greater than the distance from a focus to the opposite end o the major axis.

11. In a certain industrial process, a "good" batch is one containing 2% (or fewer) defective items. The batch is "sentenced" by taking a sample o 50 items and deciding to *accept* the batch if the sample contains c or fewe defectives, or alternatively to *reject* the batch if the sample contains more tha c defectives. Using the Poisson approximation, find the smallest integral valu of c for which, with this scheme, the probability of accepting a 'good' batc is $\geqslant 0.95$.

With this value of c, compute the probability of accepting batches contain ing (i) 5% of defectives, (ii) 10% of defectives. Sketch the function $A(p)$ givin the probability of accepting batches containing a proportion p of defectives

12. A mass-produced article is packed in cartons each containing 4 articles. Seven hundred cartons were examined for defectives with the result given in the table.

Defective articles per carton	0	1	2	3	4	5	6	More than
Frequency	390	179	59	41	18	10	3	0

Obtain the proportion of defective articles p.

Assuming that the total number of articles examined is so large that p ca be taken to represent the proportion of defectives in the population, use th binomial distribution to calculate the probability that a random sample o 5 of these articles will contain 2 defectives.

13. Prove that the total number of ways in which three non-zero positive integers can be chosen to have as their sum a given integer $6N$, where $N = 1, 2, 3, \ldots$, is N^2.

$\Bigg[$ *Hint.* Consider the coefficient of x^{6N} in the expansion of

$$(x+x^2+x^3+ \ldots)(x+x^2+x^3+ \ldots)(x+x^2+x^3+ \ldots) = \frac{x^3}{(1-x)^3}.\Bigg]$$

APPENDIX

THE DIGITAL COMPUTER

A : 1 Introduction

Many problems which arise in science and engineering do not have closed form analytical solutions; in other instances analytical solutions are of little use for obtaining numerical results. In both these situations we usually resort to numerical solutions, which may be approximate to a known degree of accuracy. Generally, this involves the use of some kind of calculating aid, such as mathematical tables, a slide rule or a desk calculator. For large-scale calculations a digital computer has to be used; this means that a precise definition of the problem, in which every step is specified in advance, must be provided and there must be no risk of ambiguity because a computer, unlike a human calculator, cannot make any kind of judgement as to which course of action is likely to give the correct solution. To explain the process of using a digital computer we compare the procedure with that employed by a human calculator using the aids mentioned above. This is illustrated diagramatically in Fig. A.1. The upper half of each rectangle gives an analysis of the process for a human calculator; the lower half gives the analysis for the solution by a digital computer.

The formulation of the problem together with the data for a particular calculation may be compared to the "input" for the computer; the storage unit corresponds to working space; the arithmetic unit performs the same functions as the calculating aid; the output corresponds to the final result sheet. The most interesting analogy lies in the control unit and the calculator—in a computer every stage of the calculation is controlled automatically—this is precisely the function of the person doing the calculation in the other case.

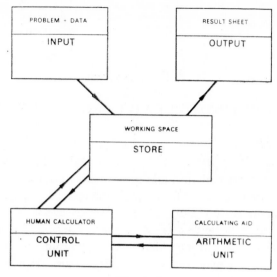

FIG. A. 1.

1. The input unit accepts the programme (i.e. instructions for the calculation) and the data and transfers them to the storage unit.

2. The storage unit or "memory" contains the data and program together with the results of any stage of the calculation.

3. The control unit draws instructions from the memory, sets up the necessary circuits in the arithmetic unit and causes the results to be transferred back to the store.

4. The arithmetic unit will perform the basic arithmetic and simple logical operations.

5. The output unit accepts results from the store and causes them to be printed out.

A : 2 Steps in the preparation of a problem for solution by computer

When we use a computer we must consider carefully all the points involved in the solution of a particular problem. These may be summarised as follows:

(a) **Specification of the problem.** This involves complete identification of the problem to be solved, the boundary conditions to be satisfied and the definition of the results which are needed. Naturally, this stage requires full understanding of the problem and its mathematical representation.

(b) **Mathematical formulation.** This consists of a mathematical analysis of the problem, carried through as far as possible. An analytical solution is better than a numerical solution since the former is a *general* solution over a continuous range of the variable, whereas a numerical solution is only given for a number (possibly a large number) of discrete points.

(c) **Numerical analysis.** At this stage we must decide whether the problem requires the use of numerical techniques—such as numerical integration—and, if so, which of the available methods should be used. This decision may involve investigating the convergence of various possible methods.

(d) **Construction of an algorithm or flow diagram.** An algorithm is a set of precise and definite instructions which must be followed when a calculation is performed. A computer program is essentially an algorithm prepared for use by the computer. The program is usually written down as a "flow diagram" which is a pictorial representation of the steps of the algorithm; the construction of a flow diagram will be considered more fully in the next section.

(e) **Coding.** Before a program, in the form of a flow diagram, can be fed into a computer it must be written in terms of a code "understood" by the machine. The use of this code enables the program to be punched on to a paper tape for feeding into the machine. There are a number of these codes or *programming languages* such as FORTRAN, ALGOL, COBOL, or PL 1.

(f) **Testing.** It is important that a numerical check (preferably independent of the actual problem) be made at each stage of a calculation. There are many types of error. Human errors, such as mistakes in the use of language or the instructions in the program, can be checked by performing a simple calculation, whose answer is known, with the program. Rounding errors arise through loss of digits on the end of a number, caused by the finite length of the register of the machine. Truncation of power series, i.e. using a finite number of terms of an infinite series to calculate, say, a sine, is another source of error. Inherent errors because of uncertainties in the data cause errors in the answer. The magnitudes of the errors arising from these sources must be estimated and allowed for. More serious errors arising from non-convergence of the numerical technique in use should be eliminated at the numerical analysis stage.

(g) **Production.** At this stage the program should be fully tested and capable of producing all the results required for the solution of the problem.

(h) **Interpretation of results.** The final stage in any problem is the analysis of results, often with the help of graphs, and the possibility of drawing physical conclusions from them.

It is clear that many of these steps are relevant for any type of calculation, whether or not a digital computer is used.

A : 3 Flow diagrams

There are various forms of notation which may be used for flow diagrams—one of the most common, and the one used here, is shown in Fig. A.2.

In the construction of a flow diagram, we must remember that in a calculation by computer every possible circumstance must be allowed for and the course of action specified in advance; even the end of data input must be indicated in some way so that the computer knows when the calculation is finished. Further, if a part of the calculation is to be repeated many times (this is known as a loop), then the instructions inside the loop must be as efficient as possible. A point at which various paths may be taken, depending on the values of the variables, is known as a *branch point* and is denoted by a diamond shape.

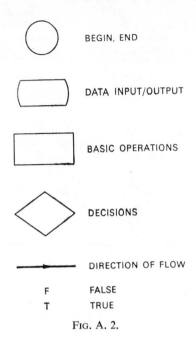

BEGIN, END

DATA INPUT/OUTPUT

BASIC OPERATIONS

DECISIONS

DIRECTION OF FLOW

F   FALSE
T   TRUE

Fig. A. 2.

Example. We illustrate the construction of a flow diagram by considering the solution of the general quadratic equation

$$ax^2 + bx + c = 0$$

from the formulae

$$x_1 = \frac{-b + \sqrt{(b^2 - 4ac)}}{2a}, \quad x_2 = \frac{-b - \sqrt{(b^2 - 4ac)}}{2a}. \tag{1}$$

The formulae (1) are qualified by certain exceptions.

(i) If $a = 0$, there is only one root $x_1 = -c/b$, the other root being infinite. (A computer cannot deal with infinity.)

(ii) If $a = 0$, $b = 0$, $c \neq 0$, no solution is possible.

(iii) If $a = 0$, $b = 0$, $c = 0$ any value of x satisfies the equation.

(iv) If $b^2 < 4ac$, the roots are complex and the computer must evaluate the real parts and the imaginary parts of the roots separately.

A program is used on any number of problems which differ in the data; in this case the values of a, b, c. Hence, when the roots have been determined corresponding to one set of data the machine is instructed to repeat the program with the next set. Since there is no loss of generality in taking $a \geqslant 0$ we can use a negative value of a to indicate the end of the calculations.

The calculation is started by reading in the first set of values of a, b, c and testing to see if $a < 0$. If this ($a < 0$) is false the machine proceeds to the

next step whereas if this ($a < 0$) is true the end of the calculation has bee
reached. The second step is to test if $a = 0$. If this ($a = 0$) is true one of th
situations (i), (ii) or (iii) must occur; if this ($a = 0$) is false the general case c
two roots occurs. When $a = 0$ the next step is to test for $b = 0$. If th
($b = 0$) is false we have situation (i); if this ($b = 0$) is true we have situatio

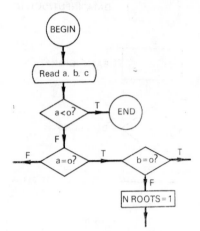

Fig. A. 3.

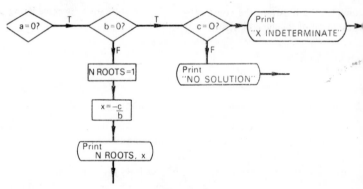

Fig. A. 4.

(ii) or (iii). The first steps in the flow diagram for this stage are shown i
Fig. A.3. We have reached the point, with the test for $b = 0$ being false, c
only one root to the equation with the value $-c/b$. These two pieces of infor
mation constitute the solution in situation (i). Another variable has to b
introduced which gives the number of roots to the equation and we give th
name N ROOTS to this variable. (It is advisable to use names describin
variables which indicate the quantities they represent; it makes the calculatio

asier to follow.) Now the machine has to give the value 1 to the variable
N ROOTS and give the value $-c/b$, after calculating this, to the variable x.

These two operations are represented by rectangles, and the solution is
printed out with the values of the two variables.

When the test for $b = 0$ is true the machine has to distinguish between
ituations (ii) and (iii). These steps are indicated in Fig. A.4. After each of the
ases of printing out solutions here the machine proceeds (as shown in
Fig. A.6) to the solution with the next set of values of a, b, c; this is indicated
by the arrows after the output "boxes" in Fig. A.4.

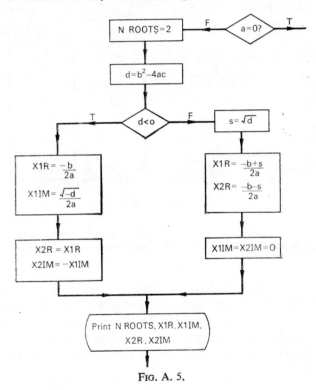

FIG. A. 5.

We now return to the test for $a = 0$ when the result is false, i.e. $a > 0$.
This is the general case of two roots; hence the variable N ROOTS is put
equal to 2. The further stages are shown in Fig. A.5. We introduce variables
X1R, X2R to represent the real parts of the two roots and X1IM, X2IM
to represent the imaginary parts. When the machine has calculated $d = b^2 -
4ac$, the path it follows is determined by the sign of d; the case of real roots
having X1IM and X2IM both zero. There is no need to deal specially with
the case, $d = 0$ of equal roots. It is more economical to go through the calculations for X1R and X2R and get the same result than it is to include a test

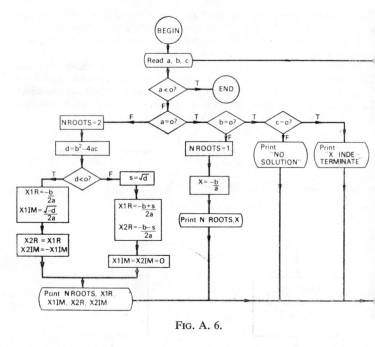

FIG. A. 6.

for $d = 0$ on every set of data. Here, as in Fig. A.6, after printing out the results the machine proceeds to the calculations with the next set of data a, b, c.

Direct methods such as the above are often not available, or are subject to considerable accumulation of rounding errors. When this is so iterative methods can often be devised which, because they rely on repetitions of the same set of operations, are easier to compute and are less prone to rounding errors.

ANSWERS TO EXERCISES

Exercises 1:1 (p. 9)

2. For **1.** (iii). (a) $-x^2$ for $0 \geqslant x \geqslant -1$, -1 for $-1 \geqslant x \geqslant -2$,
   $-(3+x)^2$ for $-2 \geqslant x \geqslant -3$;

   (b) x^2 for $0 \geqslant x \geqslant -1$, 1 for $-1 \geqslant x \geqslant -2$, $(3+x)^2$ for $-2 \geqslant x \geqslant -3$.
   For **1** (v). (a) $-\frac{1}{4}(x^2+3)$ for $0 \geqslant x \geqslant -1$,
   $-\sqrt{(-x)}$ for $-1 \geqslant x \geqslant -2$;

   (b) $\frac{1}{4}(x^2+3)$ for $0 \geqslant x \geqslant -1$, $\sqrt{(-x)}$ for $-1 \geqslant x \geqslant -2$.

3. (i) Even $|2x| - \frac{1}{2}|1-x| - \frac{1}{2}|1+x|$, odd $\frac{1}{2}|1+x| - \frac{1}{2}|1-x|$.

   (iv) Even $1-x^2$, odd x for $|x| \leqslant 1$; even $-\frac{1}{2}$, odd $3/(2x)$ for $1 \leqslant |x| \leqslant 3$.

4. (i) $1, 0$; (ii) $\dfrac{3}{4}a$, $\dfrac{1}{4}a$; (iii) $\dfrac{a}{16}$, $\dfrac{a}{16}$; (iv) $\dfrac{1}{\sqrt{2}}$, $\dfrac{1}{\sqrt{2}}$; (v) $1, -1$;
   (vi) $0, 0$.

5. (iii), (iv) and (vi) are even functions.

Exercises 1:2 (p. 18)

1. (i) -3 and -2; (ii) -3 and -2, 0 and 1, 1 and 2; (iii) -12 and -11,
   0 and 1, 2 and 3; (iv) -1 and 0, 1 and 2; (v) -3 and -2, -1
   and 0, 0 and 1, 1 and 2.

4. (i) $-2 \cdot 7$; (ii) $1 \cdot 7$; (iii) $2 \cdot 5$; (iv) $1 \cdot 4$; (v) $1 \cdot 4$. **5.** $0 \cdot 879$.

6. $k = 47$, roots $1\frac{1}{2}$, 2, $2\frac{1}{2}$.

7. (i) $x = r\pi \pm \sin^{-1}(\frac{1}{3})$; $r = 0, \pm 1, \pm 2, \ldots$;

   (ii) $x = 2r\pi \pm \alpha$, $r = 0, \pm 1, \pm 2, \ldots$;
   $x = 2r\pi \pm \cos^{-1}(2\cos\alpha)$ if $|\cos\alpha| < \frac{1}{2}$.

8. $y = 2x$, $z = 4x$, where $x = \frac{1}{2}$ or $(1 \pm \sqrt{5})/8$.

9. x, y, z can take the (six) permutations of 0, $\frac{1}{2}(7 \pm \sqrt{13})$.

11. $1 \cdot 66$.

Exercises 1:3 (p. 28)

1. (i) (a) $3x-4y = 0$, (b) $3x-4y+11 = 0$, (c) $3x-4y-7 = 0$;

   (ii) $4x+3y-11 = 0$, $2x-y-3 = 0$, $x+5y-7 = 0$, $3x-4y-2 = 0$;

(iii) $-\dfrac{1}{5}$, $-\dfrac{4}{\sqrt{5}}$, $\dfrac{8}{\sqrt{26}}$, $-\dfrac{31}{10}$; (iv) $2x+14y-13 = 0$, $14x-2y+7 = 0$;

(v) $10x+50y-91 = 0$, $44x+33y-71 = 0$, $34x-17y+20 = 0$, concurrent at $\left(\dfrac{547}{1870}, \dfrac{3294}{1870}\right)$;   (vi) $416x-258y+189 = 0$.

2. $x-2 = 0$, $\sqrt{3}y+x-2-3\sqrt{3} = 0$.   **3.** Two of the three conditions
$a_1a_3+b_1b_3 = a_3b_1-a_1b_3$, $a_2a_3+b_2b_3 = a_2b_3-a_3b_2$, $a_1a_2+b_1b_2 = 0$.

6. (i) $2y-3x-1 = 0$;   (ii) $(n+m)y-2x-2amn = 0$;

(iii) $bx \cos\left(\dfrac{\varphi+\theta}{2}\right)+ay \sin\left(\dfrac{\varphi+\theta}{2}\right)-ab \cos\left(\dfrac{\varphi-\theta}{2}\right) = 0$.

7. (i) $(-3, -\tfrac{5}{2})$, $\tfrac{1}{2}\sqrt{61}$;   (ii) $(\tfrac{3}{2}, \tfrac{7}{2})$, $\dfrac{1}{\sqrt{2}}$;   (iii) $(1, 0)$, $\sqrt{5}$;

(iv) $(-\tfrac{3}{2}, \tfrac{1}{2})$, $\tfrac{1}{2}\sqrt{(\tfrac{5}{2})}$.

8. (i) $x^2+y^2+2x-4y-4 = 0$; (ii) $x^2+y^2-4x-8y+19 = 0$;

(iii) $x^2+y^2-6x+4y-12 = 0$; (iv) $16x^2+16y^2+16x-8y-11 = 0$.

9. (i) $x^2+y^2+6x-4y = 0$, $x^2+y^2-2x-8y = 0$;

(ii) $x^2+y^2+6x-4y-4 = 0$, $x^2+y^2-2x-8y+16 = 0$.

10. $y-4x-6 = 0$, $y-4x+11 = 0$, $4x+y+3 = 0$, $4x+y-14 = 0$.

Exercises 1 : 4 (p. 34)

1. (i) a; (ii) $\dfrac{p}{q}$; (iii) 1; (iv) 1; (v) the function does not tend to any limit but *oscillates boundedly*.

2. (i) $\tfrac{1}{2}$;   (ii) 0;   (iii) 0;   (iv) $\tfrac{1}{3}$;   (v) $\tfrac{7}{4}$.

3. (i) $\dfrac{1}{\sqrt{(2a)}}$; (ii) 0.   **4.** $a = -\tfrac{1}{4}b$, $c = b$.

Exercises 1 : 5 (p. 37)

(i) (a) $O(1)$, (b) $O(1)$; (ii) (a) $O(1)$, (b) $O(x)$; (iii) (a) $O(1)$, (b) $O(x^{-1})$;
(iv) (a) $O(x^{-1})$, (b) $O(x^{-2})$; (v) (a) $O(x)$, (b) $O(x)$.

Exercises 1 : 6 (p. 47)

2. (i) $-\tfrac{4}{3} > x > -\sqrt{2}$ and $x > \sqrt{2}$; (ii) $-1 < x < 3$ and $x > 4$.

3. (i) $-2 \leqslant \lambda \leqslant 2$; (ii) $x < -5$ and $-1 < x < 5/3$.

4. (i) $x < \tfrac{1}{3}$ and $x > 1$; (ii) $(2n+1)\pi/k < x < (2n+2)\pi/k$
or $(2n+\tfrac{-}{6})\pi/k < x < (2n+\tfrac{-}{6})\pi/k$ for $n = 0, \pm1, \pm2, \dots$.

5. (i) $x < -\sqrt{3}$ or $-\sqrt{2} < x < 2$ or $x > \sqrt{3}$; (ii) $\frac{1}{3} \leqslant x \leqslant 7$.

6. (ii) $a > 2\sqrt{6}$. **8.** Greatest value of x is $1 + \sqrt{5}$.

9. $x > 0$, $y > 0$, $x > y$, $xy \leqslant 400$, $y \geqslant 10$; either $19\frac{6}{7} < x \leqslant 21\frac{1}{3}$ or $25 \leqslant x \leqslant 33$; greatest area when $x = 40$, $y = 10$.

10. Either $\lambda < -3$ or $\lambda > 2$. **12.** $p = -4$, $q = 3$, $r = 1$.

Exercises 1 : 8 (p. 56)

1. (i) $\to 0$; (ii) $\to \infty$; (iii) oscillates boundedly taking the values $1, \frac{1}{2}, -\frac{1}{2}$, $-1, -\frac{1}{2}, \frac{1}{2}, \ldots$ in succession; (iv) oscillates unboundedly taking the values in (iii) multiplied by n; (v) $\to 0$ if $|x| < 1$, $\to \infty$ if $x \geqslant 1$, oscillates unboundedly if $x \leqslant -1$.

2. (i) Any oscillating sequence u_n for which $|u_n| \to 0$.

4. If $|a| < 1$, $u_n \to -1$; if $|a| > 1$, $u_n \to 1$; if $a = 1$, $u_n = 0$; if $a = -1$, the odd members of the sequence are undefined.

Exercises 1 : 9 (p. 64)

4. When $x = 0.8$, $y = 3.801$. The polynomial is of degree 5.

5. When $x = 5$, $f(x) = 0.15867$.

6. When $x = 0.8$, $f(x) = 33.314$; transposition of the last two digits.

Miscellaneous Exercises I (p. 65)

2. (i) (a) even, (b) even, (c) odd; (ii) (a) even, (b) even, (c) odd.

4. $A = 0$, $B = 1$, $C = a^3 + a^2$, $D = 0$.

6. Three real roots, 1 negative, two positive; 0.505.

7. 0.2016.

8. $\frac{1}{2}, 2, \dfrac{5 \pm i\sqrt{11}}{6}$.

9. 5 regions; (i) 6 regions; (ii) 6 regions.

10. -0.452, $1.85(4)$. **11.** (i) $\alpha^{\frac{1}{2}}$ etc.; (ii) α^2 etc.; (iii) $\alpha + c$ etc.; (iv) $a\alpha + b$ etc.

12. $y^4 - 12y^2 + 4 = 0$; $\pm\sqrt{(6 \pm 4\sqrt{2})} - 2$, i.e., $\sqrt{2}$, $-\sqrt{2}$, $-4 + \sqrt{2}$, $-4 - \sqrt{2}$.

13. -8 and 0. **15.** (i) $2\frac{1}{5}$; (ii) 3.

16. $-\frac{2}{3} < x < 1 - \sqrt{2}$ and $0 < x < 1 + \sqrt{2}$.

18. 3.24; $l = 1 + \sqrt{5}$.

19. (i) $x = 9$; $y = -2$; (ii) $x < -2$ and $0 < x < 3$.

22. (ii) $-1 < x < 1$ and $x > 4$. **23.** $x^2 - 4x + y^2 \pm 3y + 4 = 0$.

24. It is sufficient if $f(x)$ is continuous for $a \leqslant x \leqslant b$.

25. (i) $\sqrt{2}$, -1; (ii) $2, 0$; (iii) $0, -8/27$; (iv) $8, -9/2$.

26. When $x = 5$, $f(x) = 156$.

Exercises 2 : 1 (p. 70)

(i) $\sec^2 x$; (ii) $3a(ax+b)^2$; (iii) $2x \cos(x^2)$; (iv) $\dfrac{1}{(2\sqrt{x})}$;
(v) $2 \sec 2x \tan 2x$.

Exercises 2 : 2 (p. 74)

1. $1 - 3x^2$.   **2.** $1 - 2x$.   **3.** $1 - 4x + 3x^2$.

4. $(1-x^2)(1-5x^2)$.   **5.** $2x - 4x^3$.   **6.** $4x^3 - 5x^4$.

7. $2x^3(1-x)(2-3x)$.   **8.** $mx^{m-1} - (m+n)x^{m+n-1}$.

9. $x^{m-1}(1-x^2)^{n-1}\{m - (m+2n)x^2\}$.   **10.** $1 - \dfrac{1}{x^2}$.

11. $2x - \dfrac{2}{x^3}$.   **12.** $4x^3 - 4x$.

13. $3\left(x + \dfrac{1}{2x}\right)^2\left\{1 - \dfrac{1}{(2x^2)}\right\}$.   **14.** $50x - \dfrac{2}{(9x^3)}$.

15. $3x^5\left(2x - \dfrac{1}{3x}\right)^2\left(6x - \dfrac{1}{3x}\right)$.   **16.** $\dfrac{1}{(1-x)^2}$.

17. $\dfrac{1+x^2}{(1-x^2)^2}$.   **18.** $\dfrac{x(2-x)}{(1-x)^2}$.

19. $\dfrac{2x}{(1-x^2)^2}$.

20. $nm(x^m + x^{-m})^{n-1}(x^{m-1} - x^{-m-1})$.   **21.** $\dfrac{2}{(1-x)^2}$.

22. $\dfrac{x+3}{(1-x)^3}$.   **23.** $\dfrac{1}{(1-2x)^2}$.   **24.** $\dfrac{1+3x^2}{(1-3x^2)^2}$.

25. $\dfrac{4x}{(1-x^2)^2}$.   **26.** $\dfrac{x(x^3-3x-2)}{(1+x^3)^2}$.   **27.** $\dfrac{2mx^{m-1}}{(1-x^m)^2}$.

28. $\dfrac{22x}{(1-4x^2)^2}$.   **29.** $\dfrac{(ncbx^{n-1} + mdax^{m-1} + bd(m-n)\,x^{m+n-1})}{(c-dx^m)^2}$.

30. $\dfrac{2(1-x^2)}{(1-x+x^2)^2}$.   **31.** $2 \sin x \cos x (= \sin 2x)$.

32. $\cos^2 x - \sin^2 x (= \cos 2x)$. **33.** $n \sin^{n-1} x \cos^{n-1} x \cos 2x$.

34. $2x \sec^2 (x^2)$. **35.** $3 \sec 3x \tan 3x$.

36. $-9 x^2 \operatorname{cosec}^2 (1+3x^3)$. **37.** $8 \sec^2 4x \tan 4x$.

38. $-\sin \frac{1}{2}x \cos \frac{1}{2} x (= -\frac{1}{2} \sin x)$. **39.** $2a \tan (ax+b) \sec^2 (ax+b)$.

40. $\sec^4 x$. **41.** $\dfrac{\cos x}{(1+\sin x)^2}$. **42.** $\dfrac{\cos x}{(1-\sin x)^2}$. **43.** $\dfrac{2 \sin x}{(1+\cos x)^2}$.

44. $\sec x \tan x + \sec^2 x$. **45.** $\dfrac{-4 \cos 2x}{(1+\sin 2x)^2}$.

46. $-(\sin x \cos 3x + 3 \sin 3x \cos x)$.

47. $-\{\cos (x^3) \sin x + 3x^2 \sin (x^3) \cos x\}$. **48.** $\dfrac{2}{(\cos x - \sin x)^2}$.

49. $x \cos x + \sin x$. **50.** $x^2 \sec x \tan x + 2x \sec x$. **51.** $\dfrac{(x \cos x - \sin x)}{x^2}$.

52. $x \sec^2 x + \tan x$. **53.** $-\dfrac{1}{x^2} \cos \left(\dfrac{1}{x}\right)$.

54. $\dfrac{2}{x^2} \cot \left(\dfrac{1}{x}\right) \operatorname{cosec}^2 \left(\dfrac{1}{x}\right)$. **55.** $\tan \left(\dfrac{1}{3x}\right) - \dfrac{1}{3x} \sec^2 \left(\dfrac{1}{3x}\right)$.

56. $2x \cos \left(\dfrac{4}{x}\right) + 4 \sin \left(\dfrac{4}{x}\right)$. **57.** $\dfrac{1}{2 \sqrt{(1+x)}}$.

58. $\dfrac{(a-b-2x)}{2 \sqrt{(a-x)} \cdot \sqrt{(b-x)}}$. **59.** $\dfrac{a^2 - 2x^2}{\sqrt{(a^2-x^2)}}$. **60.** $\dfrac{1+x+2x^2}{\sqrt{(1+x^2)}}$.

61. $\dfrac{-x(3-x^2)}{(1+x^2)^2 \sqrt{(1-x^2)}}$. **62.** $\dfrac{-(1+x)}{(1+x^2)^{\frac{3}{2}}}$.

63. $\dfrac{-1}{\sqrt{\{(1+x)^3 (1-x)\}}}$. **64.** $\dfrac{x}{(1-x^2)^{\frac{3}{2}}}$. **65.** $\dfrac{-a^2}{x^2 \sqrt{(a^2+x^2)}}$.

66. $\dfrac{x}{\sqrt{(1+x^2)}} - 1$. **67.** $\dfrac{x}{\sqrt{(x^2-1)}} + 1$. **68.** $\dfrac{1+2x^2}{\sqrt{(1+x^2)}} - 2x$.

69. $\dfrac{1-x^2}{\sqrt{\{(1-x+x^2)^3 (1+x+x^2)\}}}$.

70. $\dfrac{(a-b) \sin x \cos x}{\sqrt{(a \sin^2 x + b \cos^2 x)}}$. **71.** $\dfrac{2x+3}{2 \sqrt{(x^2+3x+4)}}$.

72. $\dfrac{-1}{t^2}$. **73.** $-\left(\dfrac{b}{a}\right) \tan^{n-2} t$. **74.** $\dfrac{b(t^2+1)}{a(t^2-1)}$.

Exercises 2 : 3 (p. 76)

1. (a) $m(m-1) \cdots (m-n+1)x^{m-n}$; (b) $m!$; (c) 0.

2. $a^n \cos (ax+b+\frac{1}{2}n\pi)$.

Exercises 2 : 4 (p. 83)

1. $2x e^{x^2}$.

2. $(2ax^2-1)\dfrac{e^{ax^2}}{x^2}$.

3. $e^{\sin x}\cos x$.

4. $e^{ax}(a\sin bx + b\cos bx)$.

5. $(n\cosh^2 x + m\sinh^2 x)\sinh^{n-1} x\cosh^{m-1} x$.

6. $\dfrac{2e^x}{(1+e^x)^2}$.

7. $\operatorname{sech}^2 x - \dfrac{2}{3}\tanh x\operatorname{sech}^2 x$.

8. $\cot x$.

9. $-\tan x$.

10. $\dfrac{2}{1-x^2}$.

11. $\dfrac{1}{(1-x)\sqrt{x}}$.

12. $\dfrac{1}{\sqrt{(x^2-1)}}$.

13. $\dfrac{-1}{2(1-\sqrt{x})}$.

14. $2e^{2x}$.

15. $\dfrac{-2(1+\cos x\cosh x)}{(\sinh x+\sin x)^2}$.

16. $\dfrac{1}{x}+\dfrac{1}{\sqrt{(x^2+1)}}$.

17. $b^x\ln b\cdot\sec^2(a+b^x)$.

18. $\{(\ln x)^2 + 2\ln x\}x^{x\ln x}$.

19. $\dfrac{x+1}{(x-4)(2x-3)}$.

20. $\dfrac{x^6-8x^3-9x^2}{4(x^3+1)^{\frac{1}{4}}(x^4-1)^{\frac{3}{2}}}$.

21. $\ln 3$.

22. $\dfrac{(e^{2x}-1)}{(e^{2x}+1)}$.

Exercises 2 : 5 (p. 89)

2. (i) $\pm\sqrt{y}$; (ii) $\dfrac{1-y}{1+y}$; (iii) $\dfrac{1}{y^2-1}$; (iv) $\cot^{-1}(\tan y)$;

(v) $\cot y$; (vi) $\log_{10} y$; (vii) $\pm\sin y$.

3. $\sqrt{3}$.

5. $x=\ln(3\pm\sqrt{6})$, $y=\ln(1\pm\tfrac{1}{3}\sqrt{6})$.

6. (i) $\ln\left\{\dfrac{1+\sqrt{(1+x^2)}}{x}\right\}$ for $x>0$, $\ln\left\{\dfrac{-x}{1+\sqrt{(1+x^2)}}\right\}$ for $x<0$.

9. $\dfrac{n\cos(n\sin^{-1}x)}{\sqrt{(1-x^2)}}$.

10. $\dfrac{1}{(x^2+1)\tan^{-1}(x)}$.

11. $\dfrac{x\sec^2\dfrac{x}{a}-a\tan\dfrac{x}{a}}{x^2+a^2\tan^2\dfrac{x}{a}}$.

12. $\dfrac{2}{1+x^2}$.

13. $-\dfrac{1}{2(x^2+1)}$.

14. $\dfrac{e^x(\cos x-\sin x)}{1+e^{2x}\cos^2 x}$.

15. $e^x\left[(x+1)\sin^2 x\tan^{-1}x + 2x\sin x\cos x\tan^{-1}x + \dfrac{x\sin^2 x}{1+x^2}\right]$.

16. $\dfrac{1}{x^2+1}$.

17. $\dfrac{-\sin x}{\sqrt{(1+\cos^2 x)}}$.

18. $\dfrac{2}{(1-x)^2}\sec\left(\dfrac{1+x}{1-x}\right)$.

19. $\dfrac{a}{a^2-x^2}$. **20.** $\dfrac{-a}{x\sqrt{(a^2-x^2)}}$. **21.** $\dfrac{-a}{x\sqrt{(a^2+x^2)}}$.

22. (i) 1280; (ii) 2; (iii) $1/\sqrt{6}$; (iv) $-\pi e^{-1}$; (v) 8/3.

23. $x = \ln 3$ or $-\ln 15$.

24. (i) $x = -\ln 2$, $y = \ln(3/2)$; (ii) $x = y = \pm\ln(1+\sqrt{2})$.

Exercises 2 : 6 (p. 92)

5. 1; -1; -3.

Exercises 2 : 7 (p. 98)

2. $(64x^3 + 384x^2 + 288x - 480)\, e^{2x}$.

7. (i) $120/x$; (ii) $-512e^{2x}\cos 2x$. **8.** $2^{2n-1}\{(n-1)!\}^2$.

Exercises 2 : 8 (p. 106)

3. (ii) $a = -\tfrac{5}{2}$, $b = -\tfrac{3}{2}$. **8.** (i) 2, -3; (ii) $-\tfrac{3}{2}$.

11. $a = \pm 1/5$, $b = 2$.

Miscellaneous Exercises II (p. 109)

1. $e^{cx}\sin^{m-1} rx(c\sin rx + mr\cos rx)$. **2.** $\dfrac{1}{\sqrt{(x^2+a^2)}} + \dfrac{a}{x\sqrt{(x^2-a^2)}}$.

3. $\dfrac{(1-x^2)}{(1+3x^2+x^4)}$. **4.** $\dfrac{\sqrt{3}}{(2+\cos x)}$. **5.** $-2\sec 2x$.

6. $e^x \exp(e^x)$. **7.** $\tfrac{1}{2}\ln(x^2+a^2)$. **8.** $2\sqrt{(a^2-x^2)}$.

9. $\dfrac{a(a^2-x^2)}{(a^2-ax+x^2)^{\frac{3}{2}}(a^2+ax+x^2)^{\frac{1}{2}}}$. **10.** $\dfrac{3x(x^2-1)^{\frac{1}{2}}}{(x^4+1)^{\frac{1}{3}}} - \dfrac{4x^3(x^2-1)^{\frac{3}{2}}}{3(x^4+1)^{\frac{4}{3}}}$.

11. $\dfrac{1}{2\sqrt{\{x(x+1)\}}}$. **12.** $\dfrac{0{\cdot}8686x(x-2)}{(x^2-x+1)(x^2+x-1)}$. **13.** -1.

14. $\left(\dfrac{x}{1+x^2}\right)^{\frac{x}{1-x^2}} \left[\dfrac{1}{1+x^2} + \dfrac{(1+x^2)}{(1-x^2)^2}\ln\left(\dfrac{x}{1+x^2}\right)\right]$.

15. $\cos(x^{\cos x})\cdot x^{\cos x}[x^{-1}\cos x - \sin x \ln x)]$. **16.** $ax^{\frac{a}{x}}\dfrac{(1-\ln x)}{x^2}$.

17. $\dfrac{-1}{2(1+x)\sqrt{x}}$. **18.** $(\cosh x)^x (x\tanh x + \ln\cosh x)$·

19. $\dfrac{x}{\sqrt{(x^4-1)}}$. **20.** $\dfrac{x^2-7}{\sqrt{\{(3-x)(1+x)^3\}}}$. **21.** $\dfrac{1}{(1+x)\sqrt{x}}$.

22. $\dfrac{1}{x\ln x\cdot\ln(\ln x)}$. **23.** (ii) $y=\dfrac{1}{\sqrt{(1-x)}}$.

24. $x=\ln 3,\quad y=\ln 2$. **27.** 0.

30. (i) 0; (ii) $\dfrac{n\pi}{4}$, $\quad n=0\pm 1,\ \pm 2,\ \ldots$

32. (i) $\dfrac{2(x+y)\cos(x+y)^2}{\{1-2(x+y)\cos(x+y)^2\}}$; (ii) $\dfrac{1}{3}\sec^3 2\theta \operatorname{cosec}\theta$.

35. (i) $\dfrac{6(-1)^n(n-4)!}{x^{n-3}}$;

(ii) $\dfrac{1}{4}\left\{6^n\cos\left(6x+\dfrac{n\pi}{2}\right)+3\times 2^n\cos\left(2x+\dfrac{n\pi}{2}\right)\right\}$;

(iii) $-(n-1)!\left[\dfrac{1}{(1-x)^n}+\dfrac{(-1)^{n-1}}{(1+x)^n}\right]$;

(iv) $2^n x^2\cos(2x+n\pi/2)+n2^n x\cos\{2x+(n-1)\pi/2\}$
$+n(n-1)2^{n-2}\cos\{2x+(n-2)\pi/2\}$.

40. $0,\ -2;\quad y,\ -\dfrac{y}{r^2}$. **41.** $\cos\theta,\ \dfrac{x}{r}$.

42. $A=0,\ \omega=1,\ m=1,\ B=1$.

43. 2; $3x+2$. **44.** $p,\ \varphi;\ T,\ v;\ T,\ p$.

45. (i) (a) $-\{(x+1)(x-1)^3\}^{-\frac{1}{2}}$; (b) $y^2/\{x(1-y\ln x)\}$.

49. (ii) -2 and $4/3$.

Exercises 3 : 2 (p. 122)

1. $\frac{1}{4}e^3$. **2.** $\frac{2}{33}$. **3.** $5\frac{1}{3}-4\ln 3$.

4. $1+\frac{1}{4}\pi+2\ln(1+\sqrt 2)$. **5.** $\frac{1}{2}\ln 7$. **7.** $1\frac{1}{3}$.

8. (i) $4/\omega$; (ii) 1.

Exercises 3 : 3 (p. 126)

1. $\dfrac{(6x+5)^8}{48}$. **2.** $-\dfrac{(2x+5\sin 2x)}{4}$. **3.** $-a\cos\left(\dfrac{x}{a}\right)$.

4. $\dfrac{5}{3}\ln\sec(3x+4)$. **5.** $\dfrac{3x-2\sin 2x+\frac{1}{4}\sin 4x}{8}$.

6. $\dfrac{1}{4}\left(\dfrac{1}{3}\sinh 3x+3\sinh x\right)$. **7.** $\dfrac{1}{\sqrt 2}\sinh^{-1}(\sqrt 2 x)$.

8. $\sin^{-1}\left\{\dfrac{(x-2)}{\sqrt 5}\right\}$. **9.** $\sinh^{-1}\left\{\dfrac{(2x+1)}{\sqrt 3}\right\}$.

10. $\dfrac{1}{\sqrt{2}}\sinh^{-1}(\sqrt{2}x+2\sqrt{2})$. **11.** $\sin^{-1}\left\{\dfrac{(x+3)}{\sqrt{34}}\right\}$.

12. $\sinh^{-1}\left\{\dfrac{(x-3)}{4}\right\}$. **13.** $\dfrac{1}{9}\tan^{-1}\left\{\dfrac{(3x+2)}{3}\right\}$.

14. $\dfrac{\pi}{24}$. **15.** $\dfrac{1}{4}\pi$. **16.** $\dfrac{(8-5\sqrt{2})}{12}$.

17. $\sinh^{-1}(\tfrac{3}{2})-\sinh^{-1}1=\ln\{\tfrac{1}{2}(3+\sqrt{13})\}-\ln(1+\sqrt{2})$.

18. $\sinh^{-1}1-\sinh^{-1}(\tfrac{1}{2})=\ln(1+\sqrt{2})-\ln\{\tfrac{1}{2}(1+\sqrt{5})\}$.

19. $\dfrac{1}{3}\pi-\sin^{-1}\left(\dfrac{1}{\sqrt{3}}\right)$. **20.** $\dfrac{\pi}{8}$. **21.** $\dfrac{(4x-\pi-\sin 4x)}{32}$.

Exercises 3 : 4 (p. 132)

1. $-\tfrac{1}{2}e^{-x^2}$. **2.** $\tfrac{1}{2}\tan^2 x$. **3.** $\tan x+\tfrac{1}{3}\tan^3 x$.

4. $\tfrac{1}{2}(\ln x)^2$. **5.** $\tfrac{1}{5}\sin^5 x-\tfrac{1}{7}\sin^7 x$. **6.** $-\tfrac{1}{4}\ln(1-x^4)$.

7. $\dfrac{1}{6}\tan^{-1}\left(\dfrac{x^2}{3}\right)$. **8.** $\dfrac{1}{3}(a^2+x^2)^{\frac{3}{2}}$. **9.** $\dfrac{1}{3}\ln(5+3e^x)$.

10. $-\dfrac{1}{3}a^2(a^2-x^2)^{\frac{3}{2}}+\dfrac{1}{5}(a^2-x^2)^{\frac{5}{2}}$. **11.** $-\dfrac{1}{12}\tan^{-1}\left(\dfrac{3\cos x}{4}\right)$.

12. $\dfrac{1}{a}\sinh^{-1}\left(\dfrac{e^{ax}}{b}\right)$. **13.** $c\sin^{-1}\left(\sqrt{\dfrac{x}{c}}\right)-\sqrt{\{x(c-x)\}}$.

14. $\tfrac{1}{3}\tan^{-1}(e^{3x})$. **15.** $\dfrac{\sinh^{n+1}x}{n+1}+\dfrac{\sinh^{n+3}x}{n+3}$.

16. $-\dfrac{1}{b}\ln(a+b\cos x)$. **17.** $\dfrac{1}{\sqrt{6}}\tan^{-1}\left(\dfrac{\sqrt{2}\tan x}{\sqrt{3}}\right)$.

18. $\tfrac{2}{3}\tan^{-1}(3e^x)$. **19.** $\tfrac{2}{7}\sec^{\frac{7}{2}}x-\tfrac{2}{3}\sec^{\frac{3}{2}}x$.

20. $\dfrac{1}{2}a^2\sin^{-1}\left(\dfrac{x}{a}\right)-\left(a+\dfrac{1}{2}x\right)\sqrt{(a^2-x^2)}$. **21.** $\ln(1+e^{-1})$.

22. $\dfrac{1}{2(b-a)}\ln\left(\dfrac{b}{a}\right)$. **23.** $\dfrac{7}{(3\ln 2)}$. **24.** $\dfrac{16}{63}$.

25. 1. **26.** $\dfrac{\sqrt{3}}{a^2}$. **27.** $1-\dfrac{1}{\sqrt{2}}$.

28. $\tfrac{1}{2}\ln(1+\sqrt{2})$. **29.** $\dfrac{(\sqrt{2}-1)}{a^2}$. **30.** π.

31. $\dfrac{31}{15}$. **32.** 0. **33.** $\dfrac{9\pi}{2}$.

39. $\dfrac{x^4}{4(1+x^2)^2}+\dfrac{1}{8}\tan^{-1}x-\dfrac{x(1-x^2)}{8(1+x^2)^2}$. **40.** $\dfrac{2}{3}$.

41. $-\dfrac{2}{\sqrt{(x-1)}} - 2\tan^{-1}\{\sqrt{(x-1)}\}.$ **42.** $\dfrac{2\pi}{3}.$

44. $\pi\alpha/(\sin\alpha).$ **45.** (i) $\pi^2/4$; (ii) $-\pi^2/4.$

Exercises 3 : 5 (p. 136)

1. $x\tan x + \ln\cos x.$ **2.** $\frac{1}{2}\sec x\tan x - \frac{1}{2}\ln(\sec x + \tan x).$

3. $x\ln x - x.$ **4.** $\frac{1}{2}x^2\ln x - \frac{1}{4}x^2.$

5. $x\tanh^{-1}x + \frac{1}{2}\ln(1-x^2).$ **6.** $x\sinh^{-1}\left(\dfrac{x}{a}\right) - \sqrt{(a^2+x^2)}.$

7. $x\sinh^{-1}\left(\dfrac{a}{x}\right) + a\sinh^{-1}\left(\dfrac{x}{a}\right).$

8. $\dfrac{1}{3}(x^3 - 3x^2 + 3x)\ln x - \dfrac{x^3}{9} + \dfrac{x^2}{2} - x.$

9. $\left(x + \frac{1}{3}x^3\right)\tan^{-1}x - \frac{1}{6}x^2 - \frac{1}{3}\ln(1+x^2).$

10. $-\sqrt{(1-x^2)}\sin^{-1}x + x.$ **11.** $\frac{1}{4}x^2\{2(\ln x)^2 - 2\ln x + 1\}.$

12. $\dfrac{(3x\sin^3 x + 3\cos x - \cos^3 x)}{9}.$ **13.** $x\sec^{-1}\left(\dfrac{x}{a}\right) - a\cosh^{-1}\left(\dfrac{x}{a}\right).$

14. $\dfrac{1}{2}a^2\sin^{-1}\left(\dfrac{x}{a}\right) - \dfrac{1}{2}x\sqrt{(a^2-x^2)}.$

15. $\dfrac{1}{a}(1 - a\cos x)\ln(1 - a\cos x) + \cos x.$

16. $\frac{1}{4}(2x^2-1)\sin^{-1}x + \frac{1}{4}x\sqrt{(1-x^2)}.$

17. $\dfrac{1 + \frac{1}{2}\ln 2}{\sqrt{2}} - 1.$ **18.** $\dfrac{1}{4}\pi - \dfrac{1}{2}\ln 2.$

19. $\frac{1}{4}\pi - \frac{1}{2}\ln 2 - \pi^2/32.$ **20.** $\frac{1}{2}\pi - 1.$

21. $\dfrac{1}{4}(\pi - 1).$ **22.** $\dfrac{(\pi^2+4)}{16}.$

23. $\dfrac{\pi}{6} - \dfrac{2}{9}.$ **24.** $\dfrac{(\pi - 2\ln 2)}{8}.$

27. (i) $p(1 - e^{-2n\pi p/\omega})/(p^2 + \omega^2)$; (ii) $\dfrac{\alpha}{2}\left\{\dfrac{1}{\alpha^2 + (\beta-\gamma)^2} + \dfrac{1}{\alpha^2 + (\beta+\gamma)^2}\right\}$

Exercises 3 : 6 (p. 141)

1. $\dfrac{1}{7(x+3)} - \dfrac{x-2}{7(x^2+x+1)}.$ **2.** $\dfrac{1}{2x+1} - \dfrac{1}{x^2+1}.$

3. $\dfrac{1}{x} + \dfrac{1}{x^2} - \dfrac{1}{x^2+1}.$ **4.** $\dfrac{2}{1-x} + \dfrac{2(1+x)}{1+x+x^2}.$

5. $\dfrac{1}{x} - \dfrac{2}{2x+1} + \dfrac{4}{(2x+1)^2}$.

6. $\dfrac{1}{12(x-1)} - \dfrac{1}{3(x+2)} + \dfrac{1}{4(x+3)}$.

7. $\dfrac{-4}{3(x+1)} - \dfrac{7}{3(x+1)^2} + \dfrac{(4x-1)}{3(x^2-x+1)}$.

8. $\dfrac{1}{x^2} - \dfrac{1}{x^2+1}$.

9. $\dfrac{x}{2\sqrt{2}[x^2 - \sqrt{2}x + 1]} - \dfrac{x}{2\sqrt{2}[x^2 + \sqrt{2}x + 1]}$.

10. $(-1)^n n! \left[\dfrac{-1}{(x+1)^{n+1}} + \dfrac{(n+1)}{(x+1)^{n+2}} + \dfrac{1}{(x+2)^{n+1}} \right]$.

Exercises 3 : 7 (p. 144)

1. $\dfrac{1}{7} \ln (x+3) - \dfrac{1}{14} \ln (x^2+x+1) + \dfrac{5}{7\sqrt{3}} \tan^{-1} \left(\dfrac{2x+1}{\sqrt{3}} \right)$.

2. $\dfrac{1}{2} \ln (2x+1) - \tan^{-1} x$.

3. $\ln x - \dfrac{1}{x} - \tan^{-1} x$.

4. $\ln (x^2+x+1) - 2 \ln (1-x) + \dfrac{2}{\sqrt{3}} \tan^{-1} \left(\dfrac{2x+1}{\sqrt{3}} \right)$.

5. $\ln \left(\dfrac{x}{2x+1} \right) - \dfrac{2}{(2x+1)}$.

6. $\frac{1}{12} \ln (x-1) - \frac{1}{3} \ln (x+2) + \frac{1}{4} \ln (x+3)$.

7. $-\dfrac{4}{3} \ln (x+1) + \dfrac{7}{3(x+1)} + \dfrac{2}{3} \ln (x^2-x+1) + \dfrac{2}{3\sqrt{3}} \tan^{-1} \left(\dfrac{2x-1}{\sqrt{3}} \right)$.

8. $-\dfrac{1}{x} - \tan^{-1} x$.

9. $\dfrac{1}{4\sqrt{2}} \ln \left(\dfrac{x^2 - \sqrt{2}x + 1}{x^2 + \sqrt{2}x + 1} \right) + \dfrac{1}{2\sqrt{2}} [\tan^{-1} (\sqrt{2}x - 1) + \tan^{-1} (\sqrt{2}x + 1)]$.

10. $\dfrac{\pi}{4}$.

11. $\ln 2$.

12. $2 - \sqrt{2} - \ln (\sqrt{6} - \sqrt{3})$.

13. $\dfrac{1}{6} \ln \dfrac{4}{3} + \dfrac{\pi}{6\sqrt{3}}$.

14. $\dfrac{1}{2} - \ln \dfrac{4}{3} + \dfrac{\pi}{3\sqrt{3}}$.

15. $\dfrac{3}{8} \ln \dfrac{4}{3} - \dfrac{1}{8}$.

16. $\dfrac{\pi}{12} - \dfrac{1}{6} + \dfrac{1}{6} \ln 2$.

17. $\dfrac{x^4}{4} + \dfrac{x^3}{3} + \dfrac{3x^2}{2} + 5x + \dfrac{1}{3} \ln (x+1) + \dfrac{32}{3} \ln (x-2)$.

19. (i) $-x - 1/x + \ln \{x/(1-x)^2\}$; (ii) $\frac{1}{5} \ln \{x^5/(1+x^5)\}$.

Exercises 3 : 8 (p. 147)

1. $\dfrac{-2}{(1+\tan\frac{1}{2}x)}$.

2. $x-\dfrac{3}{\sqrt{2}}\tan^{-1}\left(\dfrac{\tan\frac{1}{2}x}{\sqrt{2}}\right)$.

3. $\frac{1}{3}\tan^{-1}(3\tan x)$.

4. $2\sqrt{(x-1)}-2\tan^{-1}\sqrt{(x-1)}$.

5. $-2\ln(1-\sqrt{x})$

6. $2x-3\ln(2+\tan\frac{1}{2}x)-2\ln\sec\frac{1}{2}x$.

7. $\dfrac{1}{6}\ln(x+2\sqrt{x}+4)-\dfrac{1}{3}\ln(2-\sqrt{x})-\dfrac{1}{\sqrt{3}}\tan^{-1}\left(\dfrac{1+\sqrt{x}}{\sqrt{3}}\right)$.

8. $2\sqrt{(x-1)}+2\tan^{-1}\sqrt{(x-1)}$.

9. $2\sqrt{(2x^2+7x+3)}-\sqrt{2}\cosh^{-1}\left(\dfrac{4x+7}{5}\right)$.

10. $-\dfrac{1}{\sqrt{6}}\tan^{-1}\left(\dfrac{\sqrt{3}\cdot\cos x}{\sqrt{2}}\right)$.

11. $3\tan\frac{1}{2}x-\ln(1+\cos x)$.

12. $\dfrac{1}{\sqrt{2}}\ln\left(\dfrac{\sqrt{2}+\sqrt{(x+1)}}{\sqrt{2}-\sqrt{(x+1)}}\right)$.

13. $\ln\left(1+\tan\frac{1}{2}x\right)$.

14. $\ln(\sin x+\cos x)$.

15. $\dfrac{1}{3}(x^2+x+1)^{\frac{3}{2}}+\dfrac{3}{16}\sinh^{-1}\left(\dfrac{2x+1}{\sqrt{3}}\right)+\dfrac{1}{8}(2x+1)\sqrt{(x^2+x+1)}$.

16. $\tanh x-\dfrac{1}{3}\tanh^3 x$.

17. $\dfrac{1}{4}\ln\left(\dfrac{1+3e^x}{3+e^x}\right)$.

18. $\dfrac{1}{\sqrt{5}}\ln\left(\dfrac{5+\sqrt{5}}{5-\sqrt{5}}\right)$.

19. $\dfrac{\pi}{4\sqrt{3}}$.

20. $3-2\sqrt{2}$.

21. $\sin^{-1}\left(\frac{1}{5}\right)$.

22. $\dfrac{1}{3}\ln 4$.

23. $\dfrac{1}{2}\ln 3-\dfrac{1}{2\sqrt{2}}\ln\left(\dfrac{2\sqrt{2}+1}{2\sqrt{2}-1}\right)$.

24. 1 .

25. $4(\ln 3-1)$.

26. $\frac{1}{5}\ln 6$.

27. $\ln 2$.

28. $\dfrac{2}{1-a^2}\tan^{-1}\left|\dfrac{1+a}{1-a}\right|$.

29. $\dfrac{\pi-\alpha}{\sin\alpha}$.

30. $\dfrac{(16-5\pi)}{4}$.

31. $\ln\left(\dfrac{3}{2}\right)$.

32. $\dfrac{1}{8}\ln 3$.

33. $\dfrac{\pi}{\sqrt{3}}$.

34. $\dfrac{1}{2}\pi$.

35. $\dfrac{2}{3}\ln 4-\dfrac{\pi}{12}$.

36. (i) $(12x+8\sinh 2x+\sinh 4x)/32$;

    (ii) $(x-1)/\sqrt{(1-x^2)}-(\sin^{-1}x)/(1+x)$;

    (iii) $(1/5)\ln(\sin x-3\cos x)-3x/5$;

(iv) $-\sqrt{(4-x)} - \dfrac{1}{2} \ln\left\{\dfrac{2+\sqrt{(4-x)}}{2-\sqrt{(4-x)}}\right\}$;

(v) $\dfrac{1}{2\sqrt{2}} \ln\left\{\dfrac{x\sqrt{2}-\sqrt{(1+x^2)}}{x\sqrt{2}+\sqrt{(1+x^2)}}\right\}$;

(vi) $\dfrac{1}{\sqrt{2}} \ln\left\{\dfrac{\sqrt{2}+\sqrt{(1+x)}}{\sqrt{2}-\sqrt{(1+x)}}\right\}$;

(vii) $\ln\{x+\sqrt{(x^2-4)}\}+\frac{1}{2}\sec^{-1}(x/2)$.

37. (i) $(4-\pi)a/2$;   (ii) $2\ln\cosh\frac{1}{2} = 2\ln\left\{\left(e^{\frac{1}{2}}+e^{-\frac{1}{2}}\right)/2\right\}$;

(iii) $5/3-2\ln 2$;   (iv) $\pi/\{2a(a+b)\}$;   (v) $\ln(2+\sqrt{3})-(\sqrt{3})/2$;

(vi) $\sqrt{3}-\pi/3$.

Exercises 3 : 9 (p. 156)

1. (i) $\dfrac{63\pi}{512}$;   (ii) $\dfrac{256}{693}$;   (iii) $\dfrac{8}{1287}$;   (iv) $\dfrac{1}{60}$;   (v) $\dfrac{256}{45045}$;

(vi) $\dfrac{16}{315}$;   (vii) $\dfrac{\pi}{32}$;   (viii) $\dfrac{128}{63}$;

(ix) $(5a^2+6ab+5b^2)(b-a)^2\pi/128$.

2. $\dfrac{1}{4}\pi+\dfrac{1}{2}\ln 2-\dfrac{67}{60}$.   **3.** $\dfrac{\sqrt{2}}{64a^5}[7\sqrt{2}+3\ln(1+\sqrt{2})]$.

4. $u_3 = (x^3-6x)\sin x+(3x^2-6)\cos x$;

$v_5 = (5x^4-60x^2+120)\sin x-(x^5-20x^3+120x)\cos x$.

6. $aI_n = x^a(\ln x)^n-nI_{n-1}$.

7. $\dfrac{-x^3}{6(x^2+a^2)^3}-\dfrac{x}{8(x^2+a^2)^2}+\dfrac{x}{16a^2(x^2+a^2)}+\dfrac{1}{16a^3}\tan^{-1}\left(\dfrac{x}{a}\right)$.

10. (a) $I_n = x(\ln x)^n-nI_{n-1}$; (b) $(n-1)J_n = \sec^{n-2}x\tan x+(n-2)J_{n-2}$;

$I_3 = x[(\ln x)^3-3(\ln x)^2+6\ln x-6]$;

$J_5 = \frac{1}{4}\sec^3 x\tan x+\frac{3}{8}\sec x\tan x+\frac{3}{8}\ln(\sec x+\tan x)$.

11. $c^4\dfrac{[3\ln(1+\sqrt{2})-\sqrt{2}]}{8}$.

12. $-24\cos 2-8$.

13. $I_n = \dfrac{5(2n-3)}{9(n-1)}I_{n-1}-\dfrac{n-2}{9(n-1)}I_{n-2}-\dfrac{4\sin x}{9(n-1)(5+4\cos x)^{n-1}}$.

14. $61\pi/4$.

Exercises 3 : 10 (p. 164)

5. $\pi/12$.   **6.** 2π.   **7.** π.   **8.** $-1/9$.   **9.** 1.   **10.** $\pi/(3\sqrt{3})$.

11. (i) $\pi/8$;   (ii) $\{\sqrt{(1+a^2)}-1\}/a$;   (iii) $\pi/4$;   (iv) $\frac{1}{2}\ln 2$;

(v) $1/(a^2+1)$.

12. $\ln\{(e^x-1)/(e^x+1)\} = \ln\tanh(x/2)$; 2.

13. $F(m, n-1) = \dfrac{n-1}{n-m-2}\, F(m, n)$;

$\qquad F(m-1, n) = \dfrac{n-m-1}{m}\, F(m, n)$;

$\qquad\quad F(n, m) = \dfrac{m!(n-m-2)!}{(n-1)!}$.

14. $n!/(m-1)^{n+1}$; the integral diverges at the upper limit when $m = 1$.

Exercises 3 : 11 (p 170)

2. (i) $n!$; (ii) $n!/2^{n+1}$; (iii) $10/9$; (iv) $\frac{1}{2}\sqrt{\pi}$;

(v) $\displaystyle\int_0^\infty t^{x-1}(t^{h/2}-t^{-h/2})^2 e^{-t}\,dt$, concave upwards.

Miscellaneous Exercises III (p. 172)

1. (i) $\frac{1}{2}\{x\sin x - \frac{1}{3}x\sin 3x + \cos x - \frac{1}{9}\cos 3x\}$;

(ii) $\dfrac{1}{2}\ln(x^2+4x+6) - \dfrac{1}{\sqrt{2}}\tan^{-1}\left(\dfrac{x+2}{\sqrt{2}}\right)$; (iii) $-\dfrac{\sqrt{(1-x^2)}}{x} - \sin^{-1}x$;

(iv) $\dfrac{1}{6}\ln(x-1) - \dfrac{1}{12}\ln(x^2+x+4) - \dfrac{1}{2\sqrt{15}}\tan^{-1}\left(\dfrac{2x+1}{\sqrt{15}}\right)$;

(v) $\dfrac{2\{(x+a)^{\frac{3}{2}}+(x+b)^{\frac{3}{2}}\}}{3(a-b)}$; (vi) $3\ln(x-2) + \dfrac{2}{(x-2)} + \ln(x^2+1)$.

2. (i) $\dfrac{\pi}{12}+\dfrac{1}{2}\sqrt{3}$; (ii) $\ln(2+\sqrt{3}) - \dfrac{1}{\sqrt{3}}$; (iii) $\dfrac{\pi}{3\sqrt{3}} - \dfrac{1}{2}$;

(iv) $\dfrac{1}{2}(1-\ln 2)$; (v) $\dfrac{(5e^4-1)}{32}$; (vi) $\dfrac{(2-\sqrt{3})\pi}{4}$; (vii) $\dfrac{(\pi+2e)}{(\pi^2+4)}$;

(viii) $\pi+2$; (ix) $\dfrac{\pi}{12\sqrt{3}}$; (x) $\dfrac{9[2\sqrt{3}-\ln(2+\sqrt{3})]}{8}$;

(xi) $\dfrac{\pi}{6\sqrt{3}} - \ln\left(\dfrac{2}{\sqrt{3}}\right)$; (xii) $\dfrac{1}{2}\cosh\left(\dfrac{\pi}{2}\right)$; (xiii) $\dfrac{[2+4\ln 2 - 5\ln(\frac{5}{3})]}{4}$.

5. $\displaystyle\int_a^{na} f(x)\,dx = n\int_0^a f(x)\,dx$. **6.** $\pi\left[\cos\left(\dfrac{\pi}{n}\right) - \dfrac{1}{3}\cos^3\left(\dfrac{\pi}{n}\right)\right]$.

8. $\dfrac{\sin(2n-2)\theta}{n-1}$. **9.** $\tan^{-1}\left(\dfrac{3}{4}\right)$.

10. (iii) $\tan^{-1}x - \dfrac{1}{(1+x^2)}$. **11.** $\dfrac{(\pi^4-48\pi^2+384)}{512}$.

12. $(m+n) f(m+1, n) = m f(m, n);$ $(m+n) f(m, n+1) = n f(m, n).$

14. cosec $(x+$constant), equivalent to sec $(x+$constant).

15. $\pi \left\{ \dfrac{1}{3} - \dfrac{1}{6\sqrt{3}} \ln(2+\sqrt{3}) \right\}.$

17. $-\pi^3 - 2\pi^2 + 48\pi - 96.$ **18.** $\pi/4.$

21. $\dfrac{1}{2(1-x)} + \dfrac{1}{(1-x)^2} + \dfrac{2}{(1-x)^3} + \dfrac{1}{2(1+x)}.$

Exercises 4 : 2 (p. 179)

2. At $(1, \sqrt{2})$ tgt is $2\sqrt{2}y - x - 3 = 0$, normal is $y + 2\sqrt{2}x - 3\sqrt{2} = 0$;
at $(1, -\sqrt{2})$ tgt is $2\sqrt{2}y + x + 3 = 0$, normal is $y - 2\sqrt{2}x + 3\sqrt{2} = 0.$

3. $19x - 18y + 16 = 0$; above. **5.** $(a, 2a).$

7. $x + y - 3a = 0,$ $x - y + a = 0.$ **11.** $ty - x - at^2 = 0.$

12. $t^2y + x - 2ct = 0,$ $t^3x - ty + c - ct^4 = 0.$

14. $a = \frac{1}{2},$ $b = -3,$ $c = 7,$ $d = -7.$ **15.** $\frac{1}{2} - \frac{2}{3}\ln 2.$

Exercises 4 : 3 (p. 182)

1. (i) $-2, 0, 1$; (ii) $0.$ **4.** $\pm 1/\sqrt{3}$; $0, -1.$

Exercises 4 : 4 (p. 185)

2. $\dfrac{1}{3}.$ **6.** (i) $\dfrac{8}{3}$; (ii) $1 + \dfrac{1}{\sqrt{2}} \ln(1+\sqrt{2}).$

Exercises 4 : 5 (p. 190)

3. $4a,$ $-\dfrac{a(21\sqrt{3} - 4\pi)}{12}.$ **4.** $\dfrac{(a^2+k^2)^{\frac{3}{2}}}{ka}$; $2a + \dfrac{k^2}{a},$ $-\left(k + \dfrac{a^2}{k}\right).$

5. $(12, -16).$ **7.** $a\theta$; $a\cos\theta,$ $a\sin\theta.$

11. $5.$ **12.** $a^2/b.$

13. $4x - 16y + 5 = 0$; $\left(\frac{25}{16}, \frac{45}{64}\right)$; $\frac{1}{2}.$ **16.** $(5\sqrt{5})/6.$

Exercises 4 : 6 (p. 193)

1. $2yt = x$; $(t^2-1)^2a^2 = 4t^2 + 1.$ **3.** $(ax)^{\frac{2}{3}} - (by)^{\frac{2}{3}} = (a^2-b^2)^{\frac{2}{3}}.$

4. $1/x^2 + 1/y^2 = 1/a^2$; $4a/13.$ **5.** (ii) $a^2x^2 + b^2y^2 = (x^2+y^2)^2.$

Exercises 4 : 7 (p. 196)

1. $x = a(2\psi + \sin 2\psi), \quad y = 2a \sin^2 \psi.$

2. $s = a[\text{cosec } \psi \cot \psi + \ln (\text{cosec } \psi + \cot \psi)].$ **3.** $s = 12a \sin^2 \left(\dfrac{\psi}{4}\right).$

5. With suitable axes, $y = \cosh x.$

Exercises 4 : 8 (p. 199)

2. $\dfrac{(3+2r)^{\frac{3}{2}}}{3(r+2)}.$ **3.** $6c^2 p = \pm r^3 \left(1 + \dfrac{8c^4}{r^4}\right).$

Exercises 4 : 9 (p. 214)

5. $\frac{16}{9}.$ **6.** $\frac{1}{3}\pi.$ **9.** $(0, b), \quad (0, -b).$ **10.** $y+x = 0, \quad y-x = 0.$

13. $(-1-\sqrt{2}, \ 3-2\sqrt{2}), \quad (-1+\sqrt{2}, \ 1+\sqrt{2}), \quad (1-\sqrt{2}, \ 1+\sqrt{2}).$

14. $y = x/(x+2);$ (a) $-2 < x < 0$ and $x > 2;$
   (b) $x < -\sqrt{2}$ and $x > \sqrt{2},$ i.e., $|x| > \sqrt{2}.$

16. $8/15.$

18. $x = 2, \quad x-y+3 = 0, \quad x-3y-1 = 0;$ curve has cusp at origin.

20. $\theta = \pm \pi/3.$

Exercises 4 : 12 (p. 225)

1. (i) hyperbola, $\left(\frac{13}{16}, -\frac{1}{16}\right);$ (ii) ellipse, $\left(-\frac{6}{43}, -\frac{35}{387}\right);$ (iii) parabola;
(iv) ellipse, $(3, 2).$

2. $(1, 1);$ $11x+16y-70 = 0, \quad 16x-11y+1 = 0.$

5. $\dfrac{(pg+qf)^2 - c(p^2+q^2)^2}{[2(p^2+q^2)(pf+qg)]};$ the tangent at the vertex.

Exercises 4 : 13 (p. 229)

1. See Fig. 4.24; $\dfrac{(\lambda^2 - \mu^2)^{\frac{1}{2}}}{\lambda};$ $\dfrac{3l}{4}, \ \dfrac{l}{4};$ $\left(0, \dfrac{l}{\sqrt{2}}\right), \ \left(0, \dfrac{-l}{\sqrt{2}}\right).$

4. $\frac{1}{4}\pi;$ $3, 2.$

Exercises 4 : 14 (p. 233)

5. $(-3a, 0)$; $x+y+3a = 0$, $x-y+3a = 0$.

Exercises 4 : 17 (p. 240)

2. $-b/(a+b)^2$, $b/(a-b)^2$; $(a^2-b^2)/a$.

Miscellaneous Exercises IV (p. 241)

1. $(1, 3)$; $\dfrac{13\sqrt{13}}{2}$. **2.** $x = a(\theta+\sin\theta)$, $y = -a(1-\cos\theta)$.

4. $\pi-\tfrac{1}{2}\theta$. **6.** $x-y\tan\left(\tfrac{1}{2}\theta\right)-a\theta+2a\tan\left(\tfrac{1}{2}\theta\right) = 0$.

8. For P, $x = a(\theta-\sin\theta)$, $y = a(1-\cos\theta)$; for Q, $x = a(\theta+\sin\theta)$,
$y = a(1+\cos\theta)$.

9. $x_1+3\left(x_1 y_1^2\right)^{\frac{1}{3}}$, $y_1+3\left(x_1^2 y_1\right)^{\frac{1}{3}}$.

12. $\tfrac{16}{3}$; $4\sqrt{2}+4\ln\left(1+\sqrt{2}\right)$.

15. $a^2 y'x+b^2 x'y-(a^2+b^2)x'y' = 0$; $(a^2+b^2)x-a^2 h = 0$,
$(a^2+b^2)y-b^2 k = 0$.

19. $\left(\tfrac{13}{16}, -\tfrac{1}{16}\right)$; $8x+24y-5 = 0$, $6x-2y-5 = 0$;
$4x-28y-5 = 0$, $4x+4y-3 = 0$.

20. $\xi^2+4\xi\eta+\eta^2+3 = 0$; $\xi+\eta = 0$, i.e., $x+y-2 = 0$.

21. $\left(0, -\tfrac{36}{23}\right)$.

23. $k = 64c^3$; $\left(k^{\frac{2}{3}}, k^{\frac{1}{3}}\right)$.

24. $y^2 = 2a(x-a)$; focus $(3a/2, 0)$, directrix $x = \tfrac{1}{2}a$, limit directrix $x = 2a$.

25. $t^3 x-ty+c(1-t^4) = 0$.

26. $l/r = \pm\sin\theta+e\cos\theta$.

Exercises 5 : 1 (p. 251)

1. Convergent for $|x| \leqslant 1$, divergent for $|x| > 1$. **2.** Convergent for all x.

3. Divergent. **4.** Convergent for $|x| < a$, divergent for $|x| \geqslant a$.

5. Divergent unless $x = 0$. **6.** Divergent.

10. $\sin 3x = 3\sin x-4\sin^3 x$; $s_n = \tfrac{1}{4}[3^n \sin(\theta/3^n)-\sin\theta]$; $\tfrac{1}{4}(\theta-\sin\theta)$.

11. (i) $\dfrac{1}{4}\pi$; (ii) $\dfrac{1}{10}-\dfrac{(n+3)}{(n+5)(n+6)}$.

12. (i) $\coth x - \dfrac{1}{2^n} \coth\left(\dfrac{x}{2^n}\right)$;   (ii) $5e - 1$.

14. (i) Absolutely convergent for $|x| < 1$, convergent when $x = 1$, divergent when $x \leqslant -1$, oscillates unboundedly when $x > 1$; (ii) absolutely convergent for all x; (iii) absolutely convergent for $|x| < 2$, convergent when $x = -2$, divergent when $x \geqslant 2$, oscillates (unboundedly) when $x < -2$; (iv) absolutely convergent when $|x| < 1$, convergent when $x = -1$, divergent when $x \geqslant 1$, oscillates unboundedly for $x < -1$; (v) absolutely convergent for all x.

15. (i) Divergent; (ii) (absolutely) convergent; (iii) divergent; (iv) divergent; (v) (absolutely) convergent; (vi) (absolutely) convergent; (vii) (conditionally) convergent.

16. (i) (a) (Absolutely) convergent; (b) divergent; (ii) $|\theta| < \ln 2$.

Exercises 5 : 2 (p. 258)

9. $2x - \tan x$; $2 - \sec^2 x$.

Exercises 5 : 3 (p. 263)

1. $0{\cdot}4599$, $0{\cdot}7581$, $1{\cdot}2500$, $2{\cdot}0609$; $0{\cdot}0230$, $0{\cdot}0379$, $0{\cdot}0625$, $0{\cdot}1030$.

2. $0{\cdot}4549$, $0{\cdot}7500$, $1{\cdot}2365$, $2{\cdot}0387$; question 1 nearer, gradient of tangent to curve $y = e^x$ increases with x.

3. $0{\cdot}4872$, $0{\cdot}8033$, $1{\cdot}3244$, $2{\cdot}1835$.

Exercises 5 : 4 (p. 266)

1. $\tanh a$.   **2.** $\dfrac{1}{2} \sec a \tan a$.   **3.** $\dfrac{a}{b}$.   **4.** $\dfrac{1}{3}$.

Exercises 5 : 5 (p. 275)

2. $a = \frac{2}{3}$, $b = \frac{1}{6}$.   **3.** (i) $\frac{1}{2}(\cos x + \cosh x)$;   (ii) $\frac{1}{2}(\sinh x - \sin x)$.

5. $1 + x - \dfrac{x^3}{3} - \dfrac{x^4}{6} - \dfrac{x^5}{30}$.

6. $1 + x + \dfrac{x^2}{2} - \dfrac{x^3}{6} - \dfrac{7x^4}{24} + \dfrac{x^5}{24}$.   **7.** $x - \dfrac{3x^2}{2} + \dfrac{11x^3}{6}$.

9. $\dfrac{-69}{25(3x+2)} - \dfrac{23}{25(1-x)} - \dfrac{1}{5(1-x)^2}$; $(-1)^{n-1} \dfrac{69}{50}\left(\dfrac{3}{2}\right)^n - \dfrac{n}{5} - \dfrac{28}{25}$;

$|x| < \frac{2}{3}$.   **11.** (i) 0;   (ii) e^2.

12 (i) The greater of a and b;   (ii) $-\frac{1}{3}$;   (iii) $1/b$;   (iv) 0;

(v) $\{\ln\left(\frac{5}{4}\right)\}/\{\ln\left(\frac{3}{2}\right)\}$;   (vi) 0 if $n \neq 0$, ∞ if $n = 0$;

(vii) π;   (viii) $\frac{1}{12}$.

13. $a = -\frac{4}{3}$, $b = \frac{1}{3}$; $\lim = \frac{8}{3}$.

14.   (i) e^2;   (ii) -1;   (iii) $-\frac{1}{3}$;   (iv) $\frac{1}{2}$;   (v) $-\ln 2$;   (vi) 0;   (vii) 2;
(viii) e.

15.   (i) $\cos\alpha + x(\cos\alpha - \sin\alpha) - x^2\sin\alpha - \frac{1}{3}x^3(\sin\alpha + \cos\alpha)$;

(ii) $x - x^2/2 + x^3/6 - x^4/14$.

16. $f^n(0) = 1$ for $n > 1$.

18. $1 - \left(\dfrac{x}{2}\right)^2 + \dfrac{x^4}{2^4(2!)^2} - \dfrac{x^6}{2^6(3!)^2} + \cdots \dfrac{+(-1)^n x^{2n}}{2^{2n}(n!)^2} + \cdots$;

valid for all x.

20. $y^n(0) = 2(n-1)\,y^{n-2}(0)$; $y^{2n}(0) = 0$, $y^{2n+1}(0) = 2^{2n}(n!)$;

$y = x + \dfrac{4x^3}{3} + \dfrac{2^4 2!\,x^5}{5!} + \cdots + \dfrac{2^{2n}n!\,x^{2n+1}}{(2n+1)!} + \cdots$.

21. $y_{n+2}(0) = (n^2 - a^2)\,y_n(0)$.

Exercises 5 : 6 (p. 290)

1. $(1+k^2)^{-\frac{1}{2}}$.   **2.** $\dfrac{1}{e}$.

3. $x = 1$ gives a maximum 289; $x = 2$ gives a minimum 186.

4. (i) At $x = 0$ the function has a minimum 8,
at $x = 2$ the function has a maximum $60e^{-2}$;

(ii) $a + b + c - 3(abc)^{\frac{1}{3}}$.

7. $x = 0$ gives minimum, $x = \cos^{-1}\left(\frac{1}{3}\right)$ gives maximum, $x = \pi$ gives minimum.

8. (i) $\dfrac{2r}{\sqrt{3}}$;   (ii) $r\sqrt{2}$.   **9.** $r = 4c = h$.   **10.** $\sqrt{3}a$, $3a$.

11. $\dfrac{\pi c}{(2\pi - 1)}$.

15. (i) Maximum $8e^{-\frac{5}{4}}$ at $x = \pm\sqrt{(\frac{5}{2})}$, minimum -2 at $x = 0$; (ii) $\dfrac{a}{\sqrt{2}}$.

16. (i) Maximum at $x = a$, minimum at $x = \frac{1}{3}(a+2)$;
(ii) Maximum at $x = \frac{1}{3}(a+2)$, minimum at $x = a$;
(iii) Stationary at $x = 1$, inflexion with horizontal tangent.

17. (i) $2p\pi$ $(p = 0, \pm1, \pm2, \ldots)$;   (ii) $p\pi$ $(p = 0, \pm1, \pm2, \ldots)$.

18. $-$ gives a minimum, $+$ gives a maximum.

19. Max, $2e^{-\frac{1}{4}}$, at $x = \frac{1}{2}$; min, $-e^{-1}$, at $x = -1$.

21. $(a^2+b^2)^{\frac{1}{2}} \big/ V.$ **24.** $8\pi a^2/(3\sqrt{3}).$

25. $f'(x) = (x^2-9)(x^2-3)(x^2-1)/\{x^2(x^2+3)\}^2$;

$x = -3$ gives maximum -8, $x = -\sqrt{3}$ gives minimum $-14/\sqrt{3}$
$x = -1$ gives maximum -8, then use $f(x)$ as an odd function. Two
(distinct) roots if $|k| > 14/\sqrt{3}$, four roots (two distinct and two
equal) if $|k| = 14/\sqrt{3}$, four (distinct) roots if $14/\sqrt{3} > |k| > 8$
four (two pairs of equal) roots if $|k| = 8$, no roots if $|k| < 8$.

26. $(r-pq)^2 = 4(q^2-pr)(p^2-q)$; $(4pq-3p^3-r)/(p^2-q).$

27. $2, 2\pm 2\sqrt{3}.$ **29.** $8/\pi.$

Exercises 5:7 (p. 298)

3. 1.5% too large.   **6.** 0.0217 m².   **7.** $\pi/2.$

Exercises 5:8 (p. 304)

1. (i) $\frac{32}{27}$ m.   (ii) 2 s   (iii) 4 m/s   **2.** 63 m/s.

3. 15 m.   **4.** $\dfrac{k\sqrt{2}}{(al)}$ m/s.

5. (i) $2\pi na$ m/min.;   (ii) $\dfrac{2\pi n(x^2+a^2)}{a}$ m/min.

6. $\frac{1}{2}\pi.$ **8.** $a\omega\sin\varphi$, $\frac{1}{2}(b-2a\cos\varphi)\omega.$

10. $l\sin\varphi = r\sin\omega t.$

Exercises 5:9 (p. 317)

1. $0.879.$ **2.** Approximate roots -1.56, 0.7;   larger root $0.69.$

3. $2.20.$ **4.** $0.202.$ **5.** $3.73.$ **8.** $\dfrac{1}{8\delta}+\dfrac{\delta}{6}.$

9. $0.596.$ **10.** $1.2.$ **11.** $1.34.$ **12.** $1.875.$ **13.** $1.80.$

14. $\left\{\dfrac{\ln a}{a^2} - \dfrac{(\ln a)^2}{2a^2}\right\} x^3.$

Exercises 5:11 (p. 333)

1. 7.125; $399.$

2. $y = -0.8432$ when $x = 0.6$; $y = -0.29195$ when $x = 0.45.$

3. When $x = 3$, $y = 3.6$;   when $x = 3.5$, $y = 4.723.$

4. $f(x) = -2+3x^2+x^4.$ **5.** $12.5.$ **6.** When $x = 3$, $y = 19.$

Exercises 5:12 (p. 338)

1. $\frac{1}{6}x^3 - \frac{1}{6}x^2 + \frac{2}{3}x - 1$.

3. $A_{-1} = \dfrac{-\theta(\theta-1)(\theta-2)}{6}$, $\qquad A_0 = \dfrac{(\theta+1)(\theta-1)(\theta-2)}{2}$,

$\qquad A_1 = \dfrac{-(\theta+1)\theta(\theta-2)}{2}$, $\qquad A_2 = \dfrac{(\theta+1)\theta(\theta-1)}{6}$.

When $x = 3$, $f(x) = -0.596$; when $x = 5$, $f(x) = -0.760$; when $x = 7$, $f(x) = -0.792$.

4. $y = -2.552$ when $x = 0.2$; $\quad y = -17x^3 + 6x^2 + 1.72x - 3$.

Exercises 5:13 (p. 342)

1. $f'(2) = 11$, $\quad f''(2) = 12$. **5.** $y = 0.046$, $\quad \mathrm{d}y/\mathrm{d}x = 1.41$.

6. 0.4341; correct value $\log_{10} e = 0.4343$.

Miscellaneous Exercises V (p. 343)

4. (i) 1; (ii) 2. **5.** Max. $2(n+m^3)$, min $2(n-m^3)$.

6. (i) $-\frac{1}{3}$; (ii) $x = 0$ is a point of inflexion, $x = \frac{1}{2}\pi$ gives a min.

7. (i) 0; (ii) $-\dfrac{1}{16}$; (iii) 2. **8.** $p = \dfrac{1}{2}$, $q = 1$; $f(x) = \dfrac{3x^3}{4} + \dfrac{3x^4}{4}$.

9. $\dfrac{1}{8(1-t)} + \dfrac{1}{4(1-t)^2} + \dfrac{1}{2(1-t)^3} + \dfrac{1}{8(1+t)}$. **11.** $1 - \dfrac{x^2}{2} + \dfrac{5x^4}{24}$.

12. $x = \dfrac{1-y}{1+y}$.

13. $S = a^2(\sin\theta + \sin\theta\cos\theta)$; $\quad P = 4a\left[\cos^2\dfrac{\theta}{2} + \sin\dfrac{\theta}{2}\right]$;

$\qquad$ max S is $\dfrac{3\sqrt{3}a^2}{4}$; $\quad$ max P is $5a$.

14. $2 : 3$. **15.** $\sqrt{(a^2 + ab)} - a$. **19.** 0.0372.

21. $y = x - \dfrac{x^2}{2} + x^3 - \dfrac{9x^4}{8} + \dfrac{31x^5}{20}$; when $x = 0.1$, $y = 0.09590$.

22. $\dfrac{64a^2}{15}$.

24. (i) (a) Convergent like $\Sigma n^{-\frac{3}{2}}$; (b) divergent, $u_n \to 1$; (c) convergent, $u_n = 1/\{n(n-1)\}$ and series converges like Σn^{-2}; (ii) convergent when $|x| \leqslant 1$; when $|x| < 1$ sum is $x + (1-x)\ln(1-x)$, when $x = 1$ sum is 1, when $x = -1$ sum is $2\ln 2 - 1$.

25. (i) Absolutely convergent; (ii) absolutely convergent; (iii) oscillates boundedly, $u_n \to (-1)^n$; (iv) absolutely convergent; (v) conditionally convergent; (vi) divergent, $u_n = \pi/n + O(n^{-3})$.

26. Maximum $2e^{-2}$ at $x = 1$, minimum $-e^4$ at $x = -2$, inflexions at $x = \pm\sqrt{(5/2)}$; lim $= 9/(4e^2)$.

27. $Si(x) = x - \dfrac{x^3}{3.3!} + \dfrac{x^5}{5.5!} - \cdots + \dfrac{(-1)^n x^{2n+1}}{(2n+1).(2n+1)!} + \cdots$;   all x.

28. 1·318.   **29.** 0·88.

31. $(2n!)x^{2n+1}/\{2^{2n}(2n+1)(n!)^2\}$;   valid for $|x| < 1$.

35. $I_{n+1} + I_{n-1} = x^n/n$;

(i) $\tan^{-1} x = x - x^3/3 + x^5/5 - \cdots + (-1)^n x^{2n+1}/(2n+1) + \cdots$;

(ii) $\ln(1+x^2) = x^2 - x^4/2 + x^6/3 - \cdots + (-1)^{n-1} x^{2n}/(2n) + \cdots$.

36. (i) $-1/(2x_0)$;   (ii) 1·09.   **37.** $b = a + \varepsilon + (n-1)\,\varepsilon^2/(2a) + O(\varepsilon^3/a^2)$.

40. 2·30024.   **41.** 0·905.   **42.** $p = e^2$, $q = 3e^3/2$.   **43.** 0·13475.

44. 9119·009009.

Exercises 6 : 2 (p. 360)

1. (i) $\dfrac{4\pi a^3}{3}$;   (ii) $\dfrac{1}{3}\pi h^3 \tan^2 \alpha$.   **2.** $\dfrac{113\pi a^3}{2}$.

6. $\dfrac{(68 + 27\ln 3)\pi}{6}$.   **7.** $16\pi(3\ln 2 - 2/3)$.

11. Curves intersect at (a, a).

12. $\pi\,(40/3 - 24\ln 2 + 8(\ln 2)^2\}$.

Exercises 6 : 3 (p. 364)

1. (i) a^2;   (ii) $\dfrac{3\pi a^2}{2}$;   (iii) $\pi b(a - b)$.   **2.** $\dfrac{(2\pi^2 - 3)\pi a^2}{24}$.

5. $\frac{1}{2}\ln(2 + \sqrt{3})$.

6. $M_0 = \dfrac{8ka^3(\pi^2 - 8)}{\pi^2}$; $M_4 = \dfrac{(\pi^6 - 120\pi^4 + 5760\pi^2 - 46080)8ka^3}{\pi^6}$.

Exercises 6 : 4 (p. 372)

1. (i) On axis $\frac{1}{3}h$ from base;   (ii) on axis $\frac{1}{4}h$ from base.

2. $\bar{x} = \dfrac{2a}{5}$, $\bar{y} = a$;   (i) on Ox, $\bar{x} = \frac{1}{2}a$;   (ii) on Oy, $\bar{y} = \dfrac{5a}{4}$.

On bisecting radius, distant $\dfrac{2a\sin\alpha}{3\alpha}$ from O.

4. $V = \pi(1 - \ln 2)$; $\bar{x} = \dfrac{(3 - 4 \ln 2)}{(2 - 2 \ln 2)}$.

5. $\dfrac{32(2\sqrt{2} - 1)\pi}{3}$ m²; $\dfrac{(20 + 12\sqrt{2})}{35}$ m.

6. $\dfrac{16c^2}{15}$; $\bar{x} = \dfrac{4c}{7}$.   **7.** $\dfrac{a}{(20 - 6\pi)}$ from its vertex.

8. $\dfrac{14a}{15\pi}$, $\dfrac{a}{10}$.   **9.** $\dfrac{8(5\sqrt{5} - 1)\pi a^2}{3}$.

10. $12(\pi^2 - 8)a/\pi^3$.

12. $a = (\ln 2)/100$; $100\{(\ln 2)^{-1} - 1\}$.

Exercises 6 : 5 (p. 376)

1. $\bar{x} = \dfrac{9a}{20}$, $\bar{y} = \dfrac{9a}{10}$; $\dfrac{6\pi a^3}{5}$.

3. $\dfrac{8a^2}{15}$; $\bar{x} = \dfrac{4a}{7}$, $\bar{y} = 0$; $\dfrac{32\sqrt{2}\pi a^3}{105}$.

4. (i) If wire is in first quadrant, $\bar{x} = \dfrac{2a}{\pi}$, $\bar{y} = \dfrac{2a}{\pi}$;

(ii) $\bar{x} = \dfrac{4a}{3\pi}$, $\bar{y} = \dfrac{4b}{3\pi}$.

5. $\dfrac{1}{2}\pi ab - \dfrac{4}{3}b^2$; $\dfrac{4\pi a^2 b}{3} - \dfrac{16\pi b^3}{15}$; $\dfrac{(20a^2 - 16b^2)}{(15\pi a - 40b)}$.

6. $3\pi a^2$; $\bar{x} = \pi a$, $\bar{y} = \dfrac{5a}{6}$; $5\pi^2 a^3$.

9. 4/15 units²;   (i) $\pi/12$ units³;   (ii) $32\pi/105$ units³.

Exercises 6 : 6 (p. 383)

1. (i) $\dfrac{a^4 s \sin 2\theta \cos^2\theta}{12}$, greatest value $\dfrac{\sqrt{3}a^4 s}{32}$;

(ii) $\dfrac{1}{4}a^4 s \sin 2\theta \sin^2\theta$, greatest value $\dfrac{3\sqrt{3}a^4 s}{32}$.

3. $a\sqrt{\left\{\dfrac{(29 - 36\ln 2)}{24(1 - \ln 2)}\right\}}$.   **4.** $\sqrt{\left(\dfrac{11}{16} + \dfrac{\pi^2}{12}\right)}$.   **5.** $a\sqrt{\left(\dfrac{2}{3}\right)}$.

8. $a\sqrt{\left\{\dfrac{(2 - 5\cos^3\alpha + 3\cos^5\alpha)}{5(1 - \cos^3\alpha)}\right\}}$.   **9.** 1·2.

10. $\sqrt{\left\{\dfrac{(104 - 150\ln 2)}{10(3\ln 2 - 2)}\right\}}$.

13. (i) $a/\sqrt{3}$;   (ii) $a\sqrt{(2/3)}$;   (iii) $a/\sqrt{5}$;   (iv) $2a\sqrt{(3/5)}$.

Exercises 6 : 7 (p. 386)

2. Now $3h/8$ from base.   **4.** At depth $5a/4$; $17a/8$.

Exercises 6 : 8 (p. 390)

8. Greatest value at $x = \pi/3$, least at $x = \pi$.

Exercises 6 : 9 (p. 400)

1. (i) 0·881;   (ii) 0·413.   **2.** (i) 9·28;   (ii) 16·13;   101.

3. 0·0375.   **4.** 1125 m.   **5.** 190 m²;   750 m³/s.

6. (i) 0·448;   (ii) 0·437.   **7.** 0·493;   0·493.

8. 0·7854; $\bar{x} = 0.48$.   **9.** $V = 2.50$; $\bar{x} = 0.66$, $\bar{y} = 1.10$

10. 12·96.

11. When $x = 4$, $f(x) = 6.5536$;   27·035.

13. Error $\leqslant 2mMh^5/45 = M(b-a)^5/(2^4.\,45m^4)$;

$M = 3/8$, $m > 5/(12)^{\frac{1}{4}}$;   8 intervals.

Miscellaneous Exercises VI (p. 403)

2. a; $\frac{2}{3}a^2$.   **3.** π; on x-axis, $\bar{x} = \frac{1}{4}\pi - \frac{1}{2}\ln 2$; $\sqrt{\frac{2}{3}}$.   **5.** 15·9.

7. $\sqrt{\left\{\dfrac{b(4a+b)}{6}\right\}}$.   **8.** $\bar{x} = \dfrac{(16+5\pi)a}{2(8+3\pi)}$, $\bar{y} = \dfrac{10a}{(8+3\pi)}$;   vol $= \dfrac{5\pi a^3}{2}$.

9. 2·28.

10. $\dfrac{3\pi a^2}{16}$; $\bar{x} = 0$, $\bar{y} = \dfrac{512a}{315\pi}$; $\dfrac{2a}{3\sqrt{3}}$; $\dfrac{a[\ln(2+\sqrt{3})+2\sqrt{3}]}{\sqrt{3}}$

11. $\dfrac{\pi a^2}{12}$; $\dfrac{81\sqrt{3}a}{80\pi}$.   **13.** $\dfrac{Mh^2(3\tan^2\alpha+12)}{20}$ **14.** $\dfrac{32\pi a^3}{105}$

15. $\dfrac{1}{2}a^2$; $a\sqrt{\left[\dfrac{(3\pi-8)}{48}\right]}$.   **17.** $\dfrac{1}{2}\tan^{-1}\left(\dfrac{1}{2}\right)$, $\dfrac{1}{3}\ln 2$.

22. $a_1 = 8h/3$, $a_2 = -4h/3$, $a_3 = 8h/3$;   2753.

23. $w_{-2} = 64/(3\pi^2)$, $w_{-1} = -160/(3\pi^2)$, $w_1 = 214/(3\pi^2)$, $w_2 = 2 - 128/(3\pi^2)$;   2·2.

Exercises 7 : 1 (p. 414)

1. $\sqrt{65}$, $\tan^{-1}\left(\dfrac{7}{4}\right) = 60°15'$ approx. **3.** $\dfrac{1}{2}(w+w^*)$, $\dfrac{1}{2i}(w-w^*)$, ww^*.

4. $x = \frac{1}{2}$, $y = -\frac{3}{2}$. **6.** (ii) $\frac{1}{2}(1+i)$. **8.** 2.

Exercises 7 : 3 (p. 425)

1. The circle $|z| = a$. **3.** The circle centre $1+\frac{1}{2}i$, radius $\frac{1}{2}\sqrt{5}$.

4. (i) $\left(\dfrac{2}{5}, -\dfrac{11}{5}\right)$, $\dfrac{(11-2i)}{5}$. **5.** $z(1-i)$, $2z$, $z(1+i)$.

6. $\sqrt{13}$, $\pi-\tan^{-1}\frac{2}{3}$; $\sqrt{10}$, $\pi-\tan^{-1}\frac{1}{3}$.

7. C is $2+4\sqrt{3}+i$, D is $2+2\sqrt{3}+3i$.

8. $\dfrac{(6+8i)}{5}$.

9. (i) The circle $|z| = c\sqrt{2}$; (ii) the lower semicircular arc of the circle $|z| = c$; (iii) the ellipse with foci $\pm ic$ and major axis $4c$.

10. $\frac{1}{2}(1\pm\sqrt{3})(1+i)$.

24. $z = (\pm 1+2i)/5$.

25. $Y^2 = 4b^2(X+b^2)$, $Y \geqslant 0$.

26. $\left|\dfrac{1}{z} - \dfrac{1}{2\zeta}\right| = \dfrac{1}{2|\zeta|}$. The point $1/z$ traces out a circle, centre $1/(2\zeta)$, radius $|1/(2\zeta)|$ when z follows the straight line $z = \zeta(1+it)$. Arcs of 3 circles: centre $\dfrac{1}{2}$ radius $\dfrac{1}{2}$, centres $-\dfrac{1}{2}\pm i$ radius $\dfrac{1}{\sqrt{2}}$.

27. Lower 'half' of ellipse with foci at $\pm c$ and major axis $2d$.

Exercises 7 : 4 (p. 432)

1. i; $0.92+i0.38$, $-0.38+i0.92$, $-0.92-i0.38$, $0.38-i0.92$.

2. $\dfrac{1}{2}\left[1-i\tan\left(\dfrac{r\pi}{5}\right)\right]$, $r = 0, 1, 2, 3, 4$.

4. $2^{\frac{1}{3}}e^{-\frac{i\pi}{9}}$, $2^{\frac{1}{3}}e^{\frac{5i\pi}{9}}$, $2^{\frac{1}{3}}e^{\frac{11i\pi}{9}}$.

5. $-0.489+0.554i$, $-1.511-2.554i$. **6.** $4+i7$.

8. $z^2-2z\cos\left(\dfrac{4\pi}{7}\right)+1$, $z^2-2z\cos\left(\dfrac{6\pi}{7}\right)+1$. **11.** $0.35\pm i1.32$.

13. $e^{ir\pi/8}$ for $r = 1, 2, 3, 5, 6, 7$.

14. $2\cos(2\pi/5)$. **15.** 2.

Exercises 7 : 5 (p. 437)

2. 0 when $n = 0$; $\dfrac{(-1)^n (2^{2n} - 2 \times 4^{2n} - 6^{2n})}{(2n)!}$ when $n > 0$

3. $\theta = (2n \pm \frac{1}{3})\pi$.

4. (i) $\dfrac{(6 - 2 \cos 2\theta - 8 \cos 4\theta + 3 \cos 6\theta + 2 \cos 8\theta - \cos 10\theta)}{2^9}$;

$\dfrac{(15\pi - 16)}{5120}$;   (ii) $\dfrac{(\sin 5\theta - 5 \sin 3\theta + 10 \sin \theta)}{16}$; $\dfrac{203}{480}$.

7. $\sin (x + na + a) \dfrac{\sin na}{\sin a}$.   **8.** (i) $\dfrac{(2 \cos \theta - 1)}{(5 - 4 \cos \theta)}$; (ii) $e^{\cos \theta} \sin (\sin \theta$

10. $(\cos 5\theta + 5 \cos 3\theta + 10 \cos \theta)/16$.

Exercises 7:6 (p. 446)

1. (i) $x = (2n + 1)\pi$, $y = \pm \ln (3 + \sqrt{8})$.

7. (ii) $\frac{1}{2}\theta + n\pi - \frac{1}{4}i \ln 5$ where $\theta = \tan^{-1} 2$.   **8.** $\pm \frac{1}{2}$.

15. $\sqrt{\left(1 - \dfrac{2a^2}{r^2} \cos 2\theta + \dfrac{a^4}{r^4}\right)}$.

18. $u = \frac{1}{2} \ln (x^2 + y^2)$, $v = \tan^{-1} (y/x)$.

19. $z = \text{Log } 3 = \ln 3 + 2n\pi i$, $(n = 0, \pm 1, \pm 2, \ldots)$; any solution wit

$n > 10^6/(2\pi)$.

20. (i) $-2, 1 \pm i \sqrt{3}$; (ii) $\pm \ln (4 + \sqrt{15}) + (2n + 1)\pi i$, $n = 0, \pm 1, \pm 2, \ldots$

21. (i) $e^2/2$, $(\sqrt{3})e^2/2$;   (ii) $\{(\sqrt{3})\cosh 1\}/2$, $(\sinh 1)/2$;   (iii) $\ln 2$, $\pi/3$

Miscellaneous Exercises VII (p. 449)

1. (i) $\dfrac{(-14 + 23i)}{29}$;   (ii) $128(-1 + \sqrt{3}i)$;   (iii) $(5 - 3\sqrt{3}i)/8$.

4. (i) $x - y - 1 = 0$;   (ii) $2 + 2i$, $1 + 3i$.

5. $\cos \left[\dfrac{(8n + 1)\pi}{16}\right] + i \sin \left[\dfrac{(8n + 1)\pi}{16}\right]$, $n = 0, 1, 2, 3$.

6. (ii) $\dfrac{(\cosh \pi/4 + i \sinh \pi/4)}{\sqrt{2}}$.

7. (i) $\dfrac{1}{2} \ln 3 + (2r + 1) \dfrac{i\pi}{2}$.   **8.** $\left(m + \dfrac{1}{2}\right)\pi + \dfrac{1}{2} i \ln 2$.

9. (i) (a) $\frac{1}{2} \ln (x^2 + y^2)$; if $0 \leqslant \tan^{-1} (y/x) \leqslant \pi$, $\text{Im} (\log z) = \tan^{-1} (y/x)$

if $\pi < \tan^{-1} (y/x) \leqslant 2\pi$, $\text{Im} (\log z) = 2\pi - \tan^{-1} (y/x)$.

(b) $\dfrac{(x^2+y^2-1)}{[(x-1)^2+y^2]}$, $-\dfrac{2y}{[(x-1)^2+y^2]}$.

(ii) $r = 1\cdot122$, $\theta = 15°$, $135°$, $255°$ (or $-105°$).

10. (i) $\left| \cot \dfrac{\theta}{2} \right| \left(\cos \dfrac{\pi}{2} + \mathrm{i} \sin \dfrac{\pi}{2} \right)$; (ii) $\dfrac{1}{2} \ln 3 + (4n+1)\dfrac{\mathrm{i}\pi}{2}$.

12. $\dfrac{4(1+\sqrt{3}\mathrm{i})}{9}$.

13. $\dfrac{(\cos 12\theta + 6 \cos 8\theta + 15 \cos 4\theta + 10)}{32}$; $\dfrac{5\pi}{32}$.

18. (i) $2n\pi \pm \ln(2+\sqrt{3})$, $(2n\pm\tfrac{1}{3})\mathrm{i}\pi$.

19. (i) $\cos \dfrac{n\pi}{3} + \mathrm{i} \sin \dfrac{n\pi}{3}$, $n = 1, 2, 4, 5$; (ii) $\dfrac{6-3\sqrt{3}}{2} + \dfrac{\mathrm{i}(5+4\sqrt{3})}{2}$.

20. (i) $64 \cos^7 \theta - 112 \cos^5 \theta + 56 \cos^3 \theta - 7 \cos \theta$;

$y = -7x + 56x^3 - 112x^5 + 64x^7$.

21. (i) That part of the real axis lying between -2 and 2; (ii) ellipse, foci 0, $1+\mathrm{i}$, major axis of length 2; (iii) parabola, latus rectum $4a$, vertex $(0, -a)$; (iv) hyperbola, foci $\pm(1+\mathrm{i})$, major axis of length 2.

22. (i) (a) $z^2 = x^2 - y^2 + \mathrm{i}2xy$; (b) $\tan z = 2(\sin 2x + \mathrm{i} \sinh 2y)/(\cos 2x + \cosh 2y)$; (ii) $(1\pm\mathrm{i}\sqrt{3})/2$.

23. $(\arg z)/(\ln|z|)$.

25. (i) $|Z| = \sqrt{\{(5+4\omega+\omega^2)/(1-\omega^2-\omega^4)\}}$.

$\arg Z = \tan^{-1}\{(2+\omega-2\omega^2-\omega^3)/(1-2\omega-2\omega^2)\}$;

(ii) $|Z| = \mathrm{e}^2/\sqrt{(1+\omega^2)}$, $\arg Z = \tan^{-1}\{(1+\omega \tan \omega)/(\omega - \tan \omega)\}$.

27. $u = \cosh x \cos y$, $v = \sinh x \sin y$.

28. $2/p$ where $p = \pm1, \pm2, \pm3, \ldots.$

29. $\tfrac{1}{2}(\cos 2x + \cosh 2y)$.

Exercises 8 : 2(a) (p. 461)

1. $\omega^2 \dfrac{\left(1+\mathrm{e}^{\frac{-k\pi}{\omega}}\right)}{\pi(k^2+\omega^2)}$; $\sqrt{\left[\dfrac{\omega^3\left(1-\mathrm{e}^{\frac{-2k\pi}{\omega}}\right)}{4k\pi(k^2+\omega^2)} \right]}$.

2. $\dfrac{-1}{\omega}$; $\dfrac{(8\pi^2-3)^{\frac{1}{2}}}{\omega 2\sqrt{3}}$. **3.** $\dfrac{a}{30}$; $\dfrac{a}{3\sqrt{70}}$.

4. $3 \ln 2 - 1$; $\sqrt{\{7(\ln 2)^2 - 6 \ln 2 + 2\}}$. **6.** $\dfrac{4a}{\pi}$.

7. (i) $\dfrac{4\varrho_0 a^3}{\pi}$; (ii) $\dfrac{3\varrho_0}{\pi^2}$.

Exercises 8 : 2(b) (p. 470)

1. (a) $\bar{x} = 30$;   (b) $\sigma = 5\cdot7$.

2. (i) (a) $37\cdot6$;   (b) $6\cdot61$; median 34, u.q. 40, l.q. 30.

3. $\bar{x} = 18\cdot95$; $\sigma = 1\cdot45$.   **4.** $5\cdot82$.

5. Mean $= 50\cdot5$; standard deviation $9\cdot91$.

6. (i) a^2;   (ii) $2a$;   (iii) $a\sqrt{2}$. |

7. $A(\pi-2)/2$; $(\pi^2-8)/\{2(\pi-2)\}$; $\{\sqrt{(-2\pi^3-8\pi^2+96\pi-160)}\}/\{2(\pi-2)\}$.

8. $a = 4$, $A = 3/64$; $0\cdot14$, $2\cdot1$.

Exercises 8 : 3 (p. 483)

1. (i) $\frac{112}{125} = 0\cdot896$;   (ii) $\frac{7344}{15625} = 0\cdot47$.

2. (i) $\frac{3}{20}$;   (ii) $\frac{1}{60}$;   (iii) $\frac{59}{60}$.   **3.** $(2n+1)/3$.

4. (i) $0\cdot896$;   (ii) $0\cdot352$.   **5.** $2/\sqrt{(\pi mh)}$.

6. $A = 1$; $\bar{x} = 2$; $\sigma = \sqrt{2}$.

7. $\bar{y} = 7\pi/3$; $\sigma^2 = 34\pi^2/45$.

8. $k = 1$; mean life $= 2T$; $\sigma = T\sqrt{2}$.

9. $(b!)(w!)/\{(b+w+1)!\}$.

Exercises 8 : 4 (p. 491)

1. $\frac{1}{216}$;   (ii) $\frac{25}{216}$;   (iii) $\frac{425}{432}$;   (iv) $\frac{19}{1144}$.

2. 2.   **3.** $0\cdot41(2)$.   **4.** $0\cdot735$; 49%.

5. (i) $0\cdot532$; (ii) $0\cdot380$; (iii) $0\cdot088$.   **7.** $0\cdot26$; $0\cdot390$.   **8.** $1\cdot2$; $0\cdot0338$.

9. $0\cdot010$.   **10.** $0\cdot78$.

Exercises 8 : 5 (p. 499)

1. $\bar{x} = 96\cdot0$; $\sigma = 10\cdot5$.

x	70	74	78	82	86	90	94	98	102	106	110	114	118	122	126
f	3	6	12	23	38	55	68	73	68	54	38	22	13	5	2

2.

54 p	66 p	78 p	90 p	102 p	114 p
2	27	114	162	81	14

3. 1047 to 1083 hours; mean 1065; s.d. $25\cdot6$ hours. 1048 to 1082 hours.

4. (i) 5%;   (ii) $2\cdot4$%;   (iii) $7\cdot27$%;   (iv) $0\cdot269$.

5. 060, $4\cdot6$%.   **6.** Mean $1\cdot0055$; $\sigma = 3\cdot0393$.

Miscellaneous Exercises VIII (p. 504)

1. 15·94.　　2. (i) 0·547,　(ii) 0·0904.

3. (iii) $2/n$.　　4. (i) Yes;　(ii) 0·21.

5. (i) 0·016;　(ii) 0·060.　　6. $\bar{y} = 468·75$;　$\sigma = 252·5$.

7. Median 0·866; quartiles 0·661, 0·968.　　8. a^2, $2a$.

9. $\bar{x} = 2\ln 2$, $1/3$; median 1·33, interquartile range $1·143 \leqslant x \leqslant 1·600$.

10. $\frac{1}{4} \sqrt{\{(1+3e)(1+e)\}}$.

11. $c = 3$,　(i) 0·542,

(ii) 0·250, $A(p) = (1-p)^{50} \left\{ 1 + \dfrac{50p}{1-p} + \dfrac{1225p^2}{(1-p)^2} + \dfrac{60\,025p^3}{3(1-p)^3} \right\}$.

12. 0·02, 0·0038.

INDEX

Page numbers is parentheses after an entry refer to a headed
section on that topic